THE ANALYSIS OF

LINEAR SYSTEMS

McGRAW-HILL ELECTRICAL AND ELECTRONIC ENGINEERING SERIES

FREDERICK EMMONS TERMAN, *Consulting Editor*
W. W. HARMAN AND J. G. TRUXAL, *Associate Consulting Editors*

THE ANALYSIS OF LINEAR SYSTEMS

WAYNE H. CHEN

Professor of Electrical Engineering
University of Florida

McGRAW-HILL BOOK COMPANY, INC.

New York   San Francisco   Toronto   London

THE ANALYSIS OF LINEAR SYSTEMS

To
DOROTHY
and
AVIS *and* TIMOTHY

Preface

This is the first of two books† designed to present a unified analysis-synthesis sequence with uniform terminology and consistent viewpoint. The present book is self-contained and is completely independent of the other.

A unique style of presentation is utilized in this book for clarity and easy reference. For example, as can be seen from the table of contents and the subtopics at all levels of the text, the book is organized so that the reader will see the relative importance of, and the proper relations between, topics.

The purpose of this book is, first, to present the important concepts, principles, and techniques of linear system analysis in a systematic manner and, second, to elucidate "network relations" for better insight into network and system problems and analysis and synthesis problems. Network study is confined to linear lumped-constant networks unless otherwise specified. No attempt is made to discuss networks handling signals of a statistical nature.

This text is divided into seven parts. An introductory statement is included at the beginning of each part to indicate coverage and emphasis.

Part A includes the Introduction and a review of some network fundamentals.

In Part B, the characterization of networks in both the quantitative and qualitative (topological) senses is studied.

In Parts C to E, network responses are studied through three different approaches in the domains of the real frequency ω, the complex frequency $s = \sigma + j\omega$, and the time t, and the three are compared. Some important network relations, including those between the network characteristics and time delay, buildup time, and response waveform are discussed in conjunction with the study of the Fourier-transform approach. The Laplace-transform approach is discussed in detail as to mathematical treatment, understanding of the physical system, and applications.

The signal-flow method of analysis, its general applications, and specific applications to transistor circuits are studied in Part G.

In Part F the stability problems of a closed-loop system, e.g., a vacuum-tube or transistor feedback amplifier or a servomechanism, are discussed. Emphasis is placed upon some special studies, including an investigation of the behavior of the Nyquist diagram at infinity.

Although primarily intended for use by graduate and advanced undergraduate students in electrical engineering and by practicing engineers, this book will also be found useful by applied mathematicians, control engineers, and system designers. Since the text is a comprehensive one, a section (Art. 1.3) is included in the Introduction to aid in the selection of reading material for use of this book as a textbook, a book for self-study, or a reference.

---

† The second book, "Linear Network Design and Synthesis" (now in press), presents the important methods of synthesizing an electrical network from a prescribed network characteristic or network function, or from a prescribed set of network parameters, with particular emphasis upon underlying principles and design procedures.

The material and method of presentation in this book have been classroom-tested at the University of Florida.

The preparation of this book has left the author indebted to many people. It is his pleasure to acknowledge the encouragement of Drs. J. H. Mulligan, F. E. Terman, W. W. Harman, and E. S. Kuh during the early and formative stages of the work; and to express his deep appreciation to Drs. W. W. Harman and J. G. Truxal for their valuable suggestions.

During the writing of the book, the author enjoyed the encouragement and assistance of his colleagues and graduate students at the University of Florida. It is with much pleasure that he extends his thanks to Drs. M. E. Forsman and M. J. Larsen and Dean Joseph Weil for their continued encouragement and interest, and to Drs. M. J. Larsen and W. E. Lear for many fruitful discussions about the manuscript.

The author is particularly indebted to Prof. R. C. Harden, Missouri School of Mines and Metallurgy, and Prof. J. L. Lowry, Auburn University, for their assistance while at the University of Florida. Professor Harden assisted in the preparation of the illustrations and proofread portions of the manuscript, and Professor Lowry read the complete manuscript and checked all derivations and examples for correctness; both have contributed in a variety of ways to the improvement of this work. The author is also appreciative of the excellent work of Mrs. Alice Harden, who in a joint effort with the author's wife typed the complete manuscript. Finally, to the many others who assisted in the preparation of this book, the author expresses his sincere appreciation.

The author's special thanks go to his wife, Dorothy, who has been in many ways an important partner in this venture.

Wayne H. Chen

Contents

PART C: FREQUENCY ANALYSIS OF EXCITATION AND RESPONSE

PART G: STABILITY PROBLEMS IN CLOSED-LOOP CONTROL SYSTEMS

part A Introduction and network fundamentals

Part A provides an introduction to the text and a review of some network fundamentals. The review is primarily intended to provide uniform notation and terminology throughout the book.

Since the text contains more material than is required for a one-semester course, a section (Art. 1.3) is included in the Introduction to aid in the selection of reading material for use of this book as (1) a textbook, (2) a book for self-study, or (3) a reference.

I Introduction

This book is a study of linear system analysis with particular emphasis placed upon (1) the problems of network and system analysis and (2) the preliminary topics intended for application to network synthesis problems.

But what are the problems of network analysis and synthesis and of system analysis?

1.1. Remarks about the problems of analysis and synthesis

Problems of network analysis. We shall describe the problems of network analysis in this manner:

Network analysis:

$$[Network] \xrightarrow[\text{find}]{\text{to}} \begin{bmatrix} Network \\ function \\ or\ network \\ parameters \end{bmatrix} \xrightarrow[\text{find}]{\text{to}} \begin{bmatrix} Network \\ characteristics \\ or\ network \\ behavior \end{bmatrix} \quad (1.1)$$

We use the term "network behavior" to mean "the response of the network subject to a certain excitation."

Problems of network synthesis. The problems of network synthesis are considered the converse of the network analysis problems in (1.1); i.e.,

Network synthesis:

$$\begin{bmatrix} Network \\ characteristics \\ or\ network \\ behavior \end{bmatrix} \xrightarrow[\text{find}]{\text{to}} \begin{bmatrix} Network \\ function \\ or\ network \\ parameters \end{bmatrix} \xrightarrow[\text{find}]{\text{to}} [Network] \quad (1.2)$$

Except for some "preliminary topics," the problems of network synthesis will not be treated in this book.

Additional problem of network analysis in the study of network relations. We shall find it very important to study "network relations," e.g., the relations between two networks or between excitation and response. The network relations give us a better insight into the network problems and are, therefore, instrumental in the solution of both analysis and synthesis problems as described in (1.1) and (1.2).

The study of network relations is often considered as an additional problem of network analysis.

Problems of system analysis. Linear networks and other linear systems are usually described by the same mathematical representation with different interpretations of the variables and may, therefore, be analyzed by the same methods. In this light, we study network problems in the earlier portions of this book and then extend this study into an analysis of the closed-loop control system, with emphasis on its stability problems.

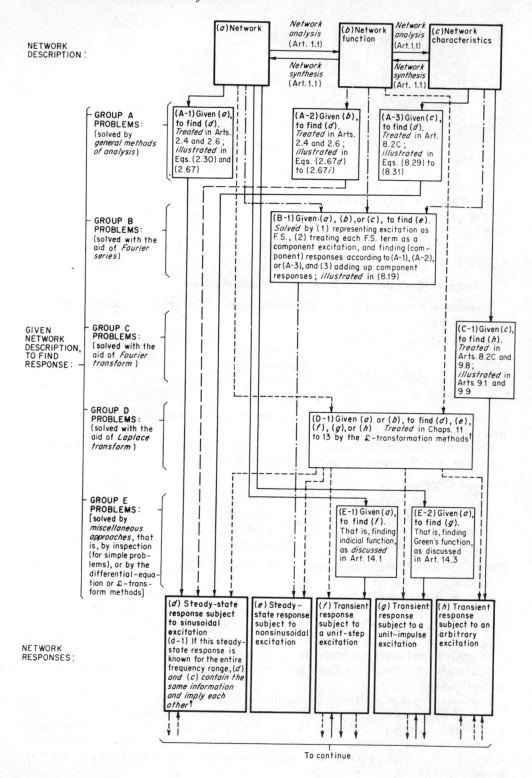

NETWORK
DESCRIPTION:

(a)Network

Network analysis (Art. 1.1)

Network synthesis (Art.1.1)

(b)Network function

Network analysis (Art.1.1)

Network synthesis (Art. 1.1)

(c)Network characteristics

GROUP A PROBLEMS: (solved by *general methods of analysis*)

(A-1)Given (a), to find (d). *Treated* in Arts. 2.4 and 2.6 ; *illustrated* in Eqs. (2.30) and (2.67)

(A-2)Given (b), to find (d). *Treated* in Arts. 2.4 and 2.6 ; *illustrated* in Eqs. (2.67d) to (2.67i)

(A-3)Given(c), to find (d). *Treated* in Art. 8.2C ; *illustrated* in Eqs. (8.29) to (8.31)

GROUP B PROBLEMS: (solved with the aid of *Fourier series*)

(B-1) Given (a), (b), or (c), to find (e). *Solved* by (1) representing excitation as F.S., (2) treating each F.S. term as a component excitation, and finding (component) responses according to (A-1), (A-2), or (A-3), and (3) adding up component responses ; *illustrated* in (8.19)

GIVEN NETWORK DESCRIPTION, TO FIND RESPONSE: —

GROUP C PROBLEMS: (solved with the aid of *Fourier transform*)

(C-1) Given (c), to find (h). *Treated* in Arts. 8.2C and 9.8 ; *illustrated* in Arts. 9.1 and 9.9

GROUP D PROBLEMS: (solved with the aid of *Laplace transform*)

(D-1) Given (a) or (b), to find (d), (e), (f), (g), or (h)   *Treated* in Chaps. 11 to 13 by the $\mathcal{L}$-transformation methods

GROUP E PROBLEMS: [solved by *miscellaneous approaches*, that is, by inspection (for simple problems), or by the differential-equation or $\mathcal{L}$-transform methods]

(E-1) Given (a), to find (f). That is, finding indicial function, as *discussed* in Art. 14.1

(E-2) Given (a), to find (g). That is, finding Green's function, as discussed in Art. 14.3

NETWORK RESPONSES:

(d) Steady-state response subject to sinusoidal excitation
(d-1) If this steady-state response is known for the entire frequency range, (d) and (c) *contain the same information and imply each other*

(e) Steady-state response subject to nonsinusoidal excitation

(f) Transient response subject to a unit-step excitation

(g) Transient response subject to a unit-impulse excitation

(h) Transient response subject to an arbitrary excitation

To continue

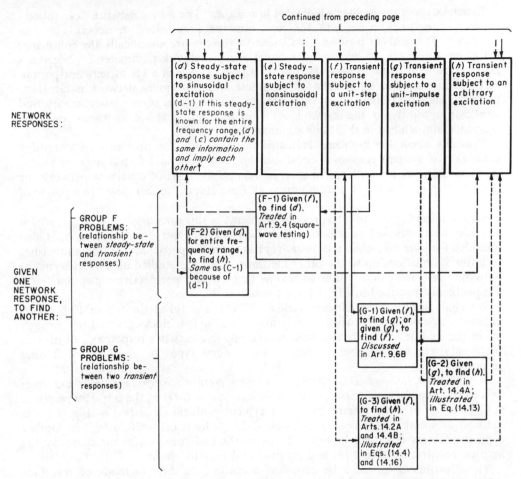

† For given (*a*), to find (*d*), (*e*), (*f*), (*g*), or (*h*), we may also use the differential-equation approach, which is only touched upon in Chap. 12 but *not treated* in this book. See any textbook on *differential equations* for the methods of solution.

‡ If we know the steady-state response E_2 for a given excitation E_1 [which represents a sinusoidal excitation as implied in Eq. (8.29*a*)] for the entire frequency range, we may evaluate the network characteristics $G_0(\omega)$ and $\theta(\omega)$ with the aid of Eq. (8.31); that is, $E_2/E_1 = G_0(\omega)e^{-j\theta(\omega)}$.

FIG. 1.1

1.2. Remarks about the coverage of this book

In view of the above remarks, this book will include the various topics belonging to the following principal subjects:

Coverage of this book:
  a. Problems of obtaining network descriptions
  b. Problems of obtaining network (or system) responses
  c. Problems of detecting unstable responses and eliminating them by improving system design
  d. Study of network relations

We shall elaborate on these subjects somewhat in the following paragraphs.

Remarks about the problems indicated in topic *a*.   The term "network description" refers to a network, a network function, network parameters, or network characteristics.   The analysis problems indicated in topic *a* are specifically the following: (1) given a network, to find network functions or network parameters; (2) given a network function, to find network characteristics; (3) given a set of network parameters, to find another set of network parameters; and (4) given network parameters, to find a network function, or vice versa.   The problems of the last category find application mostly in the methods of four-terminal network synthesis and are, therefore, not studied in this book on analysis.

Remarks about the problems indicated in topic *b*.   The problems of obtaining network (or system) responses constitute an important and broad area of study. Because there are a very large number of related methods of obtaining network (or system) responses, it is not uncommon at all for a student to feel "lost" in a jungle of techniques.

We shall use Fig. 1.1 to interpret the problems of this category.   Figure 1.1, which provides more detailed information than necessary for our present purpose, is also intended for later use, when the reader (1) has studied a particular method and wishes to know its relationship to the other methods or (2) has studied all the problems of obtaining responses and wishes to review them with a perspective viewpoint.   All the problems described in Fig. 1.1 are treated in this book.

We shall use the three blocks marked (*a*), (*b*), and (*c*) at the top of Fig. 1.1 to indicate three possible network descriptions, and the five blocks marked (*d*) through (*h*) in the middle of Fig. 1.1 to indicate five possible network responses.   With this representation, we are able to define two general types of problems of finding responses.

1. *Given the Network Description, to Obtain Network Responses.*   For example, "given (*c*) (namely, the network characteristics), to find (*h*) (i.e., the transient response subject to an arbitrary excitation)" is a typical problem described in Fig. 1.1; its method of solution is indicated in block C-1.   "Given (*a*), to find (*h*)" is another typical problem described in Fig. 1.1; its method of solution, as indicated by the arrows, requires us to find (*b*) and (*c*) first, and then to use block C-1.

These problems can also be classified according to their methods of solution; these classifications are indicated as Groups A through E in the upper half of Fig. 1.1.

2. *Given One Network Response, to Obtain Another Response.*   We shall find that it is not absolutely necessary to know the network description in order to obtain its response subject to a given excitation.   As a matter of fact, we may often find this response from another known response of the same network.

Problems of this general type are described and listed as problems of Groups F and G in the lower half of Fig. 1.1.   For example, "given (*f*), to find (*d*)" is a typical Group F problem.   Its method of solution is indicated in block F-1.

Remarks about the problems indicated in topic *c*.   In the design of a closed-loop control system or a vacuum-tube or transistor feedback amplifier, we are often interested in stability: Is this design stable?   Namely, does its response subject to a prescribed excitation have unstable components?

It is true that we may always solve for the response of a system (or network) to determine whether this response has unstable components.   But this approach is often very laborious, and if we do find the design unstable, this approach does not tell us how to improve it.

The alternative approaches call for "detecting" the unstable components in the response without solving for the response using laborious procedures.   These approaches use the various criteria or methods for determining stability and the various "methods of compensation" for improving stability; they are studied in this text.

Remarks about the problems indicated in topic *d*.   What are the relations between networks?   How do we characterize composite networks obtained by interconnecting two or more four-terminal networks?   How will the responses to two related excitations, applied individually to the same network, be related?   How are the network characteristics related to the time delay, buildup time, and waveform of the response?   How are the responses of the same network subject to different excitations related? The answers to these questions are important for the understanding and solution of

Table 1.1

Book Part	Chap. No.	(a)	(b)	(c)	(d)	(e)	(f)	(g)	(h)	(i)	(j)	(k)
		Reading coverage for the purpose described in Art. 1.3										
A. Introduction and network funda-mentals	1	O	O	O	O	O	O	O	O	O	O	O
	2	S	B[a]	B[a]	O	O	B[a]	B[a]	O	S	B[a]	B[a]
	3		B[a,b]	B[a]	O	O	B[a,b]	B[a]	O	S	B[a]	B[a]
B. Characterization of networks	4		S							S	S	S
	5		O							O		O
	6		S							S	O	O
C. Frequency analysis of excitation and response	7			S		B		S		S	S	S
	8			S		R[c]		S		S	S	S
	9			S[d]				S[d]		S[d]	S[d]	S[d]
	10			O				O		O	O	O
D. Study of network responses using Laplace-transforma-tion methods	11			S[e]	S			S	S[e]		S	S
	12			S	S			S	S		S	S
	13			S	S			S	S		S	S
E. Study of network responses using superposition integrals	14							O	O		O	S
F. The use of signal-flow diagrams as a tool in network analysis	15							S	S[f]			O
	16	S						S	S	S	S	S
	17							S	S[f]			O
G. Stability problems in closed-loop control systems	18						O[g]		S		O	S
	19						O[g]		S		O	S
	20								O			O
	21								O			O

S—Subject matter   B—Background material
O—Optional   R—read only when Referred to

[a] May be omitted if reader is already familiar with these basic subjects.
[b] Article 3.5, O (i.e., optional).
[c] Equation (8.34) in Art. 8.2C only.
[d] Articles 9.7 through 9.9, O.
[e] Omit Arts. 11.2 and 11.3A, and ignore unfamiliar terms in Art. 11.3B.
[f] May be omitted if reader is not interested in transistor circuits.
[g] Reader may either (1) study both Chaps. 18 and 19 or (2) use the Nyquist criterion in Art. 19.3C directly with the return ratio $T_{p'p}$ of the transistor feedback amplifier, as noted in the discussion following the Nyquist criterion.

numerous analysis and synthesis problems; these network relations are studied in this text.

Remark about the method of presentation.   In order to treat the four principal topics adequately and follow a logical order of presentation, this book is divided into seven parts, i.e., Parts A through G, as indicated in the table of contents.   An introductory statement is included at the beginning of each part to indicate coverage and emphasis.

1.3. Remarks about the use of this book

Although this book is comprehensive in contents, it is organized so as to permit flexibility in its use as (1) a textbook, (2) a book for self-study, or (3) a reference on *linear system (or network) analysis*.

For the purpose of using only some selected topics as a portion of a course or for self-study, the following reading coverages, which also include adequate background material, are suggested (see Table 1.1).

Selected topics or short course:
  a. For a study of *basic methods of analysis*, follow the first column in Table 1.1.
  b. For *characterization of networks*, follow the second column.
  c. For *frequency analysis*, follow the third column.
  d. For *a transient study with the Laplace transform* in which the Laplace transform is used only as a tool, follow the fourth column.
  e. For *a transient study with the Laplace transform* in which the origin of the Laplace transform is also studied, follow the fifth column.
  f. For *an analysis of transistor feedback amplifiers*, follow the sixth column.

For the purpose of using more topics on an organized basis for (1) a course with or without additional supplementary material provided by the instructor, or (2) self-study, the following reading coverages, which also include adequate background material, are suggested:

Formal course:
  g. For a study of *linear network responses, transient and steady-state*, follow the seventh column.
  h. For *transient behavior and stability of linear systems*, follow the eighth column.
  i. For *linear analysis techniques: basic methods of analysis, characterization of uetworks, and frequency analysis*, follow the ninth column.
  j. For *linear system (or network) analysis* in an abbreviated version, follow the tenth column.
  k. For *linear system (or network) analysis*, follow the eleventh column.

For courses or self-study on "network theory," this book may be used, in a number of different ways, together with the author's "Linear Network Design and Synthesis" (in press).

2 Methods of loop and nodal analysis

2.1. Network nomenclature

Most of the problems with which we shall be concerned in this book involve electrical networks. It is assumed that the reader is familiar with such basic terms† as *source, circuit element, branch, node, loop,* and *network*. A circuit is generally understood to be a simple network. However, there is no clear distinction between these terms, and we shall use them interchangeably. A simple illustration of some of these terms is given in Fig. 2.1a.

2.2. Useful network relations

In the solution of network problems, it is not always apparent which method of solution, e.g., the loop or the nodal method, will require the solution of fewer simultaneous equations. Two relations exist which are helpful in this respect. These relations, as will be proved later in Eqs. (5.12) and (5.16), are

$$l = b - n + p \tag{2.1}$$

and
$$n_p = n - p \tag{2.2}$$

where l = number of independent loops in network
b = number of branches
n = number of nodes
p = number of separate parts
n_p = number of independent node pairs

A separate part is defined as a portion of a network which may have purely inductive coupling, but no coupling through capacitance or conductance, with other parts of the network. One node in each separate part of the network is designated as a reference node, and this node in combination with any other node in that separate part constitutes a node pair.

As an example of the use of Eqs. (2.1) and (2.2), Fig. 2.1a has seven branches, four nodes, and one separate part. Therefore, $l = 4$, and $n_p = 3$; the four independent loops are numbered 1, 2, 3, and 4, and the three independent node pairs are *ad*, *bd*, and *cd*.

---

† Definitions of these terms are found in most books on electric-circuit analysis. For example, see W. R. LePage and S. Seely, "General Network Analysis," pp. 16–20, McGraw-Hill Book Company, Inc., New York, 1952.

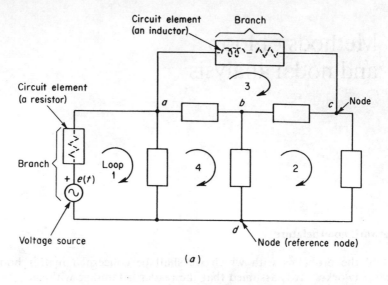

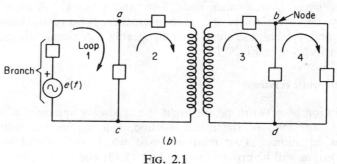

FIG. 2.1

Figure 2.1*b* provides another example which has six branches, four nodes, and two separate parts. According to Eqs. (2.1) and (2.2), $l = 4$ and $n_p = 2$; the four independent loops are numbered 1, 2, 3, and 4, and the two independent node pairs are *ac* and *bd*.

2.3. Use of $j\omega$ as frequency in the steady-state sinusoidal representation

A. *Exponential Representation*

Let us now consider the circuit in Fig. 2.2*a*; its voltage-current relation is described by the integrodifferential equation

$$e(t) = L\frac{di}{dt} + Ri + \frac{1}{C}\int i\, dt \qquad (2.3)$$

For a given sinusoidal excitation $e(t)$, what is the steady-state response $i(t)$ of this circuit?

Illustration A.   Excitation given as a sine function.   When the excitation is given in the form $e(t) = E_0 \sin(\omega t + \phi)$, we shall take advantage of the relation

$$e^{j\theta} = \cos\theta + j\sin\theta \qquad (2.4)$$

and the symbolic representations

$$\text{Re } e^{j\theta} = \text{real part of } e^{j\theta} = \cos\theta \tag{2.5a}$$

$$\text{Im } e^{j\theta} = \text{imaginary part of } e^{j\theta} = \sin\theta \tag{2.5b}$$

to find the excitation equal to

$$e(t) = E_0 \sin(\omega t + \phi) = \text{Im } (E_0 e^{j(\omega t + \phi)})$$
$$= \text{Im } (E_0 e^{j\phi} e^{j\omega t})$$
$$= \text{Im } (E e^{j\omega t}) \tag{2.6}$$

where
$$E = E_0 e^{j\phi} = E_0 (\cos\phi + j\sin\phi) \tag{2.6a}$$

However, it is customary to use exponential representations for both excitation and response:

Exponential representations:

$$e(t) = E e^{j\omega t}$$
$$i(t) = I e^{j\omega t} \tag{2.7}$$

with the *understanding* that the actual excitation and response are their imaginary parts, as illustrated in (2.6), or their real parts if the excitation is given as a cosine function, as will be illustrated in (2.11).

Procedure for Finding Steady-state Response with the Aid of Exponential Representations. For an excitation $e(t) = E_0 \sin(\omega t + \phi)$ (Fig. 2.2a), we may find the steady-state response $i(t)$ as follows:

1. Assume that both excitation $e(t)$ and response $i(t)$ have the exponential forms in (2.7). E is a known quantity of the form (2.6a), while I is an unknown quantity.

2. Substitute (2.7) into the integrodifferential equation (2.3), obtaining

$$E e^{j\omega t} = \left(j\omega L + R + \frac{1}{j\omega C} \right) I e^{j\omega t} \tag{2.8a}$$

or
$$I = \frac{E}{Z(j\omega)} \tag{2.8b}$$

Here we have impedance

Impedance:
$$Z(j\omega) = j\omega L + R + \frac{1}{j\omega C} \tag{2.9a}$$

or, letting $s = j\omega$ for brevity,

$$Z(s) = sL + R + \frac{1}{sC} \tag{2.9b}$$

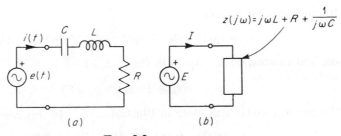

(a)   (b)

FIG. 2.2

3. Now I in (2.8b) is a known quantity, and the actual current response as a function of time is

$$i(t) = \text{Im } (Ie^{j\omega t}) = \text{Im } \left(\frac{E}{j\omega L + R + 1/j\omega C} \, e^{j\omega t} \right) \tag{2.10}$$

Complex Amplitudes of Voltages and Currents. Equations (2.8) suggest that we may represent the circuit in Fig. 2.2a in the symbolic form shown in Fig. 2.2b. E and I are called the complex amplitudes of $e(t)$ and $i(t)$, since each gives both the magnitude and the phase of its respective time function.

For example, if

$$e(t) = \text{Im } (Ee^{j\omega t}) \quad \text{and} \quad E = 2e^{j30°} = 2(\cos 30° + j \sin 30°) = 1.73 + j1$$

then $e(t) = \text{Im } (2e^{j30°}e^{j\omega t}) = 2 \sin (\omega t + 30°)$. Here $e(t)$ is said to have a complex amplitude $E = 2e^{j30°}$, that is, a magnitude of 2 and a phase angle of 30°.

Illustration B.   Excitation given as a cosine function.   When the excitation in Fig. 2.2a is given in the form $e(t) = E_0 \cos (\omega t + \phi)$, we may represent it as

$$\begin{aligned} e(t) = E_0 \cos (\omega t + \phi) &= \text{Re } (E_0 e^{j(\omega t + \phi)}) \\ &= \text{Re } (E_0 e^{j\phi}e^{j\omega t}) \\ &= \text{Re } (Ee^{j\omega t}) \end{aligned} \tag{2.11}$$

Again, we may use the exponential representations (2.7) for both excitation and response, but with the understanding that the actual excitation and response are their real parts. Following a procedure similar to that described in Illustration A, we find the actual current response in Fig. 2.2a as a function of time:

$$i(t) = \text{Re } (Ie^{j\omega t}) = \text{Re } \left(\frac{E}{j\omega L + R + 1/j\omega C} \, e^{j\omega t} \right) \tag{2.12}$$

Numerical Illustration 1.   In Fig. 2.2, letting

$$e(t) = 1 \sin 2t \qquad \text{volts} \tag{2.13a}$$

$R = 1$ ohm, $L = 1$ henry, $C = \frac{1}{2}$ farad, find $i(t)$ in amperes.

The impedance $Z(j\omega)$ at an angular frequency $\omega = 2$ rad/sec is

$$Z(j2) = j2 \times 1 + 1 + \frac{1}{j2 \times \frac{1}{2}} = 1 + j1 = \sqrt{2}e^{j45°} \tag{2.13b}$$

The complex amplitude of the current is then

$$I = \frac{E}{Z(j2)} = -\frac{1}{\sqrt{2}e^{j45°}} = 0.707e^{-j45°} \tag{2.13c}$$

and the time-varying current is

$$i(t) = \text{Im } (0.707e^{-j45°})e^{j2t} = 0.707 \sin (2t - 45°) \tag{2.13d}$$

Numerical Illustration 2.   Again in Fig. 2.2, let

$$e(t) = 1 \cos (2t + 30°) \tag{2.14a}$$

with the circuit constants as given in Illustration 1.   In this case, we have

$$e(t) = \text{Re } (1e^{j30°}e^{j2t}) = \text{Re } (Ee^{j\omega t}) \tag{2.14b}$$

The complex amplitude of the current is

$$I = \frac{E}{Z(j2)} = \frac{1e^{j30°}}{\sqrt{2}e^{j45°}} = 0.707e^{j(-15°)} \tag{2.14c}$$

The time-varying current then becomes

$$i(t) = \text{Re}\,(Ie^{j\omega t}) = \text{Re}\,(0.707e^{j(-15°)}\,e^{j2t})$$
$$= 0.707\cos(2t - 15°) \tag{2.14d}$$

B. Functions of $j\omega$

We note that, in the exponential form of representation, the angular frequency ω always appears with the operator j as a $j\omega$ term. For convenience, we shall call $j\omega$ the *frequency*, with the understanding that ω is the actual (angular) frequency. Therefore, we may consider impedance as shown in Eq. (2.9a), and other quantities such as admittance, as functions of $j\omega$.

2.4. Loop method of analysis

The loop method of analysis for both passive and active networks will be discussed in this section. Determinants will be used in the solution of the system equations.

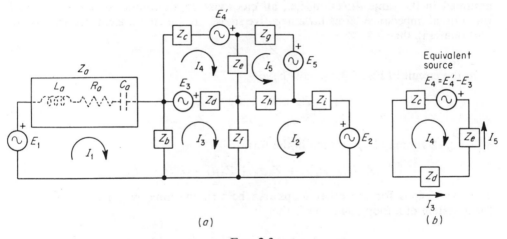

(a)   (b)

FIG. 2.3

For the present, we shall confine our discussion to the case in which all voltage sources in a network are of the same frequency.

A. Passive Networks

Loop equations. In Fig. 2.3a, we have a network composed of voltage sources and impedances as indicated. A typical impedance such as Z_a is expressed in the general form

$$Z(s) = sL_a + R_a + \frac{1}{sC_a} \tag{2.15}$$

with $s = j\omega$, as exemplified in Eq. (2.9b). The network of Fig. 2.3a has five independent loops, and since there are no current sources, there are five unknown loop currents, indicated in the figure.   Our object is to write loop equations from which we may evaluate the loop currents and define some *network functions*.

In order to have a uniform representation for the loop equations, we shall re-designate the two sources of loop 4 as an equivalent source $E_4 = E_4' - E_3$, as indicated in Fig. 2.3b.   The equation for any loop is obtained from Kirchhoff's voltage law.   For example, application of this law to loop 4 gives

$$Z_c I_4 + Z_e(I_4 + I_5) + Z_d(I_4 - I_3) = E_4$$

or
$$(Z_c + Z_e + Z_d)I_4 - Z_d I_3 + Z_e I_5 = E_4 \tag{2.16}$$

We define

Self- and mutual impedances of loop i:

Z_{ii} = self-impedance of loop i
    = sum of impedances in series in loop i $\qquad$ (2.17a)

Z_{ij} = mutual impedance between loops i and j
    = ±sum of impedances in series in branch† common to two loops   (2.17b)

where the *algebraic sign* of Z_{ij} is positive if I_i and I_j are in the same direction through the common branch, and negative if the currents are in the opposite directions. $Z_{ij} = 0$ if there is no impedance common to both loops.   If all loop currents are assumed in the same direction, i.e., all clockwise or all counterclockwise, then all the mutual-impedance terms have negative signs.   If the circuit elements are passive and bilateral, then

$$Z_{ij} = Z_{ji} \tag{2.18}$$

In the circuit in Fig. 2.3, we now have

$$\begin{aligned} Z_{44} &= Z_c + Z_e + Z_d & Z_{45} &= Z_e \\ Z_{43} &= -Z_d & Z_{41} &= 0 \end{aligned} \tag{2.19}$$

and Eq. (2.16) may be rewritten in the form

$$Z_{41}I_1 + Z_{42}I_2 + Z_{43}I_3 + Z_{44}I_4 + Z_{45}I_5 = E_4$$

The expressions for the other loops can be written similarly.   The general form for a system of n loop equations is then

$$\begin{aligned} Z_{11}I_1 + Z_{12}I_2 + \cdots + Z_{1n}I_n &= E_1 \\ Z_{21}I_1 + Z_{22}I_2 + \cdots + Z_{2n}I_n &= E_2 \\ \cdots\cdots\cdots\cdots\cdots\cdots\cdots\cdots\cdots \\ Z_{n1}I_1 + Z_{n2}I_2 + \cdots + Z_{nn}I_n &= E_n \end{aligned} \tag{2.20}$$

The loop currents $I_1, I_2, \ldots, I_n$ are simultaneous solutions of Eqs. (2.20).   With the equations arranged in symmetrical form as in (2.20), the use of determinants for obtaining the solution is a logical choice.

Solution of loop equations using determinants.   To illustrate the general use of determinants in solving the loop equations, let us consider the special case $n = 3$

---

† In the case of purely inductive coupling between two loops, Z_{ij} is due to mutual induct-ance, and its sign will be determined by the sense of the windings.   For a good discussion of this case, see M. F. Gardner and J. L. Barnes, "Transients in Linear Systems," pp. 30–33, John Wiley & Sons, Inc., New York, 1942.

in (2.20). The equation for I_1 is

$$I_1 = \frac{\begin{vmatrix} E_1 & Z_{12} & Z_{13} \\ E_2 & Z_{22} & Z_{23} \\ E_3 & Z_{32} & Z_{33} \end{vmatrix}}{\Delta}$$

$$= \frac{\begin{vmatrix} Z_{22} & Z_{23} \\ Z_{32} & Z_{33} \end{vmatrix}}{\Delta} E_1 + (-1) \frac{\begin{vmatrix} Z_{12} & Z_{13} \\ Z_{32} & Z_{33} \end{vmatrix}}{\Delta} E_2 + \frac{\begin{vmatrix} Z_{12} & Z_{13} \\ Z_{22} & Z_{23} \end{vmatrix}}{\Delta} E_3 \qquad (2.21)$$

or $\qquad\qquad I_1 = \frac{\Delta_{11}}{\Delta} E_1 + \frac{\Delta_{21}}{\Delta} E_2 + \frac{\Delta_{31}}{\Delta} E_3 \qquad\qquad\qquad (2.21a)$

where the *system determinant* Δ has the form

$$\Delta = \begin{vmatrix} Z_{11} & Z_{12} & Z_{13} \\ Z_{21} & Z_{22} & Z_{23} \\ Z_{31} & Z_{32} & Z_{33} \end{vmatrix} \qquad (2.22)$$

and the determinants Δ_{11}, Δ_{21}, Δ_{31} are the *cofactors* of Δ. The cofactor Δ_{ij} of a determinant Δ is another determinant equal to $(-1)^{i+j}$ times Δ with its ith row and jth column deleted. For example, Δ_{23} of Δ in (2.22) is

$$\Delta_{23} = (-1)^{2+3} \begin{vmatrix} Z_{11} & Z_{12} & Z_{13} \\ Z_{21} & Z_{22} & Z_{23} \\ Z_{31} & Z_{32} & Z_{33} \end{vmatrix} = (-1) \begin{vmatrix} Z_{11} & Z_{12} \\ Z_{31} & Z_{32} \end{vmatrix}$$

The currents I_2 and I_3 are found in the same manner as I_1. The three loop currents are

Current of a three-loop circuit:

$$I_1 = \frac{\Delta_{11}}{\Delta} E_1 + \frac{\Delta_{21}}{\Delta} E_2 + \frac{\Delta_{31}}{\Delta} E_3$$

$$I_2 = \frac{\Delta_{12}}{\Delta} E_1 + \frac{\Delta_{22}}{\Delta} E_2 + \frac{\Delta_{32}}{\Delta} E_3 \qquad (2.23)$$

$$I_3 = \frac{\Delta_{13}}{\Delta} E_1 + \frac{\Delta_{23}}{\Delta} E_2 + \frac{\Delta_{33}}{\Delta} E_3$$

For the general case of n loop equations given in (2.20), we have

Currents of an n-loop circuit:

$$I_k = \frac{\Delta_{1k}}{\Delta} E_1 + \frac{\Delta_{2k}}{\Delta} E_2 + \cdots + \frac{\Delta_{nk}}{\Delta} E_n \qquad k = 1, 2, \ldots, n \qquad (2.24)$$

where

System determinant:

$$\Delta = \begin{vmatrix} Z_{11} & Z_{12} & \cdots & Z_{1n} \\ Z_{21} & Z_{22} & \cdots & Z_{2n} \\ \cdots & \cdots & \cdots & \cdots \\ Z_{n1} & Z_{n2} & \cdots & Z_{nn} \end{vmatrix} \qquad (2.25)$$

and the Δ_{ik} are the cofactors of Δ. For passive, bilateral networks, Eq. (2.18) suggests that Δ in (2.25) is a determinant *symmetrical* with respect to its principal diagonal and its cofactors have the following relation:

For bilateral networks:

$$\Delta_{ik} = \Delta_{ki} \tag{2.26}$$

Passive network with a single source. In practical network problems, there is often a single source. For $E_2 = E_3 = \cdots = E_n = 0$ in (2.20) and (2.24), we have

For a single source E_1:

$$I_k = \frac{\Delta_{1k}}{\Delta} E_1 \qquad k = 1, 2, \ldots, n \tag{2.27}$$

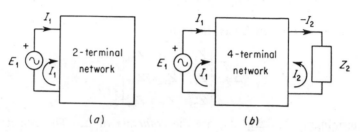

(a)   (b)

FIG. 2.4

If we consider E_1 as a source, and the rest of the circuit as a *two-terminal network*, as indicated in Fig. 2.4a, we may define the *driving-point impedance* at terminal pair 1 to be $(Z_D)_{11} = E_1/I_1$. From Eq. (2.27), it is apparent that

Driving-point impedance of two-terminal network in Fig. 2.4a:

$$Z_D = (Z_D)_{11} = \frac{E_1}{I_1} = \frac{\Delta}{\Delta_{11}} \tag{2.28}$$

A driving-point impedance relates a voltage and a current at the same terminal pair.

If we consider E_1 as a source, and the rest of the circuit as a *four-terminal network* with a load Z_2 as a part of loop 2 (Fig. 2.4b), we may define the *transfer impedance* to be $(Z_T)_{12} = E_1/I_2$. From Eq. (2.27), we now have

Transfer impedance of four-terminal network in Fig. 2.4b:

$$Z_T = (Z_T)_{12} = \frac{E_1}{I_2} = \frac{\Delta}{\Delta_{12}} \tag{2.29}$$

A transfer impedance relates a voltage at one terminal pair to a current at another. The definition of a transfer impedance is not so restrictive as is indicated in (2.29). For a single-source circuit in the example of Fig. 2.3a with $E_1 \neq 0$ and

$$E_2 = E_3 = E_4' = E_5 = 0$$

we may also have other transfer impedances, for example, $(Z_T)_{13} = E_1/I_3 = \Delta/\Delta_{13}$ and $(Z_T)_{14} = E_1/I_4 = \Delta/\Delta_{14}$.

Numerical Illustration 1. Loop system of analysis. In Fig. 2.5a, let

$$R_1 = R_2 = R_3 = R_4 = 1 \text{ ohm} \qquad L = 1 \text{ henry} \qquad C = \tfrac{1}{2} \text{ farad}$$

$$e_1(t) = 1 \cos \omega t \text{ volt} \qquad e_3(t) = \sqrt{2} \cos (\omega t + 45°) \qquad \omega = 1 \text{ rad/sec}$$

Solve for $i_1(t)$ and $i_2(t)$.

Assuming the exponential form of representation in (2.7), we now have

$$e_1(t) = E_1 e^{j\omega t} = 1 e^{j\omega t} \qquad\qquad E_1 = 1$$
$$e_3(t) = E_3 e^{j\omega t} = \sqrt{2} e^{j45°} e^{j\omega t} \qquad E_3 = \sqrt{2} e^{j45°} \qquad\qquad (2.30a)$$

and $\qquad\qquad i_1(t) = I_1 e^{j\omega t} \qquad\qquad\qquad i_2(t) = I_2 e^{j\omega t} \qquad (2.30b)$

with the understanding that the actual excitations and responses are their *real parts*. We shall now solve for I_1 and I_2.

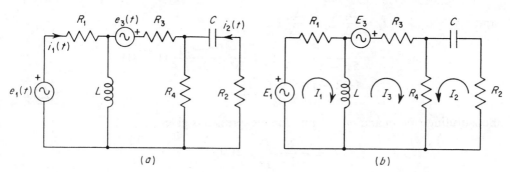

FIG. 2.5

For $s = j\omega$, the self- and mutual impedances of the loops in Fig. 2.5b are, according to (2.17),

$$Z_{11} = R_1 + Ls \qquad\qquad Z_{12} = Z_{21} = 0$$
$$Z_{22} = R_2 + R_4 + \frac{1}{Cs} \qquad Z_{13} = Z_{31} = -Ls \qquad (2.30c)$$
$$Z_{33} = R_3 + R_4 + Ls \qquad Z_{23} = Z_{32} = R_4$$

The system determinant and its cofactors are, therefore,

$$\Delta = \begin{vmatrix} R_1 + Ls & 0 & -Ls \\ 0 & R_2 + R_4 + \dfrac{1}{Cs} & R_4 \\ -Ls & R_4 & R_3 + R_4 + Ls \end{vmatrix}$$

$$= \begin{vmatrix} 1 + s & 0 & -s \\ 0 & 2 + \dfrac{2}{s} & 1 \\ -s & 1 & 2 + s \end{vmatrix} = 9 + \frac{4}{s} + 5s \qquad (2.30d)$$

$$\Delta_{11} = (-1)^{1+1} \begin{vmatrix} 2 + \dfrac{2}{s} & 1 \\ 1 & 2 + s \end{vmatrix} = 5 + \frac{4}{s} + 2s$$

$$\Delta_{12} = \Delta_{21} = (-1)^{1+2} \begin{vmatrix} 0 & 1 \\ -s & 2 + s \end{vmatrix} = -s$$

and $\qquad \Delta_{23} = \Delta_{32} = (-1)^{2+3} \begin{vmatrix} 1 + s & 0 \\ -s & 1 \end{vmatrix} = -(1 + s)$

Making use of Eqs. (2.23) and (2.24), and letting $E_1 = 1$, $E_2 = 0$, and

$$E_3 = \sqrt{2} e^{j45°} = 1 + j1$$

we have

$$I_1 = \frac{\Delta_{11}}{\Delta} E_1 + \frac{\Delta_{31}}{\Delta} E_3$$

$$= \frac{2s^2 + 5s + 4}{5s^2 + 9s + 4}(1) + \frac{2s^2 + 2s}{5s^2 + 9s + 4}(1 + j1)$$

$$= \frac{(4 + j2)s^2 + (7 + j2)s + 4}{5s^2 + 9s + 4} \qquad (2.30e)$$

and

$$I_2 = \frac{\Delta_{12}}{\Delta} E_1 + \frac{\Delta_{32}}{\Delta} E_3$$

$$= \frac{-s^2}{5s^2 + 9s + 4}(1) + \frac{-(s^2 + s)}{5s^2 + 9s + 4}(1 + j1)$$

$$= \frac{(-2 - j1)s^2 + (-1 - j1)s}{5s^2 + 9s + 4} \qquad (2.30f)$$

Substituting $s = j\omega$ and $\omega = 1$ into these expressions gives

$$I_1 = \frac{-2 + j5}{-1 + j9} = 0.60e^{j15.3°}$$

and

$$I_2 = \frac{3}{-1 + j9} = 0.33e^{j(-96.3°)}$$

The currents $i_1(t)$ and $i_2(t)$ are then

$$i_1(t) = \mathrm{Re}\,(I_1 e^{j\omega t}) = 0.60 \cos(\omega t + 15.3°) \qquad (2.30g)$$

and

$$i_2(t) = \mathrm{Re}\,(I_2 e^{j\omega t}) = 0.33 \cos(\omega t - 96.3°) \qquad (2.30h)$$

Numerical Illustration 2.   Driving-point and transfer impedances.   Let $E_3 = 0$ in Fig. 2.5b, and consider this circuit as a four-terminal network as depicted in Fig. 2.4b.   Compute the driving-point impedance $(Z_D)_{11}$ and the transfer impedance $(Z_T)_{12}$.

Making use of Eqs. (2.28) and (2.29) and the values of Δ, Δ_{11}, and Δ_{12} calculated in the previous illustration, we have

$$Z_D = (Z_D)_{11} = \frac{E_1}{I_1} = \frac{\Delta}{\Delta_{11}} = \frac{5s^2 + 9s + 4}{2s^2 + 5s + 4} \qquad (2.31a)$$

and

$$Z_T = (Z_T)_{12} = \frac{E_1}{I_2} = \frac{\Delta}{\Delta_{12}} = -\frac{5s^2 + 9s + 4}{s^2} \qquad (2.31b)$$

If we substitute $s = j\omega$ and $\omega = 1$ in these expressions, the results are

$$Z_D = (Z_D)_{11} = 1.48 + j0.79 \qquad (2.31c)$$

and

$$Z_T = (Z_T)_{12} = -1 + j9 \qquad (2.31d)$$

Parameters of four-terminal networks.   We often find that a four-terminal network does not terminate in a simple load Z_2 as in Fig. 2.4b.   For example, it may terminate in another network, as indicated in Fig. 2.6a, where the equivalent load impedance Z_2 is not readily known.   In this case, however, the output voltage $E_2 = -I_2 Z_2$, as shown in Fig. 2.6b, is usually available; both I_2 and Z_2 may in general be unknown quantities.

If we now wish to solve for I_1 and I_2, we may consider the equivalent problem of a network with two voltage sources, as in Fig. 2.6c.   This permits us to use Eq. (2.24) and obtain

Voltage-current relations of a four-terminal network:

$$I_1 = y_{11}E_1 + y_{12}E_2 \qquad I_2 = y_{21}E_1 + y_{22}E_2 \qquad (2.32)$$

where

$$y_{ij} = \frac{\Delta_{ji}}{\Delta} \qquad (2.33)$$

Here we have a set of *parameters* y_{11}, y_{12}, y_{21}, y_{22} of a four-terminal network; they may be solved for in terms of the system determinant Δ and its cofactors Δ_{ij} with the loop (or nodal) method of analysis. This set of four parameters will completely

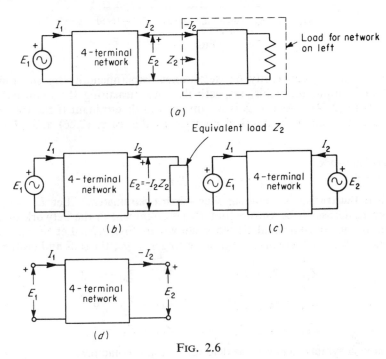

FIG. 2.6

characterize the four-terminal network, which is more conventionally represented in Fig. 2.6d, in the sense that they will prescribe the voltage-current relations as shown in (2.32). (Associated with a four-terminal network there are several sets of network parameters, and each set completely characterizes the network in terms of voltage-current relations. We shall discuss other sets of network parameters in Art. 4.2.) The parameters y_{ij} are called the *short-circuit admittances* of the network. This term is self-explanatory if we note that (1) with terminal pair 2 in Fig. 2.6d short-circuited or $E_2 = 0$ in (2.32),

$$y_{11} = \left(\frac{I_1}{E_1}\right)_{E_2=0} \qquad (2.34a)$$

$$y_{21} = \left(\frac{I_2}{E_1}\right)_{E_2=0} \qquad (2.34b)$$

and (2) with terminal pair 1 short-circuited or $E_1 = 0$ in (2.32),

$$y_{12} = \left(\frac{I_1}{E_2}\right)_{E_1=0} \qquad (2.34c)$$

$$y_{22} = \left(\frac{I_2}{E_2}\right)_{E_1=0} \qquad (2.34d)$$

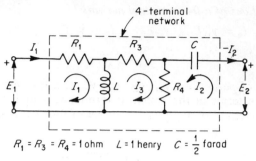

$$R_1 = R_3 = R_4 = 1\text{ ohm} \quad L = 1\text{ henry} \quad C = \tfrac{1}{2}\text{ farad}$$

Fig. 2.7

These parameters y_{ij} can easily be determined experimentally by short-circuiting the input and output terminals, respectively, and measuring the required voltages and currents in (2.34). Again, Δ is a symmetrical determinant if the four-terminal network is composed of bilateral elements. In this case, (2.26) and (2.33) imply that

For bilateral networks:

$$y_{12} = y_{21} \tag{2.35}$$

Numerical Illustration 3. Finding short-circuit parameters. Let $E_3 = 0$, and let the voltage E_2 across R_2 be known (but R_2 be unknown) in the network of Fig. 2.5. The result is the four-terminal network shown in Fig. 2.7. Let us now find the parameters y_{ij} for this network. Again, letting $s = j\omega$, the self- and mutual impedances are

$$Z_{11} = R_1 + Ls \qquad\qquad Z_{13} = Z_{31} = -Ls$$

$$Z_{22} = R_4 + \frac{1}{Cs} \qquad\qquad Z_{12} = Z_{21} = 0 \tag{2.36a}$$

$$Z_{33} = R_3 + R_4 + Ls \qquad Z_{23} = Z_{32} = R_4$$

We now have a symmetrical system determinant and cofactors:

$$\Delta = \begin{vmatrix} R_1 + Ls & 0 & -Ls \\ 0 & R_4 + \dfrac{1}{Cs} & R_4 \\ -Ls & R_4 & R_3 + R_4 + Ls \end{vmatrix}$$

$$= \begin{vmatrix} 1 + s & 0 & -s \\ 0 & 1 + \dfrac{2}{s} & 1 \\ -s & 1 & 2 + s \end{vmatrix} = \frac{2s^2 + 7s + 4}{s} \tag{2.36b}$$

$$\Delta_{11} = (-1)^{1+1} \begin{vmatrix} 1 + \dfrac{2}{s} & 1 \\ 1 & 2 + s \end{vmatrix} = \frac{s^2 + 3s + 4}{s}$$

$$\Delta_{21} = \Delta_{12} = (-1)^{2+1} \begin{vmatrix} 0 & -s \\ 1 & 2 + s \end{vmatrix} = -s$$

$$\Delta_{22} = (-1)^{2+2} \begin{vmatrix} 1 + s & -s \\ -s & 2 + s \end{vmatrix} = 3s + 2$$

The network parameters are then

$$y_{11} = \frac{\Delta_{11}}{\Delta} = \frac{s^2 + 3s + 4}{2s^2 + 7s + 4} \tag{2.36c}$$

$$y_{12} = y_{21} = \frac{\Delta_{21}}{\Delta} = \frac{-s^2}{2s^2 + 7s + 4} \tag{2.36d}$$

and

$$y_{22} = \frac{\Delta_{22}}{\Delta} = \frac{3s^2 + 2s}{2s^2 + 7s + 4} \tag{2.36e}$$

The currents I_1 and I_2 in Fig. 2.7 can now be computed for any value of angular frequency ω, with known values of E_1 and E_2, by using these parameters in Eqs. (2.32) and substituting $j\omega$ for s.

B. Active Networks

Before we attempt to analyze networks having active elements, we shall introduce the equivalent circuits of some commonly used active elements.   We shall see that *an active network, with its active elements replaced by their equivalent circuits, may be analyzed in the same manner as a passive network*.

Equivalent circuit of a vacuum tube.   Schematic diagrams are shown in Fig. 2.8a, b, and c, respectively, for a triode, a tetrode, and a pentode vacuum tube. E_g and E_p are, respectively, the alternating voltages from grid to cathode and from plate to cathode.   The d-c voltages necessary for the operation of the tubes are assumed to be applied, but are omitted from the diagrams.   In normal operation, the screen grid and suppressor grid are at the same potential as the cathode as far as alternating potential is concerned.   It is shown in elementary texts on electronics that for small values of E_g and for frequencies at which the effects of the interelectrode capacitances are negligible, the circuit of Fig. 2.8d is the equivalent of any of the other three circuits.   The amplification factor μ and the plate resistance r_p are numerical constants at fixed d-c operating potentials.   The sign of the equivalent generator voltage $-\mu E_g$, with its assumed positive direction, indicates that there is a phase reversal of this equivalent voltage from the grid voltage E_g.

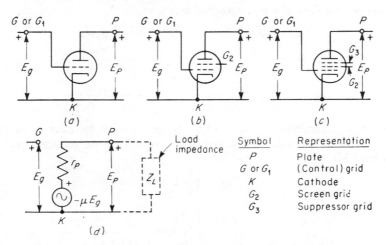

FIG. 2.8

The equivalent circuit of Fig. 2.8*d* may be used to represent a vacuum tube operating under the stated restrictions of small signal and low frequency, and the network in which the tube appears may then be analyzed as a passive network.

Equivalent circuit of a transistor.†   The schematic circuit diagram for a three-terminal transistor is shown in Fig. 2.9*a*.   As in the case of the vacuum-tube circuits, the d-c sources have been omitted, and only the alternating potentials are shown. The input voltage and current are E_1 and I_1, while E_2 and I_2 are the output voltage

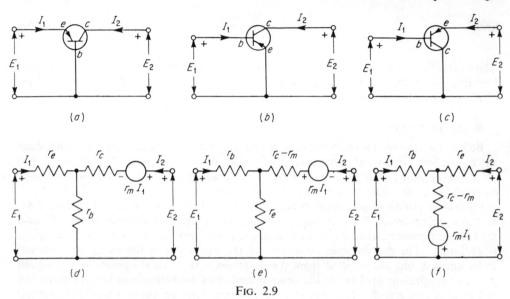

FIG. 2.9

and current.   The three elements of the transistor marked e, b, and c are, respectively, the *emitter*, the *base*, and the *collector*.

Since the circuit as shown in Fig. 2.9*a* constitutes a four-terminal network, Eqs. (2.32) apply.   We may solve for E_1 and E_2 from (2.32), finding another pair of voltage-current relations for this network:

Voltage-current relations of a four-terminal network:

$$E_1 = z_{11}I_1 + z_{12}I_2 \qquad E_2 = z_{21}I_1 + z_{22}I_2 \qquad (2.37)$$

where

$$z_{11} = \frac{y_{22}}{y_{11}y_{22} - y_{21}y_{12}} \qquad z_{12} = \frac{-y_{12}}{y_{11}y_{22} - y_{21}y_{12}}$$

$$z_{21} = \frac{-y_{21}}{y_{11}y_{22} - y_{21}y_{12}} \qquad z_{22} = \frac{y_{11}}{y_{11}y_{22} - y_{21}y_{12}} \qquad (2.38)$$

These four new parameters z_{ij} are called the *open-circuit impedances* of the four-terminal network.   The term is appropriate, since (1) with terminal pair 2 open or $I_2 = 0$ in (2.37),

$$z_{11} = \left(\frac{E_1}{I_1}\right)_{I_2=0} \qquad (2.39a)$$

$$z_{21} = \left(\frac{E_2}{I_1}\right)_{I_2=0} \qquad (2.39b)$$

† Omission of this topic will not impair reading continuity.

and (2) with terminal pair 1 open or $I_1 = 0$ in (2.37),

$$z_{12} = \left(\frac{E_1}{I_2}\right)_{I_1=0} \qquad (2.39c)$$

$$z_{22} = \left(\frac{E_2}{I_2}\right)_{I_1=0} \qquad (2.39d)$$

The parameters z_{ij} can easily be determined experimentally by open-circuiting the output and input terminals, respectively, and measuring the required voltages and currents in (2.39).

Equations (2.37) can be rearranged to give

$$\begin{aligned} E_1 &= I_1(z_{11} - z_{12}) + (I_1 + I_2)z_{12} \\ &= I_1 r_e + (I_1 + I_2)r_b \end{aligned} \qquad (2.40a)$$

$$\begin{aligned} E_2 &= I_1(z_{21} - z_{12}) + I_2(z_{22} - z_{12}) + (I_1 + I_2)z_{12} \\ &= I_1 r_m + I_2 r_c + (I_1 + I_2)r_b \end{aligned} \qquad (2.40b)$$

By letting

$$\begin{array}{cc} z_{11} - z_{12} = r_e & z_{12} = r_b \\ z_{21} - z_{12} = r_m & z_{22} - z_{12} = r_c \end{array} \qquad (2.41)$$

we see that the circuit of Fig. 2.9*d* satisfies Eqs. (2.40). The circuit of Fig. 2.9*d* is then the *equivalent circuit* for the transistor when it is used in the *grounded-base* connection of Fig. 2.9*a*. The quantities† r_e, r_b, r_m, and r_c may be obtained experimentally from the indicated open-circuit impedance measurements; with a given set of d-c operating potentials, these quantities are numerical constants.

When the transistor is used in the grounded-emitter connection of Fig. 2.9*b* or the grounded-collector connection of Fig. 2.9*c*, the same approach yields two additional circuits, different in form from that of the grounded base, but using the same circuit elements. These equivalent circuits are shown in Fig. 2.9*e* and *f*, respectively. Then, depending on the connection of the transistor, the proper equivalent circuit can be substituted for it, and the network can be solved as if it were a passive network.

Loop equations of active networks. As stated above, once the equivalent circuit has been substituted for an active element, the network containing this element may be treated using the methods described for passive networks.

As an example, let us find the loop equations of the active network in Fig. 2.10*a*. The values of μ and r_p for the prescribed operating conditions of the tube are assumed known.

We first replace the vacuum tube with its equivalent circuit as in Fig. 2.10*b*. The application of Eq. (2.1) tells us there are four independent loop currents, which are shown in the figure. Equations (2.20) may now be written for this network with $E_2 = 0$, $E_3 = -\mu E_g$, and $E_4 = -\mu E_g$. With Z_{ij} as indicated in Fig. 2.10*b*, the equation for loop 3 has the form

$$Z_{31}I_1 + Z_{32}I_2 + Z_{33}I_3 + Z_{34}I_4 = E_3 = -\mu Z_b(I_1 + I_4)$$

† The symbol r rather than z is used since, at low frequencies, these quantities are resistive. At high frequencies, the effects of capacitance and finite transit time must be taken into account. For a treatment of high-frequency equivalent circuits for transistors, see A. W. Lo, R. O. Endes, J. Zawels, F. W. Waldhauer, and C. C. Cheng, "Transistor Electronics," Prentice-Hall, Inc., Englewood Cliffs, N.J., 1955.

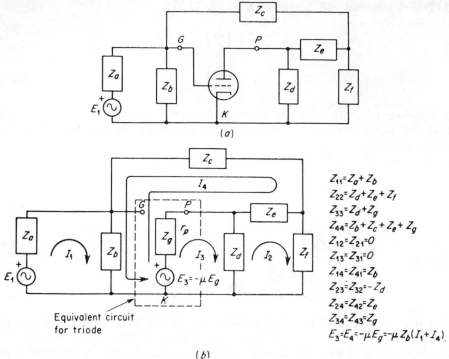

Equivalent circuit
for triode

$Z_{11}=Z_a+Z_b$
$Z_{22}=Z_d+Z_e+Z_f$
$Z_{33}=Z_d+Z_g$
$Z_{44}=Z_b+Z_c+Z_e+Z_g$
$Z_{12}=Z_{21}=0$
$Z_{13}=Z_{31}=0$
$Z_{14}=Z_{41}=Z_b$
$Z_{23}=Z_{32}=-Z_d$
$Z_{24}=Z_{42}=Z_e$
$Z_{34}=Z_{43}=Z_g$
$E_3=E_4=-\mu E_g=-\mu Z_b(I_1+I_4)$.

(*b*)

FIG. 2.10

which may be rearranged as

$$Z'_{31}I_1 + Z_{32}I_2 + Z_{33}I_3 + Z'_{34}I_4 = 0 \tag{2.42}$$

where
$$Z'_{31} = Z_{31} + \mu Z_b \tag{2.42a}$$
$$Z'_{34} = Z_{34} + \mu Z_b \tag{2.42b}$$

Similarly, the equation for loop 4 may be written as

$$Z'_{41}I_1 + Z_{42}I_2 + Z_{43}I_3 + Z'_{44}I_4 = 0 \tag{2.43}$$

where
$$Z'_{41} = Z_{41} + \mu Z_b \tag{2.43a}$$
$$Z'_{44} = Z_{44} + \mu Z_b \tag{2.43b}$$

The system of loop equations describing the active network in Fig. 2.10 now takes the form

Loop equations for active network in Fig. 2.10:

$$
\begin{aligned}
Z_{11}I_1 + Z_{12}I_2 + Z_{13}I_3 + Z_{14}I_4 &= E_1 \\
Z_{21}I_1 + Z_{22}I_2 + Z_{23}I_3 + Z_{24}I_4 &= 0 \\
Z'_{31}I_1 + Z_{32}I_2 + Z_{33}I_3 + Z'_{34}I_4 &= 0 \\
Z'_{41}I_1 + Z_{42}I_2 + Z_{43}I_3 + Z'_{44}I_4 &= 0
\end{aligned}
\tag{2.44}
$$

From (2.27), the solution for the loop currents of (2.44) is

$$I_k = \frac{\Delta_{1k}}{\Delta} E_1 \qquad k = 1, 2, 3, 4 \tag{2.45}$$

where the system determinant is

$$\Delta = \begin{vmatrix} Z_{11} & Z_{12} & Z_{13} & Z_{14} \\ Z_{21} & Z_{22} & Z_{23} & Z_{24} \\ Z'_{31} & Z_{32} & Z_{33} & Z'_{34} \\ Z'_{41} & Z_{42} & Z_{43} & Z'_{44} \end{vmatrix} \tag{2.46}$$

and the Δ_{1k} are the cofactors of Δ. In contrast to the passive-network case, we find that, in general, Δ for an active network is not symmetrical.

C. Some Network Functions

Driving-point functions. The driving-point impedance of the two-terminal passive network shown in Fig. 2.4a was defined in Eq. (2.28). We may likewise consider the active network in Fig. 2.10a as a two-terminal network having source E_1 and current I_1. Equations (2.44) suggest the same general form for the driving-point impedance as that for the passive network. Then for a passive or an active network, we have

$$Z_D = (Z_D)_{11} = \frac{E_1}{I_1} = \frac{\Delta}{\Delta_{11}} \tag{2.47}$$

for the driving-point impedance and

$$Y_D = (Y_D)_{11} = \frac{I_1}{E_1} = \frac{\Delta_{11}}{\Delta} = \frac{1}{Z_D} \tag{2.48}$$

called the *driving-point admittance*. Both Z_D and Y_D are network functions.

In the example of Fig. 2.5b with $E_3 = 0$, we found in Eq. (2.31a) that

$$Z_D = (Z_D)_{11} = \frac{5s^2 + 9s + 4}{2s^2 + 5s + 4} \tag{2.49}$$

We see that the driving-point impedance in this case is a ratio of two polynomials in s, where $s = j\omega$. Since $Y_D = 1/Z_D$, as indicated in (2.48), the driving-point admittance is also representable as a ratio of two polynomials in s. In general, a driving-point function is representable as a ratio of two polynomials in s.

Transfer functions. We have defined transfer impedance with Eq. (2.29) for the four-terminal (passive) network shown in Fig. 2.4b. We may similarly consider the active network of Fig. 2.10a as a four-terminal network having source E_1 and load impedance Z_f. Since Eqs. (2.44) as loop equations for an active network with a single source have the same general form as the loop equations of a passive network with a single source, their transfer impedances will also have the same form. Therefore, for a passive or an active network, we have

$$Z_T = (Z_T)_{12} = \frac{E_1}{I_2} = \frac{\Delta}{\Delta_{12}} \tag{2.50}$$

as the transfer impedance, and

$$Y_T = (Y_T)_{21} = \frac{I_2}{E_1} = \frac{\Delta_{12}}{\Delta} = \frac{1}{Z_T} \tag{2.51}$$

as the transfer admittance. As in the case of driving-point functions, both network functions Z_T and Y_T may be represented as a ratio of two polynomials in s. This was illustrated in Eq. (2.31b):

$$Z_T = (Z_T)_{12} = -\frac{5s^2 + 9s + 4}{s^2} \tag{2.52}$$

2.5. Voltage and current sources

A. *Exchange of Sources*

Equivalent source.   A physical voltage source inherently has some internal impedance.   For purposes of analysis, we may consider the actual source equivalent to an *idealized voltage source* in series with an impedance, as shown in Fig. 2.11*a*.

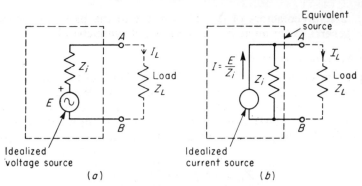

FIG. 2.11

The idealized source has no impedance and has a voltage equal to the open-circuit voltage of the actual source.   The series impedance Z_i is the internal impedance of the source.

As far as the effect on the load connected to the terminals AB is concerned, the circuit of Fig. 2.11*a* may be replaced by that of Fig. 2.11*b*.   This circuit shows that the voltage generator has been replaced by an *idealized current source*, i.e., one having zero admittance, of magnitude $I = E/Z_i$, in parallel with the impedance Z_i.   We may easily verify that, in both cases, we have (1) $E_{AB} = E$ with no load and (2) $E_{AB} = EZ_L/(Z_i + Z_L)$ and $I_L = E/(Z_i + Z_L)$ when the load Z_L is connected.   The

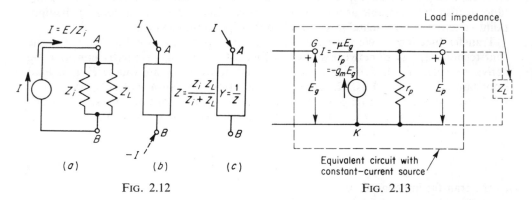

FIG. 2.12

FIG. 2.13

equivalent source of Fig. 2.11*b* applies† only for a single-frequency sinusoidal source, where direct current may be considered to be the special case of a zero-frequency sinusoid.

Notation for a constant-current source.   Since a constant-current source has infinite internal impedance, it is appropriate to represent it as an open circuit with a

† For equivalent sources under other conditions, see M. F. Gardner and J. L. Barnes, "Transients in Linear Systems," pp. 43–46, John Wiley & Sons, Inc., New York, 1942.

constant current injected into the load, as shown in Fig. 2.12b. Figure 2.12b is an alternative representation of Fig. 2.12a, which is equivalent to a circuit with a voltage source, such as that of Fig. 2.11a. The current I is shown entering the combined circuit element Z at terminal A in Fig. 2.12b and leaving (or $-I$ entering) at terminal B. Alternatively, the notation of Fig. 2.12c may be used; here only the current entering node A is shown.

As we shall see in Art. 2.6, the use of constant-current sources is of value in the nodal method of analysis, in which circuit elements are represented by their admittances, rather than impedances, as in Fig. 2.12c.

B. Alternative Representations of Some Active Elements

As a simple illustration of the discussion above, we shall find the equivalent circuit of a vacuum tube, using a constant-current source. The constant-voltage equivalent circuit was shown in Fig. 2.8d. If we compare this figure with Fig. 2.11a and its constant-current equivalent, Fig. 2.12a, we see that the vacuum tube may also be represented as in Fig. 2.13. Here, $g_m = \mu/r_p$ is the transconductance of the tube.

2.6. Nodal method of analysis

A. Passive Networks

As an illustration of the use of the nodal method of analysis, consider the circuit of Fig. 2.14a. Before proceeding with the analysis, we shall convert the given voltage sources to equivalent current sources following the procedure of Art. 2.5. We assume that E_a, E_b, E_c, and E_d are constant-voltage sources and that their internal impedances are included, respectively, in the series impedances Z_a, Z_b, Z_c, and Z_d. When these constant-voltage sources with their series impedances are converted one by one to constant-current equivalents, the circuit of Fig. 2.14b results. We then combine the currents injected into each node to obtain the circuit of Fig. 2.14c, where the circuit elements have been designated as admittances rather than impedances. The admittance Y_{ij} represents the admittance of a branch joining nodes i and j, while Y_k is the admittance of the branch between node k and ground, which is used as the reference node.

Nodal equations. A typical admittance in a network such as that of Fig. 2.14c can be expressed in the form

$$Y(s) = sC + G + \frac{1}{sL} \tag{2.53}$$

for $s = j\omega$, illustrated in Fig. 2.14d, where C, G, and L are, respectively, capacitance, conductance, and inductance.

The application of Eq. (2.2) to Fig. 2.14c indicates that there are three independent node pairs and, therefore, three unknown nodal voltages E_1, E_2, and E_3. Our object is to write the nodal equations from which we may evaluate the nodal voltages and define some additional network functions.

The equation for any node is obtained from Kirchhoff's current law. For example, application of this law to node 1 in Fig. 2.14c gives

$$Y_1 E_1 + Y_{12}(E_1 - E_2) + Y_{13}(E_1 - E_3) = I_1$$

or
$$(Y_1 + Y_{12} + Y_{13})E_1 - Y_{12}E_2 - Y_{13}E_3 = I_1 \tag{2.54}$$

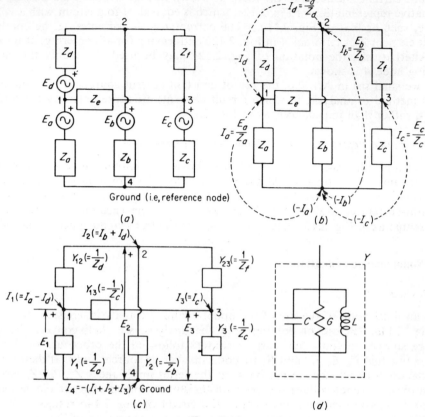

FIG. 2.14

Let us now define

Self- and mutual admittances of node i:

Y_{ii} = self-admittance of node i

= sum of admittances having node i as their common junction   (2.55*a*)

Y_{ij} = mutual admittance between node i and node j

= sum of admittances in parallel connecting nodes i and j (2.55*b*)

For node 1 in Fig. 2.14*c*, we have

$$Y_{11} = Y_1 + Y_{12} + Y_{13}$$

Unlike the mutual impedance Z_{ij} in loop equations, Y_{ij} is never negative. $Y_{ij} = 0$ if there is no admittance, i.e., no circuit element, between nodes i and j.

We may now rewrite (2.54) in the form

$$Y_{11}E_1 - Y_{12}E_2 - Y_{13}E_3 = I_1$$

The expressions for the currents at the other nodes can be written in similar form.

The *general form* for a system of n nodal equations is then

System of nodal equations:

$$Y_{11}E_1 - Y_{12}E_2 - Y_{13}E_3 - \cdots - Y_{1n}E_n = I_1$$
$$- Y_{21}E_1 + Y_{22}E_2 - Y_{23}E_3 - \cdots - Y_{2n}E_n = I_2$$
$$\cdots \cdots \cdots \cdots \cdots \cdots \cdots \cdots \cdots \cdots \cdots \cdots$$
$$- Y_{n1}E_1 - Y_{n2}E_2 - Y_{n3}E_3 - \cdots + Y_{nn}E_n = I_n$$

$$(2.56)$$

The nodal voltages $E_1, E_2, \ldots, E_n$ are the simultaneous solutions of Eqs. (2.56). As in Eq. (2.24) for loop analysis, we have

Voltages of an n-node circuit:

$$E_k = \frac{\Delta'_{1k}}{\Delta'} I_1 + \frac{\Delta'_{2k}}{\Delta'} I_2 + \cdots + \frac{\Delta'_{nk}}{\Delta'} I_n \qquad k = 1, 2, \ldots, n \qquad (2.57)$$

where

System determinant:

$$\Delta' = \begin{vmatrix} Y_{11} & -Y_{12} & -Y_{13} & \cdots & -Y_{1n} \\ -Y_{21} & Y_{22} & -Y_{23} & \cdots & -Y_{2n} \\ \cdots\cdots\cdots\cdots\cdots\cdots\cdots\cdots \\ -Y_{n1} & -Y_{n2} & -Y_{n3} & \cdots & Y_{nn} \end{vmatrix} \qquad (2.58)$$

and the Δ'_{ik} are the cofactors of Δ'. Note that the system determinant Δ' is symmetrical because $Y_{ij} = Y_{ji}$, and only its diagonal terms are positive. A numerical illustration will be given in Art. 2.6C.

B. Active Networks

To use the nodal method of analysis with active networks, we need only replace the active elements with equivalent circuits, using constant-current sources, and then proceed with the analysis as for passive networks.

Illustration. Suppose we wish to write the nodal equations for the active network of Fig. 2.15a. The values of g_m and r_p for the tube are assumed known.

We first replace the vacuum tube with its equivalent circuit, using a constant-current source as shown in Fig. 2.15b. $I_3 = 0$ indicates that there is no current source at node 3. We now have a circuit with three independent node pairs and no voltage sources; therefore we must write three nodal equations. With Y_{ij} as indicated in Fig. 2.15b, the equation for node 2 has the form

$$-Y_{21}F_1 + Y_{22}F_2 - Y_{20}F_0 = -g_m F_1$$

or

$$-Y'_{21}E_1 + Y_{22}E_2 - Y_{23}E_3 = 0$$

where

$$Y'_{21} = Y_{21} - g_m \qquad (2.59)$$

The system of nodal equations describing this active network now takes the form

$$\begin{aligned} Y_{11}E_1 - Y_{12}E_2 - Y_{13}E_3 &= I_1 \\ -Y'_{21}E_1 + Y_{22}E_2 - Y_{23}E_3 &= 0 \\ -Y_{31}E_1 - Y_{32}E_2 + Y_{33}E_3 &= 0 \end{aligned} \qquad (2.60)$$

From (2.57), the nodal voltages of (2.60) are

$$E_k = \frac{\Delta'_{1k}}{\Delta'} I_1 \qquad k = 1, 2, 3 \qquad (2.61)$$

where the system determinant is

$$\Delta' = \begin{vmatrix} Y_{11} & -Y_{12} & -Y_{13} \\ -Y'_{21} & Y_{22} & -Y_{23} \\ -Y_{31} & -Y_{32} & Y_{33} \end{vmatrix} \qquad (2.62)$$

and the Δ'_{ik} are the cofactors of Δ'. In contrast to the passive-network case, we find

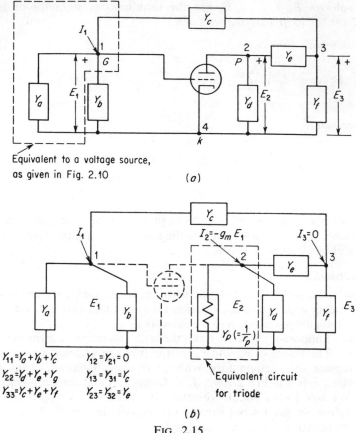

Equivalent to a voltage source,
as given in Fig. 2.10

(*a*)

$Y_{11} = Y_a + Y_b + Y_c$ $Y_{12} = Y_{21} = 0$
$Y_{22} = Y_d + Y_e + Y_g$ $Y_{13} = Y_{31} = Y_c$
$Y_{33} = Y_c + Y_e + Y_f$ $Y_{23} = Y_{32} = Y_e$

Equivalent circuit
for triode

(*b*)

FIG. 2.15

that Δ' for an active network is generally not symmetrical, since $Y_{12} = Y_{21} \neq Y_{21}'$, as indicated in Eq. (2.59).

C. *Some Network Functions*

Driving-point functions. For a network, active or passive, with a single current source I_1, Eq. (2.61) suggests that the general form for the driving-point admittance is

$$Y_D = (Y_D)_{11} = \frac{I_1}{E_1} = \frac{\Delta'}{\Delta_{11}'} \tag{2.63}$$

and for the driving-point impedance,

$$Z_D = (Z_D)_{11} = \frac{E_1}{I_1} = \frac{\Delta_{11}'}{\Delta'} = \frac{1}{Y_D} \tag{2.64}$$

Both Y_D and Z_D are network functions and are, of course, unique for a particular network and independent of the method of analysis used to determine them. As was pointed out earlier in the discussion of the loop method of analysis, these network functions are representable as ratios of two polynomials in s, where $s = j\omega$, and ω is the angular frequency.

Transfer functions. We may also determine from (2.61) the transfer admittance

$$Y_T = (Y_T)_{12} = \frac{I_1}{E_2} = \frac{\Delta'}{\Delta_{12}'} \tag{2.65}$$

and the transfer impedance

$$Z_T = (Z_T)_{21} = \frac{E_2}{I_1} = \frac{\Delta'_{12}}{\Delta'} = \frac{1}{Y_T} \qquad (2.66)$$

Again, both Y_T and Z_T are network functions representable as ratios of two poly-nomials in s.

A transfer admittance relates a current at one terminal pair to a voltage at another. In addition to (2.65), we may have other transfer admittances, for example, $(Y_T)_{13} = I_1/E_3 = \Delta'/\Delta'_{13}$, $(Y_T)_{14} = I_1/E_4 = \Delta'/\Delta'_{14}$, etc.

Numerical Illustration. In the circuit of Fig. 2.16a, let us find the voltages at nodes 1, 2, and 3 with respect to the reference node 4.

The voltage source is first converted into an equivalent current source, as shown in Fig. 2.16b, having a magnitude

$$I_1 = \frac{E_1}{R} = 1 \qquad (2.67a)$$

The values of the self- and mutual admittances, as defined in (2.55), are

$$Y_{11} = s + 2 \qquad Y_{22} = \frac{2s^2 + 2s + 1}{2s}$$

$$Y_{12} = Y_{21} = s \qquad Y_{33} = \frac{s + 1}{s} \qquad (2.67b)$$

$$Y_{13} = Y_{31} = 1 \qquad Y_{23} = Y_{32} = \frac{1}{2s}$$

The system determinant is

$$\Delta' = \begin{vmatrix} s + 2 & -s & -1 \\ -s & \dfrac{2s^2 + 2s + 1}{2s} & -\dfrac{1}{2s} \\ -1 & -\dfrac{1}{2s} & \dfrac{s + 1}{s} \end{vmatrix} = \frac{8s^3 + 14s^2 + 11s + 2}{4s^2} \qquad (2.67c)$$

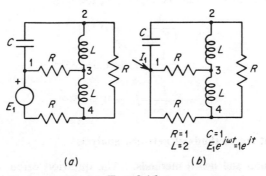

$$R = 1 \qquad C = 1$$
$$L = 2 \qquad E_1 e^{j\omega t} = 1 e^{jt}$$

(a)   (b)

FIG. 2.16

and the cofactors of interest are

$$\Delta'_{11} = (-1)^{1+1} \begin{vmatrix} \dfrac{2s^2 + 2s + 1}{2s} & -\dfrac{1}{2s} \\[2ex] -\dfrac{1}{2s} & \dfrac{s+1}{s} \end{vmatrix} = \dfrac{4s^3 + 8s^2 + 6s + 1}{4s^2}$$

$$\Delta'_{12} = (-1)^{1+2} \begin{vmatrix} -s & -\dfrac{1}{2s} \\[2ex] -1 & \dfrac{s+1}{s} \end{vmatrix} = \dfrac{2s^2 + 2s + 1}{2s}$$

$$\Delta'_{13} = (-1)^{1+3} \begin{vmatrix} -s & \dfrac{2s^2 + 2s + 1}{2s} \\[2ex] -1 & -\dfrac{1}{2s} \end{vmatrix} = \dfrac{2s^2 + 3s + 1}{2s}$$

The driving-point admittance is then

$$(Y_D)_{11} = \frac{\Delta'}{\Delta'_{11}} = \frac{8s^3 + 16s^2 + 9s + 2}{4s^3 + 8s^2 + 6s + 1} \tag{2.67d}$$

and the transfer admittances are

$$(Y_T)_{12} = \frac{\Delta'}{\Delta'_{12}} = \frac{8s^3 + 16s^2 + 9s + 2}{4s^3 + 4s^2 + 2s} \tag{2.67e}$$

$$(Y_T)_{13} = \frac{\Delta'}{\Delta'_{13}} = \frac{8s^3 + 16s^2 + 9s + 2}{4s^3 + 6s^2 + 2s} \tag{2.67f}$$

When the substitutions $s = j\omega$ and $\omega = 1$ are made, these admittances become

$$(Y_D)_{11} = \frac{-12 + j3}{-7 + j} = 1.76\underline{/-5.9°} \tag{2.67d'}$$

$$(Y_T)_{12} = \frac{-12 + j3}{-4 - 2j} = 2.77\underline{/-40.6°} \tag{2.67e'}$$

$$(Y_T)_{13} = \frac{-12 + j3}{-6 - j2} = 1.96\underline{/-32.5°} \tag{2.67f'}$$

From (2.63) and (2.65), we know that $E_1 = I_1/(Y_D)_{11}$, $E_2 = I_1/(Y_T)_{12}$, and $E_3 = I_1/(Y_T)_{13}$. The three nodal voltages are, therefore,

$$E_1 = \frac{1}{(Y_D)_{11}} I_1 = 0.568e^{j5.9°} \tag{2.67g}$$

$$E_2 = \frac{1}{(Y_T)_{12}} I_1 = 0.361e^{j40.6°} \tag{2.67h}$$

$$E_3 = \frac{1}{(Y_T)_{13}} I_1 = 0.51e^{j32.5°} \tag{2.67i}$$

2.7. Remarks about the methods of network analysis

Comparison of loop and nodal methods. The question often arises as to whether the loop or the nodal method is better in solving a particular network problem.

The answer to this question is "use the method which gives the desired solution with the least amount of labor." However, it is not always apparent which of the two methods requires the least work; to ascertain this, we may make use of Eqs. (2.1) and (2.2). (We assume that the sources will all be converted to equivalent voltage or current sources, depending on whether the loop or the nodal method is chosen.) The application of these equations to a network tells us whether there are fewer node pairs or independent loops in the network, and therefore whether we would have to write fewer nodal equations or loop equations. However, the comparison of n_p and l is not the sole criterion for determining which method of analysis to use. For example, in Fig. 2.17a, suppose that E is a known source, and we desire to find

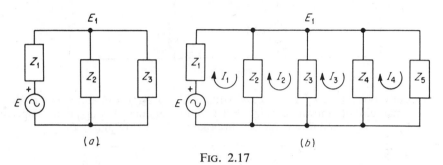

Fig. 2.17

the current in the impedance Z_3. Here $l = 2$ and $n_p = 1$; so only one nodal equation would be required, compared with two loop equations. But the dependent variable in the nodal equation is E_1, and it is still necessary to solve the equation $I = E_1/Z_3$ to obtain the desired current. In this case, then, the loop method probably involves less work, since it yields the desired current directly with two very easy loop equations and involves no exchange of sources. On the other hand, if we wish to find the current in Z_5 in Fig. 2.17b, it would be foolish indeed to solve four loop equations for I_4 simply because this dependent variable is the answer we desire.

In the usual case, the method which requires the solution of the least number of equations is the preferred method. However, in addition to such cases as that of Fig. 2.17b, there are occasions when the generator impedance may dictate the choice of method. For example, since the value of the plate resistance of a pentode vacuum tube is very large, it is often more advantageous to use the constant-current equivalent circuit, so that the effect of the plate resistance in parallel with the load can be neglected.

Remarks about the method employing signal-flow diagrams. In addition to the loop and nodal methods of network analysis, there is another method which employs signal-flow diagrams in solving for a network response or in finding a network function. The behavior of any network is described by a number of voltage-current relations. In the example of the loop method, the loop equations are the voltage-current relations; in the example of the nodal method, the nodal equations are the voltage-current relations. In the signal-flow-diagram method, these voltage-current relations are topologically represented in a graph known as the signal-flow diagram. Following a set of fixed rules, we may simplify a signal-flow diagram describing the behavior of a network and find the response of the network subject to a given excitation. Signal-flow diagrams are useful tools in network analysis as well as in the study of closed-loop control systems, although more emphasis has been placed on their applications in the latter category. We shall study the signal-flow-diagram method in Chap. 16, after we have studied the Laplace transform in Chaps. 11 to 13.

PROBLEMS

2.1. In the circuit shown in Fig. P 2.1, $e_1(t) = 1 \cos \omega t$ volt, $e_2(t) = \sqrt{2} \sin (\omega t + 45°)$ volt, $e_3(t) = 2 \cos (\omega t + 30°)$ volt, and $\omega = 1$ rad/sec. Find the currents $i_1(t)$ and $i_2(t)$. SUGGESTION: Represent $e_1(t)$, $e_2(t)$, and $e_3(t)$ as all sine (or all cosine) functions in order to use the exponential representations defined in (2.7) in the solution of the problems.

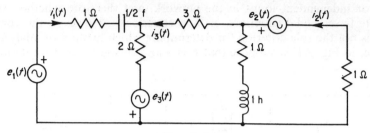

FIG. P 2.1

2.2. Repeat Prob. 2.1 for $e_1(t) = 1 \cos \omega t$ volt, $e_2(t) = 0$, $e_3(t) = 0$, and $\omega = 1$ rad/sec.

2.3. For the circuit shown in Fig. P 2.3, find (*a*) the driving-point impedance $Z_D(s) = (Z_D)_{11} = E_1/I_1$ and (*b*) the transfer impedance $Z_T(s) = (Z_T)_{12} = E_1/I_2$.

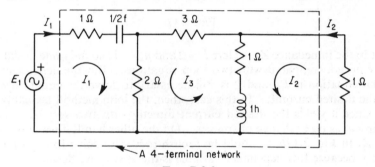

FIG. P 2.3

2.4. Note that, for $e_2(t) = e_3(t) = 0$ in Fig. P 2.1, Figs. P 2.1 and P 2.3 have identical networks. Compute $i_1(t)$ and $i_2(t)$ in Fig. P 2.1 for $e_1(t) = 1 \cos \omega t$ volt, $e_2(t) = 0$, $e_3(t) = 0$, and $\omega = 1$ rad/sec with the aid of the driving-point and transfer impedances $Z_D(s)$ and $Z_T(s)$ obtained in Prob. 2.3. Compare the answers to Probs. 2.4 and 2.2.

2.5. Repeat Prob. 2.4 for $e_1(t) = 10 \sin (\omega t + 30°)$ volts, $e_2(t) = 0$, $e_3(t) = 0$, and $\omega = 2$ rad/sec.

2.6. For the circuit shown in Fig. P 2.6, find (*a*) the driving-point impedance

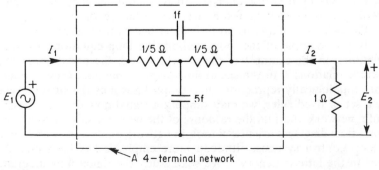

FIG. P 2.6

$Z_D(s) = (Z_D)_{11} = E_1/I_1$, (*b*) the transfer admittance $Y_T(s) = (Y_T)_{21} = I_2/E_1$, and (*c*) the transfer voltage-ratio function $G(s) = E_2/E_1$.

2.7. For the circuit shown in Fig. P 2.7, find (*a*) the transfer impedance $Z_T(s) = (Z_T)_{12} = E_1/I_2$ and (*b*) the transfer voltage-ratio function $G(s) = E_2/E_1$.

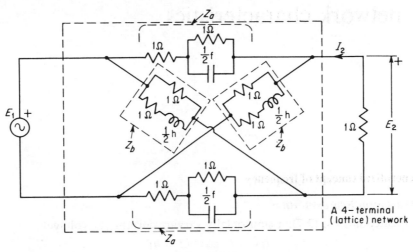

FIG. P 2.7

2.8. Find the transfer voltage-ratio function $G(s) = E_2/E_1$ of the triode amplifier in Fig. P 2.8.

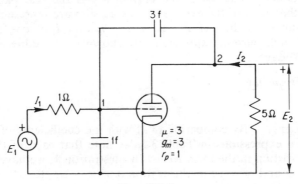

FIG. P 2.8

2.9. Assume in Fig. 2.15*a* that the circuit elements marked Y_a, Y_b, Y_d, Y_e, and Y_f are 1-ohm resistors, the circuit element Y_c is a 1-farad capacitor, and the vacuum-tube parameters are $\mu = 2$, $g_m = 2$, and $r_p = 1$. Find (*a*) the driving-point admittance $Y_D(s) = (Y_D)_{11} = I_1/E_1$ and (*b*) the transfer admittance $Y_T(s) = (Y_T)_{12} = I_1/E_2$ of this amplifier circuit.

2.10. Find the short-circuit parameters y_{11}, y_{12}, y_{21}, and y_{22} of the four-terminal network in Fig. P 2.3.

2.11. Find the short-circuit parameters y_{11}, y_{12}, y_{21}, and y_{22} of the four-terminal network in Fig. P 2.6.

3 Concept of complex frequency; network functions and network characteristics

3.1. Generalized concept of frequency

A. Waveform Representation

As indicated in Eqs. (2.7), a sinusoidally varying current (or voltage)

$$i(t) = I_m \cos(\omega t + \theta) \tag{3.1a}$$

can be expressed in the exponential form

$$i(t) = Ie^{j\omega t} = I_m e^{j\theta} e^{j\omega t} \tag{3.1b}$$

with the understanding that the actual current $i(t)$ is the real part of (3.1b). Its waveform† and the index of the exponential expression are represented in Table 3.1. In a similar manner, we have $I_m e^{-\alpha t} \cos(\omega t + \theta)$ and $I_m e^{\alpha t} \cos(\omega t + \theta)$, also in Table 3.1. Although current expressions are shown in the table, these waveforms could represent voltages.

B. Complex Frequency

We shall call

$$s = \sigma + j\omega \tag{3.2}$$

the *complex frequency*. By comparing (3.2) with the coefficients of t in the indices of the exponential expressions in Table 3.1, we note that each of these expressions could have been written in the form Ke^{st}. In Illustration 1, we have $\sigma = 0$; in Illustration 2, $\sigma = -\alpha$ and $\omega = 0$; in Illustration 3, $\sigma = -\alpha$; etc. It is evident that σ is a measure of decay (for negative σ) or runaway effect (for positive σ), while ω represents the angular frequency of a current or voltage. The complex frequency s is then a *generalized frequency* capable of describing both steady-state and transient phenomena in a response (or excitation).

3.2. Generalized impedance and admittance

A. Symbolic Representation for Instantaneous Voltage-Current Relations

In Fig. 3.1 the instantaneous voltage-current relationship is represented by the integrodifferential equation

$$e(t) = L\frac{di}{dt} + Ri + \frac{1}{C}\int i \, dt \tag{3.3}$$

† The waveform is sketched in Table 3.1 for $\theta = 0°$. For $\theta \neq 0°$, the wave is shifted along the time axis, but its waveform remains the *same*.

36

Table 3.1

Illustration	$i(t)$	Exponential expression	Index of exponential expression	Waveform
1. Sinusoid	$I_m \cos \omega t$	$I_m e^{j\omega t}$	$j\omega t$	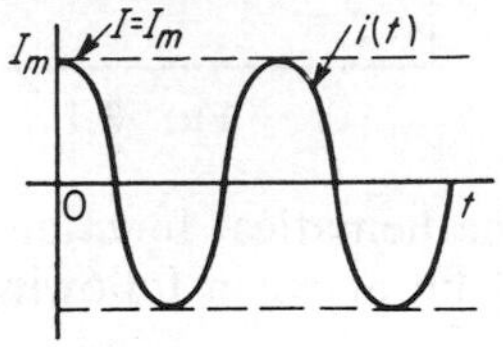
2. Decaying d-c transient	$I_m e^{-\alpha t}$ $\alpha > 0$	$I_m e^{-\alpha t}$	$-\alpha t$	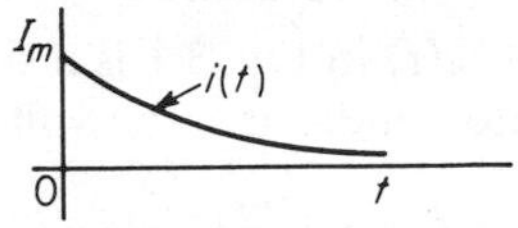
3. Decaying sinusoid	$I_m e^{-\alpha t} \cos \omega t$ $\alpha > 0$	$I_m e^{-\alpha t} e^{j\omega t}$ or $I_m e^{(-\alpha + j\omega)t}$	$(-\alpha + j\omega)t$	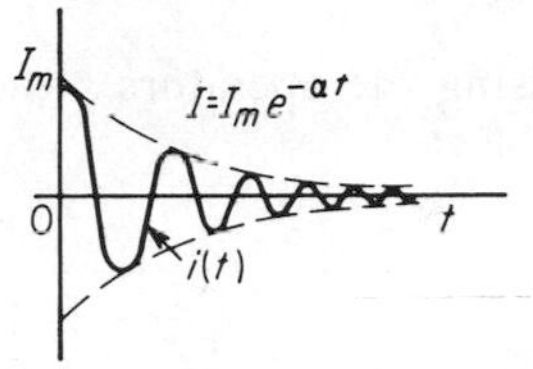
4. Runaway d-c transient	$I_m e^{\alpha t}$ $\alpha > 0$	$I_m e^{\alpha t}$	αt	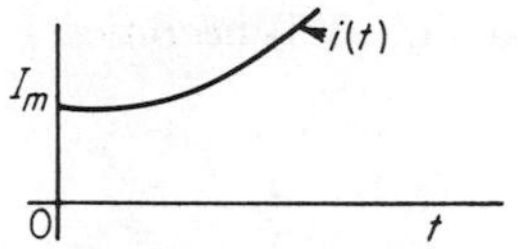
5. Runaway sinusoidal transient	$I_m e^{\alpha t} \cos \omega t$ $\alpha > 0$	$I_m e^{\alpha t} e^{j\omega t}$ or $I_m e^{(\alpha + j\omega)t}$	$(\alpha + j\omega)t$	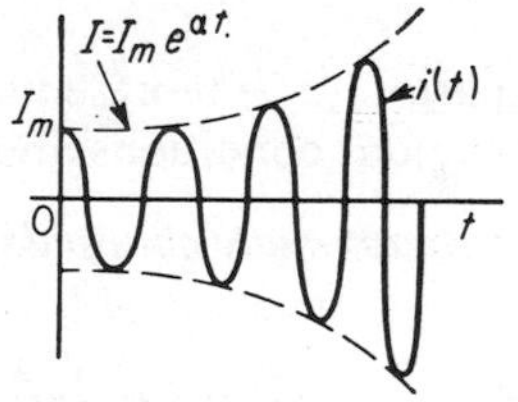

If we use the symbols s and $1/s$ as operators meaning

s and 1/s as operators:

$$s = \frac{d}{dt} \qquad \text{or} \qquad sf(t) = \frac{d}{dt} f(t) \tag{3.4a}$$

$$\frac{1}{s} = \int [\quad] \, dt \qquad \text{or} \qquad \frac{1}{s} f(t) = \int f(t) \, dt \tag{3.4b}$$

we may rewrite (3.3) as

$$e(t) = Lsi + Ri + \frac{1}{C}\frac{1}{s}i = \left(Ls + R + \frac{1}{Cs}\right) i \tag{3.5}$$

where $Ls + R + 1/Cs$ is actually an operator and (3.5) is merely another representation of the integrodifferential equation (3.3). However, Eq. (3.5) does give us the

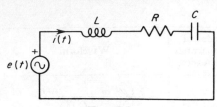

FIG. 3.1

impression that $Ls + R + 1/Cs$ is a ratio of voltage to current and has the apparent dimension of an impedance. We shall denote it by

$$Z(s) = Ls + R + \frac{1}{Cs} \tag{3.6}$$

We are not justified at this time in calling $Z(s)$ an impedance; so we shall simply regard it as a mathematical function of s having no physical meaning. Further interpretation will be given in following sections.

B. Interpretation for Steady-state Conditions

If $e(t)$ in Fig. 3.1 is a sinusoidal source, and if the circuit is operating under steady-state conditions, the voltage and current may have the exponential forms in (2.7):

$$e(t) = Ee^{j\omega t} \tag{3.7a}$$

and

$$i(t) = Ie^{j\omega t} \tag{3.7b}$$

Using the operators s and $1/s$ in (3.4), we have

$$si(t) = \frac{d}{dt} Ie^{j\omega t} = j\omega Ie^{j\omega t} = j\omega i(t)$$

and

$$\frac{1}{s} i(t) = \int Ie^{j\omega t} \, dt = \frac{1}{j\omega} Ie^{j\omega t} = \frac{1}{j\omega} i(t)$$

and Eq. (3.5) becomes

$$Ee^{j\omega t} = \left(Lj\omega + R + \frac{1}{Cj\omega} \right) Ie^{j\omega t} \tag{3.8}$$

or

$$Z(j\omega) = \frac{E}{I} = Lj\omega + R + \frac{1}{Cj\omega} \tag{3.9}$$

Equation (3.9) represents the impedance of the circuit of Fig. 3.1 under steady-state sinusoidal conditions and is identical with (3.6) for

For steady-state sinusoidal conditions:

$$s = j\omega \tag{3.10}$$

C. Generalized Interpretation

Since Eq. (3.6) with $s = j\omega$ represents the impedance of the circuit under steady-state conditions with a sinusoidal source, we shall call (3.6) with $s = \sigma + j\omega$, i.e.,

Generalized impedance:

$$Z(s) = Ls + R + \frac{1}{Cs} = \frac{LCs^2 + RCs + 1}{Cs} \tag{3.11}$$

a generalized impedance. Similarly, for a parallel RLC circuit, we shall have a generalized admittance

Generalized admittance:

$$Y(s) = Cs + G + \frac{1}{sL} = \frac{LCs^2 + GLs + 1}{Ls} \tag{3.12}$$

where $G = 1/R$ is the conductance of a resistive element. *The generalized impedances and admittances have no physical meanings in themselves, but are instrumental in the study of network realization and response*, as will be shown later.

3.3. Adpedance function $W(s)$

A. Adpedance as a Function of Complex Frequency

A comparison of (3.11) and (3.9) indicates that we may use s in place of $j\omega$ in an impedance $Z(j\omega)$ to obtain the generalized form $Z(s)$, which may be called an impedance function. Equations (3.11) and (3.12) show that the impedance or admittance function is representable in the form of a ratio of two polynomials in s.

For arbitrary networks, the various driving-point and transfer impedance and admittance functions were expressed as ratios of two determinants in Eqs. (2.28), (2.29), (2.47), (2.48), (2.50), (2.51), and (2.63) to (2.66). Since these determinants have either $Z_{ij}(s)$ in the form of (3.11) or $Y_{ij}(s)$ in the form of (3.12) as elements, we should expect that any network function (driving-point impedance or admittance, or transfer impedance or admittance) may be expressed, after its determinants are expanded, as a ratio of two polynomials in s with the general form

Adpedance function:

$$W(s) = \frac{A_m s^m + A_{m-1} s^{m-1} + \cdots + A_1 s + A_0}{B_n s^n + B_{n-1} s^{n-1} + \cdots + B_1 s + B_0} \tag{3.13}$$

We shall call $W(s)$ in (3.13) an *adpedance*† function if intended to represent either an *admittance* or an *impedance*. Equations (2.31) and (2.52) are typical adpedance functions in the form of (3.13).

In addition to adpedance, there are other network functions which may be represented in the form of (3.13). An example is the gain function of an amplifier.

B. Poles and Zeros of $W(s)$

Definitions. The polynomials in the numerator and denominator of $W(s)$ in (3.13) may be factored to give

$$W(s) = \frac{A_m(s - r_1)(s - r_2) \cdots (s - r_m)}{B_n(s - p_1)(s - p_2) \cdots (s - p_n)} \tag{3.14}$$

We shall define the *poles* and *zeros* of a function $W(s)$ as the values of s for which the function approaches infinity and zero, respectively. We note in (3.14) that, for $s \to p_1$ (i.e., s approaches p_1), $W(s) \to \infty$; p_1 is a pole of $W(s)$. We shall find that $p_1, p_2, \ldots, p_n$ are the poles, and $r_1, r_2, \ldots, r_m$ the zeros, of $W(s)$.

If $p_1 = p_2$, we say we have a *double pole* (i.e., two poles at the same location) at $s = p_1$, or a *pole of order* 2 at $s = p_1$. Likewise, we may have a pole of order j and a zero of order k, where j and k are positive integers.

Poles and zeros at infinity. We may also rewrite (3.13) as

$$W(s) = \frac{s^m}{s^n} \left[\frac{A_m + A_{m-1}(1/s) + A_{m-2}(1/s)^2 + \cdots + A_0(1/s)^m}{B_n + B_{n-1}(1/s) + B_{n-2}(1/s)^2 + \cdots + B_0(1/s)^n} \right] \tag{3.15}$$

For $s \to \infty$, the value of the terms in brackets in (3.15) approaches a constant $K = A_m/B_n$, and

$$\lim_{s \to \infty} W(s) = \lim_{s \to \infty} \frac{s^m}{s^n} K = K \lim_{s \to \infty} s^{m-n} \tag{3.15a}$$

For $m > n$ and $s \to \infty$, $W(s) \to \infty$ as $s^{m-n} \to \infty$, and $W(s)$ *has a pole of order $m - n$ at infinity* in the s plane.

† This term is believed to have been coined by H. W. Bode. See H. Bode, "Network Analysis and Feedback Amplifier Design," p. 15, D. Van Nostrand Company, Inc., Princeton, N.J., 1947.

For $m < n$ and $s \to \infty$, $W(s) \to 0$ as $s^{m-n} = (1/s)^{n-m} \to 0$, and $W(s)$ *has a zero of order $n - m$ at infinity* in the s plane.

For $m = n$, $W(s)$ *has no poles or zeros at infinity* in the s plane.

If we are given the poles and zeros of a function $W(s)$ in the finite region of the s plane, for example, $p_1, p_2, \ldots, p_n$ and $r_1, r_2, \ldots, r_m$ in (3.14), we note that the poles or zeros of $W(s)$ at infinity are always implied. For example, if $W(s)$ has $p_1 = j2$, $p_2 = -j2$, $p_3 = j5$, $p_4 = -j5$; $r_1 = 0$, $r_2 = j3$, $r_3 = -j3$, $r_4 = j7$, and $r_5 = -j7$, it has $m - n = 5 - 4 = 1$ pole at infinity. For another example, if $W(s)$ has $n = 4$ poles and $m = 3$ zeros in the finite region of the s plane, it has $n - m = 1$ zero at infinity. For this reason, we often neglect to specify the poles and zeros of an adpedance function at infinity.

Numerical illustration.   Suppose we have a driving-point impedance function

$$W(s) = \frac{s^3 + 6 \times 10^7 s^2 + 13 \times 10^{14} s + 20 \times 10^{21}}{10^4 s^2 + 4 \times 10^{11} s + 5 \times 10^{18}}$$

This expression may be rewritten in the factored form

$$W(s) = \frac{[s - (-4 \times 10^7)][s - (-10^7 + j2 \times 10^7)][s - (-10^7 - j2 \times 10^7)]}{10^4[s - (-2 \times 10^7 + j10^7)][s - (-2 \times 10^7 - j10^7)]}$$

$$(3.16)$$

Comparing (3.16) with (3.14), we see that $A_3 = 1$, $B_2 = 10^4$, $r_1 = -4 \times 10^7$, $r_2 = -10^7 + j2 \times 10^7$, $r_3 = -10^7 - j2 \times 10^7$, $p_1 = -2 \times 10^7 + j10^7$, and $p_2 = -2 \times 10^7 - j10^7$.

C. Pole-and-Zero Plot

The *pole-and-zero plot* of a network function is a graphical representation of the locations of its poles and zeros in the finite region of the s plane. For example, the network function of (3.16) has the pole-and-zero plot shown in Fig. 3.2, where a cross indicates a pole, and a small circle indicates a zero.

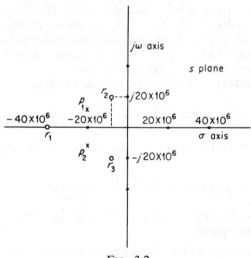

Fig. 3.2

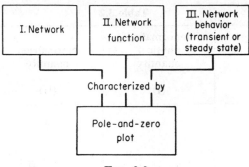

FIG. 3.3

Remarks about network problems. A network may be described by its behavior, say transient or steady-state response, or by one of its network functions. However, the network itself, the network function, and the network behavior are all characterized by the pole-and-zero plot of the network function. This relationship is shown in block-diagram form in Fig. 3.3. We may use the designations of Fig. 3.3 to classify network problems in two main categories: (1) the problems of *network analysis*, e.g., given (I) in Fig. 3.3 to find (II), or given (II) to find (III), and (2) the problems of *network synthesis* or realization, e.g., given (III) to find (II), or given (II) to find (I). The pole-and-zero plot, which is the common link joining (I), (II), and (III), is instrumental in the solution of problems belonging to either category.

3.4. Normalization

In practical problems we often encounter physical quantities of very large or very small magnitude. For example, we frequently find capacitances in millionths of a farad, inductances in thousandths of a henry, and resistance, impedance, and frequency covering extensive ranges in magnitude. In numerical computation, graphical plotting, or other mathematical manipulations, it is not usually convenient to work with these very large or very small numerical values. *Normalization, to be introduced in the following sections, will convert unwieldy numbers to normalized values of medium magnitude for purposes of manipulation.* In our illustrations of circuit problems in following chapters, we shall use normalized circuit elements.

A. Normalization of Circuit Elements

To normalize a circuit element, we set up two standards of reference called the normalizing quantities; these are the *normalizing frequency* ω_0 and the *normalizing impedance* R_0. If we know the approximate ranges of operating frequency and of network impedances, we may arbitrarily choose ω_0 and R_0 from those ranges. The normalizing quantities may also be chosen according to a procedure to be discussed in the next section.

The process of normalization is shown in Table 3.2. The circuit relations existing among the unnormalized quantities in column I must be preserved among the normalized quantities in column II. In column III, items 1 to 5, we define the normalized value to be the unnormalized value divided by an appropriate normalizing quantity, i.e., (1) ω_0, used in normalizing the frequency, or (2) R_0, used in normalizing all quantities with the dimensions of impedance. For consistency we require the relations of normalized inductance and capacitance as shown in column III,

Table 3.2

	(Unnormalized) physical quantity (I)	Normalized quantity (II)	Relation between physical and normalized quantities (III)
1. Frequency	$s = j\omega$	$\bar{s}$	$\bar{s} = \dfrac{s}{\omega_0}$
2. Inductive impedance . . .	$Z_L = sL$	$\bar{Z}_L = \bar{s}\bar{L}$	$\bar{Z}_L = \dfrac{Z_L}{R_0}$
3. Capacitive impedance . .	$Z_C = \dfrac{1}{sC}$	$\bar{Z}_C = \dfrac{1}{\bar{s}\bar{C}}$	$\bar{Z}_C = \dfrac{Z_C}{R_0}$
4. Resistance	R	$\bar{R}$	$\bar{R} = \dfrac{R}{R_0}$
5. Impedance.	Z	$\bar{Z}$	$\bar{Z} = \dfrac{Z}{R_0}$
6. Inductance.	L	$\bar{L}$	$\bar{L} = \dfrac{\omega_0 L}{R_0}$
7. Capacitance.	C	$\bar{C}$	$\bar{C} = \omega_0 C R_0$

items 6 and 7, to hold.   These relations are derived from items 2 and 3 as follows:

$$\bar{Z}_L = \bar{s}\bar{L} = \frac{Z_L}{R_0} = \frac{sL}{R_0} = \frac{s}{\omega_0}\frac{\omega_0 L}{R_0} \tag{3.17a}$$

requires, for $\bar{s} = s/\omega_0$,

$$\bar{L} = \frac{\omega_0 L}{R_0} \tag{3.17b}$$

Similarly,

$$\bar{Z}_C = \frac{1}{\bar{s}\bar{C}} = \frac{Z_C}{R_0} = \frac{1}{sCR_0} = \frac{1}{(s/\omega_0)\omega_0 CR_0} \tag{3.18a}$$

requires, for $\bar{s} = s/\omega_0$,

$$\bar{C} = \omega_0 C R_0 \tag{3.18b}$$

Numerical illustration.   In the circuit of Fig. 3.4a, we shall normalize the circuit elements and find the normalized value of the impedance Z_D.   Let us suppose that a knowledge of the operating frequency range makes a choice of $\omega_0 = 5 \times 10^4$ rad/sec a convenient one, and let $R_0 = 500$ ohms.   Using the relations of Table 3.2, we have

$$\bar{R} = \frac{R}{R_0} = 1$$

$$\bar{L}_1 = \frac{\omega_0 L_1}{R_0} = \frac{5 \times 10^4 \times 10 \times 10^{-3}}{500} = 1 \qquad \bar{L}_2 = 1$$

$$\bar{C}_1 = \omega_0 C_1 R_0 = 5 \times 10^4 \times 0.1 \times 10^{-6} \times 500 = 2.5$$

$$\bar{C}_2 = 2\bar{C}_1 = 5 \qquad \bar{C}_3 = 2.5$$

as shown in Fig. 3.4b. The normalized impedance in Fig. 3.4b is then

$$Z_D = \cfrac{\left\{\left[\cfrac{\dfrac{1(1/2.5\bar{s})}{1 + 1/2.5\bar{s}} + 1\bar{s}\right]\dfrac{1}{5\bar{s}}}{\left[\dfrac{1(1/2.5\bar{s})}{1 + 1/2.5\bar{s}} + 1\bar{s}\right] + \dfrac{1}{5\bar{s}}} + 1\bar{s}\right\}\dfrac{1}{2.5\bar{s}}}{\cfrac{\left[\dfrac{1(1/2.5\bar{s})}{1 + 1/2.5\bar{s}} + 1\bar{s}\right]\dfrac{1}{5\bar{s}}}{\left[\dfrac{1(1/2.5\bar{s})}{1 + 1/2.5\bar{s}} + 1\bar{s}\right] + \dfrac{1}{5\bar{s}}} + 1\bar{s} + \dfrac{1}{2.5\bar{s}}} \tag{3.19a}$$

The form of Z_D illustrates the convenient method of writing the driving-point impedance of a ladder network of this type by starting at the elements farthest from the

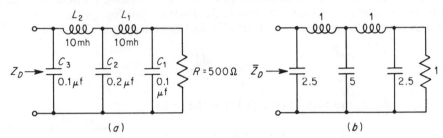

FIG. 3.4

input terminals and writing the expressions for the various series and parallel combinations of elements while progressing toward the input terminals. After reduction, the normalized impedance expression becomes

$$Z_D = \frac{12.5\bar{s}^4 + 5\bar{s}^3 + 10\bar{s}^2 + 2\bar{s} + 1}{31.25\bar{s}^5 + 12.5\bar{s}^4 + 37.5\bar{s}^3 + 10\bar{s}^2 + 10\bar{s} + 1} \tag{3.19b}$$

From relations 1 and 5 in Table 3.2, we see that $Z_D = Z_D/R_0$ and $\bar{s} = s/\omega_0$. The driving-point impedance function is, therefore,

$$Z_D = R_0 Z_D$$
$$= \frac{500[12.5(s/5 \times 10^4)^4 + 5(s/5 \times 10^4)^3 + 10(s/5 \times 10^4)^2 + 2(s/5 \times 10^4) + 1]}{31.25(s/5 \times 10^4)^5 + 12.5(s/5 \times 10^4)^4 + 37.5(s/5 \times 10^4)^3 + 10(s/5 \times 10^4)^2 + 10(s/5 \times 10^4) + 1}$$
$$\tag{3.19c}$$

Remarks. The network in Fig. 3.4b and its network function Z_D (say computed from the network diagram as in the above illustration) represent the network in Fig. 3.4a and its network function if we specify $\omega_0 = 5 \times 10^4$ rad/sec and $R_0 = 500$ ohms. However, if we specify other values for ω_0 and R_0, the network in Fig. 3.4b and its network function Z_D represent a different network and its network function. Therefore, we see that *normalization enables us to study a single network with circuit values of medium magnitudes, with results applicable to a number of networks related through their common normalized form.*

B. Normalization of Network Functions

We note in the preceding discussion that normalization puts frequency $\bar{s} = s/\omega_0$ and impedance $Z = Z/R_0$ on a relative basis, using the normalizing quantities ω_0

and R_0 for comparison.   This amounts to a "change of scale factor" for all the physical quantities in order to facilitate mathematical manipulation.   There is no reason why this process should be limited to impedance functions.   We shall now extend the process of normalization to include any network function of the general form of (3.13) or (3.14).

We shall again require two normalizing quantities: ω_0, the normalizing frequency, and W_0, a normalizing quantity having a dimension determined by the function being normalized. ω_0 and W_0 may be either (1) *arbitrarily chosen*† in the same manner in which we chose ω_0 and R_0 in Art. 3.4A or (2) *chosen according to a procedure* to be discussed in the following paragraphs.

A procedure frequently used in choosing values for these quantities is to let W_0 be the value of $W(s)$ for $s = 0$ (zero frequency), or sometimes for $s = \infty$ (infinite frequency), and then to calculate ω_0 using an expression to be derived below.   We note that, in the numerical illustration given in the preceding section, $R_0 = Z(0)$. That is, the normalizing impedance used is the value of $Z(s)$ for $s = 0$.

$W(0)$ **as a normalizing quantity.**   From Eq. (3.13) we see that

$$W(0) = \frac{A_0}{B_0}$$

Letting $K = A_m/B_n$, we may rewrite (3.14) in the form

$$\frac{W(s)}{W(0)} = \frac{K(s - r_1)(s - r_2) \cdots (s - r_m)}{W(0)(s - p_1)(s - p_2) \cdots (s - p_n)}$$

and then as

$$\frac{W(s)}{W(0)} = \frac{K[(s - r_1)/\omega_0][(s - r_2)/\omega_0] \cdots [(s - r_m)/\omega_0]\omega_0{}^m}{W(0)[(s - p_1)/\omega_0][(s - p_2)/\omega_0] \cdots [(s - p_n)/\omega_0]\omega_0{}^n} \tag{3.20}$$

Letting

$$\frac{K}{W(0)} \frac{\omega_0{}^m}{\omega_0{}^n} = 1$$

or

Normalizing frequency:

$$\omega_0 = \left[\frac{K}{W(0)}\right]^{1/(n-m)} = \left(\frac{A_m}{B_n} \frac{B_0}{A_0}\right)^{1/(n-m)} \tag{3.21}$$

and letting

$$\bar{s} = \frac{s}{\omega_0}$$

$$\bar{r}_i = \frac{r_i}{\omega_0} \qquad i = 1, 2, \ldots, m \tag{3.22}$$

$$\bar{p}_j = \frac{p_j}{\omega_0} \qquad j = 1, 2, \ldots, n$$

† With "arbitrarily chosen" ω_0 and W_0, the normalized function has the form $W(s) = \bar{H}$ [right-hand side of (3.23)] with $\bar{H} \neq 1$, rather than (3.23) itself.   For many problems we *prefer to choose* ω_0 and W_0 *arbitrarily*, since (1) the normalized form of the network function is usually good enough for easy manipulation, and we are not concerned with $\bar{H} \neq 1$, and (2) it eliminates all the work of determining ω_0 to make $\bar{H} = 1$, as described in subsequent paragraphs.

we may rewrite (3.20) as the normalized version of (3.14) in the form

Normalized function:

$$\bar{W}(\bar{s}) = \frac{W(s)}{W(0)} = \frac{(\bar{s} - \bar{r}_1)(\bar{s} - \bar{r}_2) \cdots (\bar{s} - \bar{r}_m)}{(\bar{s} - \bar{p}_1)(\bar{s} - \bar{p}_2) \cdots (\bar{s} - \bar{p}_n)} \tag{3.23}$$

The normalizing frequency is defined in (3.21), and $\bar{s}$, $\bar{r}_i$, and $\bar{p}_j$ are, respectively, complex frequency, zeros, and poles in normalized forms. In later work in which it will be understood that normalized quantities are being used, we shall for simplicity sometimes omit the bars over W, s, r_i, and p_j.

Numerical illustration. We shall find the network function representing the high-frequency gain of a shunt-compensated video amplifier and normalize it. The circuit of the amplifier is shown in Fig. 3.5a, where R is the load resistance, L is the

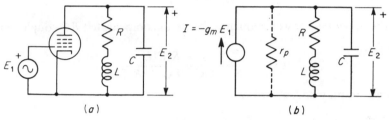

$$I = -g_m E_1$$

(a)   (b)

FIG. 3.5

compensating inductance, and C is the total shunt capacitance. The frequency is assumed high enough so that the effect of the series coupling capacitor may be neglected.

The equivalent circuit for the amplifier is shown in Fig. 3.5b. It is assumed that, as in most practical cases, the plate resistance r_p of the pentode is much greater than the impedance in parallel with it, so that it can be omitted from our analysis. Now, writing the expression for E_2 with $s = j\omega$, we have

$$E_2 = -g_m E_1 \frac{(1/sC)(R + sL)}{1/sC + R + sL} = -g_m E_1 \frac{(L/C)s + R/C}{Ls^2 + Rs + 1/C}$$

The gain expression is then

$$G(s) = \frac{E_2}{E_1} = -\frac{g_m}{C} \frac{s + R/L}{s^2 + (R/L)s + 1/LC} = -\frac{g_m(s - r_1)}{C(s - p_1)(s - p_2)} \tag{3.24a}$$

where

$$r_1 = -\frac{R}{L}$$

$$p_1, p_2 = -\frac{R}{2L} \pm \frac{1}{2}\sqrt{\left(\frac{R}{L}\right)^2 - \frac{4}{LC}}$$

As a typical example, let $R = 2{,}000$ ohms, $L = 40 \times 10^{-6}$ henry, $C = 25 \times 10^{-12}$ farad, and $g_m = 10{,}000 \times 10^{-6}$ ohm. We then have

$$G(s) = -\frac{10^{-2}}{25 \times 10^{-12}} \frac{s + 2{,}000/40 \times 10^{-6}}{s^2 + (2{,}000/40 \times 10^{-6})s + 1/(40 \times 10^{-6} \times 25 \times 10^{-12})}$$

$$= -4 \times 10^8 \frac{s + 5 \times 10^7}{s^2 + 5 \times 10^7 s + 10^{15}}$$

or $\quad G(s) = -4 \times 10^8 \dfrac{s - (-5 \times 10^7)}{[s - 10^7(-2.5 + j1.9)][s - 10^7(-2.5 - j1.9)]} \tag{3.24b}$

We note that r_1, p_1, and p_2 in this expression are very large numbers.

Let us now normalize this network function. We choose the value of gain for $s = 0$ as the normalizing quantity $W(0)$; that is,†

$$W(0) = G(0) = -g_m R \tag{3.25a}$$

Then
$$\frac{G(s)}{G(0)} = \frac{1}{-g_m R} \frac{-g_m}{C} \frac{s + R/L}{s^2 + (R/L)s + 1/LC}$$

$$= \frac{1}{RC} \frac{[(s + R/L)/\omega_0]\omega_0}{\{[s^2 + (R/L)s + 1/LC]/\omega_0^2\}\omega_0^2}$$

Letting
$$\frac{1}{RC} \frac{\omega_0}{\omega_0^2} = 1$$

or
$$\omega_0 = \frac{1}{RC} \tag{3.25b}$$

which is the upper half-power frequency for an uncompensated RC-coupled amplifier, we have

$$\bar{G}(\bar{s}) = \frac{\bar{s} + R^2 C/L}{\bar{s}^2 + (R^2 C/L)\bar{s} + R^2 C/L} \tag{3.26a}$$

This expression may be factored to give

$$\bar{G}(\bar{s}) = \frac{\bar{s} - \bar{r}_1}{(\bar{s} - \bar{p}_1)(\bar{s} - \bar{p}_2)} \tag{3.26b}$$

where
$$\bar{s} = \frac{s}{\omega_0} = RCs$$

$$\bar{r}_1 = \frac{r_1}{\omega_0} = -\frac{R^2 C}{L} \tag{3.26c}$$

$$\bar{p}_1, \bar{p}_2 = \frac{p_1}{\omega_0}, \frac{p_2}{\omega_0} = -\frac{R^2 C}{L} \pm j\frac{R^2 C}{2L}\sqrt{\frac{4L}{R^2 C} - 1}$$

Equations (3.26a) and (3.26b) are alternative representations of the normalized gain function. When the values of the circuit constants are substituted in (3.26b), we have

$$\bar{G}(\bar{s}) = \frac{\bar{s} - (-2.5)}{[\bar{s} - (-1.25 + j0.97)][\bar{s} - (-1.25 - j0.97)]} \tag{3.27}$$

$W(\infty)$ **as a normalizing quantity.** Under certain conditions we shall find that $W(0)$ is not a suitable normalizing quantity. For example,

$$G(s) = \frac{A_1 s}{B_1 s + B_0} \tag{3.28}$$

may represent the gain function of a low-frequency compensated video amplifier. Here, $G(0) = 0$ and is not of any value in normalization. However, since this expression results from the use of the low-frequency equivalent circuit for the amplifier, $G(\infty)$ will be found to represent the mid-frequency gain. We may then use $G(\infty)$ as a normalizing quantity and follow the method previously described to obtain

$$\bar{G}(\bar{s}) = \frac{G(s)}{G(\infty)} = \frac{\bar{s} - \bar{r}_1}{s - \bar{p}_1} \tag{3.29}$$

† The gain expression (3.24a) was derived using the high-frequency equivalent circuit for the amplifier. Equation (3.24a), evaluated for $s = 0$, then actually represents the gain in the mid-frequency range, and $G(s)/G(0)$ is therefore the relative gain of the amplifier.

In this case it will be found that no solution for ω_0 may be obtained from (3.21) if $G(\infty)$ is used in place of $G(0)$, as $m = n$ and $\omega_0{}^m/\omega_0{}^n = 1$. In general, if the polynomials in the numerator and denominator of $W(s)$ are of the same degree, it is necessary to choose ω_0 arbitrarily from the operating range. A choice of ω_0 of some physical significance (such as a half-power frequency) would be helpful. For instance, the use of the lower half-power frequency as ω_0 in normalizing s, r_1, and p_1 to obtain (3.29) would be a logical choice. It is obvious from (3.28) that $\bar{r}_1 = r_1/\omega_0 = 0$ in (3.29).

3.5. Remarks about network functions and network characteristics

A. Some General Remarks

We shall describe, in general terms, "network functions" and "network characteristics," in order to clarify the various network problems stated in Chap. 1.

Network function. *A network function is a (complex) function of the complex frequency s capable of describing the behavior of the network subject to an arbitrary excitation.* For example, the adpedance function $W(s)$ in (3.13), as illustrated in (2.31) and (2.52), is a network function; the transfer voltage-ratio function $G(s)$ (also known as the voltage-gain function) in (3.24) is another.

Network characteristics. *A network characteristic is a (real) function of the real frequency ω capable of describing some partial behavior of the network subject to an arbitrary excitation;* it is related to a network function of the network. For example, if we measure the ratio of magnitudes of output voltage to input voltage for an amplifier at different frequencies ω, we obtain a function $G_0(\omega)$ of the real frequency ω. This function $G_0(\omega)$, known as the "gain characteristic" of the amplifier, is a network characteristic; it is related to the transfer voltage-ratio function $G(s)$ by $G_0(\omega) = |G(j\omega)|$.

Network function $N(s)$ at real frequencies $s = j\omega$. In general, we may represent a network function $N(s)$ at real frequencies $s = j\omega$ in one of the two alternative forms

$$N(j\omega) = N_1(\omega) + jN_2(\omega) \tag{3.30}$$

and
$$N(j\omega) = N_0(\omega)e^{-j\theta(\omega)} \tag{3.31}$$

As an illustration, let us consider the driving-point impedance of an inductance $L = 1$ and a resistance $R = 1$ connected in parallel:

$$Z_D(s) = \frac{sLR}{sL + R} = \frac{s}{1 + s} \tag{3.32a}$$

which may be represented in the form of (3.30):

$$Z_D(j\omega) = N_1(\omega) + jN_2(\omega) = \frac{\omega^2}{1 + \omega^2} + j\frac{-\omega}{1 + \omega^2} \tag{3.32b}$$

To represent (3.32a) in the form of (3.31), we may use $N_1(\omega)$ and $N_2(\omega)$ as defined in (3.32b) in the computation of

$$N_0(\omega) = |N(j\omega)| = \sqrt{[N_1(\omega)]^2 + [N_2(\omega)]^2}$$

$$\theta(\omega) = -\tan^{-1}\frac{N_2(\omega)}{N_1(\omega)} \tag{3.33}$$

Network function and its associated network characteristics. We usually associate a network function $N(s)$ with a set of two network characteristics. For example, $N_1(\omega)$ and $N_2(\omega)$ in (3.30) form a set for the network function $N(s)$; $N_0(\omega)$ and $\theta(\omega)$ form another. Also, there are other forms of network characteristics which we have not yet defined. A network function is completely characterized by a set of two network characteristics.

B. Network Functions and Associated Network Characteristics for Two-terminal Networks

Let us consider the network functions and associated network characteristics of the two-terminal network in Fig. 3.6a.

Driving-point impedance function. A driving-point impedance function

$$Z_D(s) = \frac{E_1}{I_1}$$

is associated with the following set of network characteristics: (1) The *real* characteristic $R(\omega)$ represents the "equivalent resistance" of the network at the

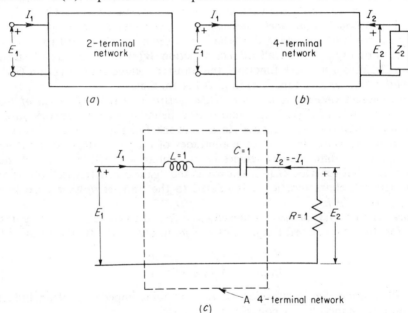

(a)   (b)

(c)

Fig. 3.6

frequency ω, and (2) the *imaginary* characteristic $X(\omega)$ represents the "equivalent reactance," where

$$Z_D(j\omega) = N_1(\omega) + jN_2(\omega) = R(\omega) + jX(\omega) \tag{3.34}$$

An illustration has been provided in Eqs. (3.32).

Driving-point admittance function. Similarly, a driving-point admittance function $Y_D(s) = I_1/E_1$ is associated with the following set of network characteristics: (1) The *real* characteristic $G(\omega)$ represents the "equivalent conductance" of the network at the frequency ω, and (2) the *imaginary* characteristic $B(\omega)$ represents the "equivalent susceptance," where

$$Y_D(j\omega) = N_1(\omega) + jN_2(\omega) = G(\omega) + jB(\omega) \tag{3.35}$$

C. Some Network Functions and Associated Network Characteristics for Four-terminal Networks

Let us now consider the four-terminal network arrangement in Fig. 3.6b. To characterize such a network arrangement, we need transfer functions. We have already discussed some transfer functions in Chap. 2, e.g., the transfer impedance function $Z_T(s) = (Z_T)_{12} = E_1/I_2$ and the transfer admittance function $Y_T(s) = (Y_T)_{21} = I_2/E_1$. We shall now introduce some additional commonly used transfer functions.

Transfer voltage-ratio function. We shall define the transfer voltage-ratio function (also known as the *voltage-gain function*) of the four-terminal network in Fig. 3.6*b* to be $G = E_2/E_1$. It is obvious that $G = E_2/E_1 = Z_2(-I_2)/E_1 = Z_2[-(Y_T)_{21}]$. When the transfer admittance $Y_T = (Y_T)_{21}$ is obtained, as in the loop (or nodal) method of analysis, the transfer voltage-ratio function is also obtained.

A Simple Illustration. As a simple (trivial) illustration, the four-terminal network in Fig. 3.6*c* has transfer voltage-ratio function

$$G(s) = \frac{E_2}{E_1} = \frac{R}{sL + R + 1/sC} = \frac{s}{s^2 + s + 1} \tag{3.36}$$

Representing (3.36) in the form of (3.30), i.e.,

$$G(j\omega) = G_1(\omega) + jG_2(\omega) \tag{3.37}$$

we immediately obtain a set of *real* and *imaginary* network characteristics of $G(s)$:

Set of network characteristics of $G(s)$ in (3.36):

$$G_1(\omega) = \frac{\omega^2}{(1 - \omega^2)^2 + \omega^2} \qquad G_2(\omega) = \frac{\omega(1 - \omega^2)}{(1 - \omega^2)^2 + \omega^2} \tag{3.38}$$

Representing (3.36) in the form of (3.31), i.e.,

$$G(j\omega) = G_0(\omega)e^{-j\theta(\omega)} \tag{3.39}$$

and taking advantage of the relations in (3.33), we have another set of network characteristics of $G(s)$:

Another set of network characteristics of $G(s)$ in (3.36):

$$G_0(\omega) = |G(j\omega)| = \sqrt{[G_1(\omega)]^2 + [G_2(\omega)]^2}$$

$$\theta(\omega) = -\tan^{-1}\frac{G_2(\omega)}{G_1(\omega)} \tag{3.40}$$

where $G_1(\omega)$ and $G_2(\omega)$ are defined in (3.38). The network characteristics in (3.40) are often referred to as the "frequency characteristics" of a four-terminal network. The $G_0(\omega)$ characteristic is also called a *gain characteristic* (or an *absolute-gain characteristic*). This is obvious from (3.36) and (3.39), where we note that $G_0(\omega) = |G(j\omega)| = |E_2/E_1|$ for $s = j\omega$. The $\theta(\omega)$ characteristic, being a measure of the phase angle by which the input E_1 leads the output E_2, is also called a *phase characteristic*.

Logarithmic (voltage) gain function. We shall define the logarithmic gain function $\Theta(s)$ of a four-terminal network to be the natural logarithm of its voltage-gain function; that is, $\Theta(s) = \ln[G(s)]$. At real frequency $s = j\omega$, we have

$$\Theta(j\omega) = \ln[G(j\omega)] = \ln[G_0(\omega)e^{-j\theta(\omega)}] \tag{3.41a}$$

which is often expressed in the form

$$\Theta(j\omega) = \ln[G(j\omega)] = A(\omega) + jB(\omega) \tag{3.41b}$$

where

Network characteristics of logarithmic gain function:

$$A(\omega) = \ln\,[G_0(\omega)] \qquad B(\omega) = -\theta(\omega) \qquad (3.42)$$

form a set of network characteristics of the logarithmic gain function

$$\Theta(s) = \ln\,[G(s)]$$

The real characteristic $A(\omega)$ is also called the *logarithmic gain characteristic*. $A(\omega_1)$ gives the logarithmic gain of the four-terminal network in nepers at a particular frequency ω_1. The imaginary characteristic $B(\omega)$, representing the phase angle by which E_2 leads E_1, is also called a *phase characteristic*.

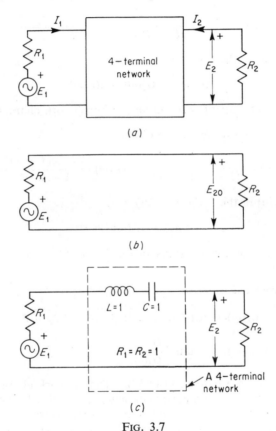

(a)

(b)

(c)

Fig. 3.7

Insertion voltage-ratio function. Suppose we have a network arrangement as in Fig. 3.7a. We define the *insertion voltage-ratio function* of this four-terminal network to be

$$e^\theta = \frac{E_{20}}{E_2} \qquad (3.43)$$

where E_2 is the potential drop across the load R_2 with the network in the circuit as in Fig. 3.7a; and E_{20}, that with the network removed as in Fig. 3.7b. It can be easily shown that e^θ is also a transfer function: From Fig. 3.7b, we have

$$\frac{E_{20}}{E_1} = \frac{R_2}{R_1 + R_2}$$

Therefore, $e^\theta = E_{20}/E_2 = (E_{20}/E_1)(E_1/E_2) = [R_2/(R_1 + R_2)](E_1/E_2)$. Since $[G(s)]_{12} = E_1/E_2$ is a transfer function and $R_2/(R_1 + R_2)$ is a constant, e^θ is a transfer function.

A Simple Illustration. For the circuit arrangement in Fig. 3.7c, and with the aid of Fig. 3.7b, we have

$$e^\theta = \frac{E_{20}}{E_2} = \frac{R_1 + sL + 1/sC + R_2}{R_1 + R_2} \tag{3.44a}$$

$$e^\theta = \frac{s^2 + 2s + 1}{2s} \tag{3.44b}$$

Insertion Transmission Function. Take the logarithm of (3.43):

$$\theta = \theta(s) = \ln \frac{E_{20}}{E_2}$$

is another network function, called the *insertion transmission function* (or insertion transmission parameter). Letting $s = j\omega$ and expressing $\theta(j\omega)$ in the form of (3.30), we have

$$\theta(j\omega) = \ln \left(\frac{E_{20}}{E_2}\right)_{s=j\omega} = \alpha(\omega) + j\beta(\omega) \tag{3.45}$$

Here we have two network characteristics $\alpha(\omega)$ and $\beta(\omega)$ associated with the network functions e^θ and $\theta(s)$: $\alpha(\omega)$, representing *insertion loss* and measured in nepers, and $\beta(\omega)$, representing *insertion phase* and measured in radians.

PROBLEMS

3.1. Given:
$$W(s) = 360 \times 10^6 \, \frac{s^2 + 21 \times 10^6 s + 90 \times 10^{12}}{s^3 + 33 \times 10^6 s^2 + 306 \times 10^{12} s + 648 \times 10^{18}}$$

Obtain a normalized expression in the form
$$W(s) = W^*(\bar{s}) = H \, \frac{\bar{s}^2 + a_1 \bar{s} + a_0}{\bar{s}^3 + b_2 \bar{s}^2 + b_1 \bar{s} + b_0}$$

by normalizing the complex-frequency variable s with an *arbitrarily chosen* normalizing frequency ω_0, where $\bar{s} = s/\omega_0$ for (a) $\omega_0 = 3 \times 10^5$ rad/sec and (b) $\omega_0 = 10^5$ rad/sec.

Note that (a) yields an expression with coefficients of medium magnitude, while the result of (b) still has rather large numbers as its coefficients. $\omega_0 = 3 \times 10^5$ rad/sec in (a) may therefore be considered a better choice as the normalizing frequency.

3.2. (a) Normalize the network function $W(s)$ given in Prob. 3.1 into the form
$$\bar{W}(\bar{s}) = \frac{W(s)}{W_0} = \bar{H} \, \frac{\bar{s}^2 + a_1 \bar{s} + a_0}{\bar{s}^3 + b_2 \bar{s}^2 + b_1 \bar{s} + b_0}$$

with the *arbitrarily chosen* normalizing quantities $\omega_0 = 3 \times 10^6$ rad/sec and $W_0 = 100$. Note that $\bar{H}$ is a number of medium magnitude.

(b) What are the poles and zeros of the normalized function $\bar{W}(\bar{s})$? Sketch a pole-and-zero plot.

(c) Determine the poles and zeros of $W(s)$ from the poles and zeros of $\bar{W}(\bar{s})$ obtained in (b).

3.3. (a) Normalize the network function $W(s)$ given in Prob. 3.1 into the form
$$\bar{W}(\bar{s}) = \frac{W(s)}{W(0)} = \bar{H} \, \frac{\bar{s}^2 + a_1 \bar{s} + a_0}{\bar{s}^3 + b_2 \bar{s}^2 + b_1 \bar{s} + b_0} \qquad \bar{H} = 1$$

with the *normalizing procedure* described in Art. 3.4B.

(b) What are the poles and zeros of the normalized function $\bar{W}(\bar{s})$? Sketch a pole-and-zero plot.

(c) Determine the poles and zeros of $W(s)$ from the poles and zeros of $\bar{W}(\bar{s})$ obtained in (b).

3.4. Given:
$$W(s) = 2,920 \times 10^4 \frac{s^4 + 90 \times 10^8 s^2 + 1,296 \times 10^{16}}{s^4 + 126 \times 10^8 s^2 + 3,240 \times 10^{16}}$$

(*a*) Normalize $W(s)$ with $\omega_0 = 3\sqrt{2} \times 10^4$ rad/sec and $W_0 = 1,000$.

(*b*) What are the poles and zeros of the normalized function $\bar{W}(\bar{s})$? Sketch a pole-and-zero plot.

(*c*) Determine the poles and zeros of $W(s)$ from the poles and zeros of $\bar{W}(\bar{s})$ obtained in (*b*).

3.5. Given:
$$W(s) = 5.5 \times 10^{-9} \frac{s^3 + 17.5 \times 10^{-12} s^2 + 125 \times 10^{-24} s + 375 \times 10^{-36}}{s^4 + 45 \times 10^{-12} s^3 + 675 \times 10^{-24} s^2 + 4,375 \times 10^{-36} s}$$

Repeat Prob. 3.4 for $\omega_0 = 5 \times 10^{-12}$ rad/sec and $W_0 = 1,000$.

3.6. Refer to the circuit in Fig. P 3.6.

(*a*) Normalize the circuit elements with the normalizing quantities $\omega_0 = 7\pi \times 10^6$ rad/sec and $R_0 = 72$ ohms.

(*b*) Find the driving-point impedance $\bar{Z}_D(\bar{s}) = \bar{E}_1/\bar{I}_1$ of the normalized circuit.

(*c*) Find the transfer admittance $\bar{Y}_T(\bar{s}) = \bar{I}_2/\bar{E}_1$ of the normalized circuit.

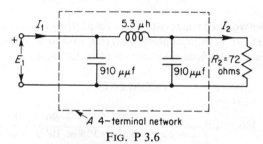

FIG. P 3.6

(*d*) Determine the driving-point impedance $Z_D(s) = E_1/I_1$ of the original circuit in Fig. P 3.6 from $\bar{Z}_D(\bar{s})$ obtained in (*b*).

(*e*) Determine the transfer admittance $Y_T(s) = I_2/E_1$ of the original circuit in Fig. P 3.6 from $\bar{Y}_T(\bar{s})$ obtained in (*c*).

3.7. Refer to the circuit in Fig. P 3.7.

(*a*) Find the insertion voltage-ratio function e^θ defined in (3.43).

(*b*) Obtain the insertion loss and insertion phase characteristics $\alpha(\omega)$ and $\beta(\omega)$ defined in (3.45).

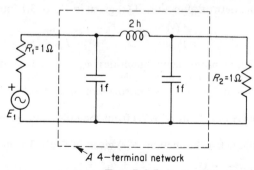

FIG. P 3.7

3.8. Using the transfer voltage-ratio function $G(s)$ obtained in Prob. 2.7 for the circuit in Fig. P 2.7, obtain the network characteristics $G_0(\omega)$ and $\theta(\omega)$ as defined in Eq. (3.39).

3.9. Using the transfer voltage-ratio function $G(s)$ in (3.36) for the circuit in Fig. 3.6*c*, (*a*) obtain the network characteristics $G_0(\omega)$ and $\theta(\omega)$ and (*b*) plot them versus the frequency ω. Note that $G_0(\omega)$ is an even function of ω, and $\theta(\omega)$, an odd function.

part **B** Characterization
of networks

Part B contains a discussion of the means of characterizing networks and a study of some network relations obtained in the process of network characterization.

Among the topics treated here are (1) characterization of the composite networks obtained by interconnecting two or more four-terminal networks and (2) network relations such as network equivalence (including the equivalence between ladder and lattice structures), network duality, and reciprocal networks.

Chapter 5 is primarily intended to introduce to the reader the concept of network topology. Two network relations given in Art. 2.2 are proved here as topological properties. The omission of this chapter will not impair reading continuity.

4 Network parameters and methods of interconnecting networks

4.1. Some simple matrix operations for use as mathematical tools in expressing voltage-current relations and studying network interconnections

A brief discussion of matrices and their simple operations is included in this section to provide the reader with adequate mathematical background for studying (1) the voltage-current relations of a four-terminal network as characterized by network parameters in Art. 4.2 and (2) the interconnections of four-terminal networks in Art. 4.3. The reader already familiar with matrix algebra may omit this section and proceed directly to Art. 4.2.

A. Definitions and Terminology

Collection of numbers. In ordinary arithmetic and algebra, we often operate on *single* numbers (or functions); the operations are addition, subtraction, multiplication, division, etc. For interpretation, let us consider the illustration associated with Eqs. (2.13) and Fig. 2.2. In this one-loop circuit, we are given a *single* excitation $e(t)$, and we operate on this quantity, finding a single response $i(t)$.

However, there are many problems in which it is desirable to operate on a *collection* of numbers (or functions). In an n-loop circuit, we have a *collection* of excitations $E_1, E_2, \ldots, E_n$ and wish to determine a *collection* of responses $I_1, I_2, \ldots, I_n$; this problem may be solved by (1) solving for each single response I_k one by one as described in Eqs. (2.20) through (2.24) *or* (2) solving for all the responses $I_1, I_2, \ldots, I_n$ *collectively*. The latter approach employs matrices and matrix operations which we shall introduce in this section.

As another example, let us consider a four-terminal network as in Fig. 2.6d. Let us assume that we have a *collection* of known voltages E_1, E_2 and wish to determine a *collection* of currents I_1, I_2. We may solve for I_1 and I_2 collectively, using matrix representation.

Matrix as an array of numbers or functions. We shall define a matrix of *order* $m \times n$:

Matrix of order $m \times n$:

$$A = \begin{bmatrix} a_{11} & a_{12} & \cdots & a_{1n} \\ a_{21} & a_{22} & \cdots & a_{2n} \\ \cdots\cdots\cdots\cdots\cdots\cdots \\ a_{m1} & a_{m2} & \cdots & a_{mn} \end{bmatrix} \tag{4.1}$$

to be an array of *elements* a_{ij}, numbers or functions, arranged in m rows and n

columns as shown in Eq. (4.1).   If $m = n$ in (4.1), we have a *square matrix* of order n:

Square matrix:

$$A = \begin{bmatrix} a_{11} & a_{12} & \cdots & a_{1n} \\ a_{21} & a_{22} & \cdots & a_{2n} \\ \cdots & \cdots & \cdots & \cdots \\ a_{n1} & a_{n2} & \cdots & a_{nn} \end{bmatrix} \tag{4.2}$$

Illustration 1.   Let us now consider the following matrices:

Matrix of order 3×4:

$$A_1 = \begin{bmatrix} 3 & 7 & 2 & 1 \\ 1 & 7 & 8 & 4 \\ 5 & 0 & 6 & 3 \end{bmatrix} \tag{4.3a}$$

Square matrix of order 3:

$$A_2 = \begin{bmatrix} 1 & 0 & 3 \\ 2 & -3 & 7 \\ 11 & 2 & 6 \end{bmatrix} \tag{4.3b}$$

Matrix with complex numbers as elements:

$$A_3 = \begin{bmatrix} 1+j & 2 & -j \\ 0 & 3 & 1-j \\ 1 & 2j & 5 \end{bmatrix} \tag{4.3c}$$

Zero matrix:

$$A_4 = \Lambda = \begin{bmatrix} 0 & 0 & 0 \\ 0 & 0 & 0 \\ 0 & 0 & 0 \end{bmatrix} \tag{4.3d}$$

Unit matrix:

$$A_5 = \mathbf{I} = \begin{bmatrix} 1 & 0 & 0 & 0 \\ 0 & 1 & 0 & 0 \\ 0 & 0 & 1 & 0 \\ 0 & 0 & 0 & 1 \end{bmatrix} \tag{4.3e}$$

Row matrix:

$$A_6 = [x, y, z] = [3, 7, 2] \tag{4.3f}$$

Column matrix:

$$A_7 = \begin{bmatrix} x \\ y \\ z \end{bmatrix} = \begin{bmatrix} 3 \\ 7 \\ 2 \end{bmatrix} \tag{4.3g}$$

Matrix with functions of time as elements:

$$A_8 = \begin{bmatrix} v_x(t) \\ v_y(t) \\ v_z(t) \end{bmatrix} = \begin{bmatrix} 100 \\ 50 \\ 32t \end{bmatrix} \tag{4.3h}$$

Note in (4.3) that a matrix may have real numbers, complex numbers, or parametric functions as its members, as exemplified in A_1, A_3, and A_8. A *zero matrix* Λ (elements all zeros) is illustrated in (4.3*d*); a zero matrix need not be a square matrix. A *unit matrix* is a square matrix whose diagonal elements are all 1s and whose nondiagonal elements are all 0s, as illustrated in (4.3*e*).

A matrix of order $1 \times n$, having 1 row and n columns, is called a *row matrix* of order n; an illustration is provided by A_6. A matrix of order $m \times 1$, having m rows and 1 column, is called a *column matrix* of order m; an illustration is provided by A_7. Now, we may represent a vector in space having the three components $x = 3, y = 7, z = 2$ *either* as a row matrix as in (4.3*f*) *or* as a column matrix as in (4.3*g*). However, the choice between these two forms is sometimes dictated by the matrix operation we wish to perform. For example, if we wish to perform a matrix multiplication $T \times A$, matrices T and A must be conformable (Art. 4.1C). This means that, if T is a matrix of order 3×3, A must be a matrix of order 3×1, i.e., a *column matrix* as illustrated in (4.3*g*), and must *not* be a row matrix such as (4.3*f*).

The elements of a matrix may be either numbers or functions. Consider a moving projectile having the velocity components $v_x(t) = 100$ due east, $v_y(t) = 50$ due north, and $v_z(t) = gt = 32t$ toward the earth; matrix A_8 in (4.3*h*) certainly represents this collection of velocity components and has functions of time as its elements.

Illustration 2. Matrices Associated with an n-loop Circuit. For an *n*-loop circuit, we have, in general, a collection of n excitations $E_1, E_2, \ldots, E_n$ as indicated in Eqs. (2.20), and a collection of $n \times n$ impedances $Z_{11}, Z_{12}, \ldots, Z_{nn}$ as defined in Eqs. (2.17) and used in Eqs. (2.20). Usually we wish to solve for a collection of n unknown responses $I_1, I_2, \ldots, I_n$. With the definition of a matrix as an array of numbers (or functions), we may represent the excitations, impedances, and responses of an *n*-loop circuit in the matrix forms

Excitation matrix:

$$E = \begin{bmatrix} E_1 \\ E_2 \\ \cdot \\ \cdot \\ \cdot \\ E_n \end{bmatrix} \tag{4.4a}$$

Impedance matrix:

$$Z = \begin{bmatrix} Z_{11} & Z_{12} & \cdots & Z_{1n} \\ Z_{21} & Z_{22} & \cdots & Z_{2n} \\ \multicolumn{4}{c}{\dotfill} \\ Z_{n1} & Z_{n2} & \cdots & Z_{nn} \end{bmatrix} \tag{4.4b}$$

Response matrix:

$$I = \begin{bmatrix} I_1 \\ I_2 \\ \cdot \\ \cdot \\ \cdot \\ I_n \end{bmatrix} \tag{4.4c}$$

where E is a column matrix of order n, Z is a square matrix of order n, and I is another column matrix of order n. We are only illustrating some matrices here; we shall discuss how the three matrices of an *n*-loop circuit in (4.4) are related in Art. 4.1C, and show how the response matrix I may be evaluated from the excitation and impedance matrices E and Z in Art. 4.1D.

Illustration 3.   *Some Matrices Associated with a Four-terminal Network.*   There are a number of different sets of matrices associated with a four-terminal network. We shall, at present, confine ourselves to one particular set for illustration.

For a four-terminal network as in Fig. 2.6d, we assume that we have a collection of two known voltages E_1, E_2 and a collection of four short-circuit admittances y_{11}, y_{12}, y_{21}, y_{22} as used and interpreted in Eqs. (2.32) through (2.34).   We wish to solve for a collection of two currents I_1, I_2.   Remembering the definition of a matrix as an array of numbers or functions, we may represent the voltages, admittances and currents of a four-terminal network in the matrix forms

Voltage matrix:

$$E = \begin{bmatrix} E_1 \\ E_2 \end{bmatrix} \tag{4.5a}$$

Short-circuit admittances:

$$Y = \begin{bmatrix} y_{11} & y_{12} \\ y_{21} & y_{22} \end{bmatrix} \tag{4.5b}$$

Current matrix:

$$I = \begin{bmatrix} I_1 \\ I_2 \end{bmatrix} \tag{4.5c}$$

where E and I are two column matrices of order 2, and Y is a square matrix of order 2×2.   We are only illustrating some matrices here; we shall discuss how these three matrices are related in Art. 4.2A.

Singular and regular matrices.   Associated with each square matrix A, there is a determinant A.   For example, the square matrix

$$A = \begin{bmatrix} 3 & 7 \\ 5 & 2 \end{bmatrix} \tag{4.6a}$$

has an *associated determinant*

$$|A| = \begin{vmatrix} 3 & 7 \\ 5 & 2 \end{vmatrix} = 3 \times 2 - 5 \times 7 = -29 \tag{4.6b}$$

In this case, the value of the determinant $|A|$ associated with the matrix A is -29. It is incorrect to say that the matrix A in (4.6a) has a value of -29, since a matrix is an array of numbers and has no defined value.

A square matrix A is called a *singular matrix* if its associated determinant vanishes. For example,

$$A_1 = \begin{bmatrix} 3 & 6 \\ 1 & 2 \end{bmatrix} \tag{4.7a}$$

and

$$A_2 = \begin{bmatrix} 1 & 3 & 2 \\ 3 & 7 & 5 \\ 2 & 6 & 4 \end{bmatrix} \tag{4.7b}$$

are singular matrices.   It is easy to verify that the values of their associated determinants $|A_1|$ and $|A_2|$ are zero.   A nonsingular matrix is often referred to as a *regular matrix*, and Eq. (4.6a) provides an illustration.

B. Addition of Matrices

Rule. We may add corresponding elements a_{ij} and b_{ij} of two matrices A and B of the same order $m \times n$ to obtain the elements $a_{ij} + b_{ij}$ of the sum $A + B$:

Sum of A and B:

$$A + B = \{a_{ij}\} + \{b_{ij}\} = \{a_{ij} + b_{ij}\} = \begin{bmatrix} a_{11} + b_{11} & a_{12} + b_{12} & \cdots & a_{1n} + b_{1n} \\ a_{21} + b_{21} & a_{22} + b_{22} & \cdots & a_{2n} + b_{2n} \\ \cdots\cdots\cdots\cdots\cdots\cdots\cdots\cdots\cdots\cdots\cdots\cdots \\ a_{m1} + b_{m1} & a_{m2} + b_{m2} & \cdots & a_{mn} + b_{mn} \end{bmatrix}$$

$$(4.8)$$

Addition with zero matrix. For a zero matrix Λ of order $m \times n$ and an arbitrary matrix A of order $m \times n$, it is easy to see that

$$A + \Lambda = A \qquad (4.9)$$

This is analogous to $a + 0 = a$ in ordinary algebra; the zero matrix Λ is analogous to the zero element 0.

C. Multiplication of Matrices

Conformable matrices and their product. If A is a matrix of order $m \times k$ (i.e., having m rows and k *columns*) and B is a matrix of order $k \times n$ (i.e., having k *rows* and n columns), A is said to be *conformable* to B; their product AB is a matrix of order $m \times n$ (i.e., having m rows and n columns).

We can multiply only conformable matrices. Multiplication is not defined for nonconformable matrices.

Procedure of matrix multiplication. We shall see that the row-by-column operation to be illustrated here defines matrix multiplication.

Let us consider two conformable matrices: A with m rows $R_1, R_2, \ldots, R_m$, and B with n columns $C_1, C_2, \ldots, C_n$. The product of A and B is

Product of matrices A and B:

$$AB = \{R_i * C_j\} = \begin{bmatrix} R_1 * C_1 & R_1 * C_2 & \cdots & R_1 * C_n \\ R_2 * C_1 & R_2 * C_2 & \cdots & R_2 * C_n \\ \cdots\cdots\cdots\cdots\cdots\cdots\cdots\cdots\cdots \\ R_m * C_1 & R_m * C_2 & \cdots & R_m * C_n \end{bmatrix}$$

$$(4.10)$$

where

$$R_i * C_j = \sum \begin{bmatrix} \text{products of corresponding} \\ \text{elements in } R_i \text{ and } C_j \end{bmatrix}$$

$$= \sum_{r=1}^{k} x_r y_r = x_1 y_1 + x_2 y_2 + \cdots + x_k y_k \qquad (4.11a)$$

and

$$R_i = i\text{th row of } A = [x_1 \quad x_2 \quad \cdots \quad x_k] \qquad (4.11b)$$

$$C_j = j\text{th column of } B = \begin{bmatrix} y_1 \\ y_2 \\ \cdot \\ \cdot \\ \cdot \\ y_k \end{bmatrix} \qquad (4.11c)$$

Illustration. We wish to find the product AB of two conformable matrices

$$A = \begin{bmatrix} 1 & 2 & 5 & 0 \\ -2 & 1 & 3 & 1 \\ 4 & -3 & 7 & 1 \end{bmatrix} \qquad B = \begin{bmatrix} 2 & 1 \\ 0 & 2 \\ 3 & 1 \\ 1 & 5 \end{bmatrix} \tag{4.12a}$$

According to (4.11), we have

$$\begin{aligned}
R_1 * C_1 &= \text{(row 1 of } A) * \text{(column 1 of } B) \\
&= 1 \times 2 + 2 \times 0 + 5 \times 3 + 0 \times 1 = 17 \\
R_1 * C_2 &= \text{(row 1 of } A) * \text{(column 2 of } B) \\
&= 1 \times 1 + 2 \times 2 + 5 \times 1 + 0 \times 5 = 10 \\
R_2 * C_1 &= -2 \times 2 + 1 \times 0 + 3 \times 3 + 1 \times 1 = 6 \\
R_2 * C_2 &= -2 \times 1 + 1 \times 2 + 3 \times 1 + 1 \times 5 = 8 \\
R_3 * C_1 &= 4 \times 2 + (-3) \times 0 + 7 \times 3 + 1 \times 1 = 30 \\
R_3 * C_2 &= 4 \times 1 + (-3) \times 2 + 7 \times 1 + 1 \times 5 = 10
\end{aligned} \tag{4.12b}$$

which may be substituted into (4.10), yielding

$$AB = \begin{bmatrix} 17 & 10 \\ 6 & 8 \\ 30 & 10 \end{bmatrix} \tag{4.12c}$$

Note here that A is a matrix of order 3×4, B is a matrix of order 4×2, and their product AB is a matrix of order 3×2.

Noncommutative property. It is obvious that two square matrices A and B of the same order are conformable to each other; both products AB and BA are defined. However, we shall find that, in general,

Noncommutative property:

$$AB \neq BA \tag{4.13}$$

This means that we cannot change the order of multiplication or *commute* the two matrices A and B in multiplication. We say that matrix multiplication is noncommutative.

To verify the noncommutative property in (4.13), let us consider

$$A = \begin{bmatrix} 1 & 1 \\ 1 & 1 \end{bmatrix} \qquad B = \begin{bmatrix} 3 & 0 \\ 0 & 2 \end{bmatrix}$$

Following the procedure of multiplication in (4.10), we find

$$AB = \begin{bmatrix} 3 & 2 \\ 3 & 2 \end{bmatrix} \qquad BA = \begin{bmatrix} 3 & 3 \\ 2 & 2 \end{bmatrix}$$

and (4.13) is verified by this simple illustration.

Multiplication by unit matrix. For an arbitrary matrix A and a unit matrix $\mathbf{I}$ [a square matrix whose diagonal elements are all 1s, and whose nondiagonal elements are all 0s, as illustrated in (4.3e)],

$$A\mathbf{I} = \mathbf{I}A = A \tag{4.14}$$

If A is a square matrix of order n, the unit matrix $\mathbf{I}$ in (4.14) must also be a square matrix of order n. If $A_{m \times n}$ is a matrix of order $m \times n$, Eq. (4.14) means $A_{m \times n} \mathbf{I}_n = \mathbf{I}_m A_{m \times n} = A_{m \times n}$, where $\mathbf{I}_m$ and $\mathbf{I}_n$ are, respectively, unit (square) matrices of orders m and n.

To verify (4.14), let us consider

$$A = \begin{bmatrix} 1 & 2 \\ 4 & 3 \end{bmatrix} \qquad \mathbf{I} = \begin{bmatrix} 1 & 0 \\ 0 & 1 \end{bmatrix}$$

Following the procedure for multiplication in (4.10), we find

$$A\mathbf{I} = \begin{bmatrix} 1 & 2 \\ 4 & 3 \end{bmatrix}\begin{bmatrix} 1 & 0 \\ 0 & 1 \end{bmatrix} = \begin{bmatrix} 1 & 2 \\ 4 & 3 \end{bmatrix} = A$$

$$\mathbf{I}A = \begin{bmatrix} 1 & 0 \\ 0 & 1 \end{bmatrix}\begin{bmatrix} 1 & 2 \\ 4 & 3 \end{bmatrix} = \begin{bmatrix} 1 & 2 \\ 4 & 3 \end{bmatrix} = A$$

and (4.14) is verified by this simple illustration. Equation (4.14) is analogous to $a \times 1 = 1 \times a = a$ in ordinary algebra; the unit matrix $\mathbf{I}$ is analogous to the unit element 1.

Multiplication by a scalar quantity k. The product of a matrix A and a scalar quantity k, that is, a constant, is

$$kA = k\begin{bmatrix} a_{11} & a_{12} & \cdots & a_{1n} \\ a_{21} & a_{22} & \cdots & a_{2n} \\ \cdots\cdots\cdots\cdots\cdots \\ a_{m1} & a_{m2} & \cdots & a_{mn} \end{bmatrix} = \begin{bmatrix} ka_{11} & ka_{12} & \cdots & ka_{1n} \\ ka_{21} & ka_{22} & \cdots & ka_{2n} \\ \cdots\cdots\cdots\cdots\cdots\cdots \\ ka_{m1} & ka_{m2} & \cdots & ka_{mn} \end{bmatrix} \qquad (4.15)$$

a matrix whose elements ka_{ij} are the elements a_{ij} of A multiplied by the scalar quantity k.

Matrix representation of loop equations. For an n-loop circuit, we have a system of n loop equations in Eqs. (2.20), where $E_1, E_2, \ldots, E_n$ are the voltage excitations, $Z_{11}, Z_{12}, \ldots, Z_{nn}$ are the self- or mutual impedances, and $I_1, I_2, \ldots, I_n$ are the *unknown* current responses.

We introduced excitation matrix E, impedance matrix Z, and response matrix I in (4.4). The loop equations (2.20) may now be represented in an alternative matrix form:

$$E = ZI \qquad \text{or} \qquad \begin{bmatrix} E_1 \\ E_2 \\ \cdot \\ \cdot \\ \cdot \\ E_n \end{bmatrix} = \begin{bmatrix} Z_{11} & Z_{12} & \cdots & Z_{1n} \\ Z_{21} & Z_{22} & \cdots & Z_{2n} \\ \cdots\cdots\cdots\cdots\cdots \\ Z_{n1} & Z_{n2} & \cdots & Z_{nn} \end{bmatrix}\begin{bmatrix} I_1 \\ I_2 \\ \cdot \\ \cdot \\ \cdot \\ I_n \end{bmatrix} \qquad (4.16)$$

By multiplying out the right-hand side of (4.16) according to the procedure of multiplication in (4.10), we find

$$\begin{bmatrix} E_1 \\ E_2 \\ \cdot \\ \cdot \\ \cdot \\ E_n \end{bmatrix} = \begin{bmatrix} Z_{11}I_1 + Z_{12}I_2 + \cdots + Z_{1n}I_n \\ Z_{21}I_1 + Z_{22}I_2 + \cdots + Z_{2n}I_n \\ \cdots\cdots\cdots\cdots\cdots\cdots\cdots\cdots \\ Z_{n1}I_1 + Z_{n2}I_2 + \cdots + Z_{nn}I_n \end{bmatrix} \qquad (4.17)$$

The two column matrices in (4.17) are equal; therefore, their corresponding elements are also equal. It is now easy to see that (4.17) or (4.16) is an equivalent representation of Eqs. (2.20).

D. Inversion of a Matrix

Inverse of a square matrix. The inverse (or reciprocal) of a nonsingular square matrix A is another square matrix $B = A^{-1}$ such that

$$BA = AB = \mathbf{I} \qquad A^{-1}A = AA^{-1} = \mathbf{I} \qquad (4.18)$$

We are now interested in finding the inverse A^{-1} of a given nonsingular square matrix A. Before we consider this problem, we shall define some terms, e.g., *cofactor* of a determinant and *transpose* of a matrix.

Associated determinant $|A|$ of a matrix A and its cofactors. We have already introduced and illustrated the term *associated determinant* of a square matrix in (4.6). For the square matrix A in (4.2), we have the associated determinant

$$|A| = \begin{vmatrix} a_{11} & a_{12} & \cdots & a_{1n} \\ a_{21} & a_{22} & \cdots & a_{2n} \\ \cdots\cdots\cdots\cdots\cdots\cdots \\ a_{n1} & a_{n2} & \cdots & a_{nn} \end{vmatrix} \qquad (4.19)$$

The cofactor A_{ij} of this determinant $|A|$ is another determinant having the form

$$A_{ij} = (-1)^{i+j} \begin{pmatrix} \text{determinant } |A| \\ \text{with } i\text{th row and} \\ j\text{th column deleted} \end{pmatrix} \qquad (4.19a)$$

For illustration, let us consider the determinant

$$|A'| = \begin{vmatrix} a & d & g \\ b & e & h \\ c & f & i \end{vmatrix} \qquad (4.20)$$

According to (4.19a), its cofactors are

$$A_{11} = (-1)^{1+1} \begin{vmatrix} e & h \\ f & i \end{vmatrix} = ei - fh$$

$$A_{12} = (-1)^{1+2} \begin{vmatrix} b & h \\ c & i \end{vmatrix} = -(bi - ch)$$

$$A_{13} = (-1)^{1+3} \begin{vmatrix} b & e \\ c & f \end{vmatrix} = bf - ce$$

$$\qquad (4.20a)$$

$$A_{21} = (-1)^{2+1} \begin{vmatrix} d & g \\ f & i \end{vmatrix} = -(di - fg)$$

and, similarly,

$$A_{22} = ai - cg \qquad A_{23} = -(af - cd)$$
$$A_{31} = dh - eg \qquad A_{32} = -(ah - bg) \qquad (4.20b)$$
$$A_{33} = ae - bd$$

Transpose A' of a matrix A.   The transpose A' of a given matrix A is defined as

$$A' = \text{matrix obtained by interchanging rows and columns of } A \qquad (4.21)$$

For illustration, A' below is the transpose of matrix A:

$$A = \begin{bmatrix} a & b & c \\ d & e & f \\ g & h & i \end{bmatrix} \qquad A' = \begin{bmatrix} a & d & g \\ b & e & h \\ c & f & i \end{bmatrix} \qquad (4.22)$$

Procedure for finding the inverse matrix A^{-1} of a given matrix A.   Given a non-singular square matrix A, obtain its inverse A^{-1} as follows:

Find its transpose A' $\qquad\qquad$ (4.23a)

Replace each element of A' by its cofactor $\qquad\qquad$ (4.23b)

Divide each element in the result of (4.23b) by the determinant $|A|$
associated with the original matrix A; $|A| \neq 0$ for A nonsingular;
the matrix thus obtained is the inverse matrix A^{-1} $\qquad\qquad$ (4.23c)

Illustration of finding the inverse matrix.   Let us find the inverse matrix A^{-1} of the matrix

$$A = \begin{bmatrix} a & b & c \\ d & e & f \\ g & h & i \end{bmatrix} \qquad (4.24a)$$

by following procedure (4.23):
1. We first find its transpose, which was obtained earlier in (4.22):

$$A' = \begin{bmatrix} a & d & g \\ b & e & h \\ c & f & i \end{bmatrix} \qquad (4.24b)$$

2. We then find the cofactors of the elements in A', which are identical with those in Eqs. (4.20), and use them to replace the elements in (4.24b):

$$\begin{bmatrix} ei - fh & -(bi - ch) & bf - ce \\ -(di - fg) & ai - cg & -(af - cd) \\ dh - eg & -(ah - bg) & ae - bd \end{bmatrix} \qquad (4.24c)$$

3. The inverse matrix of A is now

$$A^{-1} = \begin{bmatrix} \dfrac{ei - fh}{|A|} & -\dfrac{bi - ch}{|A|} & \dfrac{bf - ce}{|A|} \\[2mm] -\dfrac{di - fg}{|A|} & \dfrac{ai - cg}{|A|} & -\dfrac{af - cd}{|A|} \\[2mm] \dfrac{dh - eg}{|A|} & -\dfrac{ah - bg}{|A|} & \dfrac{ae - bd}{|A|} \end{bmatrix} = \dfrac{1}{|A|} \text{ [Eq. (4.24c)]} \quad (4.24d)$$

where $|A|$ is the determinant associated with the original matrix A. Since $1/|A|$ is a scalar quantity, we have taken it outside the matrix symbols [ ] in (4.24d).

As a numerical illustration, we shall consider

$$A = \begin{bmatrix} 3 & 2 & 7 \\ 0 & 5 & 1 \\ 1 & 0 & 2 \end{bmatrix} \tag{4.25a}$$

Following (4.24), we find its inverse matrix:

$$A^{-1} = \frac{1}{-3}\begin{bmatrix} 10 & 4 & -33 \\ 1 & -1 & -3 \\ -5 & 2 & 15 \end{bmatrix} = \begin{bmatrix} -\frac{10}{3} & -\frac{4}{3} & 11 \\ -\frac{1}{3} & \frac{1}{3} & 1 \\ \frac{5}{3} & -\frac{2}{3} & -5 \end{bmatrix} \tag{4.25b}$$

But how can we be sure that (4.25b) is the correct representation of the inverse matrix A^{-1} of the given matrix A? According to the definition of A^{-1}, it must satisfy the expression in (4.18):

$$A^{-1}A = AA^{-1} = \mathbf{I}$$

We may therefore verify (4.25b) by computing the product of A^{-1} and A in (4.25) according to (4.10):

$$A^{-1}A = \frac{1}{-3}\begin{bmatrix} 10 & 4 & -33 \\ 1 & -1 & -3 \\ -5 & 2 & 15 \end{bmatrix}\begin{bmatrix} 3 & 2 & 7 \\ 0 & 5 & 1 \\ 1 & 0 & 2 \end{bmatrix}$$

$$= \frac{1}{-3}\begin{bmatrix} -3 & 0 & 0 \\ 0 & -3 & 0 \\ 0 & 0 & -3 \end{bmatrix} = \begin{bmatrix} 1 & 0 & 0 \\ 0 & 1 & 0 \\ 0 & 0 & 1 \end{bmatrix} = \mathbf{I} \tag{4.25c}$$

and finding that it checks with (4.18).

Finding the loop currents of an *n*-loop circuit using matrices. For an *n*-loop circuit, we may write either a system of loop equations [Eqs. (2.20)] or its equivalent matrix representation $E = ZI$ [Eq. (4.16)].

If we wish to find the loop currents $I_1, I_2, \ldots, I_n$ of this *n*-loop circuit, we may follow the approach described in Chap. 2 and find these currents in Eqs. (2.24).

We now wish to find the loop currents by using matrix operations. For $E = ZI$ in (4.16), we find

$$Z^{-1}E = Z^{-1}ZI = (Z^{-1}Z)I = \mathbf{I}I = I$$

where $\mathbf{I} = Z^{-1}Z$ is a unit matrix, and

$$I = Z^{-1}E \qquad \begin{bmatrix} I_1 \\ I_2 \\ \cdot \\ \cdot \\ \cdot \\ I_n \end{bmatrix} = Z^{-1}\begin{bmatrix} E_1 \\ E_2 \\ \cdot \\ \cdot \\ \cdot \\ E_n \end{bmatrix} \tag{4.26}$$

This means that we use the following procedure in finding the loop currents of an *n*-loop circuit:

Set up the loop equations in the matrix form of (4.16) instead of the form of (2.20)   (4.27*a*)

Find the inverse matrix Z^{-1} of the impedance matrix Z in (4.16) according to the procedure in (4.23)   (4.27*b*)

Find the product of the matrices Z^{-1} and E following the procedure of multiplication in (4.10); this product is the current matrix I according to (4.26); its elements $I_1, I_2, \ldots, I_n$ are the required loop currents   (4.27*c*)

Numerical illustration of finding loop currents.   We shall apply matrix operations to the illustration associated with Eqs. (2.30). For the three-loop network in Fig. 2.5*b*, we have the following matrices from Eqs. (2.30*a*) and (2.30*c*):

$$E = \begin{bmatrix} E_1 \\ E_2 \\ E_3 \end{bmatrix} = \begin{bmatrix} 1 \\ 0 \\ \sqrt{2}e^{j45°} \end{bmatrix} = \begin{bmatrix} 1 \\ 0 \\ 1+j1 \end{bmatrix} \tag{4.28a}$$

$$Z = \begin{bmatrix} Z_{11} & Z_{12} & Z_{13} \\ Z_{21} & Z_{22} & Z_{23} \\ Z_{31} & Z_{32} & Z_{33} \end{bmatrix} = \begin{bmatrix} s+1 & 0 & -s \\ 0 & \dfrac{2s+2}{s} & 1 \\ -s & 1 & s+2 \end{bmatrix} \tag{4.28b}$$

As suggested in (4.27*b*), we shall follow the procedure in (4.23) to find the inverse matrix Z^{-1}.

1. We first find the transpose of Z:

$$Z' = \begin{bmatrix} 1+s & 0 & -s \\ 0 & 2+\dfrac{2}{s} & 1 \\ -s & 1 & 2+s \end{bmatrix} \tag{4.28c}$$

2. We then find the cofactors of the elements in Z' and use them to replace the elements in (4.28*c*):

$$\begin{bmatrix} \dfrac{2s^2+5s+4}{s} & -s & 2(s+1) \\ -s & 3s+2 & -(s+1) \\ 2(s+1) & -(s+1) & \dfrac{2s^2+4s+2}{s} \end{bmatrix} \tag{4.28d}$$

3. We find the determinant $|Z|$ associated with the original Z matrix in (4.28*b*):

$$|Z| = 9 + \frac{4}{s} + 5s = \frac{5s^2+9s+4}{s} \tag{4.28e}$$

The inverse matrix is now

$$Z^{-1} = \frac{1}{|Z|} \text{ [Eq. (4.28d)]} = \begin{bmatrix} \dfrac{2s^2 + 5s + 4}{5s^2 + 9s + 4} & \dfrac{-s^2}{5s^2 + 9s + 4} & \dfrac{2s(s+1)}{5s^2 + 9s + 4} \\[2mm] \dfrac{-s^2}{5s^2 + 9s + 4} & \dfrac{s(3s+2)}{5s^2 + 9s + 4} & \dfrac{-s(s+1)}{5s^2 + 9s + 4} \\[2mm] \dfrac{2s(s+1)}{5s^2 + 9s + 4} & \dfrac{-s(s+1)}{5s^2 + 9s + 4} & \dfrac{2s^2 + 4s + 2}{5s^2 + 9s + 4} \end{bmatrix} \quad (4.28f)$$

According to (4.27c), with the value of matrix E in (4.28a), the current matrix is now

$$I = \begin{bmatrix} I_1 \\ I_2 \\ I_3 \end{bmatrix} = Z^{-1} \begin{bmatrix} 1 \\ 0 \\ 1+j1 \end{bmatrix} = \text{[Eq. (4.28f)]} \begin{bmatrix} 1 \\ 0 \\ 1+j1 \end{bmatrix} \quad (4.28g)$$

The elements I_1, I_2, I_3 of the product of the two matrices on the right-hand side of (4.28g) are the loop currents. I_1 and I_2, thus computed, are found to check with Eqs. (2.30e) and (2.30f).

$$I_3 = \frac{1}{5s^2 + 9s + 4} \, 2s(s+1)(1) + 0 + (2s^2 + 4s + 2)(1 + j1)$$

$$= \frac{(4 + j2)s^2 + (6 + j4)s + 2 + j2}{5s^2 + 9s + 4} \quad (4.28h)$$

I_3 was not computed in the earlier illustration in Chap. 2.

4.2. Voltage-current relations of a four-terminal network; network parameters

There are two voltages E_1, E_2 and two currents I_1, I_2 associated with the four-terminal network in Fig. 4.1. Our present interest is to study the voltage-current relations among these four quantities E_1, E_2, I_1, I_2 of a four-terminal network.

We may either consider $-I_2$ as current flowing out of the network (and into the load) or consider I_2 as current flowing into the network

A. Currents I_1, I_2 Expressed in Terms of Voltages E_1, E_2

We have already obtained in Eqs. (2.32) the voltage-current relations of a four-terminal network in algebraic form:

Algebraic form:

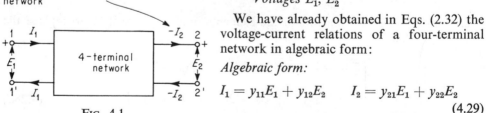

FIG. 4.1

$$I_1 = y_{11}E_1 + y_{12}E_2 \qquad I_2 = y_{21}E_1 + y_{22}E_2$$
$$(4.29)$$

where y_{11}, y_{12}, y_{21}, y_{22} are a set of *network parameters*. This set of four parameters completely characterizes a four-terminal network in the sense that it prescribes the voltage-current relations of the network in (4.29).

We have introduced in Eqs. (4.5) a set of matrices associated with the four-terminal network in Fig. 4.1. Using these matrices, we may also rewrite (4.29) in matrix form:

Matrix form:

$$I = YE \quad \text{or} \quad \begin{bmatrix} I_1 \\ I_2 \end{bmatrix} = \begin{bmatrix} y_{11} & y_{12} \\ y_{21} & y_{22} \end{bmatrix} \begin{bmatrix} E_1 \\ E_2 \end{bmatrix} \tag{4.30}$$

To show that (4.29) and (4.30) are equivalent expressions, we find the product of the two matrices on the right-hand side of (4.30) according to (4.10), obtaining

$$\begin{bmatrix} I_1 \\ I_2 \end{bmatrix} = \begin{bmatrix} y_{11}E_1 + y_{12}E_2 \\ y_{21}E_1 + y_{22}E_2 \end{bmatrix}$$

This expression implies $I_1 = y_{11}E_1 + y_{12}E_2$ and $I_2 = y_{21}E_1 + y_{22}E_2$ and is, therefore, the same as (4.29).

Computation of y_{ij} from loop analysis. We have already studied how to compute y_{ij} by the method of loop analysis in Chap. 2; we shall now summarize the procedure with reference to Fig. 2.7 for notation.

1. Assume E_1 and E_2 are two voltage sources, and set up current loops as depicted in Fig. 2.7.
2. Determine the self-impedances Z_{ii} and mutual impedances Z_{ij} of these loops according to (2.17).
3. Set up loop equations similar to Eqs. (2.20) with $E_3 = E_4 = \cdots = E_n = 0$ (since we have only two sources E_1 and E_2).
4. Solve for loop currents with the aid of Eqs. (2.24), finding

$$I_1 = \frac{\Delta_{11}}{\Delta} E_1 + \frac{\Delta_{21}}{\Delta} E_2 \qquad I_2 = \frac{\Delta_{12}}{\Delta} E_1 + \frac{\Delta_{22}}{\Delta} E_2 \tag{4.31a}$$

where the system determinant Δ is defined in (2.25), and the Δ_{ij} are its cofactors.

5. Identifying (4.31a) with (4.29), find

$$y_{11} = \frac{\Delta_{11}}{\Delta} \qquad y_{12} = \frac{\Delta_{21}}{\Delta} \qquad y_{21} = \frac{\Delta_{12}}{\Delta} \qquad y_{22} = \frac{\Delta_{22}}{\Delta} \tag{4.31b}$$

where Δ and its cofactors Δ_{ij} may be evaluated as determinants according to their definitions.

The above procedure tells how to compute the parameters y_{ij}, as well as the reasoning behind the method. If we are only interested in computing the parameters y_{ij}, we may follow only steps 1, 2, and 5, omitting the rest.

Illustration 1. The y_{ij} of the four-terminal network in Fig. 4.2a, which is identical with Fig. 2.7, have already been calculated in the illustration associated with Eqs. (2.36); thus

$$y_{11} = \frac{\Delta_{11}}{\Delta} = \frac{s^2 + 3s + 4}{2s^2 + 7s + 4}$$

$$y_{12} = y_{21} = \frac{\Delta_{21}}{\Delta} = \frac{\Delta_{12}}{\Delta} = \frac{-s^2}{2s^2 + 7s + 4}$$

$$y_{22} = \frac{\Delta_{22}}{\Delta} = \frac{3s^2 + 2s}{2s^2 + 7s + 4}$$

where $s = j\omega$, and ω is the angular frequency in radians per second.

Interpretation of y_{ij} as short-circuit admittances; measurement of y_{ij}. What are physical interpretations of these network parameters y_{ij} as defined and illustrated? We have already discussed them in the paragraph associated with Eqs. (2.34). The parameters y_{ij} are the *short-circuit admittances* of a four-terminal network. For

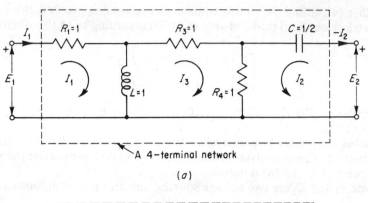

(a)

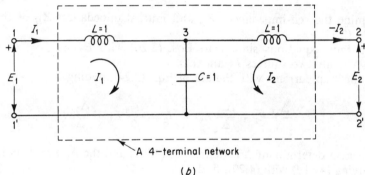

(b)

Fig. 4.2

example, we may short-circuit terminal pair 22′ in Fig. 4.1, i.e., let $E_2 = 0$ in (4.29), and obtain the two short-circuit admittances

$$y_{11} = \left(\frac{I_1}{E_1}\right)_{E_2=0} \qquad y_{21} = \left(\frac{I_2}{E_1}\right)_{E_2=0} \tag{4.32a}$$

by (1) applying E_1 to the circuit, (2) *measuring I_1 and I_2*, and (3) finding the current/ voltage ratios in (4.32a). Similarly, we may short-circuit terminal pair 11′ in Fig. 4.1, i.e., let $E_1 = 0$ in (4.29), and obtain the other two short-circuit admittances

$$y_{12} = \left(\frac{I_1}{E_2}\right)_{E_1=0} \qquad y_{22} = \left(\frac{I_2}{E_2}\right)_{E_1=0} \tag{4.32b}$$

by (1) applying E_2, (2) *measuring I_1 and I_2*, and (3) finding the current/voltage ratios in (4.32b).

In (2.35), one condition was imposed upon these short-circuit network parameters; i.e.,

$$y_{12} = y_{21} \tag{4.33}$$

for bilateral networks.

Illustration 2. We shall now find the short-circuit parameters y_{ij} of the simple four-terminal network in Fig. 4.2b by taking advantage of their physical interpretations in (4.32). For example, we find

$$y_{11} = \left(\frac{I_1}{E_1}\right)_{E_2=0} = \frac{1}{\left(\dfrac{E_1}{I_1}\right)_{E_2=0}} = \frac{1}{\text{driving-point impedance looking into } 11' \text{ with } 22' \text{ short-circuited}}$$

$$= \frac{1}{sL + sL\,(1/sC)/(sL + 1/sC)} = \frac{s^2 + 1}{s^3 + 2s} \qquad (4.34a)$$

$$y_{21} = \left(\frac{I_2}{E_1}\right)_{E_2=0} = -\frac{1}{s^3 + 2s}\; † \qquad (4.34b)$$

$$y_{12} = \left(\frac{I_1}{E_2}\right)_{E_1=0} = -\frac{1}{s^3 + 2s} \qquad (4.34c)$$

$$y_{22} = \left(\frac{I_2}{E_2}\right)_{E_1=0} = \frac{1}{\left(\dfrac{E_2}{I_2}\right)_{E_1=0}} = \frac{1}{\text{driving-point impedance looking into } 22' \text{ with } 11' \text{ short-circuited}}$$

$$= \frac{1}{sL + sL(1/sC)/(sL + 1/sC)} = \frac{s^2 + 1}{s^3 + 2s} \qquad (4.34d)$$

B. Voltages E_1, E_2 Expressed in Terms of Currents I_1, I_2

We have already expressed I_1, I_2 in terms of E_1, E_2 in (4.29) for the four-terminal network in Fig. 4.1. We shall find in subsequent paragraphs that we may also express E_1, E_2 in terms of I_1, I_2 in the following algebraic form:

Algebraic form:

$$E_1 = z_{11}I_1 + z_{12}I_2 \qquad E_2 = z_{21}I_1 + z_{22}I_2 \qquad (4.35)$$

where z_{11}, z_{12}, z_{21}, z_{22} are a set of *network parameters*. This set of four parameters completely characterizes a four-terminal network in the sense that it prescribes the voltage-current relations of the network in (4.35).

In the same manner in which we represent (4.29) in its equivalent matrix form (4.30), we may represent (4.35) in matrix form:

Matrix form:

$$E = ZI \qquad \text{or} \qquad \begin{bmatrix} E_1 \\ E_2 \end{bmatrix} = \begin{bmatrix} z_{11} & z_{12} \\ z_{21} & z_{22} \end{bmatrix} \begin{bmatrix} I_1 \\ I_2 \end{bmatrix} \qquad (4.36)$$

To show that (4.35) and (4.36) are equivalent expressions, we may find the product of the two matrices on the right-hand side of (4.36) according to (4.10), obtaining

$$\begin{bmatrix} E_1 \\ E_2 \end{bmatrix} = \begin{bmatrix} z_{11}I_1 + z_{12}I_2 \\ z_{21}I_1 + z_{22}I_2 \end{bmatrix}$$

† With $22'$ short-circuited (as $E_2 = 0$) in Fig. 4.2b, and with E_3 the voltage at node 3, it is easy to see that $E_3 = E_1[sL(1/sC)/(sL + 1/sC)]/[sL + sL(1/sC)/(sL + 1/sC)] = E_1 s/(s^3 + 2s)$ and $-I_2 = E_3/sL = [E_1 s/(s^3 + 2s)]/s = E_1/(s^3 + 2s)$, which implies $I_2/E_1 = -1/(s^3 + 2s)$ in (4.34b). We may obtain y_{12} in (4.34c) in a similar manner or according to (4.33).

This expression implies $E_1 = z_{11}I_1 + z_{12}I_2$ and $E_2 = z_{21}I_1 + z_{22}I_2$ and is, therefore, the same as (4.35).

Computation of z_{ij} from nodal analysis. Let us now use the four-terminal network in Fig. 4.3 for notations and illustration for our present problem. Considering I_1 and I_2 as two current sources entering the network at nodes 1 and 2, we may express the nodal voltages E_1, E_2 in terms of I_1, I_2 in the form of (4.35). To compute z_{ij} by the method of nodal analysis, we may use the following procedure:

1. Assume I_1 and I_2 are two current sources and define nodes as the junctions of three or more circuit branches. Figure 4.3 depicts three nodes.

2. Determine the self-admittances Y_{ii} and mutual admittances Y_{ij} of these nodes according to (2.55).

3. Set up nodal equations similar to Eqs. (2.56) with $I_3 = I_4 = \cdots = I_n = 0$ (since we have only two sources I_1 and I_2).

4. Solve for nodal voltages with the aid of Eq. (2.57), finding

$$E_1 = \frac{\Delta'_{11}}{\Delta'} I_1 + \frac{\Delta'_{21}}{\Delta'} I_2 \qquad E_2 = \frac{\Delta'_{12}}{\Delta'} I_1 + \frac{\Delta'_{22}}{\Delta'} I_2 \qquad (4.37a)$$

where the system determinant Δ' is defined in (2.58), and the Δ'_{ij} are its cofactors.

5. Identifying (4.37a) with (4.35), find

$$z_{11} = \frac{\Delta'_{11}}{\Delta'} \qquad z_{12} = \frac{\Delta'_{21}}{\Delta'} \qquad z_{21} = \frac{\Delta'_{21}}{\Delta'} \qquad z_{22} = \frac{\Delta'_{22}}{\Delta'} \qquad (4.37b)$$

where Δ' is defined in (2.58), and its cofactors Δ'_{ij} are determinants and may be evaluated accordingly.

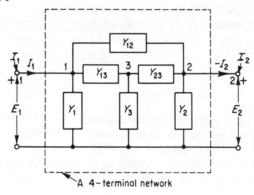

A 4-terminal network

FIG. 4.3

The above procedure tells us how to compute the parameters z_{ij} as well as the reasoning behind the method. If we are interested only in computing the parameters z_{ij}, we may follow only steps 1, 2, and 5, omitting the others.

Remarks about the methods of evaluating z_{ij}. We have described above a method of evaluating z_{ij} using the method of nodal analysis. However, the more commonly used methods of evaluating z_{ij} are (1) the *method of identities*—for example, once we have evaluated the short-circuit admittances y_{ij} as described in the preceding section, we may compute the parameters z_{ij} from the *known* values of y_{ij} through certain relations called identities—and (2) the *method taking advantage of the physical interpretations of z_{ij} as open-circuit impedances* in much the same way that the y_{ij}, as short-circuit admittances, are evaluated in (4.32) and (4.34). These methods will be discussed in subsequent paragraphs.

Computation of z_{ij} from known short-circuit admittances y_{ij} through identities.
Assuming that the short-circuit admittances y_{ij} in (4.29),

$$I_1 = y_{11}E_1 + y_{12}E_2 \qquad I_2 = y_{21}E_1 + y_{22}E_2 \tag{4.37c}$$

are *known* quantities, we now wish to compute the parameters z_{ij}. This can be
easily accomplished by solving for E_1, E_2 in terms of I_1, I_2 in (4.37c):

$$E_1 = \frac{\begin{vmatrix} I_1 & y_{12} \\ I_2 & y_{22} \end{vmatrix}}{\Delta} = \frac{y_{22}}{\Delta} I_1 + \frac{-y_{12}}{\Delta} I_2$$

$$E_2 = \frac{\begin{vmatrix} y_{11} & I_1 \\ y_{21} & I_2 \end{vmatrix}}{\Delta} = \frac{-y_{21}}{\Delta} I_1 + \frac{y_{11}}{\Delta} I_2 \tag{4.38}$$

where
$$\Delta = \begin{vmatrix} y_{11} & y_{12} \\ y_{21} & y_{22} \end{vmatrix} = y_{11}y_{22} - y_{12}y_{12}$$

Identifying the above expressions with (4.35), we obtain a set of *identities*, i.e.,
identical relations, between a set of network parameters y_{ij} and another set of
network parameters z_{ij}:

Identities of z_{ij} in terms of y_{ij}:

$$z_{11} = \frac{y_{22}}{y_{11}y_{22} - y_{12}y_{21}} \qquad z_{12} = \frac{-y_{12}}{y_{11}y_{22} - y_{12}y_{21}}$$

$$z_{21} = \frac{-y_{21}}{y_{11}y_{22} - y_{12}y_{21}} \qquad z_{22} = \frac{y_{11}}{y_{11}y_{22} - y_{12}y_{21}} \tag{4.39}$$

For bilateral networks, we have

$$z_{12} = z_{21} \tag{4.40}$$

which may be obtained by imposing (4.33) upon (4.39).

Obtaining the identities in (4.39) by matrix inversion. We may also obtain the
identities in (4.39) by a different approach. Suppose that, instead of using (4.29)
and (4.35), we use their *matrix forms* in (4.30) and (4.36). In (4.30), we multiply
both sides by the inverse matrix Y^{-1}, finding

$$Y^{-1}I = Y^{-1}YE = Y^{-1}Y E = IE = E \tag{4.41a}$$

or
$$E = Y^{-1}I \tag{4.41b}$$

Identifying (4.41b) with (4.36), we have

$$Z = Y^{-1} \qquad \text{or} \qquad \begin{bmatrix} z_{11} & z_{12} \\ z_{21} & z_{22} \end{bmatrix} = \begin{bmatrix} y_{11} & y_{12} \\ y_{21} & y_{22} \end{bmatrix}^{-1} \tag{4.42}$$

This means that the Z matrix is the inverse of the Y matrix. To find the inverse of
Y, we follow the procedure in (4.23):
1. Find the transpose:

$$Y' = \begin{bmatrix} y_{11} & y_{21} \\ y_{12} & y_{22} \end{bmatrix} \tag{4.43a}$$

2. Replace each element of Y' by its cofactor:

$$\begin{bmatrix} y_{22} & -y_{12} \\ -y_{21} & y_{11} \end{bmatrix} \tag{4.43b}$$

3. The determinant with Y is

$$|Y| = \begin{vmatrix} y_{11} & y_{12} \\ y_{21} & y_{22} \end{vmatrix} = y_{11}y_{22} - y_{12}y_{21} \tag{4.43c}$$

The inverse of Y is

$$Y^{-1} = \begin{bmatrix} \dfrac{y_{22}}{y_{11}y_{22} - y_{12}y_{21}} & \dfrac{-y_{12}}{y_{11}y_{22} - y_{12}y_{21}} \\[3ex] \dfrac{-y_{21}}{y_{11}y_{22} - y_{12}y_{21}} & \dfrac{y_{11}}{y_{11}y_{22} - y_{12}y_{21}} \end{bmatrix} \tag{4.43d}$$

which, according to (4.42), is the Z matrix. Our results here do check with (4.39).

Illustration 1. We may now compute the parameters z_{ij} of the network in Fig. 4.2b by substituting its known parameters y_{ij} [Eqs. (4.34)] into (4.39), finding

$$z_{11} = \frac{s^2 + 1}{s} \qquad z_{12} = \frac{1}{s}$$

$$z_{21} = \frac{1}{s} \qquad z_{22} = \frac{s^2 + 1}{s} \tag{4.44}$$

Remarks about identities. We have now introduced two sets of parameters: y_{ij} and z_{ij}. We shall introduce four more sets of network parameters in Art. 4.2C to F; so there are a total of *six* sets of network parameters associated with the four-terminal networks in Fig. 4.1.

At the beginning of Art. 4.2A, we said that the set of parameters y_{11}, y_{12}, y_{21}, y_{22} completely characterizes a four-terminal network in the sense that it prescribes the voltage-current relations in (4.29). At the beginning of Art. 4.2B, we said that the set of parameters z_{11}, z_{12}, z_{21}, z_{22} completely characterizes a four-terminal network in the sense that it prescribes the voltage-current relations in (4.35). Actually, each of the six sets of network parameters completely characterizes a four-terminal network in the same sense. This means that, knowing any one set of parameters, we shall be able to find the other five sets through the relations called *identities*. Given a set of parameters y_{ij}, we can find the set of parameters z_{ij} using the identities in (4.39). In the same manner in which we obtained the identities (4.39), using the approach in (4.38) of solving simultaneous equations or the approach in (4.43) of finding the inverse matrix, we may find the 30 sets of identities in Table 4.1. *Given any set of parameters, we may find any other set of parameters with the aid of Table 4.1.* For example, column b of Table 4.1 lists all sets of identities for finding the parameters z_{ij} in terms of other sets of parameters.

Interpretation of z_{ij} as open-circuit impedances; measurement of z_{ij}. We have interpreted the parameters y_{ij} as the short-circuit impedances of a four-terminal network in Eqs. (4.32). What then are the physical interpretations of the network parameters z_{ij} as defined and illustrated above? We shall find that the z_{ij} are the *open-circuit impedances* of a four-terminal network. For example, we may open-circuit the terminal pair 22' in Fig. 4.1, i.e., let $I_2 = 0$ in (4.35), and obtain the two open-circuit impedances

$$z_{11} = \left(\frac{E_1}{I_1}\right)_{I_2=0} \qquad z_{21} = \left(\frac{E_2}{I_1}\right)_{I_2=0} \tag{4.45a}$$

by (1) applying I_1 (i.e., injecting I_1 into terminal 1) in the circuit, (2) *measuring E_1 and E_2*, and (3) finding the voltage/current ratios in (4.45a). Similarly, we may open-circuit the terminal pair 11' in Fig. 4.1, i.e., let $I_1 = 0$ in (4.35), and obtain the other two open-circuit impedances

$$z_{12} = \left(\frac{E_1}{I_2}\right)_{I_1=0} \qquad z_{22} = \left(\frac{E_2}{I_2}\right)_{I_1=0} \tag{4.45b}$$

by (1) applying I_2 to the circuit, (2) *measuring E_1 and E_2*, and (3) finding the voltage/current ratios in (4.45b).

For bilateral networks, we have

$$z_{12} = z_{21} \tag{4.46}$$

We may consider (4.46) as the equivalent of condition (4.33) through the identities in (4.39) or Table 4.1.

Illustration 2. We shall now find the open-circuit parameters z_{ij} of the simple four-terminal network in Fig. 4.2b by taking advantage of their physical interpretations in (4.45). For example, we find

$$z_{11} = \left(\frac{E_1}{I_1}\right)_{I_2=0} = \begin{array}{l} \text{driving-point impedance looking} \\ \text{into 11' with 22' open-circuited} \end{array}$$

$$= sL + \frac{1}{sC} = \frac{s^2+1}{s} \tag{4.47a}$$

$$z_{21} = \left(\frac{E_2}{I_1}\right)_{I_2=0} = \left(\frac{E_3}{I_1}\right)_{I_2=0} = \frac{1}{s}^{\dagger} \tag{4.47b}$$

$$z_{12} = \left(\frac{E_1}{I_2}\right)_{I_1=0} = \frac{1}{s} \tag{4.47c}$$

$$z_{22} = \left(\frac{E_2}{I_2}\right)_{I_1=0} = \begin{array}{l} \text{driving-point impedance looking} \\ \text{into 22' with 11' open-circuited} \end{array}$$

$$= sL + \frac{1}{sC} = \frac{s^2+1}{s} \tag{4.47d}$$

Note that (4.47) agrees with (4.44) although they result from two different methods of computing the parameters z_{ij}.

C. E_1, I_1 Expressed in Terms of E_2, I_2

For the four-terminal network in Fig. 4.1, we have already expressed I_1, I_2 in terms of E_1, E_2 in (4.29), and E_1, E_2 in terms of I_1, I_2 in (4.35). We shall find in subsequent paragraphs that we may express E_1, I_1 at the terminal pair 11' in terms of E_2, I_2 at the terminal pair 22' in the following algebraic form:

Algebraic form:

$$E_1 = aE_2 - bI_2 \qquad I_1 = cE_2 - dI_2 \tag{4.48}$$

where a, b, c, d are a set of *network parameters*. This set of four parameters completely characterizes a four-terminal network in the sense that it prescribes the voltage-current relations of the network in (4.48).

† With 22' open-circuited (as $I_2 = 0$) in Fig. 4.2b, and with E_3 the voltage at node 3, it is easy to see that $E_2 = E_3 = I_1(1/sC) = I_1/s$ or $E_2/I_1 = 1/s$. We may obtain z_{12} in (4.47c) in a similar manner *or* according to (4.46).

Table 4.1

Given parameters in	To find parameters in	
	(a)	(b)
(1) $I_1 = y_{11}E_1 + y_{12}E_2$ $I_2 = y_{21}E_1 + y_{22}E_2$ For bilateral networks $y_{12} = y_{21}$		$E_1 = z_{11}I_1 + z_{12}I_2$ $E_2 = z_{21}I_1 + z_{22}I_2$ **(b1)** $z_{11} = \dfrac{y_{22}}{y_{11}y_{22} - y_{12}y_{21}}$ $z_{12} = \dfrac{-y_{12}}{y_{11}y_{22} - y_{12}y_{21}}$ $z_{21} = \dfrac{-y_{21}}{y_{11}y_{22} - y_{12}y_{21}}$ $z_{22} = \dfrac{y_{11}}{y_{11}y_{22} - y_{12}y_{21}}$ For bilateral networks $z_{12} = z_{21}$ as $y_{12} = y_{21}$
(2) $E_1 = z_{11}I_1 + z_{12}I_2$ $E_2 = z_{21}I_1 + z_{22}I_2$ For bilateral networks $z_{12} = z_{21}$	**(a2)** $y_{11} = \dfrac{z_{22}}{z_{11}z_{22} - z_{12}z_{21}}$ $y_{12} = \dfrac{-z_{12}}{z_{11}z_{22} - z_{12}z_{21}}$ $y_{21} = \dfrac{-z_{21}}{z_{11}z_{22} - z_{12}z_{21}}$ $y_{22} = \dfrac{z_{11}}{z_{11}z_{22} - z_{12}z_{21}}$ For bilateral networks $y_{12} = y_{21}$ as $z_{12} = z_{21}$	
(3) $E_1 = aE_2 - bI_2$ $I_1 = cE_2 - dI_2$ For bilateral networks $ad - bc = 1$	**(a3)** $y_{11} = \dfrac{d}{b}$ $\qquad y_{12} = \dfrac{-(ad - bc)}{b}$ $y_{21} = \dfrac{-1}{b}$ $\qquad y_{22} = \dfrac{a}{b}$ For bilateral networks $y_{12} = y_{21}$ as $ad - bc = 1$	**(b3)** $z_{11} = \dfrac{a}{c}$ $\qquad z_{12} = \dfrac{ad - bc}{c}$ $z_{21} = \dfrac{1}{c}$ $\qquad z_{22} = \dfrac{d}{c}$ For bilateral networks $z_{12} = z_{21}$ as $ad - bc = 1$

(4) $$E_2 = d^*E_1 - b^*I_1$$ $$I_2 = c^*E_1 - a^*I_1$$ For bilateral networks $$d^*a^* - b^*c^* = 1$$	(a4) $$y_{11} = \frac{d^*}{b^*} \qquad y_{12} = \frac{-1}{b^*}$$ $$y_{21} = \frac{-(d^*a^* - b^*c^*)}{b^*} \qquad y_{22} = \frac{a^*}{b^*}$$ For bilateral networks $$y_{12} = y_{21} \qquad \text{as } d^*a^* - b^*c^* = 1$$	(b4) $$z_{11} = \frac{a^*}{c^*} \qquad z_{12} = \frac{1}{c^*}$$ $$z_{21} = \frac{d^*a^* - b^*c^*}{c^*} \qquad z_{22} = \frac{d^*}{c^*}$$ For bilateral networks $$z_{12} = z_{21} \qquad \text{as } d^*a^* - b^*c^* = 1$$
(5) $$E_1 = h_{11}I_1 + h_{12}E_2$$ $$I_2 = h_{21}I_1 + h_{22}E_2$$ For bilateral networks $$h_{12} = -h_{21}$$	(a5) $$y_{11} = \frac{1}{h_{11}} \qquad y_{12} = \frac{-h_{12}}{h_{11}}$$ $$y_{21} = \frac{h_{21}}{h_{11}} \qquad y_{22} = \frac{h_{11}h_{22} - h_{12}h_{21}}{h_{11}}$$ For bilateral networks $$y_{12} = y_{21} \qquad \text{as } h_{12} = -h_{21}$$	(b5) $$z_{11} = \frac{h_{11}h_{22} - h_{12}h_{21}}{h_{22}} \qquad z_{12} = \frac{h_{12}}{h_{22}}$$ $$z_{21} = \frac{-h_{21}}{h_{22}} \qquad z_{22} = \frac{1}{h_{22}}$$ For bilateral networks $$z_{12} = z_{21} \qquad \text{as } h_{12} = -h_{21}$$
(6) $$I_1 = g_{11}E_1 + g_{12}I_2$$ $$E_2 = g_{21}E_1 + g_{22}I_2$$ For bilateral networks $$g_{12} = -g_{21}$$	(a6) $$y_{11} = \frac{g_{11}g_{22} - g_{12}g_{21}}{g_{22}} \qquad y_{12} = \frac{g_{12}}{g_{22}}$$ $$y_{21} = \frac{-g_{21}}{g_{22}} \qquad y_{22} = \frac{1}{g_{22}}$$ For bilateral networks $$y_{12} = y_{21} \qquad \text{as } g_{12} = -g_{21}$$	(b6) $$z_{11} = \frac{1}{g_{11}} \qquad z_{12} = \frac{-g_{12}}{g_{11}}$$ $$z_{21} = \frac{g_{21}}{g_{11}} \qquad z_{22} = \frac{g_{11}g_{22} - g_{12}g_{21}}{g_{11}}$$ For bilateral networks $$z_{12} = z_{21} \qquad \text{as } g_{12} = -g_{21}$$

Table 4.1 (continued)

Given parameters in	To find parameters in	

(1)

$$I_1 = y_{11}E_1 + y_{12}E_2$$
$$I_2 = y_{21}E_1 + y_{22}E_2$$

For bilateral networks

$$y_{12} = y_{21}$$

(c)

$$E_1 = aE_2 - bI_2$$
$$I_1 = cE_2 - dI_2$$

(c1)

$$a = \frac{-y_{22}}{y_{21}} \qquad b = \frac{-1}{y_{21}}$$

$$c = \frac{-(y_{11}y_{22} - y_{12}y_{21})}{y_{21}} \qquad d = \frac{-y_{11}}{y_{21}}$$

For bilateral networks

$$D = ad - bc = 1 \qquad \text{as } y_{12} = y_{21}$$

(d)

$$E_2 = d^*E_1 - b^*I_1$$
$$I_2 = c^*E_1 - a^*I_1$$

(d1)

$$d^* = \frac{-y_{11}}{y_{21}}\frac{1}{D} \qquad b^* = \frac{-1}{y_{21}}\frac{1}{D}$$

$$c^* = \frac{-(y_{11}y_{22} - y_{12}y_{21})}{y_{21}}\frac{1}{D} \qquad a^* = \frac{-y_{22}}{y_{21}}\frac{1}{D}$$

where

$$D = \frac{y_{12}}{y_{21}} \qquad D = 1 \text{ for bilateral networks}$$

(2)

$$E_1 = z_{11}I_1 + z_{12}I_2$$
$$E_2 = z_{21}I_1 + z_{22}I_2$$

For bilateral networks

$$z_{12} = z_{21}$$

(c2)

$$a = \frac{z_{11}}{z_{21}} \qquad b = \frac{z_{11}z_{22} - z_{12}z_{21}}{z_{21}}$$

$$c = \frac{1}{z_{21}} \qquad d = \frac{z_{22}}{z_{21}}$$

For bilateral networks

$$D = ad - bc = 1 \qquad \text{as } z_{12} = z_{21}$$

(d2)

$$d^* = \frac{z_{22}}{z_{21}}\frac{1}{D} \qquad b^* = \frac{z_{11}z_{22} - z_{12}z_{21}}{z_{21}}\frac{1}{D}$$

$$c^* = \frac{1}{z_{21}}\frac{1}{D} \qquad a^* = \frac{z_{11}}{z_{21}}\frac{1}{D}$$

where

$$D = \frac{z_{12}}{z_{21}} \qquad D = 1 \text{ for bilateral networks}$$

(3)

$$E_1 = aE_2 - bI_2$$
$$I_1 = cE_2 - dI_2$$

For bilateral networks

$$ad - bc = 1$$

(d3)

$$d^* = d\frac{1}{D} \qquad b^* = b\frac{1}{D}$$

$$c^* = c\frac{1}{D} \qquad a^* = a\frac{1}{D}$$

where

$$D = ad - bc \qquad D = 1 \text{ for bilateral networks}$$

	(c4)	(d5)
(4) $E_2 = d^*E_1 - b^*I_1$ $I_2 = c^*E_1 - a^*I_1$ For bilateral networks $d^*a^* - b^*c^* = 1$	$a = a^*\dfrac{1}{D^*}$ $b = b^*\dfrac{1}{D^*}$ $c = c^*\dfrac{1}{D^*}$ $d = d^*\dfrac{1}{D^*}$ where $D^* = d^*a^* - b^*c^*$ $D^* = 1$ for bilateral networks	
	(c5)	(d5)
(5) $E_1 = h_{11}I_1 + h_{12}E_2$ $I_2 = h_{21}I_1 + h_{22}E_2$ For bilateral networks $h_{12} = -h_{21}$	$a = \dfrac{-(h_{11}h_{22} - h_{12}h_{21})}{h_{21}}$ $b = \dfrac{-h_{11}}{h_{21}}$ $c = \dfrac{-h_{22}}{h_{21}}$ $d = \dfrac{-1}{h_{21}}$ For bilateral networks $ad - bc = 1$ as $h_{12} = -h_{21}$	$d^* = \dfrac{-1}{h_{21}}\dfrac{1}{D}$ $b^* = \dfrac{-h_{11}}{h_{21}}\dfrac{1}{D}$ $c^* = \dfrac{-h_{22}}{h_{21}}\dfrac{1}{D}$ $a^* = \dfrac{-(h_{11}h_{22} - h_{12}h_{21})}{h_{21}}\dfrac{1}{D}$ where $D = -\dfrac{h_{12}}{h_{21}}$ $D = 1$ for bilateral networks
	(c6)	(d6)
(6) $I_1 = g_{11}E_1 + g_{12}I_2$ $E_2 = g_{21}E_1 + g_{22}I_2$ For bilateral networks $g_{12} = -g_{21}$	$a = \dfrac{1}{g_{21}}$ $b = \dfrac{g_{22}}{g_{21}}$ $c = \dfrac{g_{11}}{g_{21}}$ $d = \dfrac{g_{11}g_{22} - g_{12}g_{21}}{g_{21}}$ For bilateral networks $ad - bc = 1$ as $g_{12} = -g_{21}$	$d^* = \dfrac{g_{11}g_{22} - g_{12}g_{21}}{g_{21}}\dfrac{1}{D}$ $b^* = \dfrac{g_{22}}{g_{21}}\dfrac{1}{D}$ $c^* = \dfrac{g_{11}}{g_{21}}\dfrac{1}{D}$ $a^* = \dfrac{1}{g_{21}}\dfrac{1}{D}$ where $D = \dfrac{-g_{12}}{g_{21}}$ $D = 1$ for bilateral networks

Table 4.1 (continued)

Given parameters in	To find parameters in	
	(e) $E_1 = h_{11}I_1 + h_{12}E_2$ $\quad$ $I_2 = h_{21}I_1 + h_{22}E_2$	(f) $I_1 = g_{11}E_1 + g_{12}I_2$ $\quad$ $E_2 = g_{21}E_1 + g_{22}I_2$
(1) $I_1 = y_{11}E_1 + y_{12}E_2$ $I_2 = y_{21}E_1 + y_{22}E_2$ For bilateral networks $y_{12} = y_{21}$	(e1) $h_{11} = \dfrac{1}{y_{11}}$ $\qquad$ $h_{12} = \dfrac{-y_{12}}{y_{11}}$ $h_{21} = \dfrac{y_{21}}{y_{11}}$ $\qquad$ $h_{22} = \dfrac{y_{11}y_{22} - y_{12}y_{21}}{y_{11}}$ For bilateral networks $h_{12} = -h_{21}$ $\quad$ as $y_{12} = y_{21}$	(f1) $g_{11} = \dfrac{y_{11}y_{22} - y_{12}y_{21}}{y_{22}}$ $\qquad$ $g_{12} = \dfrac{y_{12}}{y_{22}}$ $g_{21} = \dfrac{-y_{21}}{y_{22}}$ $\qquad$ $g_{22} = \dfrac{1}{y_{22}}$ For bilateral networks $g_{12} = -g_{21}$ $\quad$ as $y_{12} = y_{21}$
(2) $E_1 = z_{11}I_1 + z_{12}I_2$ $E_2 = z_{21}I_1 + z_{22}I_2$ For bilateral networks $z_{12} = z_{21}$	(e2) $h_{11} = \dfrac{z_{11}z_{22} - z_{12}z_{21}}{z_{22}}$ $\qquad$ $h_{12} = \dfrac{z_{12}}{z_{22}}$ $h_{21} = \dfrac{-z_{21}}{z_{22}}$ $\qquad$ $h_{22} = \dfrac{1}{z_{22}}$ For bilateral networks $h_{12} = -h_{21}$ $\quad$ as $z_{12} = z_{21}$	(f2) $g_{11} = \dfrac{1}{z_{11}}$ $\qquad$ $g_{12} = \dfrac{-z_{12}}{z_{11}}$ $g_{21} = \dfrac{z_{21}}{z_{11}}$ $\qquad$ $g_{22} = \dfrac{z_{11}z_{22} - z_{12}z_{21}}{z_{11}}$ For bilateral networks $g_{12} = -g_{21}$ $\quad$ as $z_{12} = z_{21}$
(3) $E_1 = aE_2 - bI_2$ $I_1 = cE_2 - dI_2$ For bilateral networks $ad - bc = 1$	(e3) $h_{11} = \dfrac{b}{d}$ $\qquad$ $h_{12} = \dfrac{ad - bc}{d}$ $h_{21} = \dfrac{-1}{d}$ $\qquad$ $h_{22} = \dfrac{c}{d}$ For bilateral networks $h_{12} = -h_{21}$ $\quad$ as $ad - bc = 1$	(f3) $g_{11} = \dfrac{c}{a}$ $\qquad$ $g_{12} = \dfrac{-(ad - bc)}{a}$ $g_{21} = \dfrac{1}{a}$ $\qquad$ $g_{22} = \dfrac{b}{a}$ For bilateral networks $g_{12} = -g_{21}$ $\quad$ as $ad - bc = 1$

(4)

$$E_2 = d^*E_1 - b^*I_1$$

$$I_2 = c^*E_1 - a^*I_1$$

For bilateral networks

$$d^*a^* - b^*c^* = 1$$

(e4)

$$h_{11} = \frac{b^*}{d^*} \qquad h_{12} = \frac{1}{d^*}$$

$$h_{21} = \frac{-(d^*a^* - b^*c^*)}{d^*} \qquad h_{22} = \frac{c^*}{d^*}$$

For bilateral networks

$$h_{12} = -h_{21} \qquad \text{as } d^*a^* - b^*c^* = 1$$

(f4)

$$g_{11} = \frac{c^*}{a^*} \qquad g_{12} = \frac{-1}{a^*}$$

$$g_{21} = \frac{d^*a^* - b^*c^*}{a^*} \qquad g_{22} = \frac{b^*}{a^*}$$

For bilateral networks

$$g_{12} = -g_{21} \qquad \text{as } d^*a^* - b^*c^* = 1$$

(5)

$$E_1 = h_{11}I_1 + h_{12}E_2$$

$$I_2 = h_{21}I_1 + h_{22}E_2$$

For bilateral networks

$$h_{12} = -h_{21}$$

(f5)

$$g_{11} = \frac{h_{22}}{h_{11}h_{22} - h_{12}h_{21}} \qquad g_{12} = \frac{-h_{12}}{h_{11}h_{22} - h_{12}h_{21}}$$

$$g_{21} = \frac{-h_{21}}{h_{11}h_{22} - h_{12}h_{21}} \qquad g_{22} = \frac{h_{11}}{h_{11}h_{22} - h_{12}h_{21}}$$

For bilateral networks

$$g_{12} = -g_{21} \qquad \text{as } h_{12} = -h_{21}$$

(6)

$$I_1 = g_{11}E_1 + g_{12}I_2$$

$$E_2 = g_{21}E_1 + g_{22}I_2$$

For bilateral networks

$$g_{12} = -g_{21}$$

(e6)

$$h_{11} = \frac{g_{22}}{g_{11}g_{22} - g_{12}g_{21}} \qquad h_{12} = \frac{-g_{12}}{g_{11}g_{22} - g_{12}g_{21}}$$

$$h_{21} = \frac{-g_{21}}{g_{11}g_{22} - g_{12}g_{21}} \qquad h_{22} = \frac{g_{11}}{g_{11}g_{22} - g_{12}g_{21}}$$

For bilateral networks

$$h_{12} = -h_{21} \qquad \text{as } g_{12} = -g_{21}$$

In the same manner in which we represent (4.29) in its matrix form (4.30), we may represent (4.48) in the matrix form

Matrix form:

$$\begin{bmatrix} E_1 \\ I_1 \end{bmatrix} = T \begin{bmatrix} E_2 \\ -I_2 \end{bmatrix} \quad \text{or} \quad \begin{bmatrix} E_1 \\ I_1 \end{bmatrix} = \begin{bmatrix} a & b \\ c & d \end{bmatrix} \begin{bmatrix} E_2 \\ -I_2 \end{bmatrix} \tag{4.49}$$

Multiplying out the right-hand side of (4.49), we find that it is the same as (4.48).

Computation of a, b, c, d from known short-circuit admittances; a set of identities. Assuming that the short-circuit admittances y_{ij} in (4.29),

$$I_1 = y_{11}E_1 + y_{12}E_2 \tag{4.50a}$$
$$I_2 = y_{21}E_1 + y_{22}E_2 \tag{4.50b}$$

are *known* quantities, we now wish to compute the parameters a, b, c, d.

This can be easily accomplished by rearranging Eqs. (4.50). From (4.50b), we have

$$E_1 = \frac{-y_{22}}{y_{21}} E_2 - \frac{-1}{y_{21}} I_2 \tag{4.51a}$$

Substituting the above into (4.50a), we find

$$I_1 = y_{11} \left(\frac{-y_{22}}{y_{21}} E_2 - \frac{-1}{y_{21}} I_2 \right) + y_{12}E_2 = \left(y_{12} - \frac{y_{11}y_{22}}{y_{21}} \right) E_2 - \frac{-y_{11}}{y_{21}} I_2 \tag{4.51b}$$

Identifying (4.51) with (4.48), we have a set of *identities* between a set of network parameters y_{ij} and another set of network parameters a, b, c, d:

Identities:

$$a = \frac{-y_{22}}{y_{21}} \qquad\qquad b = \frac{-1}{y_{21}}$$

$$c = \frac{-(y_{11}y_{22} - y_{12}y_{21})}{y_{21}} \qquad d = \frac{-y_{11}}{y_{21}} \tag{4.52}$$

For bilateral networks, we have

$$\begin{vmatrix} a & b \\ c & d \end{vmatrix} = ad - bc = 1 \tag{4.53}$$

which is equivalent to condition (4.33). By imposing $y_{12} = y_{21}$ on (4.52), we may easily verify (4.53).

Remarks about other sets of identities. Using the identities in (4.52), we may compute parameters a, b, c, d in terms of *known* parameters y_{ij}. We have earlier remarked that there are six sets of network parameters associated with the four-terminal network in Fig. 4.1. What if we wish to compute parameters a, b, c, d from other sets of *known* parameters? Table 4.1, column c, provides the solution. For example, if we are given parameters z_{ij}, the identities in (c2) of Table 4.1 may be used. Other sets of identities are listed in (c4) to (c6) of Table 4.1.

Illustration 1. We shall now compute the parameters a, b, c, d of the network in Fig. 4.2b by substituting its known parameters y_{ij} [in Eqs. (4.34)] into (4.52), finding

$$a = s^2 + 1 \qquad b = s^3 + 2s$$
$$c = s \qquad\qquad d = s^2 + 1 \tag{4.54}$$

This network is bilateral, and we note that (4.53) is satisfied.

Physical interpretations of the parameters a, b, c, d. By open-circuiting the terminal pair 22' in Fig. 4.1, i.e., letting $I_2 = 0$ in (4.48), we obtain

$$a = \left(\frac{E_1}{E_2}\right)_{I_2=0} = \text{transfer voltage ratio } E_1/E_2 \text{ measured} \qquad (4.55a)$$
$$\text{with 22' open-circuited}$$

$$c = \left(\frac{I_1}{E_2}\right)_{I_2=0} = \text{transfer admittance } I_1/E_2 \text{ measured} \qquad (4.55b)$$
$$\text{with 22' open-circuited}$$

Similarly, by short-circuiting the terminal pair 22' in Fig. 4.1, i.e., letting $E_2 = 0$ in (4.48), we have

$$b = \left(\frac{E_1}{-I_2}\right)_{E_2=0} = \text{transfer impedance } E_1/(-I_2) \text{ measured} \qquad (4.55c)$$
$$\text{with 22' short-circuited}$$

$$d = \left(\frac{I_1}{-I_2}\right)_{E_2=0} = \text{transfer current ratio } I_1/(-I_2) \text{ measured} \qquad (4.55d)$$
$$\text{with 22' short-circuited}$$

This means that parameters a, b, c, d are transfer functions measured under certain open-circuit and short-circuit conditions.

Illustration 2. We shall now show that we may obtain the parameters a, b, c, d of a four-terminal network by taking advantage of their physical interpretations in (4.55). For example, considering the simple network in Fig. 4.2b, we find

$$a = \left(\frac{E_1}{E_2}\right)_{I_2=0} = \frac{sL + 1/sC}{1/sC} = s^2 + 1 \dagger \qquad (4.56)$$

which checks with (4.54). Similarly, we may obtain the other network parameters b, c, d of this network according to Eqs. (4.55b) through (4.55d), finding that they also check with (4.54).

D. E_2, I_2 Expressed in Terms of E_1, I_1

We shall find in subsequent paragraphs that, for the four-terminal network in Fig. 4.1, we may express E_2, I_2 at terminal pair 22' in terms of E_1, I_1 at terminal pair 11' in the following algebraic form:

Algebraic form:
$$E_2 = d^*E_1 - b^*I_1 \qquad I_2 = c^*E_1 - a^*I_1 \qquad (4.57)$$

where d^*, b^*, c^*, a^* are a set of *network parameters*. This set of four parameters completely characterizes a four-terminal network in the sense that it prescribes the voltage-current relations of the network in (4.57).

In the same manner in which we represent (4.48) in its matrix form (4.49), we may also represent (4.57) in the matrix form

Matrix form:
$$\begin{bmatrix} E_2 \\ I_1 \end{bmatrix} = T^* \begin{bmatrix} E_1 \\ -I_1 \end{bmatrix} \quad \text{or} \quad \begin{bmatrix} E_2 \\ I_2 \end{bmatrix} = \begin{bmatrix} d^* & b^* \\ c^* & a^* \end{bmatrix} \begin{bmatrix} E_1 \\ -I_1 \end{bmatrix} \qquad (4.58)$$

Multiplying out the right-hand side of (4.58), we find that it is the same as (4.57).

---

† With 22' open-circuited (as $I_2 = 0$) in Fig. 4.2b, and with E_3 the voltage at node 3, it is easy to see that $E_2 = E_3 = (1/sC)I_1 = (1/sC)E_1/(sL + 1/sC) = E_1/(s^2 + 1)$ or $E_1/E_2 = s^2 + 1$.

Computation of $d*$, $b*$, $c*$, $a*$ through identities. By rearranging (1) Eqs. (4.29), (4.35), and (4.48) [in much the same way as we rearranged (4.29) or (4.50) into the form of (4.51) or (4.48) in obtaining the identities in (4.52)] and (2) other voltage-current relations (which will be given in Art. 4.2E and F) into the form of (4.57), we find the identities in Table 4.1, column d. Using these sets of identities, we may compute the parameters $d*$, $b*$, $c*$, $a*$ from any *given set* of network parameters of a four-terminal network.

For example, we may compute the parameters $d*$, $b*$, $c*$, $a*$ of the simple four-terminal network in Fig. 4.2b by (1) substituting (4.34) into the identities in (d1) of Table 4.1, (2) substituting (4.44) into the identities in (d2), or (3) substituting (4.54) into the identities in (d3).

For bilateral networks, we have

$$\begin{vmatrix} d* & b* \\ c* & a* \end{vmatrix} = d*a* - b*c* = 1 \qquad (4.59)$$

which is equivalent to conditions (4.33) and (4.53). By imposing $y_{12} = y_{21}$ on the identities in (d1) of Table 4.1, we may easily verify (4.59).

Physical interpretations of the parameters $a*$, $b*$, $c*$, $d*$. By open-circuiting the terminal pair $11'$ in Fig. 4.1, i.e., letting $I_1 = 0$ in (4.57), we have

$$d* = \left(\frac{E_2}{E_1}\right)_{I_1=0} = \textit{transfer voltage ratio } E_2/E_1 \textit{ measured} \qquad (4.60a)$$
$$\textit{with } 11' \textit{ open-circuited}$$

$$c* = \left(\frac{I_2}{E_1}\right)_{I_1=0} = \textit{transfer admittance } I_2/E_1 \textit{ measured} \qquad (4.60b)$$
$$\textit{with } 11' \textit{ open-circuited}$$

Similarly, by short-circuiting the terminal pair $11'$ in Fig. 4.1, i.e., letting $E_1 = 0$ in (4.57), we obtain

$$b* = \left(\frac{E_2}{-I_1}\right)_{E_1=0} = \textit{transfer impedance } E_2/(-I_1) \textit{ measured} \qquad (4.60c)$$
$$\textit{with } 11' \textit{ short-circuited}$$

$$a* = \left(\frac{I_2}{-I_1}\right)_{E_1=0} = \textit{transfer current ratio } I_2/(-I_1) \textit{ measured} \qquad (4.60d)$$
$$\textit{with } 11' \textit{ short-circuited}$$

This means that parameters $d*$, $b*$, $c*$, $a*$ are transfer functions measured under certain open-circuit and short-circuit conditions.

Illustration. We shall now show that we may obtain the parameters $d*$, $b*$, $c*$, $a*$ of a four-terminal network by taking advantage of their physical interpretations in (4.60). For example, considering the simple network in Fig. 4.2b, we find

$$d* = \left(\frac{E_2}{E_1}\right)_{I_1=0} = s^2 + 1\dagger \qquad (4.61a)$$

$$c* = \left(\frac{I_2}{E_1}\right)_{I_1=0} = s \qquad (4.61b)$$

$$b* = \left(\frac{E_2}{-I_1}\right)_{E_1=0} = s(s^2 + 3) \qquad (4.61c)$$

$$a* = \left(\frac{I_2}{-I_1}\right)_{E_1=0} = s^2 + 1 \qquad (4.61d)$$

† With $11'$ open-circuited (as $I_1 = 0$) in Fig. 4.2b, and with E_3 the voltage at node 3, $E_1 = E_3 = (1/sC)I_2 = (1/sC)E_2/(sL + 1/sC) = E_2/(s^2 + 1)$ or $E_2/E_1 = s^2 + 1$. Similarly, we may obtain $c*$, $b*$, and $a*$ in (4.61).

E. E_1, I_2 Expressed in Terms of I_1, E_2

For the four-terminal network in Fig. 4.1, we now express E_1, I_2 in terms of I_1, E_2 in the algebraic form

Algebraic form:

$$E_1 = h_{11}I_1 + h_{12}E_2 \qquad I_2 = h_{21}I_1 + h_{22}E_2 \tag{4.62}$$

where h_{11}, h_{12}, h_{21}, h_{22} are a set of *network parameters*. This set of four parameters completely characterizes a four-terminal network in the sense that it prescribes the voltage-current relations of the network in (4.62).

In the same manner in which we represent (4.29) in its matrix form (4.30), we may also represent (4.62) in the matrix form

Matrix form:

$$\begin{bmatrix} E_1 \\ I_2 \end{bmatrix} = H \begin{bmatrix} I_1 \\ E_2 \end{bmatrix} \quad \text{or} \quad \begin{bmatrix} E_1 \\ I_2 \end{bmatrix} = \begin{bmatrix} h_{11} & h_{12} \\ h_{21} & h_{22} \end{bmatrix} \begin{bmatrix} I_1 \\ E_2 \end{bmatrix} \tag{4.63}$$

Multiplying out the right-hand side of (4.63), we find that it is the same as (4.62).

Computation of h_{ij} through identities. By rearranging (1) Eqs. (4.29), (4.35), (4.48), and (4.57) [in much the same way as we rearranged (4.29) or (4.50) into the form of (4.51) or (4.48) in obtaining the identities in (4.52)] and (2) another voltage-current relation (which will be given in Art. 4.2F) into the form of (4.62), we find the identities in Table 4.1, column *e*. Using these sets of identities, we may compute the parameters h_{ij} from any *given* set of network parameters of a four-terminal network. For example, we may compute the parameters h_{11}, h_{12}, h_{21}, h_{22} of the simple four-terminal network in Fig. 4.2b by (1) substituting (4.34) into the identities in (e1) of Table 4.1, (2) substituting (4.44) into (e2), (3) substituting (4.54) into (e3), or (4) substituting (4.61) into (e4).

For bilateral networks, we have

$$h_{12} = -h_{21} \tag{4.64}$$

as an equivalent to condition (4.33); this is obvious according to the identities in (e1) of Table 4.1.

Physical interpretations of the parameters h_{ij}. By short-circuiting terminal pair 22' in Fig. 4.1, i.e., letting $E_2 = 0$ in (4.62), we obtain

$$h_{11} = \left(\frac{E_1}{I_1} \right)_{E_2=0} = \text{\textit{driving-point impedance } } E_1/I_1 \text{ \textit{measured}} \tag{4.65a}$$
$$\text{\textit{with 22' short-circuited}}$$

$$h_{21} = \left(\frac{I_2}{I_1} \right)_{E_2=0} = \text{\textit{transfer current ratio } } I_2/I_1 \text{ \textit{measured}} \tag{4.65b}$$
$$\text{\textit{with 22' short-circuited}}$$

Similarly, by open-circuiting terminal pair 11' in Fig. 4.1, i.e., letting $I_1 = 0$ in (4.62), we obtain

$$h_{12} = \left(\frac{E_1}{E_2} \right)_{I_1=0} = \text{\textit{transfer voltage ratio } } E_1/E_2 \text{ \textit{measured}} \tag{4.65c}$$
$$\text{\textit{with 11' open-circuited}}$$

$$h_{22} = \left(\frac{I_2}{E_2} \right)_{I_1=0} = \text{\textit{driving-point admittance } } I_2/E_2 \text{ \textit{measured}} \tag{4.65d}$$
$$\text{\textit{with 11' open-circuited}}$$

This means that parameters h_{ij} are driving-point or transfer functions measured under certain open-circuit or short-circuit conditions.

Illustration. We shall now show that we may obtain the parameters h_{11}, h_{12}, h_{21}, h_{22} of a four-terminal network by taking advantage of their physical interpretations in (4.65). For example, considering the simple network in Fig. 4.2b, we find

$$h_{11} = \left(\frac{E_1}{I_1}\right)_{E_2=0} = \frac{s^3 + 2s}{s^2 + 1} \tag{4.66a}$$

$$h_{21} = \left(\frac{I_2}{I_1}\right)_{E_2=0} = \frac{-1}{s^2 + 1} \,\dagger \tag{4.66b}$$

$$h_{12} = \left(\frac{E_1}{E_2}\right)_{I_1=0} = \frac{1}{s^2 + 1} \tag{4.66c}$$

$$h_{22} = \left(\frac{I_2}{E_2}\right)_{I_1=0} = \frac{s}{s^2 + 1} \tag{4.66d}$$

F. I_1, E_2 Expressed in Terms of E_1, I_2

For the four-terminal network in Fig. 4.1, we now express I_1, E_2 in terms of E_1, I_2 in the algebraic form

Algebraic form:
$$I_1 = g_{11}E_1 + g_{12}I_2 \qquad E_2 = g_{21}E_1 + g_{22}I_2 \tag{4.67}$$

where g_{11}, g_{12}, g_{21}, g_{22} are a set of *network parameters*. This set of four parameters completely characterizes a four-terminal network in the sense that it prescribes the voltage-current relations of the network in (4.67).

In the same manner in which we represent (4.29) in its matrix form (4.30), we may represent (4.67) in the matrix form

Matrix form:
$$\begin{bmatrix} I_1 \\ E_2 \end{bmatrix} = G \begin{bmatrix} E_1 \\ I_2 \end{bmatrix} \qquad \text{or} \qquad \begin{bmatrix} I_1 \\ E_2 \end{bmatrix} = \begin{bmatrix} g_{11} & g_{12} \\ g_{21} & g_{22} \end{bmatrix} \begin{bmatrix} E_1 \\ I_2 \end{bmatrix} \tag{4.68}$$

Multiplying out the right-hand side of (4.68), we find that it is the same as (4.67).

Computation of g_{ij} through identities. By rearranging (4.29), (4.35), (4.48), (4.57), and (4.62) [in much the same way as we rearranged (4.29) or (4.50) into the form of (4.51) or (4.48) in obtaining the identities in (4.52)] into the form of (4.67), we find the identities in Table 4.1, column *f*. Using these sets of identities, we may compute the parameters g_{ij} from any *given* set of network parameters of a four-terminal network. For example, we may compute the parameters g_{11}, g_{12}, g_{21}, g_{22} of the simple four-terminal network in Fig. 4.2b by (1) substituting (4.34) into the identities in (*f*1) of Table 4.1, (2) substituting (4.44) into (*f*2), (3) substituting (4.54) into (*f*3), (4) substituting (4.61) into (*f*4), or (5) substituting (4.66) into (*f*5).

For bilateral networks, we have

$$g_{12} = -g_{21} \tag{4.69}$$

as equivalent to condition (4.33); this is obvious according to the identities in (*f*1) of Table 4.1.

---

† With 22′ short-circuited (as $E_2 = 0$) in Fig. 4.2b and with E_3 the voltage at node 3, $E_3 = I_1 Z_{LC}$ and $I_2 = -E_3/sL$, where $Z_{LC} = (sL)(1/sC)/(sL + 1/sC) = s/(s^2 + 1)$ is the impedance between 3 and 2′ with 22′ short-circuited. We therefore have $I_2/I_1 = -Z_{LC}/sL = -1/(s^2 + 1)$. We may obtain h_{12} in (4.66c) in a similar manner.

Physical interpretations of the parameters g_{ij}. By open-circuiting terminal pair 22' in Fig. 4.1, i.e., letting $I_2 = 0$ in (4.67), we have

$$g_{11} = \left(\frac{I_1}{E_1}\right)_{I_2=0} = \text{driving-point admittance } I_1/E_1 \text{ measured} \qquad (4.70a)$$
$$\text{with 22' open-circuited}$$

$$g_{21} = \left(\frac{E_2}{E_1}\right)_{I_2=0} = \text{transfer voltage ratio } E_2/E_1 \text{ measured} \qquad (4.70b)$$
$$\text{with 22' open-circuited}$$

Similarly, by short-circuiting terminal pair 11' in Fig. 4.1, i.e., letting $E_1 = 0$ in (4.67), we have

$$g_{12} = \left(\frac{I_1}{I_2}\right)_{E_1=0} = \text{transfer current ratio } I_1/I_2 \text{ measured} \qquad (4.70c)$$
$$\text{with 11' short-circuited}$$

$$g_{22} = \left(\frac{E_2}{I_2}\right)_{E_1=0} = \text{driving-point impedance } E_2/I_2 \text{ measured} \qquad (4.70d)$$
$$\text{with 11' short-circuited}$$

This means that parameters g_{ij} are driving-point or transfer functions measured under certain open-circuit or short-circuit conditions.

Illustration. We shall now show that we may obtain the parameters $g_{11}, g_{12}, g_{21}, g_{22}$ of a four-terminal network by taking advantage of their physical interpretations in (4.70). For example, considering the simple network in Fig. 4.2b, we find

$$g_{11} = \left(\frac{I_1}{E_1}\right)_{I_2=0} = \frac{s}{s^2+1} \qquad (4.71a)$$

$$g_{21} = \left(\frac{E_2}{E_1}\right)_{I_2=0} = \frac{1}{s^2+1} \; \dagger \qquad (4.71b)$$

$$g_{12} = \left(\frac{I_1}{I_2}\right)_{E_1=0} = \frac{-1}{s^2+1} \qquad (4.71c)$$

$$g_{22} = \left(\frac{E_2}{I_2}\right)_{E_1=0} = \frac{s^3+2s}{s^2+1} \qquad (4.71d)$$

G. Some Summarizing Remarks about Network Parameters

From previous sections (Art. 4.2A through F), we note:

1. *There are six sets of network parameters associated with a four-terminal network as depicted in Fig. 4.1. Each set completely characterizes the network in the sense that the four parameters of the set prescribe the voltage-current relations of the network.* These sets of parameters and their associated voltage-current relations are listed as headings in Table 4.1.

2. *Knowing any one set of parameters of a four-terminal network, we are able to compute the other five sets through identities.* All 30 sets of identities are listed in Table 4.1.

3. *All network parameters may be physically interpreted and measured as driving-point and transfer functions under certain open-circuit or short-circuit conditions.* Reference is made to Eqs. (4.32), (4.45), (4.55), (4.60), (4.65), and (4.70).

4. *For bilateral networks, there is a dependence relation in each set of four network parameters. It actually only takes three independent parameters to characterize a bilateral network.* These dependence relations are Eqs. (4.33), (4.40), (4.53), (4.59), (4.64), and (4.69).

† With 22' open-circuited (as $I_2 = 0$) in Fig. 4.2b, and with E_3 the voltage at node 3, $E_2 = E_3 = (1/sC)I_1 = (1/sC)E_1/(sL + 1/sC) = E_1/(s^2 + 1)$ or $E_2/E_1 = 1/(s^2 + 1)$. We may obtain g_{12} in (4.71c) in a similar manner.

4.3. Interconnection of four-terminal networks; composite network parameters

We shall make one "basic assumption" for our discussion of interconnection: *When four-terminal networks are interconnected, the current entering each terminal pair is equal to the current leaving this terminal pair*, as depicted in Fig. 4.4f1. Note that I_1 enters terminal 1 and leaves terminal 1'; I_2 enters terminal 2 and leaves terminal 2'.

But what if some of the networks do not satisfy this basic assumption? We have only two choices: (1) do not use the network in this interconnection or (2) add a 1:1 turns-ratio isolating transformer to the network and use this modified network as depicted in Fig. 4.4f2 in the interconnection.

However, it is not often obvious whether several given networks, when interconnected in a prescribed manner, meet the requirements of the basic assumption. For this reason, we shall discuss "precautions" to take in the interconnection of networks, with concrete examples, using the readily recognizable "short-circuit conditions" as violations of the basic assumption.

A. Two Four-terminal Networks in Cascade

Let us assume that the parameters a, b, c, d of the four-terminal network I and the parameters a', b', c', d', of the four-terminal network II, in Fig. 4.4a, are *known* quantities. The voltage-current relations of these two networks, according to (4.49), may then be given in the matrix forms

For network I:

$$\begin{bmatrix} E_1 \\ I_1 \end{bmatrix} = T \begin{bmatrix} E_2 \\ -I_2 \end{bmatrix} \quad \text{or} \quad \begin{bmatrix} E_1 \\ I_1 \end{bmatrix} = \begin{bmatrix} a & b \\ c & d \end{bmatrix} \begin{bmatrix} E_2 \\ -I_2 \end{bmatrix} \tag{4.72a}$$

For network II:

$$\begin{bmatrix} E_1' \\ I_1' \end{bmatrix} = T' \begin{bmatrix} E_2' \\ -I_2' \end{bmatrix} \quad \text{or} \quad \begin{bmatrix} E_1' \\ I_1' \end{bmatrix} = \begin{bmatrix} a' & b' \\ c' & d' \end{bmatrix} \begin{bmatrix} E_2' \\ -I_2' \end{bmatrix} \tag{4.72b}$$

Composite network parameters. Networks I and II are cascaded into a composite four-terminal network in Fig. 4.4a; we wish to find its parameters. We note in Fig. 4.4a that $E_1' = E_2$ and $I_1' = -I_2$, or

$$\begin{bmatrix} E_2 \\ -I_2 \end{bmatrix} = \begin{bmatrix} E_1' \\ I_1' \end{bmatrix}$$

in matrix form. Applying this relation to (4.72), we find

$$\begin{bmatrix} E_1 \\ I_1 \end{bmatrix} = T \begin{bmatrix} E_2 \\ -I_2 \end{bmatrix} = T \begin{bmatrix} E_1' \\ I_1' \end{bmatrix} = TT' \begin{bmatrix} E_2' \\ -I_2' \end{bmatrix} \tag{4.73a}$$

or $\quad$ $$\begin{bmatrix} E_1 \\ I_1 \end{bmatrix} = \begin{bmatrix} a & b \\ c & d \end{bmatrix} \begin{bmatrix} a' & b' \\ c' & d' \end{bmatrix} \begin{bmatrix} E_2' \\ -I_2' \end{bmatrix} = \begin{bmatrix} aa' + bc' & ab' + bd' \\ ca' + dc' & cb' + dd' \end{bmatrix} \begin{bmatrix} E_2' \\ -I_2' \end{bmatrix} \tag{4.73b}$$

with the aid of (4.10). The composite network in Fig. 4.4a is now completely characterized by its parameters in

Composite parameters:

$$TT' = \begin{bmatrix} \mathbf{a} & \mathbf{b} \\ \mathbf{c} & \mathbf{d} \end{bmatrix} = \begin{bmatrix} aa' + bc' & ab' + bd' \\ ca' + dc' & cb' + dd' \end{bmatrix} \tag{4.74}$$

Voltage-current relations of the composite network.   The matrix form of the voltage-current relations of the composite network in Fig. 4.4*a* is given in Eqs. (4.73); by multiplying out the matrices on the right-hand side of (4.73*b*), we find the voltage-current relations in algebraic form:

$$\begin{aligned} E_1 &= \mathbf{a}E_2' - \mathbf{b}I_2' = (aa' + bc')E_2' - (ab' + bd')I_2' \\ I_1 &= \mathbf{c}E_2' - \mathbf{d}I_2' = (ca' + dc')E_2' - (cb' + dd')I_2' \end{aligned} \tag{4.75}$$

Remarks about other sets of composite parameters.   In the above discussion, we were given the parameters a, b, c, d of network I and the parameters a', b', c', d' of network II, and we found the parameters $\mathbf{a}$, $\mathbf{b}$, $\mathbf{c}$, $\mathbf{d}$ of the composite network consisting of networks I and II in cascade.

What if we are given the parameters z_{11}, z_{12}, z_{21}, z_{22} of network I and the parameters z_{11}', z_{22}', z_{21}', z_{22}' of network II and wish to find the parameters $\mathbf{z}_{11}$, $\mathbf{z}_{12}$, $\mathbf{z}_{21}$, $\mathbf{z}_{22}$ of the composite network? Using the identities in Table 4.1, we may proceed as follows:

Find a, b, c, d from z_{11}, z_{12}, z_{21}, z_{22} through identities in (*c*2) of Table 4.1   (4.76*a*)

Find a', b', c', d' from z_{11}', z_{12}', z_{21}', z_{22}' in similar manner   (4.76*b*)

Find the composite parameters $\mathbf{a}$, $\mathbf{b}$, $\mathbf{c}$, $\mathbf{d}$ according to (4.74); then find the composite parameters $\mathbf{z}_{11}$, $\mathbf{z}_{12}$, $\mathbf{z}_{21}$, $\mathbf{z}_{22}$ through identities in (*b*3) of Table 4.1   (4.76*c*)

Similarly, we may find the other sets of composite parameters with the aid of identities in Table 4.1 when two networks are connected in cascade as in Fig. 4.4*a*.

B. *Two Four-terminal Networks in Parallel*

Let us now assume that the parameters y_{11}, y_{12}, y_{21}, y_{22} of the four-terminal network I and the parameters y_{11}', y_{12}', y_{21}', y_{22}' of the four-terminal network II, in Fig. 4.4*b*, are known quantities.   The voltage-current relations of these two networks, according to (4.30), may then be given in the matrix forms

For network I:

$$I = YE \qquad \text{or} \qquad \begin{bmatrix} I_1 \\ I_2 \end{bmatrix} = \begin{bmatrix} y_{11} & y_{12} \\ y_{21} & y_{22} \end{bmatrix} \begin{bmatrix} E_1 \\ E_2 \end{bmatrix} \tag{4.77a}$$

For network II:

$$I' = Y'E' \qquad \text{or} \qquad \begin{bmatrix} I_1' \\ I_2' \end{bmatrix} = \begin{bmatrix} y_{11}' & y_{12}' \\ y_{21}' & y_{22}' \end{bmatrix} \begin{bmatrix} E_1' \\ E_2' \end{bmatrix} \tag{4.77b}$$

Composite network parameters.   Networks I and II are now connected in parallel, forming a composite four-terminal network as depicted in Fig. 4.4*b*; we wish to find its parameters.   We note in Fig. 4.4*b* that $E_1 = E_1'$ and $E_2 = E_2'$, or

$$\begin{bmatrix} E_1 \\ E_2 \end{bmatrix} = \begin{bmatrix} E_1' \\ E_2' \end{bmatrix} \qquad \text{or} \qquad E = E'$$

in matrix form.   Applying this relation to (4.77), we find

$$I + I' = (Y + Y')E \tag{4.78a}$$

or
$$\begin{bmatrix} I_1 + I_1' \\ I_2 + I_2' \end{bmatrix} = (Y + Y') \begin{bmatrix} E_1 \\ E_2 \end{bmatrix} = \begin{bmatrix} y_{11} + y_{11}' & y_{12} + y_{12}' \\ y_{21} + y_{21}' & y_{22} + y_{22}' \end{bmatrix} \begin{bmatrix} E_1 \\ E_2 \end{bmatrix} \tag{4.78b}$$

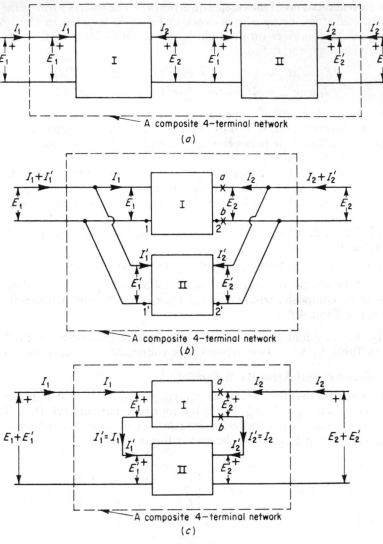

FIG. 4.4

The composite network in Fig. 4.4*b* is now completely characterized by its parameters in

Composite parameters:

$$Y + Y' = \begin{bmatrix} \mathbf{y}_{11} & \mathbf{y}_{12} \\ \mathbf{y}_{21} & \mathbf{y}_{22} \end{bmatrix} = \begin{bmatrix} y_{11} + y'_{11} & y_{12} + y'_{12} \\ y_{21} + y'_{21} & y_{22} + y'_{22} \end{bmatrix} \tag{4.79}$$

Voltage-current relations of the composite network. The matrix form of the voltage-current relations of the composite network in Fig. 4.4*b* is already given in Eqs. (4.78); by multiplying out the matrices on the right-hand side of (4.78*b*), we find the voltage-current relations in algebraic form:

$$
\begin{aligned}
I_1 + I'_1 &= \mathbf{y}_{11}E_1 + \mathbf{y}_{12}E_2 = (y_{11} + y'_{11})E_1 + (y_{12} + y'_{12})E_2 \\
I_2 + I'_2 &= \mathbf{y}_{21}E_1 + \mathbf{y}_{22}E_2 = (y_{21} + y'_{21})E_1 + (y_{22} + y'_{22})E_2
\end{aligned} \tag{4.80}
$$

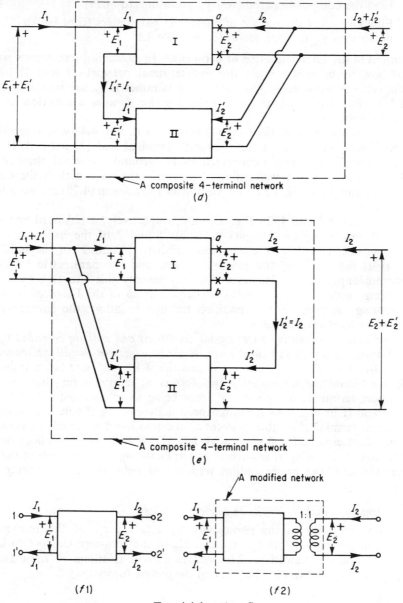

FIG. 4.4 (*continued*)

Remarks about other sets of composite parameters. In the above discussion, we were given the parameters y_{ij} and y'_{ij} of networks I and II, and we found the parameters y_{ij} of the composite network consisting in networks I and II in parallel, as in Fig. 4.4b. We may find any other set of composite parameters by the following procedure:

From any given set of parameters of network I in Fig. 4.4b, find the parameters y_{ij} through identities in Table 4.1   (4.81a)

From any given set of parameters of network II, find the parameters y'_{ij} through identities in Table 4.1   (4.81b)

Find the composite parameters y_{ij} according to (4.79)   (4.81c)

Find any other desired set of composite parameters from *known* parameters y_{ij} through identities in Table 4.1   (4.81d)

Precautions in the interconnection of networks. In preceding paragraphs we have discussed how to parallel-connect the four-terminal networks I and II into the composite network depicted in Fig. 4.4b whose parameters y_{ij} are indicated by relations (4.79). But are relations (4.79) valid for the parallel connection of any 2 four-terminal networks?

For two unbalanced networks,† say (1) network I in Fig. 4.4b whose terminals 1 and 2 are directly connected as its "ground" terminal and (2) network II whose terminals 1′ and 2′ are directly connected as its "ground" terminal, the composite network in Fig. 4.4b has a well-defined "ground" terminal which is the common terminal represented by 1, 2, 1′, 2′; the parameter relations in (4.79) are valid for this interconnection.

Suppose networks I and II in Fig. 4.4b are, respectively, a balanced and an unbalanced network. The two distinct terminals 1 and 2 of the balanced network I are now short-circuited by the common terminals 1′ and 2′ of the unbalanced network II as the result of the interconnection, and the parametric relations in (4.79) are no longer valid. However, we may remedy this situation by inserting a "transformer with a 1:1 turns ratio" at terminals *ab* of the balanced network I, thus preventing the short-circuit condition through isolation; the parametric relations (4.79) are then again valid.

The precaution of preventing short-circuit conditions and making remedies by using isolating transformers with 1:1 *turns ratio should be exercised for all interconnections studied in Art.* 4.3. For example, (1) if network I in Fig. 4.4c is an unbalanced network, we should use an isolating transformer at terminals *ab*, thus preventing the two upper terminals of network II from being short-circuited; (2) if both the networks I and II in Fig. 4.4d are unbalanced networks, we should use an isolating transformer at terminals *ab*, thus preventing the two input terminals of network II from being short-circuited; (3) if network I in Fig. 4.4e is an unbalanced network, we should use an isolating transformer at terminals *ab*, thus preventing the lower input terminal and the upper output terminal of network II from being short-circuited; etc.

C. Two Four-terminal Networks in Series

Let us now assume that the parameters z_{11}, z_{12}, z_{21}, z_{22} of the four-terminal network I and the parameters z'_{11}, z'_{12}, z'_{21}, z'_{22} of the four-terminal network II, in Fig. 4.4c, are known quantities. The voltage-current relations of these two networks, according to (4.36), may be given in the matrix forms

For network I:

$$E = ZI \quad \text{or} \quad \begin{bmatrix} E_1 \\ E_2 \end{bmatrix} = \begin{bmatrix} z_{11} & z_{12} \\ z_{21} & z_{22} \end{bmatrix} \begin{bmatrix} I_1 \\ I_2 \end{bmatrix} \tag{4.82a}$$

For network II:

$$E' = Z'I' \quad \text{or} \quad \begin{bmatrix} E'_1 \\ E'_2 \end{bmatrix} = \begin{bmatrix} z'_{11} & z'_{12} \\ z'_{21} & z'_{22} \end{bmatrix} \begin{bmatrix} I'_1 \\ I'_2 \end{bmatrix} \tag{4.82b}$$

† A four-terminal network whose input- and output-terminal pairs have a common "ground" terminal is called an *unbalanced network*. For example, a ladder network in the form of Fig. 4.2a is an unbalanced network, while a lattice in the general form of Fig. 6.5a is a *balanced network*.

Composite network parameters. Networks I and II are now connected in series, forming a composite four-terminal network as in Fig. 4.4c; we wish to find its parameters. We note in Fig. 4.4c that $I_1 = I_1'$ and $I_2 = I_2'$, or

$$\begin{bmatrix} I_1 \\ I_2 \end{bmatrix} = \begin{bmatrix} I_1' \\ I_2' \end{bmatrix} \qquad \text{or} \qquad I = I'$$

in matrix form. Applying this relation to (4.82), we find

$$E + E' = (Z + Z')I \tag{4.83a}$$

or
$$\begin{bmatrix} E_1 + E_1' \\ E_2 + E_2' \end{bmatrix} = (Z + Z') \begin{bmatrix} I_1 \\ I_2 \end{bmatrix} = \begin{bmatrix} z_{11} + z_{11}' & z_{12} + z_{12}' \\ z_{21} + z_{21}' & z_{22} + z_{22}' \end{bmatrix} \begin{bmatrix} I_1 \\ I_2 \end{bmatrix} \tag{4.83b}$$

The composite network in Fig. 4.4c is now completely characterized by its parameters in

$$Z + Z' = \begin{bmatrix} \mathbf{z}_{11} & \mathbf{z}_{12} \\ \mathbf{z}_{21} & \mathbf{z}_{22} \end{bmatrix} = \begin{bmatrix} z_{11} + z_{11}' & z_{12} + z_{12}' \\ z_{21} + z_{21}' & z_{22} + z_{22}' \end{bmatrix} \tag{4.84}$$

Voltage-current relations of the composite network. The matrix form of the voltage-current relations of the composite network in Fig. 4.4c is given in Eqs. (4.83); by multiplying out the matrices on the right-hand side of (4.83b), we find the voltage-current relations in algebraic form:

$$\begin{aligned} E_1 + E_1' &= \mathbf{z}_{11}I_1 + \mathbf{z}_{12}I_2 = (z_{11} + z_{11}')I_1 + (z_{12} + z_{12}')I_2 \\ E_2 + E_2' &= \mathbf{z}_{21}I_1 + \mathbf{z}_{22}I_2 = (z_{21} + z_{21}')I_1 + (z_{22} + z_{22}')I_2 \end{aligned} \tag{4.85}$$

Remarks. Taking advantage of the identities in Table 4.1 and following procedures similar to (4.81), we may find any set of composite parameters for the composite network consisting of networks I and II in series as in Fig. 4.4c.

D. Two Four-terminal Networks in Series-Parallel Connection

Let us now assume that the parameters h_{11}, h_{12}, h_{21}, h_{22} of the four-terminal network I and the parameters h_{11}', h_{12}', h_{21}', h_{22}' of the four-terminal network II in Fig. 4.4d are known quantities. The voltage-current relations of these two networks, according to (4.63), may then be given in the matrix forms

For network I:
$$\begin{bmatrix} E_1 \\ I_2 \end{bmatrix} = H \begin{bmatrix} I_1 \\ E_2 \end{bmatrix} \qquad \text{or} \qquad \begin{bmatrix} E_1 \\ I_2 \end{bmatrix} = \begin{bmatrix} h_{11} & h_{12} \\ h_{21} & h_{22} \end{bmatrix} \begin{bmatrix} I_1 \\ E_2 \end{bmatrix} \tag{4.86a}$$

For network II:
$$\begin{bmatrix} E_1' \\ I_2' \end{bmatrix} = H' \begin{bmatrix} I_1' \\ E_2' \end{bmatrix} \qquad \text{or} \qquad \begin{bmatrix} E_1' \\ I_2' \end{bmatrix} = \begin{bmatrix} h_{11}' & h_{12}' \\ h_{21}' & h_{22}' \end{bmatrix} \begin{bmatrix} I_1' \\ E_2' \end{bmatrix} \tag{4.86b}$$

Composite network parameters. Networks I and II are now connected with input terminal pairs in *series* and output terminal pairs in *parallel*, forming a composite four-terminal network as in Fig. 4.4d; we wish to find its parameters. We note in Fig. 4.4d that $I_1 = I_1'$ and $E_2 = E_2'$, or

$$\begin{bmatrix} I_1 \\ E_2 \end{bmatrix} = \begin{bmatrix} I_1' \\ E_2' \end{bmatrix}$$

in matrix form.   Applying this relation to (4.86), we find

$$\begin{bmatrix} E_1 \\ I_2 \end{bmatrix} + \begin{bmatrix} E_1' \\ I_2' \end{bmatrix} = (H + H') \begin{bmatrix} I_1 \\ E_2 \end{bmatrix} \tag{4.87a}$$

or
$$\begin{bmatrix} E_1 + E_1' \\ I_2 + I_2' \end{bmatrix} = (H + H') \begin{bmatrix} I_1 \\ E_2 \end{bmatrix} = \begin{bmatrix} h_{11} + h_{11}' & h_{12} + h_{12}' \\ h_{21} + h_{21}' & h_{22} + h_{22}' \end{bmatrix} \begin{bmatrix} I_1 \\ E_2 \end{bmatrix} \tag{4.87b}$$

The composite network in Fig. 4.4d is now completely characterized by its parameters in

Composite parameters:

$$H + H' = \begin{bmatrix} \mathbf{h}_{11} & \mathbf{h}_{12} \\ \mathbf{h}_{21} & \mathbf{h}_{22} \end{bmatrix} = \begin{bmatrix} h_{11} + h_{11}' & h_{12} + h_{12}' \\ h_{21} + h_{21}' & h_{22} + h_{22}' \end{bmatrix} \tag{4.88}$$

Voltage-current relations of the composite network.   The matrix form of the voltage-current relations of the composite network in Fig. 4.4d is given in Eqs. (4.87); by multiplying out the matrices on the right-hand side of (4.87b), we find the voltage-current relations in algebraic form:

$$\begin{aligned} E_1 + E_1' &= \mathbf{h}_{11} I_1 + \mathbf{h}_{12} E_2 = (h_{11} + h_{11}') I_1 + (h_{12} + h_{12}') E_2 \\ I_2 + I_2' &= \mathbf{h}_{21} I_1 + \mathbf{h}_{22} E_2 = (h_{21} + h_{21}') I_1 + (h_{22} + h_{22}') E_2 \end{aligned} \tag{4.89}$$

Remarks.   Taking advantage of the identities in Table 4.1 and following procedures similar to (4.81), we may find any set of composite parameters for the composite network consisting of networks I and II in series-parallel connection as in Fig. 4.4d.

E. Two Four-terminal Networks in Parallel-Series Connection

Let us now assume that parameters g_{11}, g_{12}, g_{21}, g_{22} of the four-terminal network I and parameters g_{11}', g_{12}', g_{21}', g_{22}' of the four-terminal network II in Fig. 4.4e are known quantities.   The voltage-current relations of these two networks, according to (4.68), may then be given in the matrix forms

For network I:
$$\begin{bmatrix} I_2 \\ E_2 \end{bmatrix} = G \begin{bmatrix} E_1 \\ I_2 \end{bmatrix} \quad \text{or} \quad \begin{bmatrix} I_1 \\ E_2 \end{bmatrix} = \begin{bmatrix} g_{11} & g_{12} \\ g_{21} & g_{22} \end{bmatrix} \begin{bmatrix} E_1 \\ I_2 \end{bmatrix} \tag{4.89a}$$

For network II:
$$\begin{bmatrix} I_1' \\ E_2' \end{bmatrix} = G' \begin{bmatrix} E_1' \\ I_2' \end{bmatrix} \quad \text{or} \quad \begin{bmatrix} I_1' \\ E_2' \end{bmatrix} = \begin{bmatrix} g_{11}' & g_{12}' \\ g_{21}' & g_{22}' \end{bmatrix} \begin{bmatrix} E_1' \\ I_2' \end{bmatrix} \tag{4.89b}$$

Composite network parameters.   Networks I and II are now connected with input terminal pairs in *parallel* and output terminal pairs in *series*, forming a composite four-terminal network as in Fig. 4.4e; we wish to find its parameters.   We note in Fig. 4.4e that $E_1 = E_1'$ and $I_2 = I_2'$, or

$$\begin{bmatrix} E_1 \\ I_2 \end{bmatrix} = \begin{bmatrix} E_1' \\ I_2' \end{bmatrix}$$

in matrix form.   Applying this relation to (4.89), we find

$$\begin{bmatrix} I_1 \\ E_2 \end{bmatrix} + \begin{bmatrix} I_1' \\ E_2' \end{bmatrix} = (G + G') \begin{bmatrix} E_1 \\ I_2 \end{bmatrix} \tag{4.90a}$$

or
$$\begin{bmatrix} I_1 + I_1' \\ E_2 + E_2' \end{bmatrix} = (G + G') \begin{bmatrix} E_1 \\ I_2 \end{bmatrix} = \begin{bmatrix} g_{11} + g_{11}' & g_{12} + g_{12}' \\ g_{21} + g_{21}' & g_{22} + g_{22}' \end{bmatrix} \begin{bmatrix} E_1 \\ I_2 \end{bmatrix} \tag{4.90b}$$

The composite network in Fig. 4.4e is now completely characterized by its parameters in

Composite parameters:

$$G + G' = \begin{bmatrix} \mathbf{g}_{11} & \mathbf{g}_{12} \\ \mathbf{g}_{21} & \mathbf{g}_{22} \end{bmatrix} = \begin{bmatrix} g_{11} + g'_{11} & g_{12} + g'_{12} \\ g_{21} + g'_{21} & g_{22} + g'_{22} \end{bmatrix} \tag{4.91}$$

Voltage-current relations of the composite network. The matrix form of the voltage-current relations of the composite network in Fig. 4.4e is given in Eqs. (4.90); by multiplying out the matrices on the right-hand side of (4.90b), we find the voltage-current relations in algebraic form:

$$\begin{aligned} I_1 + I'_1 &= \mathbf{g}_{11}E_1 + \mathbf{g}_{12}I_2 = (g_{11} + g'_{11})E_1 + (g_{12} + g'_{12})I_2 \\ E_2 + E'_2 &= \mathbf{g}_{21}E_1 + \mathbf{g}_{22}I_2 = (g_{21} + g'_{21})E_1 + (g_{22} + g'_{22})I_2 \end{aligned} \tag{4.92}$$

Remarks. Taking advantage of the identities in Table 4.1 and following procedures similar to (4.81), we may find any set of composite parameters for the composite network consisting of network I and II in parallel-series connection as in Fig. 4.4e.

F. Simple Illustrations of Finding the Parameters of a Four-terminal Network by Considering It as a Composite Network

Illustration 1. We now wish to find a set of network parameters for the T network in Fig. 4.5a, where Z_a, Z_b, Z_c are the impedances of the circuit elements.

Stretching our imagination a little, we may regard this network as a composite of the two networks I and II *in series* as in Fig. 4.5b.

According to earlier discussion and Fig. 4.4c, Eq. (4.84) applies here. This means that we may (1) compute matrix Z_I for network I in Fig. 4.5b, (2) compute matrix Z_{II} for network II, and (3) find the parameters z_{11}, z_{12}, z_{21}, z_{22} of the composite network in Fig. 4.5a or b as the elements of the matrix $Z_I + Z_{II}$.

For network I in Fig. 4.5b, we may find the elements z_{ij} of matrix Z_I according to their physical interpretations in (4.45); this matrix must have the form

$$Z_I = \begin{bmatrix} Z_a & 0 \\ 0 & Z_b \end{bmatrix} \tag{4.93a}$$

Similarly, for network II we have

$$Z_{II} = \begin{bmatrix} Z_c & Z_c \\ Z_c & Z_c \end{bmatrix} \tag{4.93b}$$

The network in Fig. 4.5a must, therefore, have parameters z_{ij} as the elements of the matrix

$$Z_I + Z_{II} = \begin{bmatrix} \mathbf{z}_{11} & \mathbf{z}_{12} \\ \mathbf{z}_{21} & \mathbf{z}_{22} \end{bmatrix} = \begin{bmatrix} Z_a + Z_c & Z_c \\ Z_c & Z_b + Z_c \end{bmatrix} \tag{4.93c}$$

From the parameters z_{ij} in (4.93c), we may find other sets of parameters of the network in Fig. 4.5a through identities in Table 4.1.

Illustration 2. We now wish to find a set of network parameters for the Π network in Fig. 4.6a, where Y_d, Y_e, Y_f are the admittances of the circuit elements.

Stretching our imagination a little, we may regard this network as a composite of the two networks I and II *in parallel* as in Fig. 4.6b.

According to earlier discussion and Fig. 4.4b, Eq. (4.79) applies here. This means that we may (1) compute matrix Y_I for network I in Fig. 4.6b, (2) compute matrix

Y_{II} for network II, and (3) find the parameters y_{11}, y_{12}, y_{21}, y_{22} of the composite network in Fig. 4.6a or b as the elements of the matrix $Y_I + Y_{II}$.

For network I in Fig. 4.6b, we may find the elements y_{ij} of the matrix Y_I according to their physical interpretations in (4.32); this matrix must have the form

$$Y_I = \begin{bmatrix} Y_e & 0 \\ 0 & Y_f \end{bmatrix} \tag{4.94a}$$

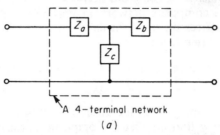

A 4-terminal network

(a)

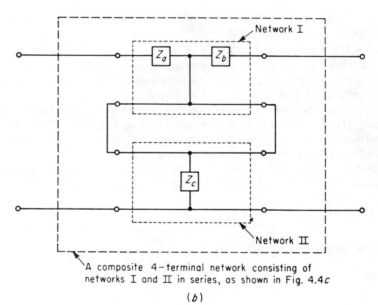

A composite 4-terminal network consisting of
networks I and II in series, as shown in Fig. 4.4c

(b)

FIG. 4.5

Similarly, for network II we have

$$Y_{II} = \begin{bmatrix} Y_d & -Y_d \\ -Y_d & Y_d \end{bmatrix} \tag{4.94b}$$

The network in Fig. 4.6a must, therefore, have parameters y_{ij} as the elements of the matrix

$$Y_I + Y_{II} = \begin{bmatrix} y_{11} & y_{12} \\ y_{21} & y_{22} \end{bmatrix} = \begin{bmatrix} Y_e + Y_d & -Y_d \\ -Y_d & Y_f + Y_d \end{bmatrix} \tag{4.94c}$$

From the parameters y_{ij} in (4.94c), we may find other sets of parameters of the network in Fig. 4.6a through identities in Table 4.1.

Illustration 3.   We now wish to find a set of network parameters for the bridged-T network in Fig. 4.7a, where Z_a, Z_b, Z_c, Z_d are the impedances of the circuit elements, and $Y_d = 1/Z_d$ is the admittance of one of these circuit elements.

Stretching our imagination a little, we may regard this network as a composite of the two networks I and II *in parallel* as in Fig. 4.7b.

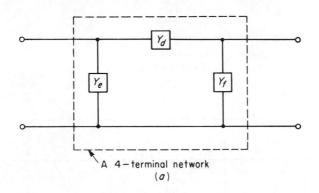

A 4—terminal network
(a)

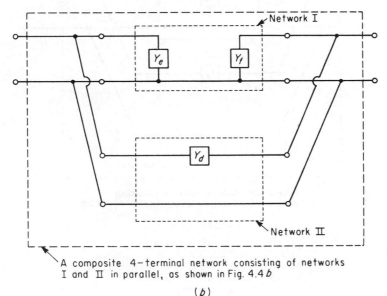

A composite 4—terminal network consisting of networks
I and II in parallel, as shown in Fig. 4.4b

(b)

FIG. 4.6

According to earlier discussion and Fig. 4.4b, Eq. (4.79) applies here.   This means that we may (1) compute matrix Y_I for network I in Fig. 4.7b, (2) compute matrix Y_{II} for network II, and (3) find the parameters y_{11}, y_{12}, y_{21}, y_{22} of the composite network in Fig. 4.7a or b as the elements of the matrix $Y_I + Y_{II}$.   This procedure is carried out as follows:

1. *Computing Matrix Y_I.*   Network I in Fig. 4.7b is identical with the network in Fig. 4.5a and, therefore, must have the Z matrix in (4.93c):

$$Z_I = \begin{bmatrix} z_{11} & z_{12} \\ z_{21} & z_{22} \end{bmatrix} = \begin{bmatrix} Z_a + Z_c & Z_c \\ Z_c & Z_b + Z_c \end{bmatrix}$$

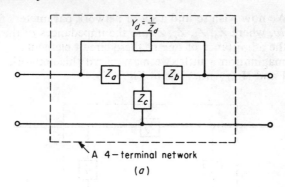

A 4−terminal network

(*a*)

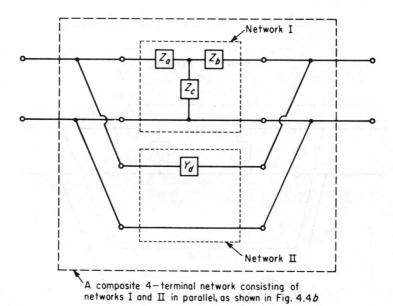

A composite 4−terminal network consisting of
networks I and II in parallel, as shown in Fig. 4.4*b*

(*b*)

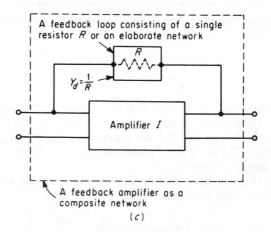

A feedback amplifier as a
composite network

(*c*)

FIG. 4.7

Using identities in (*a*2) of Table 4.1, or calculating the inverse matrix according to the procedure in (4.23), we find

$$Y_I = \begin{bmatrix} y_{11} & y_{12} \\ y_{21} & y_{22} \end{bmatrix} = [Z_I]^{-1} = \begin{bmatrix} \dfrac{Z_b + Z_c}{\Delta} & \dfrac{-Z_c}{\Delta} \\[2mm] \dfrac{-Z_c}{\Delta} & \dfrac{Z_a + Z_c}{\Delta} \end{bmatrix} \tag{4.95a}$$

where

$$\Delta = Z_a Z_b + Z_b Z_c + Z_c Z_a \tag{4.95a'}$$

2. *Computing* Y_{II}. Network II in Fig. 4.7*b* is identical with network II in Fig. 4.6*b* and, therefore, must have the Y matrix in (4.94*b*):

$$Y_{II} = \begin{bmatrix} Y_d & -Y_d \\ -Y_d & Y_d \end{bmatrix} \tag{4.95b}$$

3. *Finding the Parameter* y_{ij}. The parameters y_{11}, y_{12}, y_{21}, y_{22} of the composite network in Fig. 4.7*a* or *b* must be the elements of the matrix

$$Y_I + Y_{II} = \begin{bmatrix} y_{11} & y_{12} \\ y_{21} & y_{22} \end{bmatrix} = \begin{bmatrix} \dfrac{Z_b + Z_c}{\Delta} + Y_d & -\dfrac{Z_c}{\Delta} - Y_d \\[2mm] -\dfrac{Z_c}{\Delta} - Y_d & \dfrac{Z_a + Z_c}{\Delta} + Y_d \end{bmatrix} \tag{4.95c}$$

where

$$\Delta = Z_a Z_b + Z_b Z_c + Z_c Z_a \tag{4.95c'}$$

From the parameters y_{ij} in (4.95*c*), we may find other sets of parameters of the network in Fig. 4.7*a* through identities in Table 4.1.

Remarks. We have illustrated the method of finding network parameters with a rather simple problem. However, the method is applicable to a number of more difficult networks. For example, if we know the parameters y_{ij} of amplifier I in Fig. 4.7*c*, we may readily find the parameters y_{ij} of a feedback amplifier consisting of the given amplifier and a feedback loop by following the above-described procedure.

Illustration 4. We now wish to find a set of network parameters for the simple ladder network in Fig. 4.8*a*, where Z_a, Z_b, Z_c are the impedances of three circuit elements, and Y_e, Y_f are the admittances of two other circuit elements.

Following the discussion and procedure described in the preceding illustration, and identifying network I here with network I in Fig. 4.7*b*, and network II here with network I in Fig. 4.6*b*, we find the parameters y_{ij} of the composite network in Fig. 4.8*a* or *b* as the elements of the matrix

$$Y_I + Y_{II} = \begin{bmatrix} y_{11} & y_{12} \\ y_{21} & y_{22} \end{bmatrix} = \begin{vmatrix} \dfrac{Z_b + Z_c}{\Delta} + Y_e & -\dfrac{Z_c}{\Delta} \\[2mm] -\dfrac{Z_c}{\Delta} & \dfrac{Z_a + Z_c}{\Delta} + Y_f \end{vmatrix} \tag{4.96}$$

where matrix Y_I is obtained from (4.95*a*), and matrix Y_{II} is obtained from (4.94*a*).

From the parameters y_{ij} in (4.96), we may find other sets of parameters of the network in Fig. 4.8*a* through identities in Table 4.1.

Remarks. This, too, is a comparatively simple illustration of the method of finding network parameters, but the method may be applied to a number of more difficult problems. For example, if we know the parameters y_{ij} of amplifier I in Fig. 4.8*c*, we may readily find the parameters y_{ij} of this "amplifier with wiring capacitances" by following the above-described procedure.

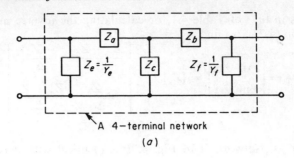

A 4−terminal network

(*a*)

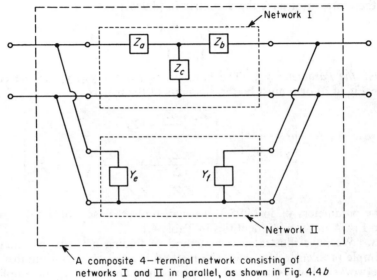

A composite 4−terminal network consisting of
networks I and II in parallel, as shown in Fig. 4.4*b*

(*b*)

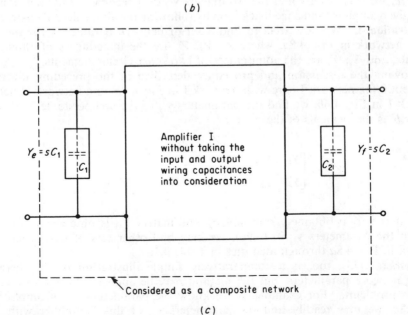

Considered as a composite network

(*c*)

FIG. 4.8

PROBLEMS

The following matrices are for use in Probs. 4.1 through 4.4:

$$A = \begin{bmatrix} 1 \\ 0 \\ 1 \\ 2 \end{bmatrix} \qquad B = \begin{bmatrix} 1 & 3 & -1 & 0 & 2 \end{bmatrix} \qquad C = \begin{bmatrix} 3 \\ 2 \\ 0 \\ 1 \\ -1 \end{bmatrix}$$

$$D = \begin{bmatrix} 2 & 1 \\ 0 & 1 \end{bmatrix} \qquad E = \begin{bmatrix} 1 & 7 & 6 \\ 0 & 2 & 5 \end{bmatrix} \qquad F = \begin{bmatrix} 1 & 2 & 3 \\ 3 & 1 & 0 \\ -1 & 0 & 3 \end{bmatrix}$$

$$G = \begin{bmatrix} \dfrac{s^2+1}{s} & \dfrac{1}{s} \\ \dfrac{1}{s} & \dfrac{s^2+1}{s} \end{bmatrix} \qquad H = \begin{bmatrix} 1 \\ 1+j \end{bmatrix} \qquad I = \begin{bmatrix} 2+j & 1 \\ 0 & 1-j \end{bmatrix}$$

$$J = \begin{bmatrix} 4 & 10 & -11 \\ -1 & 1 & -1 \\ 2 & -5 & 5 \end{bmatrix} \qquad K = \begin{bmatrix} 2+j & 2 & 1-j \\ 2-j & 1+j & j \\ 1 & 1-j & 1 \end{bmatrix}$$

$$L = \begin{bmatrix} 0 & 4 & 4 & -1 \\ 1 & 2 & 1 & -4 \\ 1 & 1 & 0 & -1 \\ -1 & 2 & -1 & 3 \end{bmatrix}$$

4.1. Evaluate the following matrix products: (*a*) *AB*; (*b*) *BC*; (*c*) *DE*; (*d*) *FJ*; (*e*) *GH* for $s = j2$; (*f*) *GI* for $s = j7$; (*g*) *LA*.

4.2. Determine the values of *x* such that each of the following matrices is singular and therefore does not have an inverse:

$$(a) \quad M = \begin{bmatrix} 1-x & 1 & 1 & 1 \\ 1 & 1-x & 1 & 1 \\ 1 & 1 & 1-x & 1 \\ 1 & 1 & 1 & 1-x \end{bmatrix} \qquad (b) \quad N = \begin{bmatrix} 2 & 1 & -1 \\ 9+x & 5 & 0 \\ 8-2x & 5-2x & 1 \end{bmatrix}$$

4.3. Find the inverses of the following matrices: (*a*) *I*; (*b*) *F*; (*c*) *J*; (*d*) *K*; (*e*) *L*. Verify the results with the aid of (4.18).

4.4. Evaluate the following matrix expressions: (*a*) F^2; (*b*) $DE + E$; (*c*) $(D + I)H$; (*d*) $E(F - J)$.

4.5. Establish the identities in (*d*1), (*e*1), and (*f*1) of Table 4.1.

4.6. Establish the identities in (*a*2), (*c*2), (*d*2), (*e*2), and (*f*2) of Table 4.1.

4.7. Establish the identities in (*a*3), (*b*3), (*d*3), (*e*3), and (*f*3) of Table 4.1.

4.8. Establish the identities in (*a*4), (*b*4), (*c*4), (*e*4), and (*f*4) of Table 4.1.

4.9. Establish the identities in (*a*5), (*b*5), (*c*5), (*d*5), and (*f*5) of Table 4.1.

4.10. Establish the identities in ($a6$), ($b6$), ($c6$), ($d6$), and ($e6$) of Table 4.1.

4.11. Given: The network arrangement in Fig. P 4.11 and its special cases $R_2 = 0$ and $R_2 = \infty$.

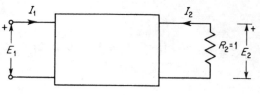

Fig. P 4.11

Establish the following relations between the transfer function and the network parameters:

(a) $\quad Z_T(s) = \dfrac{E_2}{I_1} = \dfrac{z_{21}}{1 + z_{22}}$

(b) $\quad A(s) = \dfrac{I_2}{I_1} = -\dfrac{z_{21}}{1 + z_{22}}$

(c) $\quad Y_T(s) = \dfrac{I_2}{E_1} = \dfrac{y_{21}}{1 + y_{22}}$

(d) $\quad G(s) = \dfrac{E_2}{E_1} = -\dfrac{y_{21}}{1 + y_{22}}$

(e) $\quad A^*(s) = \left(\dfrac{I_2}{I_1}\right)_{R_2=0} = -\dfrac{z_{21}}{z_{22}}$

(f) $\quad G^*(s) = \left(\dfrac{E_2}{E_1}\right)_{R_2=\infty} = -\dfrac{y_{21}}{y_{22}}$

(g) $\quad Z_T^*(s) = \left(\dfrac{E_2}{I_1}\right)_{R_2=\infty} = z_{21}$

(h) $\quad Y_T^*(s) = \left(\dfrac{I_2}{E_1}\right)_{R_2=0} = y_{21}$

To find a four-terminal network from a given transfer function, for example, $Z_T(s)$, we often find its related network parameters, say z_{21} and z_{22}, with the aid of one of the above relations and then realize a network having these parameters. The above expressions are, therefore, regarded as the *basic relations* in transfer-function synthesis.

4.12. Refer to the four-terminal network in Fig. P 2.6.

(a) Find the short-circuit parameters y_{ij} by the method of loop analysis (this is identical to Prob. 2.11).

(b) Find the other five sets of parameters for this network through identities in Table 4.1.

4.13. Refer to the four-terminal network in Fig. P 2.6.

(a) Find the open-circuit parameters z_{ij} by the method of nodal analysis. SUGGESTION: Considering I_1 and I_2 as the currents injected into nodes 1 and 2 of the four-terminal network by two current sources, measure the voltages E_1 and E_2 across these nodes to the reference ground.

(b) Find the other five sets of parameters for this network through identities in Table 4.1. Compare the results of Probs. 4.12 and 4.13.

4.14. Verify the given parameters of the four-terminal networks in Fig. P 4.14. These networks will be used as the component networks in subsequent problems.

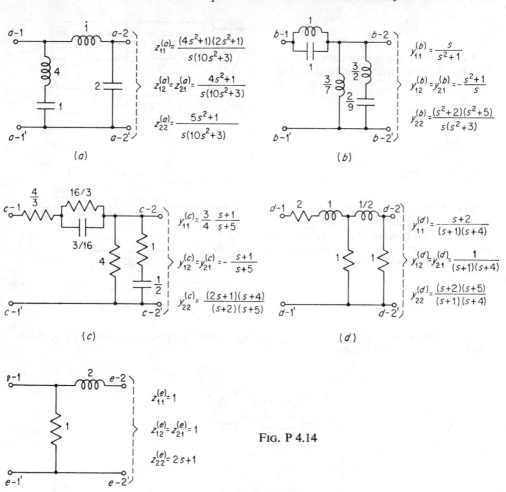

$$z_{11}^{(a)} = \frac{(4s^2+1)(2s^2+1)}{s(10s^2+3)}$$

$$z_{12}^{(a)} = z_{21}^{(a)} = \frac{4s^2+1}{s(10s^2+3)}$$

$$z_{22}^{(a)} = \frac{5s^2+1}{s(10s^2+3)}$$

(a)

$$y_{11}^{(b)} = \frac{s}{s^2+1}$$

$$y_{12}^{(b)} = y_{21}^{(b)} = -\frac{s^2+1}{s}$$

$$y_{22}^{(b)} = \frac{(s^2+2)(s^2+5)}{s(s^2+3)}$$

(b)

$$y_{11}^{(c)} = \frac{3}{4}\frac{s+1}{s+5}$$

$$y_{12}^{(c)} = y_{21}^{(c)} = -\frac{s+1}{s+5}$$

$$y_{22}^{(c)} = \frac{(2s+1)(s+4)}{(s+2)(s+5)}$$

(c)

$$y_{11}^{(d)} = \frac{s+2}{(s+1)(s+4)}$$

$$y_{12}^{(d)} = y_{21}^{(d)} = \frac{1}{(s+1)(s+4)}$$

$$y_{22}^{(d)} = \frac{(s+2)(s+5)}{(s+1)(s+4)}$$

(d)

$$z_{11}^{(e)} = 1$$

$$z_{12}^{(e)} = z_{21}^{(e)} = 1$$

$$z_{22}^{(e)} = 2s+1$$

(e)

FIG. P 4.14

4.15. Obtain the parameters **a, b, c, d** of the composite network in Fig. P 4.15.

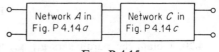

FIG. P 4.15

4.16. Obtain the parameters y_{11}, y_{12}, y_{21}, y_{22} of the composite network in Fig. P 4.16.

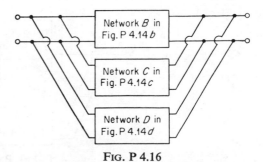

FIG. P 4.16

4.17. Obtain the parameters h_{11}, h_{12}, h_{21}, h_{22} of the composite network in Fig. P 4.17.

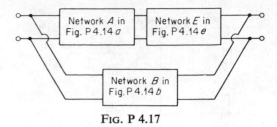

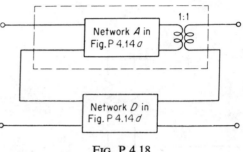

FIG. P 4.17

4.18. Obtain the parameters z_{11}, z_{12}, z_{21}, z_{22} of the composite network in Fig. P 4.18. Explain why it is necessary to use an isolating transformer with a 1:1 turns ratio in this network arrangement.

FIG. P 4.18

4.19. Obtain the parameters h_{11}, h_{12}, h_{21}, h_{22} of the composite network in Fig. P 4.19. Explain the use of the isolating transformer.

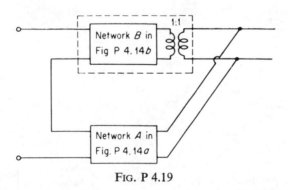

FIG. P 4.19

4.20. Obtain the parameters g_{11}, g_{12}, g_{21}, g_{22} of the composite network in Fig. P 4.20. Explain the use of the isolating transformer.

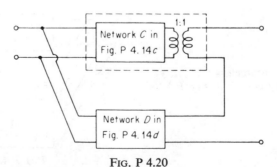

FIG. P 4.20

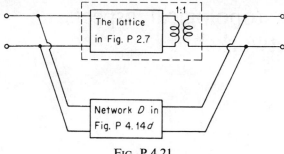

FIG. P 4.21

4.21. (*a*) Represent the parameters y_{11}, y_{12}, y_{21}, y_{22} of the four-terminal lattice network in Fig. P 2.7 in terms of Z_a and Z_b.

(*b*) Obtain the parameters y_{11}, y_{12}, y_{21}, y_{22} of this network as functions of the complex-frequency variable s.

(*c*) Obtain the parameters y_{11}, y_{12}, y_{21}, y_{22} of the composite network in Fig. P 4.21. Explain the use of the isolating transformer.

5 Some topological aspects of networks[†]

5.1. Description of problem

In this chapter we shall study some of the topological properties of network configurations.

What are topological properties? For our present purpose, we shall describe topological properties with the following statements:

Statement 1. *A topological property is an invariant property. That is, it does not vary under continuous transformation.*

Illustration. For an intuitive interpretation of the above remark, let us print on a rubber sheet

$$\text{A closed curve } C \tag{5.1a}$$

$$\text{A point } P \text{ contained in } C \tag{5.1b}$$

and distort them into C' and P' by nonuniform stretching of the rubber sheet without cutting it. It is obvious that C' is also a closed curve and P' is a point contained in C'. The properties which are invariant under the "continuous transformation" of nonuniform stretching may be called topological properties. The geometrical configurations of (1) the closed curve C and point P and (2) the closed curve C' and point P' are said to be *topologically equivalent* or topologically identical.

Remark about Rubber-sheet Geometry. The above illustration suggests consideration of topological properties as the properties of the "rubber-sheet geometry."

Statement 2. *A topological property is a qualitative property.*

This statement is obvious from the illustration associated with (5.1). For example, we are not concerned with the exact mathematical function (i.e., quantitative relationship) that defines the transformation. Instead, we are interested only in the qualitative properties as illustrated in (5.1).

Statement 3. *To study the topological properties of a geometrical configuration, we may study the configuration or any of its topologically equivalent patterns.*

This is again obvious from the illustration associated with (5.1). Two topologically equivalent geometrical configurations, by definition, have the same set of topological properties.

Problems under consideration. In this chapter, we shall study some topological properties of network configurations using the following approach:

Approach:

> All networks of the same geometrical configuration are considered topologically equivalent; *we shall use a single graph consisting of branches and vertices to represent all topologically equivalent networks* $\hspace{2em}$ (5.2a)

[†] Omission of this chapter will not impair reading continuity.

We shall study some of the topological properties of a given graph; these qualitative properties are readily applicable to all networks represented by the same graph (5.2*b*)

For quantitative properties, e.g., finding the response subject to a given excitation, we must know the circuit-element values in addition to the network configuration. With the exception of this chapter, the entire book is devoted to the quantitative properties of the networks.

The following topics will be covered in this chapter:

Topological properties of network configurations to be studied:

The description of network configurations by means of linear graphs and matrices (5.3*a*)

Finding the independent loop currents and node-pair potentials in a network with particular emphasis on the derivations of some relations which have been given and used in Chap. 2 (5.3*b*)

Network duality in the topological (i.e., qualitative) sense, which will be extended to a study on network duality in the quantitative sense in Chap. 6 (5.3*c*)

This chapter, confined to the above topics with direct applications in mind, is only intended to introduce the reader to the topological concept of network configurations. For more extensive study on "network topology," references† are suggested.

5.2. Preliminary subjects for consideration

Linear graph. A linear graph is a geometrical configuration consisting in a set of "vertices," also known as nodes in network applications, and the "edges," also known as branches, that connect them. Two illustrations are provided in Fig. 5.1*a*.

Network as a graph. For the geometrical consideration of a network, i.e., of the topological properties of the network configuration, we may represent the network by a graph and then study the graph.

For illustration, a graph of the network in Fig. 5.2*a*1 is given in Fig. 5.2*a*2.

Remarks about the Branch in a Network Graph. We are often concerned with the question, "What constitutes a network branch?" In general, a branch in a network graph corresponds to

A network branch:

A single *R*, *L*, or *C* element *or* (5.4*a*)

A series combination of *R*, *L*, and *C* elements (5.4*b*)

As illustration, the network in Fig. 5.2*b*1 has Fig. 5.2*b*3 and 4 as its graphs according to the interpretations in (5.4); the network in Fig. 5.2*b*2 has Fig. 5.2*b*4 as its graph. The networks in Fig. 5.2*b*1 and 2 may, therefore, be considered topologically equivalent in the sense that they have the same graph.

Remarks about Representations of Voltage and Current Sources in a Network Graph. We have discussed in Art. 2.5 how to replace a physical voltage source by (1) an idealized voltage source *e* or *E* in series with an internal impedance R_i or

---

† See S. Seshu and M. B. Reed, "Linear Graphs and Electrical Networks," Addison-Wesley Publishing Company, Inc., Reading, Mass., 1961, and the works cited in its bibliography.

Z_i as in Fig. 5.2a1 or (2) an idealized current source i or I in parallel with an internal impedance R_i or Z_i as in Fig. 5.2c. Therefore, we need only consider the idealized voltage and current sources.

Since an idealized voltage source e or E has no internal impedance, we may consider it a short-circuited element. In the example of Fig. 5.2a1, we may short-circuit the idealized voltage source in the network and obtain its graph in Fig. 5.2a2.

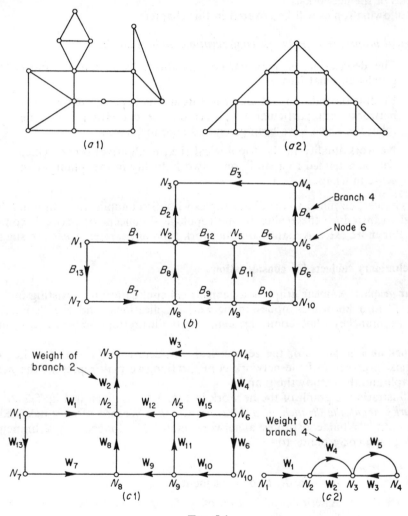

FIG. 5.1

Since an idealized current source i or I has no internal admittance, we may consider it an open-circuited element. In the example of Fig. 5.2c1, we may open-circuit the idealized current source in the network by leaving it out of the network entirely and obtain its graph in Fig. 5.2c2 or 3.

Remarks about the Vertices in a Separate Part. A *separate part* is defined as a portion of a network which, while it may have purely inductive coupling, has no coupling through capacitance or conductance with the other parts of the network. For example, there are three separate parts in the network in Fig. 5.2c1; according to the discussion in the preceding paragraphs, this network would have an un-connected graph as in Fig. 5.2c2.

The potential between a pair of nodes is called a node-pair potential. We shall study the node-pair potentials of a network in Art. 5.6. For a network having separate parts such as the one in Fig. 5.2c1, how are we going to define the potential between nodes N_{16} and N_2 of two separate parts? To define this and any other node-pair potentials properly, *we must form a "connected graph" by letting two related separate parts share a common node.* This is also a common practice in actual circuits—we usually use the same ground terminal, i.e., ground node, for all separate parts. For illustration, Fig. 5.2c3 depicts a *connected graph*, in which N_{12} is a common node of two separate parts and N_4 is another, for the network in Fig. 5.2c1.

Oriented linear graph. By arbitrarily assigning the directions of the edges of a graph, we form an oriented graph as depicted in Fig. 5.1b.

In an oriented graph considered as a network graph, the directions of the branches may be used conveniently to represent the directions of the currents in the branches.

Oriented linear graph with weighted edges. We may also assign a *weight* (or weighting function) W_i to each edge (or branch) B_i of an oriented graph as in Fig. 5.1c1 and 2.

5.3. Remarks about different interpretations of linear graphs; matrix representation of linear graphs

A linear graph may be used to describe physical systems other than network configurations. We shall now tabulate some of the more important interpretations of linear graphs.

Interpretation 1. *A linear graph may be used to represent a network configuration as a network graph.* As discussed in the preceding paragraphs, we may find the graph of a network with the following correspondences:

Correspondences between network and graph:

For network	For graph	
Node	Vertex	(5.5a)
Branch	Edge	(5.5b)
Direction of a branch current	Orientation of an edge	(5.5c)
Impedance of a branch	Weight of an edge	(5.5d)

Since this chapter is primarily devoted to the study of network graphs, *the terms in the two columns in (5.5) are considered synonyms, and we shall use them interchangeably.*

A network graph may be (1) a nonoriented linear graph as in Fig. 5.2a2, (2) an oriented linear graph as in Fig. 5.1b, or (3) an oriented linear graph with weighted branches as in Fig. 5.1c1, with the interpretations in (5.5). Only the first two categories will be discussed in this chapter.

Interpretation 2. *An oriented linear graph with weighted edges may be used to describe the voltage-current relations of a network as a signal-flow diagram.* The correspondences are then as follows:

Correspondences between network and graph:

For network	For graph	
Voltage or current, an electrical quantity	Vertex	(5.6a)
Relation between two electrical quantities, say A and B	Edge between two vertices	(5.6b)

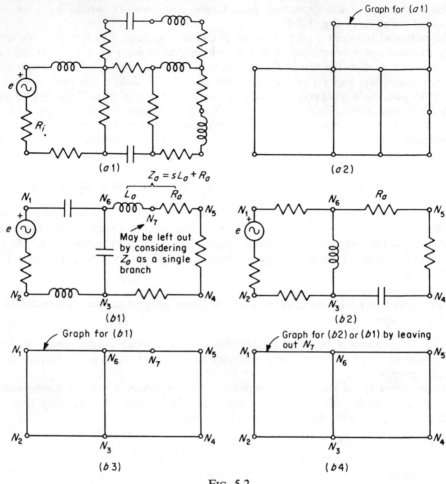

FIG. 5.2

	For network		For graph	
	Contributivity of a relation, showing whether A contributes to B, or B to A		*Orientation* of an edge	(5.6c)
	Impedance, admittance, voltage ratio, or *current ratio* which relates two electrical quantities		*Weight* of an edge	(5.6d)

For example, let us consider the simple network in Fig. 5.3a whose voltage-current relations (a1), (a2), and (a3) are indicated in the figure. Relation (a1),

$$\frac{1}{Z_a} E_1 + \frac{-1}{Z_a} E_2 = I_1$$

may be described graphically as in Fig. 5.3b1 in the following manner:

Finding a partial graph:

Represent voltages E_1, E_2 and current I_1 by three *vertices*   (5.7a)

Draw two directed (i.e., *oriented*) *edges* from E_1 and E_2 to I_1, indicating that E_1 and E_2 contribute to I_1,   (5.7b)

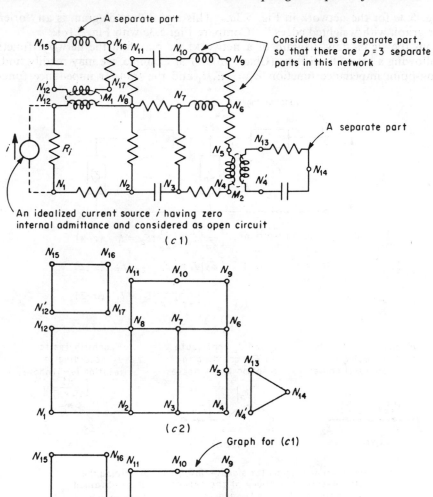

An idealized current source *i* having zero
internal admittance and considered as open circuit

(*c* 1)

(*c* 2)

(*c* 3)

FIG. 5.2 (*continued*)

Use $1/Z_a$ and $-1/Z_a$ as the *weights* of the two directed edges   (5.7*c*)

We now have the *partial graph* in Fig. 5.3*b*1 describing the voltage-
current relation (*a*1)   (5.7*d*)

Similarly, we may construct the partial graph in Fig. 5.3*b*2 describing the voltage-
current relation (*a*2) and the partial graph in Fig. 5.3*b*3 describing the voltage-current
relation (*a*3). Combining Figs. 5.3*b*1, 2, and 3, we have the signal-flow diagram

in Fig. 5.3c for the network in Fig. 5.3a.   This signal-flow diagram is an "oriented linear graph with weighted edges."   Compare Fig. 5.3c with Fig. 5.1c1.

From the signal-flow diagram of a network, we may find the network functions by following a set of fixed rules (Chap. 16).   For example, we may readily find the driving-point impedance function $Z_D = E_1/I_1$ and the transfer impedance function

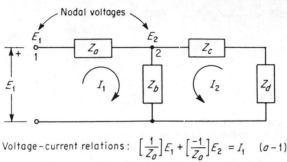

Nodal voltages

Voltage-current relations:

$$\left[\frac{1}{Z_a}\right]E_1 + \left[\frac{-1}{Z_a}\right]E_2 = I_1 \quad (a-1)$$

$$\left[Z_b\right]I_1 + \left[Z_b\right]I_2 = E_2 \quad (a-2)$$

$$\left[\frac{-1}{Z_c + Z_d}\right]E_2 = I_2 \quad (a-3)$$

(a)

E_1 and E_2 contribute to I_1 according to relation $(a-1)$ above:

I_1 and I_2 contribute to E_2 according to relation $(a-2)$ above:

E_2 contributes to I_2 according to relation $(a-3)$ above:

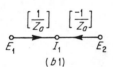

(b1)

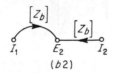

(b2)

(b3)

Signal-flow diagram (or signal-flow graph) describing the voltage-current relations of the network in (a) — obtained by combining (b1), (b2), and (b3):

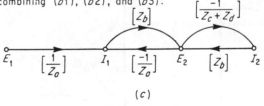

(c)

FIG. 5.3

$Z_T = E_1/I_2$ of the network in Fig. 5.3a from its signal-flow diagram in Fig. 5.3c. Signal-flow diagrams are important tools in network analysis and in the study of closed-loop control systems and will be studied in Chaps. 15 through 17.

Interpretation 3.   *An oriented linear graph with weighted edges may be used to describe the probability relations of a system as in a state diagram.*   For example, "states" and "transitional probabilities" are used in the study of codes, e.g., telegraphic codes.   We may use† oriented linear graphs with weighted edges, in which

† See figs. 3 through 5 in C. E. Shannon, A Mathematical Theory of Communication, *Bell System Tech. J.*, vol. 27, pp. 379–429, 623–656, July, October, 1948.

each vertex represents a "state" and each weight represents a "probability," in this and other communication problems.

Description of a network with a matrix. We may describe an oriented network graph such as that in Fig. 5.1*b* with a matrix of the form of (4.1), where the rows correspond to different nodes N_i, and the columns to different branches B_j. An element a_{ij} is $+1$, -1, or 0 according to the following rules:

Elements of incidence matrix A of the form of (4.1):

$$a_{ij} = +1 \text{ if branch } B_j \text{ is connected to node } N_i \text{ and directed}$$
$$\text{toward } N_i \tag{5.8a}$$

$$a_{ij} = -1 \text{ if } B_j \text{ is connected to } N_i \text{ and directed away from } N_i \tag{5.8b}$$

$$a_{ij} = 0 \text{ if } B_j \text{ is not connected to } N_i \tag{5.8c}$$

This matrix is called an *incidence matrix*.

For the oriented network graph in Fig. 5.1*b* we find the following incidence matrix:

For graph of Fig. 5.1b:

$$
A = \begin{bmatrix}
-1 & 0 & 0 & 0 & 0 & 0 & 0 & 0 & 0 & 0 & 0 & 0 & -1 \\
+1 & -1 & 0 & 0 & 0 & 0 & 0 & +1 & 0 & 0 & 0 & +1 & 0 \\
0 & +1 & +1 & 0 & 0 & 0 & 0 & 0 & 0 & 0 & 0 & 0 & 0 \\
0 & 0 & -1 & +1 & 0 & 0 & 0 & 0 & 0 & 0 & 0 & 0 & 0 \\
0 & 0 & 0 & 0 & -1 & 0 & 0 & 0 & 0 & 0 & +1 & -1 & 0 \\
0 & 0 & 0 & -1 & +1 & -1 & 0 & 0 & 0 & 0 & 0 & 0 & 0 \\
0 & 0 & 0 & 0 & 0 & 0 & -1 & 0 & 0 & 0 & 0 & 0 & +1 \\
0 & 0 & 0 & 0 & 0 & 0 & +1 & -1 & +1 & 0 & 0 & 0 & 0 \\
0 & 0 & 0 & 0 & 0 & 0 & 0 & 0 & -1 & +1 & -1 & 0 & 0 \\
0 & 0 & 0 & 0 & 0 & +1 & 0 & 0 & 0 & -1 & 0 & 0 & 0
\end{bmatrix}
$$
$$\tag{5.9}$$

We have now used an (incidence) matrix to describe an oriented network graph.

We may use a matrix having 0s and 1s as elements to describe the network configuration of a nonoriented network graph.

Remarks about the use of matrices as equivalent representations of linear graphs. Similarly, we may (1) use a matrix of the form of (4.1) in which $m = n$ and the a_{ij} depict "weights" to describe the system in interpretation 2 above and (2) use a matrix of the form of (4.1) in which $m = n$ and the a_{ij} depict "probabilities" to describe the system in interpretation 3. The rows of the matrix are made to correspond to the n vertices (of the linear graph of the system concerned); the columns also correspond to these n vertices.

It is now obvious that we may use either (1) a linear graph or (2) a matrix as alternative representations to describe certain physical or mathematical systems.

5.4. Terminology used in network graphs

We shall now define some of the basic terms associated with network graphs.

Branch. *A branch (or edge) is a line segment in a network graph corresponding to a single circuit element or to a combination of circuit elements* as described in (5.4).

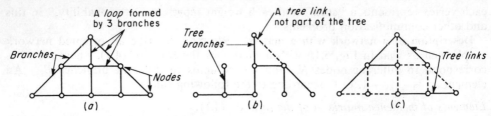

FIG. 5.4   (*a*) Graph; (*b*) tree of (*a*); (*c*) tree complement represented by solid lines (as tree links), where the dashed lines depicting the tree in (*b*) are given for reference.

Node.   *A node (or vertex) is the intersection of two or more branches in a network graph* as shown in Fig. 5.4a.

Loop.   *A loop is a set of branches forming a closed path in a network graph.*   A three-branch loop is shown in Fig. 5.4a.

Tree (definition 1).   *A tree includes all nodes of a network graph and an open set* (i.e., one which includes no loop) *of network branches which connects all these nodes.* For example, Fig. 5.4*b* shows a tree for the graph in Fig. 5.4*a*; Fig. 5.5*a*2 and 3 depicts

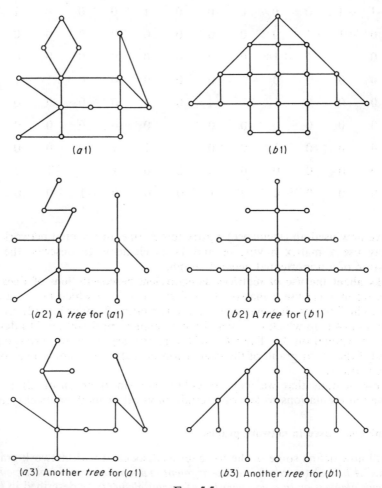

FIG. 5.5

two trees for the graph in Fig. 5.5*a*1; Fig. 5.5*b*2 and 3, two trees for the graph in Fig. 5.5*b*1. We note that there are often a number of trees associated with a given graph.

Tree (definition 2). *A tree consists in* b_t *network branches connecting all n nodes of a network graph, where*

$$b_t = n - 1 \tag{5.10}$$

It is easy to see in the illustrations that the two definitions of a tree are consistent.

Tree branch and tree link. By choosing a particular tree of a network graph, we separate all the network branches into two categories: (1) those network branches belonging to the tree, called *tree branches*, and (2) those network branches not belonging to the tree, called *tree links* (or *links*). The collection of all tree links is called the *tree complement*. Illustrations of these terms are provided in Fig. 5.4*b* and *c*.

Remarks about planar and nonplanar networks. A network is called a *planar network* if all the branches of its graph can be placed in the same plane with no branch crossing another. Graphs of some planar networks are shown in Figs. 5.1*a*, 5.2*a*2, 5.3*c*, and 5.4*a*.

A network is called a *nonplanar network* if some branches of its graph cross others when they are all placed in the same plane. Graphs of some nonplanar networks are shown in Fig. 5.6.

Although we shall use planar graphs for most of the illustrations in this chapter, we shall find that much of our discussion is applicable to both planar and nonplanar graphs, although network duality, as discussed in Art. 5.7, applies only to planar networks.

5.5. Independent loop currents in a network

We now wish to determine the number of independent loop currents in a given network or its graph. We shall state a theorem and three corollaries and prove them.

Theorem A. *The number of independent loop currents in a network is equal to the number of tree links.*

Proof. Let us consider the network graph in Fig. 5.7*a*1 and one of its possible trees in Fig. 5.7*b*1. We first add a tree link L_1 to the tree in Fig. 5.7*b*2, creating a loop and permitting a loop current i_{Lp-1} which, for example, may be caused by a voltage source in link L_1. We then add another tree link L_2, creating another loop and permitting another independent loop current i_{Lp-2} in Fig. 5.7*b*3. Repeating this process, we obtain six loops by adding six tree links in Fig. 5.7*b*7. Although we have used the particular network graph in Fig. 5.7*a*1, this property is also true for other networks and is, therefore, stated as Theorem A.

Corollary A1. *All branch currents of a network can be expressed in terms of its independent loop currents.*

Theorem A obviously implies Corollary A1. However, let us clarify it with an illustration. In the network graph in Fig. 5.7*a*1, we arbitrarily assign directions to the branch currents and label them $i_1, i_2, \ldots, i_{14}$, as in Fig. 5.7*a*2. Identifying Fig. 5.7*a*2 with Fig. 5.7*b*7 as in Fig. 5.7*c*1, we see that any one of the 14 branch currents may be expressed as a linear combination of the six independent loop currents.

This illustration uses the loops defined in Fig. 5.7*b*7. Figure 5.7*c*2 provides another illustration in which the loops are defined somewhat differently.

Corollary A2. *In a connected network with n nodes and b branches, the number of independent loop currents is*

Number of independent loop currents:

$$l = b - n + 1 \tag{5.11}$$

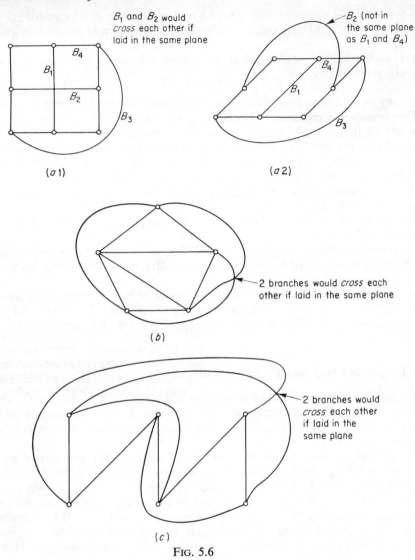

B_1 and B_2 would
cross each other if
laid in the same plane

B_2 (not in
the same plane
as B_1 and B_4)

$(a1)$ $(a2)$

2 branches would *cross* each
other if laid in the same plane

(b)

2 branches would
cross each other
if laid in the
same plane

(c)

FIG. 5.6

In a network graph with b (network) branches and an associated tree with b_t tree branches there are $b - b_t$ tree links according to the definitions in Art. 5.4. Corollary A2 is the natural consequence of replacing b_t with (5.10) and applying Theorem A.

Illustration. Let us consider the network graph in Fig. 5.7a. For $b = 14$ and $n = 9$, Eq. (5.11) implies that we must have $l = 6$ independent loop currents. This checks our earlier result in Fig. 5.7b7, c1, or c2.

Corollary A3. *In a network with p separate parts, n nodes, and b branches, the number of independent loop currents is*

Number of independent loop currents:

$$l = b - n + p \qquad (5.12)$$

We must use a "connected graph" as the network graph of a network with separate parts (Art. 5.2); in so doing, we lose one node by making two related separate parts share a common node. In the example of Fig. 5.2c, we have $n = 19$ nodes and $p = 3$ separate parts in Fig. 5.2c1, and only

$$n' = n - (p - 1) \tag{5.13a}$$
$$n' = 19 - (3 - 1) = 17 \tag{5.13b}$$

nodes in the "connected graph" in Fig. 5.2c3.

Equation (5.11) applies to a connected graph with n' nodes; i.e.,

$$l = b - n' + 1 \tag{5.14}$$

Equation (5.12) results from substituting (5.13a) into (5.14).

Illustration. For the network in Fig. 5.2c1, we have $p = 3$, $n = 19$, and $b = 22$; Eq. (5.12) implies that we must have $l = 6$ independent loop currents. This result may be verified by defining a set of independent loop currents for this network.

5.6. Independent node-pair potentials in a network

We now wish to determine the number of independent node-pair potentials in a given network or its graph. We shall state a theorem and three corollaries and prove them.

Theorem B. *The number of independent node-pair potentials in a network is equal to the number of tree branches.*

Proof. Let us consider the network graph in Fig. 5.8a1 and one of its possible trees in Fig. 5.8a3.

We first use tree branch B_1 in Fig. 5.8b1 to define a node-pair potential e_1, which may be considered as the potential between the pair of nodes if a voltage source is inserted in branch B_1. We then add tree branch B_2, defining another independent node-pair potential e_2 in Fig. 5.8b2. Repeating this process, we obtain eight independent node-pair potentials by using all eight tree branches in Fig. 5.8b8. Although we have used the particular network graph in Fig. 5.8a1, this property is also true for other networks and is, therefore, stated as Theorem B.

Corollary B1. *All branch potentials of a network can be expressed in terms of its independent node-pair potentials.*

Theorem B obviously implies Corollary B1. However, let us clarify it with an illustration. In the network graph in Fig. 5.8a1, we arbitrarily assign polarities to the branch potentials and label them $v_1, v_2, \ldots, v_{14}$ as in Fig. 5.8a2. Identifying Fig. 5.8a2 with Fig. 5.8b8 as in Fig. 5.8c, we see that any one of the 14 branch potentials may be expressed as a linear combination of the eight independent node-pair potentials.

Corollary B2. *In a connected network with n nodes, the number of independent node-pair potentials is*

Number of independent node-pair potentials:

$$n_p = n - 1 \tag{5.15}$$

Corollary B2 is an embodiment of Theorem B and (5.10).

Illustration. Let us consider the network graph in Fig. 5.8a1. For $n = 9$, Eq. (5.15) implies that we must have $n_p = 8$ independent node-pair potentials. This checks with our earlier result in Fig. 5.8b8 or c.

Corollary B3. *In a network with p separate parts and n nodes, the number of independent node-pair potentials is*

Number of independent node-pair potentials:

$$n_p = n - p \tag{5.16}$$

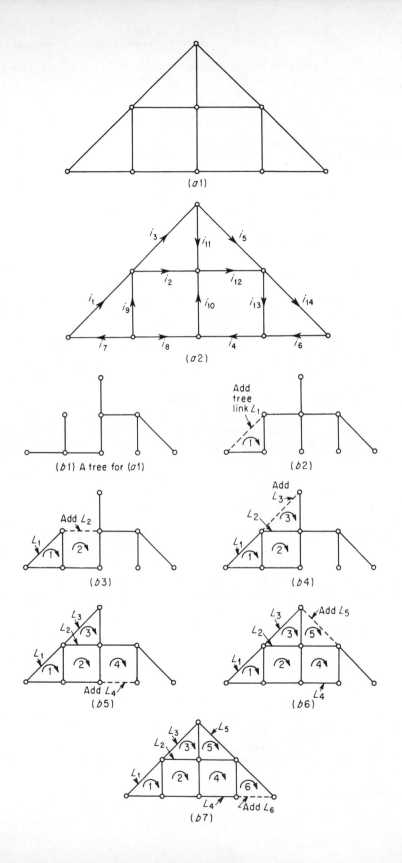

(a1)

(a2)

(b1) A tree for (a1)

(b2)

Add tree link L_1

(b3)

Add L_2

(b4)

Add L_3

(b5)

Add L_4

(b6)

Add L_5

(b7)

Add L_6

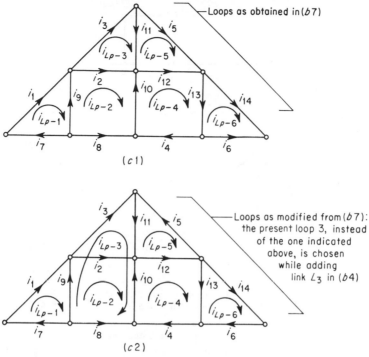

FIG. 5.7 (*a*1) Network graph. (*a*2) Branch currents indicated with arbitrarily assigned directions. (*c*1) Any one of the 14 branch currents of all branches of the network graph may be expressed in terms of the 6 independent loop currents; for example, $i_1 = i_{Lp-1}$, $i_2 = i_{Lp-2} - i_{Lp-3}, \ldots, i_9 = -i_{Lp-1} + i_{Lp-2}$, etc. (*c*2) Any one of the 14 branch currents may be expressed in terms of the 6 independent loop currents; for example, $i_1 = i_{Lp-1}$, $i_2 = i_{Lp-2}, \ldots, i_9 = -i_{Lp-1} + i_{Lp-2} + i_{Lp-3}$, etc.

Reference is made to the discussion following Corollary A3 (Art. 5.5). Equation (5.15) applies to a connected graph with n' nodes, i.e.,

$$n_p = n' - 1 \qquad (5.17)$$

Equation (5.16) results from substituting (5.13*a*) into (5.17).

Illustration. For the network in Fig. 5.2*c*1, we have $p = 3$ and $n = 19$; Eq. (5.16) implies that we must have $n_p = 16$ independent node-pair potentials. This result may be verified by defining a set of independent node-pair potentials using the network graph in Fig. 5.2*c*3.

5.7. Network duality

In the discussions in the two preceding sections we have noticed a one-to-one correspondence between (1) the quantities and relations used and implied in the study of independent loop currents in Art. 5.5 and (2) the quantities and relations used and implied in the study of independent node-pair potentials in Art. 5.6. We shall now tabulate these correspondences in (5.18). Ignore the captions "original network" and "dual network" for the time being.

Dual networks. In Arts. 5.5 and 5.6, we have demonstrated the one-to-one correspondences in (5.18*a*) and those in (5.18*b*). Now, let us consider them together: *Do networks exist in pairs such that the networks of the same pair have one-to-one*

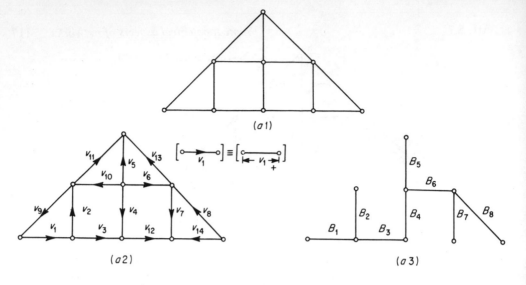

(a1)

(a2)

(a3)

Define e_3 and *note independence* among e_1, e_2, and e_3 (that is, e_3 cannot be represented as a linear combination of e_1 and e_2):

Define a *node-pair potential* e_1:

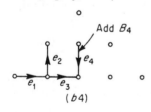

(b1)

Define e_2 and *note independence* between e_1 and e_2 (that is, $e_2 \neq \pm e_1$):

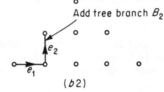

Add tree branch B_2

(b2)

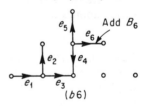

Add B_3

(b3)

Define e_4 and *note independence* among e_1, e_2, e_3, and e_4:

Add B_4

(b4)

Define e_5 and *note independence* among $e_1, \ldots, e_5$:

Add B_5

(b5)

Define e_6 and *note independence* among $e_1, \ldots, e_6$:

Add B_6

(b6)

Define e_7 and *note independence* among $e_1, \ldots, e_7$:

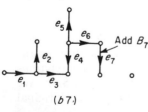

Add B_7

(b7)

Define e_8 and *note independence* among $e_1, \ldots, e_8$:

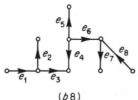

(b8)

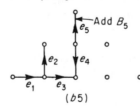

(c)

FIG. 5.8 (a1) Network graph. (a2) Branch potentials indicated with arbitrarily assigned polarities. (a3) Tree of (a1). (c) Any one of the 14 branch potentials may be expressed in terms of the 8 independent node-pair potentials; for example, $v_1 = e_1, \ldots, v_8 = e_8, v_9 = -e_1 - e_2$ (since $v_9 + v_1 + v_2 = v_9 + e_1 + e_2 = 0$ in a loop), $v_{10} = e_2 - e_3 + e_4$ (since $v_{10} - v_2 + v_3 - v_4 = v_{10} - e_2 + e_3 - e_4 = 0$ in a loop), $v_{11} = -e_2 + e_3 - e_4 + e_5$, etc.

118

	Original network, with quantities and relations in both (5.18a) and (5.18b) (1)	Dual network, with quantities and relations in both (5.18a) and (5.18b) (2)	
One-to-one correspondences between quantities and relations in Art. 5.5 (column 1) and Art. 5.6 (column 2)	Loop Current Tree link Closed circuit Series connection	Node pair Potential Tree branch Open circuit Parallel connection	(5.18a)
One-to-one correspondences between quantities and relations in Art. 5.6 (column 1) and Art. 5.5 (column 2)	Node pair Potential Tree branch Open circuit Parallel connection	Loop Current Tree link Closed circuit Series connection	(5.18b)

correspondences between their quantities and relations as tabulated in Eqs. (5.18)? The answer is "yes" for planar networks (Art. 5.4) and "no" for nonplanar networks. We now confine our discussion to planar networks.

We shall define dual networks with this statement: *Two networks are said to be topologically or qualitatively dual to each other if there are one-to-one correspondences between all entries in columns 1 and 2 in Eqs.* (5.18) *for these two networks.* One of these two networks may be designated as the original (or given) network, and the other its dual.

We shall postpone our illustration of dual networks until after we have introduced the procedure for finding the dual of a network.

Procedure for finding the dual of a planar network. To find the dual of a given network in the topological sense, we proceed as follows:

Step 1. Mark a point in each loop of the original network, designating it as a node N_K^* *of the dual network; mark a point exterior to the original network, designating it as the reference node*† N_0^* *of the dual network.*

Reference is now made to Fig. 5.9a for illustration. We have marked and designated the nodes $N_1^*, N_2^*, \ldots, N_6^*$ associated with the six loops of the original network, and the reference node N_0^* associated with the loop consisting of the exterior branches of the original network.

Step 2. Connect two nodes obtained in Step 1 with a network branch of the dual network, crossing a network branch of the original network. Repeat Step 2 for all branches. With nodes obtained in Step 1 and network branches obtained here, we now have the dual of the original network.

In Fig. 5.9a, we have now obtained the network branches (broken lines) of the dual network; each of these network branches connects two nodes and crosses a network branch (solid lines) of the original network. The dual network thus obtained is the broken-line representation in Fig. 5.9a or b.

The condition in Step 2 that each network branch of the dual network *crosses* a network branch of the original network ensures that *there is a one-to-one correspondence between the two dual networks*, i.e., the original and its dual. The dual of

---

† In an actual physical network, we usually ground a node, calling it a "ground node" or "reference node," and using it as a zero-potential reference. The so-called "node potential" at a particular node is then the potential at this node with respect to the reference node. *Whether we ground N_0^* or not, we may use it as a "reference node" in the sense described here.*

Note one-one correspondences between (1) the node N_k^* of the dual network and (2) the loops of the original network, in which the nodes N_k^* are placed:

$$\left[\text{node } N_1^*\right] \xleftrightarrow{1:1} \left[\text{loop } cdbc\right]$$
$$\left[\text{node } N_6^*\right] \xleftrightarrow{1:1} \left[\text{loop } fghf\right]$$
$$\left[\text{reference node } N_0^*\right] \longleftrightarrow \left[\text{loop } abcdefgha\right]$$

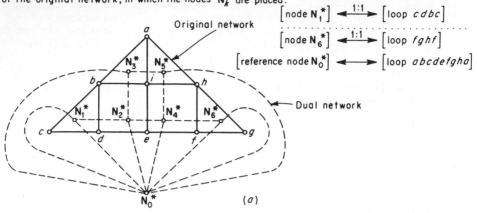

Original network

Dual network

(a)

Original network (solid line):
Tree branches B_h (heavy), $h = 1, 2, \ldots, 8$
Links L_k (light), $k = 1, 2, \ldots, 6$

$\xrightleftharpoons[1:1]{1:1}$

Dual network (broken line):
Links L_h^* (heavy), $h = 1, 2, \ldots, 8$
Tree branches B_k^* (light), $k = 1, 2, \ldots, 6$

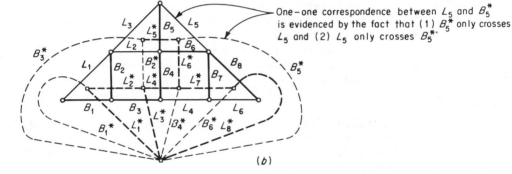

One-one correspondence between L_5 and B_5^* is evidenced by the fact that (1) B_5^* only crosses L_5 and (2) L_5 only crosses B_5^*.

(b)

Original network showing tree branches B_h (heavy line); links L_k (light line); loops M_k (only $k = 1$ indicated); nodes N_0 (reference node) and N_h (only $h = 5$ indicated); loop currents i_k (only $k = 1$ indicated); node-pair potential e_h (only $h = 5$ indicated), where $h = 1, 2, \ldots, 8$ and $k = 1, 2, \ldots, 6$

$$\left[\circ \xrightarrow{e} \circ\right] \equiv \left[\circ \xleftarrow{\quad e \quad} \circ \atop - \qquad +\right]$$

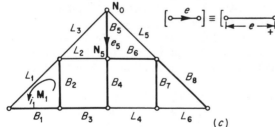

(c)

Dual network showing tree branches B_k^* (light line); links L_h^* (heavy line); loops M_h^* (only $h = 5$ indicated); nodes N_0^* (reference node) and N_k^* (only $k = 1$ indicated); loop currents i_h^* (only $h = 5$ indicated); node-pair potential e_k^* (only $k = 1$ indicated), where $k = 1, 2, \ldots, 6$ and $h = 1, 2, \ldots, 8$

(d)

Fig. 5.9

120

an original network having 14 network branches must also have 14 network branches; this is illustrated in Fig. 5.9a.

An illustration.   Establishing duality for the result of the above procedure.   We have claimed that we may find the dual of a given network by the above procedure. But is the result of this procedure really the dual of the given network in the sense that the two networks have one-to-one correspondences for all the entries in Eqs. (5.18)?   We shall try to furnish an affirmative answer to this question.

For easy reference, we first resketch the original network and its dual in Fig. 5.9a with modifications in Fig. 5.9b such that the tree branches B_h (*heavy* solid lines) and the links L_K (*light* solid lines) of the original network are distinguishable, and the corresponding elements L_h^* and B_K^* (*heavy* and *light* broken lines, respectively) of the dual network are also distinguishable.   By examining the dual network, it is easy to see that the collection of B_K^* (*light* broken lines) in Fig. 5.9b is a tree and L_h^* are the tree links.

We then resketch the original network (Fig. 5.9a and b) in Fig. 5.9c and label its various quantities; we resketch the dual network (Fig. 5.9a and b) in Fig. 5.9d and label its various quantities.   With reference to these figures, we are now in a position to establish the one-to-one correspondence for duality as listed in Eqs. (5.18):

Illustration for duality in Fig. 5.9:

Original network as depicted in Fig. 5.9c (1)	*Dual network as depicted in Fig. 5.9d* (2)	
Loop associated with link L_K (only $K = 1$ is indicated in the figure): $\mathbf{M}_K$	*Node pair* associated with tree branch B_K^* (only $K = 1$ is indicated in the figure): $\mathbf{N}_K^* \mathbf{N}_0^*$	(5.19a)
Current in loop $\mathbf{M}_K$ (only $K = 1$ is indicated in the figure): i_K	*Potential* in node pair $\mathbf{N}_K^* \mathbf{N}_0^*$ (only $K = 1$ is indicated in the figure): e_K^*	(5.19b)
Tree link (light line): L_K	*Tree branch* (light line): B_K^*	(5.19c)
Closed circuit and *series connection* described, e.g., by B_1, B_2, L_1 contained in a loop $\mathbf{M}_1$	*Open circuit* and *parallel connection* described, e.g., by L_1^*, L_2^*, B_1^* joined at a node $\mathbf{N}_1^*$	(5.19d)
Node pair associated with tree branch B_h (only $h = 5$ is indicated in the figure): $\mathbf{N}_h \mathbf{N}_0$	*Loop* associated with link L_h^* (only $h = 5$ is indicated in the figure): $\mathbf{M}_h^*$	(5.19e)
Potential in node pair $\mathbf{N}_h \mathbf{N}_0$ (only $h = 5$ is indicated in the figure): e_h	*Current* in loop $\mathbf{M}_h^*$ (only $h = 5$ is indicated in the figure): i_h^*	(5.19f)
Tree branch (heavy line): B_h	*Tree link* (heavy line): L_h^*	(5.19g)
Open circuit and *parallel connection* described, e.g., by L_2, B_4, B_6, B_5 joined at a node $\mathbf{N}_5$	*Closed circuit* and *series connection* described, e.g., by B_2^*, L_4^*, L_6^*, L_5^* contained in a loop $\mathbf{M}_5^*$	(5.19h)

We have now established duality between the two networks in Fig. 5.9a.

Additional illustrations.   Two additional illustrations of finding the dual of a planar network with the procedure described above are provided in Fig. 5.10a and b.   Although "duality" in these illustrations is understood and assured, the reader may wish to carry out an analysis for each of them to establish duality in the same manner as we did in (5.19) for the illustration in Fig. 5.9.

Remarks about "quantitative" duality.   As remarked in (5.2), we have been investigating some of the topological or qualitative properties of networks throughout

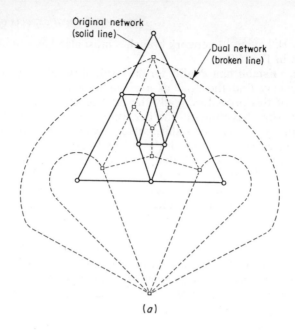

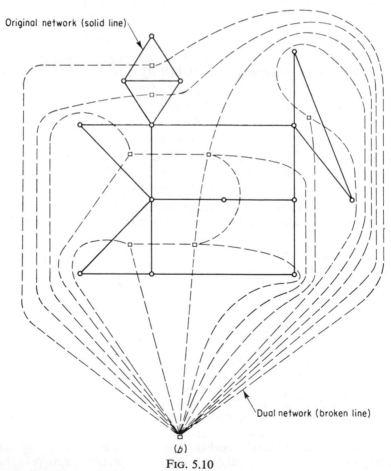

FIG. 5.10

the present chapter. We have also only studied the "qualitative aspect" of duality. For example, we have established one-to-one correspondences between the quantities and relations of two dual networks in (5.19); these are *qualitative* relations. We did not investigate the numerical relationships between the quantities in two dual systems—the *quantitative* relations.

We shall study the quantitative aspects of duality in Art. 6.2.

PROBLEMS

5.1. Given: The network graphs in Fig. P 5.1.
(*a*) Determine whether any of these graphs is nonplanar. Find the dual of each planar graph.
(*b*) Obtain a tree for each graph.

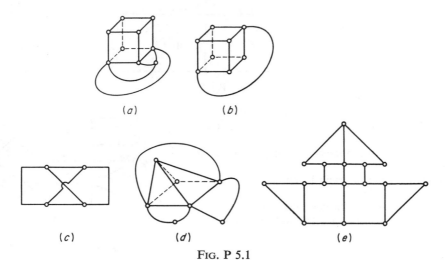

FIG. P 5.1

5.2. Refer to the network graph in Fig. P 5.1e.
(*a*) Find a set of tree links.
(*b*) Identify a set of independent loop currents with these tree links.
(*c*) Show that any branch current of the network graph can be expressed in terms of these independent loop currents.

5.3. Refer to the network graph in Fig. P 5.1e.
(*a*) Find a set of tree branches.
(*b*) Identify a set of independent node-pair potentials with these tree branches.
(*c*) Show that any branch potential of the network graph can be expressed in terms of these independent node-pair potentials.

5.4. Given: The oriented graph in Fig. P 5.4.
(*a*) Obtain its incidence matrix.
(*b*) Use a 5 × 5 matrix to describe the graph. Explain how you define this matrix.

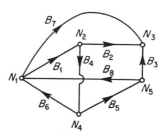

FIG. P 5.4

5.5. The impedance matrix of a three-loop network of the general configuration of Fig. P 5.5 is given as

$$
Z = [Z_{ij}] = \begin{bmatrix} 2s + 3 + \dfrac{1}{2s} & 2 + \dfrac{1}{2s} & -2s \\[2ex] 2 + \dfrac{1}{2s} & 5 + \dfrac{1}{s} & 2 + \dfrac{1}{2s} \\[2ex] -2s & 2 + \dfrac{1}{2s} & 5s + 4 + \dfrac{1}{2s} \end{bmatrix}
$$

Identify the circuit elements together with circuit values in the network.

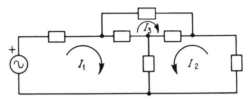

FIG. P 5.5

5.6. Given: The network graph in Fig. P 5.6.

(*a*) Determine the number of independent loop currents.

(*b*) Determine the number of independent node-pair potentials.

Obtain a connected graph by connecting N_a with N_a', and N_b with N_b'; then

(*c*) Obtain a tree of the connected graph.

(*d*) Find the dual of the connected graph.

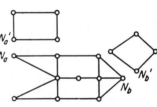

FIG. P 5.6

5.7. Given: The planar graph in Fig. P 5.7.

Find its dual, and show the one-to-one correspondences between *all* quantities and relations listed in (5.18).

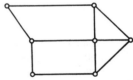

FIG. P 5.7

6 Equivalence, duality, and reciprocal networks

In this chapter we study the relations between networks; these have extensive application in the problems of network synthesis. Although we have briefly studied network equivalence and network duality in the topological (qualitative) sense in Chap. 5, and we now wish to study network equivalence and network duality in the quantitative sense, the omission of Chap. 5 will not be a handicap in the reading of this chapter.

6.1. Network equivalence

Remarks about network equivalence in the topological sense. As discussed in Arts. 5.1 and 5.2 and in (5.2), two networks are said to be *topologically (qualitatively) equivalent* if they have the same geometrical configurations. For example, the two networks in Fig. 5.2*b*1 and 2 are topologically equivalent networks. However, because they have different types of circuit elements in their corresponding network branches, these two networks are expected to have *different* quantitative relations, i.e., voltage-current relations.

Remarks about network equivalence in the voltage-current sense. Two networks, considered as two black boxes with external leads, are said to be equivalent in the voltage-current sense if they have the *same* voltage-current relations in their external leads while operating under identical conditions, e.g., open-circuit, short-circuit, or equal-load conditions. These two networks need not have the same network configuration or circuit-element values. For example, we shall show later that (1) all four networks in Fig. 6.1*b* are equivalent in the voltage-current sense and (2) the two networks in Fig. 6.2*b* are also equivalent in the voltage-current sense.

In this chapter, *we shall consistently use the term "network equivalence" to mean "network equivalence in the voltage-current sense,"* unless otherwise indicated.

A. Description of Network Equivalence

Equivalence of two-terminal networks. A two-terminal network, as depicted in Fig. 6.1*a*, is associated with only one voltage E_1 and one current I_1; its voltage-current relation is described by its driving-point impedance $Z_D(s) = E_1/I_1$ or driving-point admittance $Y_D(s) = I_1/E_1$.

Two 2-terminal networks **A** and **B**, as depicted in Fig. 6.1*a*, are said to be equivalent if (1) they have the same voltage-current relations or (2) their driving-point impedances or admittances are identical; i.e.,

Equivalence for two-terminal networks in Fig. 6.1a:

$$Z_D(s) = Z'_D(s) \quad \text{or} \quad Y_D(s) = Y'_D(s) \tag{6.1}$$

125

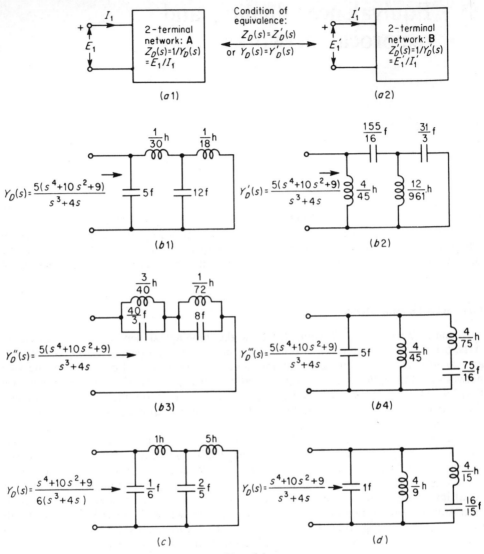

FIG. 6.1

Illustration. By alternately adding admittance and impedance, from left to right, in the network in Fig. 6.1b1 {e.g., impedance of first element $= \frac{1}{18}s$; admittance of first two elements $= 12s + (\frac{1}{18}s)^{-1}$; impedance of first three elements $= \frac{1}{30}s + [12s + (\frac{1}{18}s)^{-1}]^{-1}$; etc.}, we calculate the driving-point admittance

For network in Fig. 6.1b1:

$$Y_D(s) = 5s + \{\tfrac{1}{30}s + [12s + (\tfrac{1}{18}s)^{-1}]^{-1}\}^{-1} = \frac{5(s^4 + 10s^2 + 9)}{s^3 + 4s} \qquad (6.2a)$$

Similarly, for the network in Fig. 6.1b2, we have

For network in Fig. 6.1b2:

$$Y'_D(s) = \frac{5(s^4 + 10s^2 + 9)}{s^3 + 4s} \qquad (6.2b)$$

By taking the reciprocal of the sum of all the series impedances in the network in Fig. 6.1b3, we find

For network in Fig. 6.1b3:

$$Y_D''(s) = \left(\frac{\frac{3}{40}s \times \frac{3}{40}/s}{\frac{3}{40}s + \frac{3}{40}/s} + \frac{\frac{1}{72}s \times \frac{1}{8}/s}{\frac{1}{72}s + \frac{1}{8}/s}\right)^{-1} = \frac{5(s^4 + 10s^2 + 9)}{s^3 + 4s} \qquad (6.2c)$$

By adding all the parallel admittances in the network in Fig. 6.1b4, we find

For network in Fig. 6.1b4:

$$Y_D'''(s) = \frac{5(s^4 + 10s^2 + 9)}{s^3 + 4s} \qquad (6.2d)$$

There are 4 two-terminal networks in Fig. 6.1b having identical driving-point admittances as indicated in Eqs. (6.2); according to (6.1), these are four *equivalent* networks.

If we are given the driving-point admittance function

$$Y_D(s) = \frac{5(s^4 + 10s^2 + 9)}{s^3 + 4s}$$

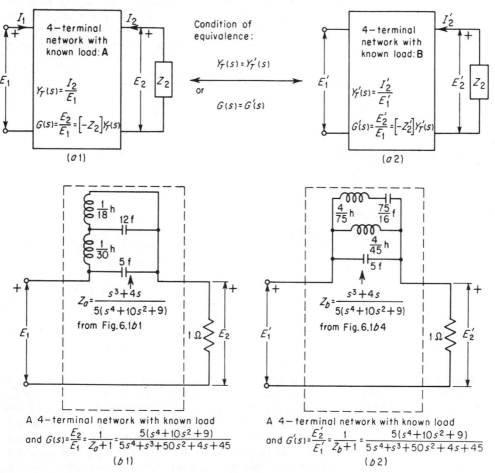

A 4-terminal network with known load
and $G(s) = \dfrac{E_2}{E_1} = \dfrac{1}{Z_a + 1} = \dfrac{5(s^4 + 10s^2 + 9)}{5s^4 + s^3 + 50s^2 + 4s + 45}$

(b1)

A 4-terminal network with known load
and $G'(s) = \dfrac{E_2'}{E_1'} = \dfrac{1}{Z_b + 1} = \dfrac{5(s^4 + 10s^2 + 9)}{5s^4 + s^3 + 50s^2 + 4s + 45}$

(b2)

Fig. 6.2

we may readily find the four networks in Fig. 6.1*b* by established methods of network synthesis. This indicates that network synthesis is not a unique process in the sense that it yields *different* networks for the *same* given specification, say a prescribed network characteristic or a given network function as above; the different results are usually related as equivalent networks.

Potential equivalence of two-terminal networks.   Two 2-terminal networks **A** and **B** are said to be *potentially equivalent* if (1) they have similar voltage-current relations in the sense that, for the same excitation, their responses have the same waveforms but have magnitudes differing by a constant scale factor k [for example, they may have the responses $i_1(t) = \cos \omega t + 2e^{\alpha_1 t} - 3e^{\alpha_2 t}$ and $i_1'(t) = 3(\cos \omega t + 2e^{\alpha_1 t} - 3e^{\alpha_2 t})$ for $k = 3$] or (2) their driving-point impedances or admittances differ only by a constant scale factor k; i.e.,

Potential equivalence for 2 *two-terminal networks:*

$$Z_D(s) = kZ_D'(s) \quad \text{or} \quad Y_D(s) = \frac{1}{k} Y_D'(s) \tag{6.3}$$

Statements 1 and 2 above can be shown to be consistent with each other with the aid of the Laplace-transform methods which will be studied in Chaps. 11 to 13.

Potential equivalence may be described in an alternative way: 2 two-terminal networks are said to be *potentially equivalent* if their driving-point impedances $Z_D(s)$ and $Z_D'(s)$ have the same set of poles and zeros, but differ by a constant.

Illustration.   Any of the four networks in Fig. 6.1*b* whose driving-point admittance is

$$Y_D(s) = \frac{5(s^4 + 10s^2 + 9)}{s^3 + 4s} = \frac{5(s^2 + 1)(s^2 + 9)}{s(s^2 + 4)}$$

$$= \frac{5(s + j)(s - j)(s + j3)(s - j3)}{s(s + j2)(s - j2)} \tag{6.4a}$$

is potentially equivalent to the network in Fig. 6.1*c* whose driving-point admittance is

$$Y_D(s) = \frac{s^4 + 10s^2 + 9}{6(s^3 + 4s)} = \frac{(s + j)(s - j)(s + j3)(s - j3)}{6s(s + j2)(s - j2)} \tag{6.4b}$$

We note that the driving-point admittances in (6.4) differ only by a constant scale factor; they have the same set of poles and zeros.

Similarly, we may establish "potential equivalence" between (1) any network in Fig. 6.1*b* and the network in Fig. 6.1*d* and (2) the network in Fig. 6.1*c* and the network in Fig. 6.1*d*.

Remarks.   With reference to Art. 3.4, we note that two network functions $Z_D(s)$ and $Z_D'(s)$ related in (6.3) must have the *same* normalized form $\bar{Z}_D(s)$; if we use R_0' to normalize $Z_D'(s)$ into $\bar{Z}_D(s)$, we use $R_0 = kR_0'$ to normalize $Z_D(s)$ into $\bar{Z}_D(s)$. The concept of normalization may therefore be considered in this light: *Normalization enables us to study a single network or network function with results applicable to a number of "potentially equivalent" networks.*

Equivalence of four-terminal networks with known load.   For a four-terminal network with a known load as depicted in Fig. 6.2*a*1, we have *one* excitation, say E_1, and *one* interested response, say I_2 (or E_2); there is always a transfer function, say $Y_T(s) = (Y_T)_{21} = I_2/E_1$, relating these two quantities. So far as the voltage-current relation is concerned, a four-terminal network is not unlike a two-terminal network which has *one* excitation, say E_1, *one* response, say I_1, and a driving-point function, say $Y_D = I_1/E_1$, relating these two quantities; we may therefore prescribe "equivalence" relation in a similar manner.

Two 4-terminal networks **A** and **B** with known and equal loads Z_2, as in Fig. 6.2*a*, are said to be equivalent if (1) they have the same voltage-current relations or (2) their corresponding transfer functions relating an interested response to the excitation are identical; i.e.,

Equivalence for four-terminal networks with known loads in Fig. 6.2a:

$$Y_T(s) = Y_T'(s) \qquad \text{or} \qquad G(s) = G'(s) \tag{6.5}$$

We may also use I_1 as the excitation and $Z_T(s) = E_2/I_1$ or $G_i(s) = I_2/I_1$ as the transfer function; the condition of equivalence becomes $Z_T(s) = Z_T'(s)$ or $G_i(s) = G_i'(s)$ instead of (6.5).

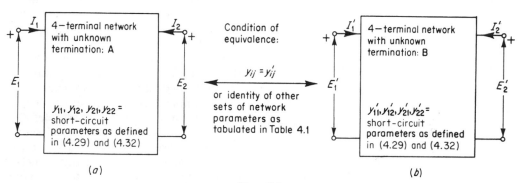

FIG. 6.3

Illustration. We may readily find the transfer voltage-ratio functions $G(s)$ and $G'(s)$ of the four-terminal networks with equal and known loads in Fig. 6.2*b* to be

$$G(s) = G'(s) = \frac{5(s^4 + 10s^2 + 9)}{5s^4 + s^3 + 50s^2 + 4s + 45} \tag{6.6}$$

According to (6.5), these two networks are equivalent.

Equivalence of four-terminal networks with unknown termination. There are two voltages E_1, E_2 and two currents I_1, I_2 associated with the general four-terminal network with unknown termination as depicted in Fig. 6.3*a*. As discussed in Art. 4.2, it takes any one of six sets of network parameters to completely characterize a four-terminal network in the sense that it prescribes the voltage-current relations of the network; for example, the parameters y_{ij} prescribe the voltage-current relations of the network in (4.29).

Two four-terminal networks **A** and **B**, as in Fig. 6.3, are said to be equivalent if (1) they have the same voltage-current relations or (2) their corresponding sets of network parameters are identical; i.e.,

Equivalence for four-terminal networks in Fig. 6.3:

	$y_{11} = y_{11}'$	$y_{12} = y_{12}'$	$y_{21} = y_{21}'$	$y_{22} = y_{22}'$	(6.7*a*)
or	$z_{11} = z_{11}'$	$z_{12} = z_{12}'$	$z_{21} = z_{21}'$	$z_{22}' = z_{22}'$	(6.7*b*)
or	$a = a'$	$b = b'$	$c = c'$	$d = d'$	(6.7*c*)
or	$d^* = (d^*)'$	$b^* = (b^*)'$	$c^* = (c^*)'$	$a^* = (a^*)'$	(6.7*d*)
or	$h_{11} = h_{11}'$	$h_{12} = h_{12}'$	$h_{21} = h_{21}'$	$h_{22} = h_{22}'$	(6.7*e*)
or	$g_{11} = g_{11}'$	$g_{12} = g_{12}'$	$g_{21} = g_{21}'$	$g_{22} = g_{22}'$	(6.7*f*)
or	*Identical sets of other parameters* not yet defined				(6.7*g*)

The first six sets of parameters in (6.7) are defined in Art. 4.2; given one set of parameters for a network, we may readily compute the other five sets with the aid of Table 4.1.

Remarks.   *The remaining portion of Art. 6.1 will be devoted primarily to the "equivalence" of four-terminal networks in the sense described in Fig. 6.3 and Eqs. (6.7).* Illustrations of the equivalence of four-terminal networks will be postponed for the time being and given in Art. 6.1B and C.

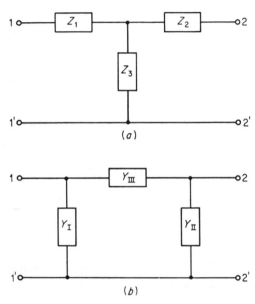

(a)

(b)

FIG. 6.4   (a) T network; (b) Π network.

B. Some Basic Ladder Structures and Their Equivalence

We shall introduce two basic ladder structures commonly used in filters and corrective networks and establish equivalence between them.

The T network.   The T network is shown in Fig. 6.4a, where Z_1, Z_2, and Z_3 are the impedances of its branches.

For simple illustration, we may have two inductances L_1 and L_2 in place of Z_1 and Z_2 in the figure, and a capacitance C_3 in the place of Z_3, where $Z_1 = sL_1$, $Z_2 = sL_2$, and $Z_3 = 1/sC_3$; this T network may be a section of a low-pass filter.

Parameters of the T Network.   In order to use (6.7) to establish equivalence between a T network and any other four-terminal network, we must first find the parameters for the T network.

According to the physical interpretations of z_{ij} in (4.45), we may readily find the open-circuit parameters z_{ij} of the T network in Fig. 6.4a, and from them other sets of parameters, with the aid of Table 4.1.

Parameters of the T network in Fig. 6.4a:

$$z_{11} = Z_1 + Z_3 \qquad z_{12} = Z_3$$
$$z_{21} = Z_3 \qquad z_{22} = Z_2 + Z_3$$
(6.8a)

Other sets of parameters obtained by substituting
z_{ij} from (6.8a) into Table 4.1   (6.8b)

T Network as the Equivalent of an Arbitrary Network.   Solving for Z_1, Z_2, Z_3 in (6.8a), we have

Equivalent T network of an arbitrary network:

$$Z_1 = z_{11} - z_{12} \qquad Z_2 = z_{22} - z_{12} \qquad Z_3 = z_{12}$$
(6.9)

We may readily measure the open-circuit parameters z_{11}, $z_{12} = z_{21}$, and z_{22} of any passive, linear, bilateral network; knowing these parameters, we may substitute them into (6.9), obtaining Z_1, Z_2, Z_3 for the equivalent T network. Illustrations of finding an equivalent T network for a given Π network will be given later.

Remarks about the Equivalent T Network as a Physical Network. It is true that we may always find an equivalent T network for an arbitrary passive, linear, bilateral network mathematically with the aid of (6.9). But is this network physically realizable?

Since z_{11}, z_{12}, z_{21}, z_{22} of the arbitrary network are functions of s, Z_1, Z_2, and Z_3, computed with the aid of (6.9), are also functions of s and are the driving-point impedances of the 3 two-terminal networks in Fig. 6.4a. To find a two-terminal network from its driving-point impedance, for example, Z_1, Z_2, or Z_3 as computed with (6.9), is a problem† of network synthesis and is beyond the scope of this book. However, we shall use the following simple illustrations to explain "physical realizability":

Five simple illustrations:

Assumed form of Z_1 computed with (6.9)	Impedance of known circuit-element combination		
(1)	(2)		
$Z_1 = 2s + 3$	$Z = sL + R$	(series LR)	(6.10a)
$Z_1 = s + 3 + \dfrac{1}{2s}$	$Z = sL + R + \dfrac{1}{sC}$	(series LRC)	(6.10b)
$Z_1 = -3s + 1$	$Z = sL + R$	(series LR)	(6.10c)
$Z_1 = s - 2 + \dfrac{1}{2s}$	$Z = sL + R + \dfrac{1}{sC}$	(series LRC)	(6.10d)
$Z_1 = \dfrac{2s}{s^2 + 3}$	$Z = \dfrac{sL(1/sC)}{sL + 1/sC} = \dfrac{(1/C)s}{s^2 + 1/LC}$	(parallel LC)	(6.10e)

In (6.10a), we find that the driving-point impedance Z_1 is readily realizable with a series combination of an inductance $L = 2$ and a resistance $R = 3$. Similarly, Z_1 in (6.10b) is readily realizable with a series combination of $L = 1$, $R = 3$, and $C = 2$, and Z_1 in (6.10e) with a parallel combination of $L = \frac{2}{3}$ and $C = \frac{1}{2}$. The three driving-point impedances Z_1 in (6.10a), (6.10b), and (6.10e) are said to be *physically realizable* since they can be realized (i.e., synthesized) with physical circuit elements.

On the other hand, Z_1 in (6.10c) may be realized only with a mathematical, i.e., *nonphysical*, network as a series combination of a negative inductance $L = -3$ and a resistance $R = 1$. A negative inductance is not a physical circuit element. This is also true for Z_1 in (6.10d), as a negative resistance $R = -2$ is not physical. Therefore, the driving-point impedances Z_1 in (6.10c) and (6.10d) are said to be *physically nonrealizable*, since they can be realized only with mathematical circuit elements.

We may therefore make the following statement: *For each passive, linear, bilateral four-terminal network, there always exists an equivalent T network; this equivalent T network may or may not be physical.* A nonphysical equivalent T network may possess negative circuit elements.

The Π network. The Π network is shown in Fig. 6.4b, where Y_{I}, Y_{II}, and Y_{III} are the admittances of its branches.

For simple illustration, we may have two capacitances C_1 and C_2 in place of Y_{I} and Y_{II} in the figure, and an inductance L_3 in the place of Y_{III}, where $Y_{\mathrm{I}} = sC_1$, $Y_{\mathrm{II}} = sC_2$, and $Y_{\mathrm{III}} = 1/sL_3$; this Π network may be a section of a low-pass filter.

† For two-terminal network-synthesis problems, see chaps. 3 through 9 of the author's "Linear Network Design and Synthesis" (in press).

Parameters of the Π Network. In order to use (6.7) to establish equivalence between a Π network and any other four-terminal network, we must first find the parameters for the Π network.

According to the physical interpretations of y_{ij} in (4.32), we may readily find the short-circuit parameters y_{ij} of the Π network in Fig. 6.4b, and from them other sets of parameters, with the aid of Table 4.1:

Parameters of the Π network in Fig. 6.4b:

$$y_{11} = Y_\mathrm{I} + Y_\mathrm{III} \qquad y_{12} = -Y_\mathrm{III}$$
$$y_{21} = -Y_\mathrm{III} \qquad y_{22} = Y_\mathrm{II} + Y_\mathrm{III} \tag{6.11a}$$

Other sets of parameters obtained by substituting
y_{ij} from (6.11a) into Table 4.1 $\hfill$ (6.11b)

Π *Network as the Equivalent of an Arbitrary Network.* Solving for Y_I, Y_II, Y_III in (6.11a), we have

Equivalent Π network of an arbitrary network:

$$Y_\mathrm{I} = y_{11} + y_{12} \qquad Y_\mathrm{II} = y_{22} + y_{12} \qquad Y_\mathrm{III} = -y_{12} \tag{6.12}$$

We may readily measure the short-circuit parameters y_{11}, $y_{12} = y_{21}$, and y_{22} of any passive, linear, bilateral network; knowing these parameters, we may substitute them into (6.12), obtaining Y_I, Y_II, Y_III for the equivalent Π network. Like the equivalent T network discussed above, this equivalent Π network may or may not be physical. A nonphysical equivalent Π network may possess negative circuit elements.

T-Π equivalence. Suppose we are given a Π network, as in Fig. 6.4b, whose parameters are available in (6.11), and we wish to find its equivalent T network in the form of Fig. 6.4a. According to the above discussion, we only need (1) find the z_{ij} parameters of the Π network according to (6.11b) [namely, with the substitution of (6.11a) into (b1) of Table 4.1] and (2) substitute these z_{ij} parameters into (6.9), obtaining

$$Z_1 = \frac{y_{22}}{y_{11}y_{22} - y_{12}y_{21}} - \frac{-y_{12}}{y_{11}y_{22} - y_{12}y_{21}} \qquad \text{replacing } y_{ij} \text{ with (6.11a)} \quad (6.13)$$

and similar expressions for Z_2 and Z_3, which are readily reducible to

Equivalent T network of a given Π network with notations indicated in Fig. 6.4:

$$Z_1 = \frac{Y_\mathrm{II}}{Y_\mathrm{I}Y_\mathrm{II} + Y_\mathrm{II}Y_\mathrm{III} + Y_\mathrm{III}Y_\mathrm{I}}$$

$$Z_2 = \frac{Y_\mathrm{I}}{Y_\mathrm{I}Y_\mathrm{II} + Y_\mathrm{II}Y_\mathrm{III} + Y_\mathrm{III}Y_\mathrm{I}} \tag{6.14}$$

$$Z_3 = \frac{Y_\mathrm{III}}{Y_\mathrm{I}Y_\mathrm{II} + Y_\mathrm{II}Y_\mathrm{III} + Y_\mathrm{III}Y_\mathrm{I}}$$

Since terminals $1'$ and $2'$ in Fig. 6.4 are directly connected, we actually have only three terminals in each network. The T and Π networks may then also be called Y and Δ networks because of their configurations. Equations (6.14) are often considered the equations for a Δ-Y transformation.

Similarly, we may find the equivalent Π network for a given T network by (1) finding the y_{ij} parameters of the T network according to (6.8b) [namely, with the substitution of (6.8a) into (a2) of Table 4.1] and (2) substituting these y_{ij} parameters into (6.12), obtaining

Equivalent Π network of a given T network with notations indicated in Fig. 6.4:

$$Y_{\mathrm{I}} = \frac{Z_2}{Z_1 Z_2 + Z_2 Z_3 + Z_3 Z_1}$$

$$Y_{\mathrm{II}} = \frac{Z_1}{Z_1 Z_2 + Z_2 Z_3 + Z_3 Z_1} \qquad (6.15)$$

$$Y_{\mathrm{III}} = \frac{Z_3}{Z_1 Z_2 + Z_2 Z_3 + Z_3 Z_1}$$

Equations (6.15) are often considered the equations for a Y-Δ transformation. The Δ-Y transformations in (6.14) and (6.15) are much used in the study of electric power systems.

C. Lattice Structure; Its Equivalence with Other Symmetrical Networks

A lattice, as a basic network structure, is shown in Fig. 6.5a1. Network synthesis using lattices is often simple compared with that using other network configurations.

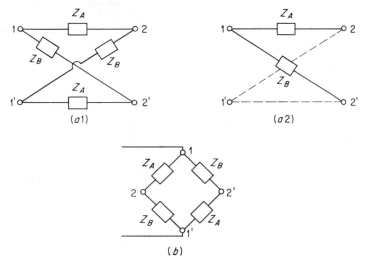

FIG. 6.5   (*a*1) Lattice; (*a*2) representation; (*b*) lattice as a bridge circuit.

However, a lattice is a balanced circuit and therefore does not provide a common ground between the input and output terminal pairs. Note that, unlike those in the T and Π networks in Fig. 6.4, 1' and 2' in Fig. 6.5a1 do not form a common terminal. This is certainly a disadvantage with regard to application.

Although Fig. 6.5a1 depicts the actual lattice structure, it is customary to use the symbolic representation in Fig. 6.5a2 to indicate a lattice.

Characterization of the lattice. We shall now find some of the sets of network parameters associated with a lattice. As remarked in Art. 4.2, each set of four network parameters completely characterizes a four-terminal network in the sense that it prescribes the voltage-current relations of the network.

The Parameters z_{ij} of a Lattice.   It is easy to see that the lattice in Fig. 6.5a1 may be conveniently represented as the bridge circuit in Fig. 6.5b.

According to the physical interpretations of the open-circuit parameters z_{ij} in (4.45a), we may readily find

$$z_{11} = \begin{pmatrix} driving\text{-}point\ impedance \\ looking\ into\ terminal \\ pair\ 11'\ in\ Fig.\ 6.5b \end{pmatrix}_{\substack{terminal\ pair \\ 22'\ open\text{-}circuited}} = \tfrac{1}{2}(Z_A + Z_B) \tag{6.16a}$$

$$z_{21} = \left(\frac{E_2}{I_1}\right)_{\substack{terminal\ pair \\ 22'\ open\text{-}circuited \\ or\ I_2 = 0}} = \left(\frac{V_2 - V_{2'}}{I_1}\right)_{I_2 = 0}^{\dagger} = \frac{(I_1/2)Z_B - (I_1/2)Z_A}{I_1} = \frac{Z_B - Z_A}{2}$$

$$\tag{6.16b}$$

With the aid of (4.45b), we may also find z_{12} and z_{22}.   However, since the lattice is a symmetrical bilateral network, we expect that $z_{11} = z_{22}$ and $z_{12} = z_{21}$, and, therefore, we need not obtain z_{22} and z_{21} independently.   Summarizing, the lattice as depicted in Fig. 6.5a has the following open-circuit parameters:

Parameters z_{ij} of the lattice in Fig. 6.5a:

$$z_{11} = z_{22} = \tfrac{1}{2}(Z_A + Z_B) \qquad z_{12} = z_{21} = \tfrac{1}{2}(Z_B - Z_A) \tag{6.17}$$

The Parameters y_{ij} of a Lattice.   Labeling the circuit elements in Fig. 6.5a and b with their admittances $Y_A = 1/Z_A$ and $Y_B = 1/Z_B$ instead of their impedances Z_A and Z_B, taking advantage of the physical interpretations of the short-circuit parameters y_{ij} in (4.32), and following steps and discussion similar to those that led to Eqs. (6.16) and (6.17), we find the short-circuit parameters of the lattice:

Parameters y_{ij} of the lattice in Fig. 6.5a:

$$y_{11} = y_{22} = \frac{1}{2}(Y_A + Y_B) = \frac{1}{2}\left(\frac{1}{Z_A} + \frac{1}{Z_B}\right)$$

$$\tag{6.18}$$

$$y_{12} = y_{21} = \frac{1}{2}(Y_B - Y_A) = \frac{1}{2}\left(\frac{1}{Z_B} - \frac{1}{Z_A}\right)$$

Four Other Sets of Parameters of a Lattice as Defined in Art. 4.2.   We have defined six sets of parameters associated with a four-terminal network in Art. 4.2 and listed them in Table 4.1.

Now, knowing the z_{ij} parameters of a lattice in (6.17), we may readily find the other sets of parameters with the aid of (a2), (c2), (d2), (e2), and (f2) of Table 4.1; knowing the y_{ij} parameters of a lattice in (6.18), we may find the other sets of parameters with the aid of (b1), (c1), (d1), (e1), and (f1) of Table 4.1.

Additional sets of parameters for the characterization of the lattice.   We have either obtained or discussed methods for obtaining the six sets of network parameters of a lattice as defined in Art. 4.2.   But are there other sets of network parameters suitable for a lattice?

From (6.17) and (6.18), we note that it takes only *two* independent parameters (the remaining two parameters of the set are dependent parameters) to characterize a lattice structure.   Let us now try to find some additional sets of two parameters to characterize a lattice.

---

† Injecting current I_1 into terminal 1 in Fig. 6.5b, we have current $I_1/2$ in each of the two branches 121' and 12'1'. E_2, being the potential across 22', is then equal to $V_2 - V_{2'}$, where $V_2 = (I_1/2)Z_B$ is the potential across 21', and $V_{2'} = (I_1/2)Z_A$ is the potential across 2'1'.

The Open-circuit and Short-circuit Impedances z_{oc} and z_{sc} of a Whole Lattice as Lattice Parameters. We shall utilize the "whole network," i.e., the "whole lattice" in Fig. 6.5*a*. We open-circuit one terminal pair, say 22' (it does not matter which pair we use, because the lattice is a "symmetrical network"), and measure the driving-point impedance at the other terminal pair, say 11', calling it the *open-circuit imped-ance z_{oc}*. We then short-circuit one terminal pair, say 22', and measure the driving-point impedance at the other terminal pair, say 11', calling it the *short-circuit impedance z_{sc}*.

We now have a set of two parameters to characterize a lattice:

Set of "whole-network" parameters of a lattice (definitions):

z_{oc} = driving-point impedance Z_D at one terminal pair 11' (or 22') with
      other terminal pair 22' (or 11') *open-circuited*   (6.19*a*)

z_{sc} = Z_D at one terminal pair 11' (or 22') with other pair *short-circuited*   (6.19*b*)

Comparing (6.19) with (4.45) and (4.32), we see that

$$z_{oc} = z_{11} \qquad z_{sc} = \frac{1}{y_{11}} \tag{6.20}$$

Substituting z_{11} and y_{11} from (6.17) and (6.18) into (6.20), we readily find the parameters z_{oc} and z_{sc} of a lattice:

Parameters z_{oc} and z_{sc} of the lattice in Fig. 6.5a:

$$z_{oc} = \frac{1}{2}(Z_A + Z_B) \qquad z_{sc} = \frac{2}{Y_A + Y_B} = \frac{2Z_A Z_B}{Z_A + Z_B} \tag{6.21}$$

From (6.21), we also note an interesting property of these parameters:

$$z_{oc} z_{sc} = Z_A Z_B$$

The Open-circuit and Short-circuit Impedances Z_{oc} and Z_{sc} of a "Half Lattice" as Lattice Parameters. Because of the symmetry of a lattice with respect to its two terminal pairs, we may use one-half of the lattice to define a set of two network parameters to characterize the lattice itself.

Let us split the lattice in the middle as in Fig. 6.6*a* and utilize a "half network," i.e., a "half lattice." We define the *open-circuit impedance Z_{oc}* and *short-circuit impedance Z_{sc}* in the following manner:

Set of "half-network" parameters of a lattice (definitions):

Z_{oc} = driving-point impedance Z_D at terminal pair 11' with terminals at
      other end of "half network" *open-circuited*, with the exception of
      cross-element terminals, as in Fig. 6.6*b*   (6.22*a*)

Z_{sc} = Z_D at 11' with terminals at other end of "half-network" *short-circuited*
      with the exception of cross-element terminals, as in Fig. 6.6*c*   (6.22*b*)

We now have another set of two parameters to characterize a lattice.

For the typical lattice structure in Fig. 6.5*a*, split in Fig. 6.6 to obtain the param-eters Z_{oc} and Z_{sc} as defined in (6.22), we may readily evaluate these parameters by examining Fig. 6.6*b* and *c*, obtaining

Parameters Z_{oc} and Z_{sc} of the lattice in Fig. 6.5a:

$$Z_{oc} = \frac{Z_B}{2} + \frac{Z_B}{2} = Z_B \qquad Z_{sc} = \frac{Z_A}{2} + \frac{Z_A}{2} = Z_A \tag{6.23}$$

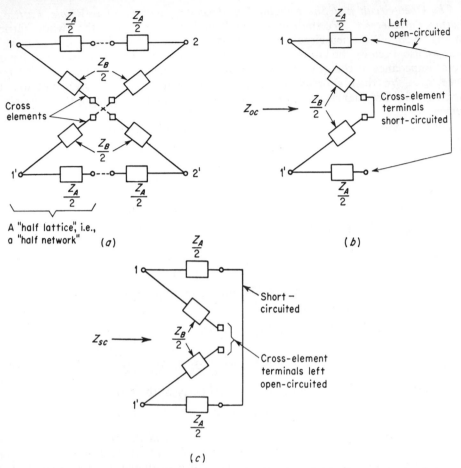

FIG. 6.6   (a) Splitting in the middle to obtain a half lattice; (b) finding open-circuit imped-ance Z_{oc}; (c) finding short-circuit impedance Z_{sc}.

Remarks about the "whole-network" and "half-network" parameters of a symmetrical network.   Let us first try to differentiate between the two general categories of network parameters.

The "Whole-network" Parameters.   In the preceding paragraphs we have obtained various sets of parameters of a symmetrical network, a "lattice" in this particular instance.

We note that, in the process of obtaining the z_{ij} parameters in (6.17), the y_{ij} parameters in (6.18), the four other sets of parameters (defined in Art. 4.2) in the paragraph following (6.18), and the z_{oc} and z_{sc} parameters, we have used the "whole network." We shall therefore call these sets of parameters the "whole-network" parameters.

"Whole-network" parameters:

z_{ij} as defined in Art. 4.2	(6.24a)
y_{ij} as defined in Art. 4.2	(6.24b)
Four other sets of parameters defined in Art. 4.2	(6.24c)
z_{oc} and z_{sc} as defined in (6.19)	(6.24d)

The "Half-network" Parameters. We also note that, in the process of obtaining the Z_{oc} and Z_{sc} parameters in (6.22), we have used a "half network." We shall therefore call this set of parameters the "half-network" parameters.

"Half-network" parameters:

> Z_{oc} and Z_{sc}, as defined in (6.22) for a lattice and defined in (6.26) for
> a general symmetrical network   (6.25)

"Half-network" Parameters of a General Symmetrical Network. The "half-network" parameters Z_{oc} and Z_{sc} in (6.22) are defined for a lattice network. We shall now consider the general symmetrical network in Fig. 6.7a.

Let us first split this network in the middle as in Fig. 6.7b and use a "half network." We define the *open-circuit impedance* Z_{oc} and *short-circuit impedance* Z_{sc} in the following manner:

Set of "half-network" parameters of a symmetrical network (definitions):

$Z_{oc} = $ driving-point impedance Z_D at terminal pair 11′ with terminals at
           other end of "half network" *open-circuited* with exception of cross-
           element terminals, as in Fig. 6.7c   (6.26a)

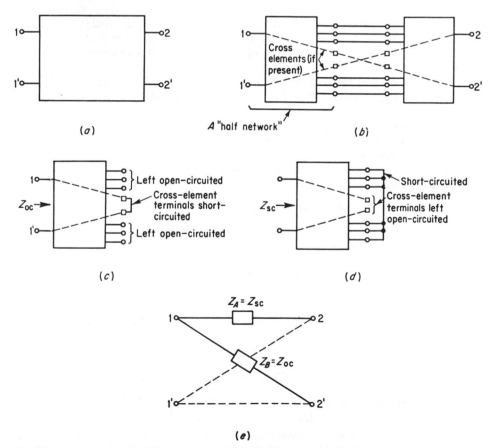

FIG. 6.7   (a) Symmetrical network; (b) splitting in the middle; (c) finding open-circuit impedance Z_{oc}; (d) finding short-circuit impedance Z_{sc}; (e) equivalent lattice.

$Z_{sc} = Z_D$ at 11' with terminals at other end of "half network" *short-circuited* with exception of cross-element terminals, as in Fig. 6.7d   (6.26b)

An illustration of finding Z_{oc} and Z_{sc} for a lattice has been given in Fig. 6.6 and Eqs. (6.23). Illustrations of finding Z_{oc} and Z_{sc} for symmetrical ladder networks will be postponed until Art. 6.1E.

Lattice as the equivalent of an arbitrary symmetrical network obtained with the aid of "whole-network" parameters. Solving for Z_A and Z_B from (6.17) *or* Y_A and Y_B in (6.18), we have

Equivalent lattice of any symmetrical network:

$$Z_A = z_{11} - z_{12} \qquad Z_B = z_{11} + z_{12} \qquad (6.27)$$

Alternative of the above:

$$Y_A = \frac{1}{Z_A} = y_{11} - y_{12} \qquad Y_B = \frac{1}{Z_B} = y_{11} + y_{12} \qquad (6.28)$$

We may readily measure the open-circuit parameters z_{11} and z_{12} *or* the short-circuit parameters y_{11} and y_{12} of any passive, linear, bilateral, symmetrical network; knowing z_{11} and z_{12}, we may substitute them into (6.27), obtaining Z_A and Z_B for the equivalent lattice in the form of Fig. 6.5a; *or* knowing the short-circuit parameters y_{11} and y_{12}, we may substitute them into (6.28), obtaining $Y_A = 1/Z_A$ and $Y_B = 1/Z_B$ for the equivalent lattice. This means that *we may use either* (6.27) *or* (6.28) *to obtain the equivalent lattice of an arbitrary passive, linear, bilateral symmetrical network; this equivalent lattice,* like the equivalent T network discussed above, *may or may not be physical.*

Remarks. We have introduced in (6.27) and (6.28) two alternative approaches for obtaining an equivalent lattice for any symmetrical network with the aid of the two sets of "whole-network" parameters z_{ij} and y_{ij}.

Similarly, we may introduce additional alternative approaches using other sets of "whole-network" parameters; all these alternative approaches will result in the same equivalent lattice.

Lattice as the equivalent of an arbitrary symmetrical network obtained with the aid of "half-network" parameters. Solving for Z_A and Z_B from (6.23), we have

Equivalent lattice of any symmetrical network:

$$Z_A = Z_{sc} \qquad Z_B = Z_{oc} \qquad (6.29)$$

For any passive, linear, bilateral, symmetrical network, we may readily measure the "half-network" parameters Z_{sc} and Z_{oc} according to their definitions in (6.26); knowing Z_{sc} and Z_{oc} and substituting them in (6.29), we may find Z_A and Z_B of the equivalent lattice in the form of Fig. 6.5a.

Remarks. Equations (6.29) introduce an alternative approach for obtaining an equivalent lattice for any symmetrical network. This approach will yield the same result as the approaches in (6.27) and (6.28).

The approaches in (6.27) and (6.28) will be used in Art. 6.1D in finding the equivalent lattice of some ladder structures (T networks, Π networks, etc.); the approach in (6.29) will be used in Art. 6.1E. Their results are consistent.

D. *Equivalence between Symmetrical Ladder Structure and Lattice as Established with the Aid of "Whole-network" Parameters*

We shall use the z_{ij} and y_{ij} parameters here; these parameters are called "whole-network" parameters in (6.24) to distinguish them from the "half-network" parameters in (6.25).

Equivalence between a lattice and a T network. We shall now use the z_{ij} parameters and impose the conditions in (6.7) to establish equivalence between a lattice and a symmetrical T network.

Given a Lattice, to Find Its Equivalent T Network. Suppose we are given the lattice in Fig. 6.8a2 whose parameters are available in (6.17) to (6.19), and we wish to find its equivalent symmetrical T network in the form of Fig. 6.8a1. According

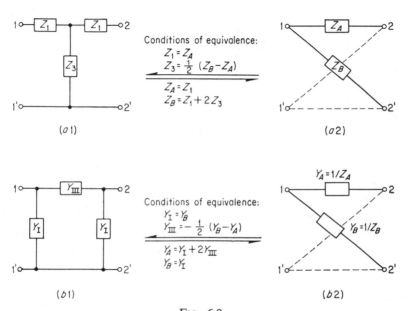

Conditions of equivalence:
$$Z_1 = Z_A$$
$$Z_3 = \tfrac{1}{2}(Z_B - Z_A)$$
$$\overline{\qquad\qquad}$$
$$Z_A = Z_1$$
$$Z_B = Z_1 + 2Z_3$$

(a1)   (a2)

Conditions of equivalence:
$$Y_1 = Y_B$$
$$Y_{III} = -\tfrac{1}{2}(Y_B - Y_A)$$
$$\overline{\qquad\qquad}$$
$$Y_A = Y_1 + 2Y_{III}$$
$$Y_B = Y_1$$

(b1)   (b2)

FIG. 6.8

to Art. 6.1B, we need only substitute the z_{ij} parameters of the lattice in (6.17) into (6.9), whose Z_2 in Fig. 6.4a now becomes another Z_1 in Fig. 6.8a1. We obtain

Equivalent T network for a given lattice with notation in Fig. 6.8a:

$$Z_1 = Z_A \qquad Z_3 = \tfrac{1}{2}(Z_B - Z_A) \tag{6.30}$$

Given a T Network, to Find Its Equivalent Lattice. We may find the equivalent lattice of a given symmetrical T network by (1) substituting the z_{ij} parameters of the T network in (6.8a) into (6.27) *or* (2) solving for Z_A and Z_B in (6.30), obtaining

Equivalent lattice of a given T network with notation in Fig. 6.8a:

$$Z_A = Z_1 \qquad Z_B = Z_1 + 2Z_3 \tag{6.31}$$

Remarks. If we compare the T network and lattice as two equivalent networks in Fig. 6.8a, we note that the T network provides a common ground for the input and output terminal pairs, while its equivalent lattice does not.

Figure 6.8b depicts a Π network and a lattice as two equivalent networks; their equivalent relations will be studied in the following paragraphs.

Equivalence between a lattice and a Π network. We shall now use the y_{ij} parameters and impose the conditions in (6.7) to establish equivalence between a lattice and a symmetrical Π network.

Given a Lattice, to Find Its Equivalent Π Network. Suppose we are given the lattice in Fig. 6.8b2 whose parameters are available in (6.17) to (6.19), and we wish

T network:

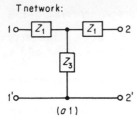

(a1)

Split in the middle:

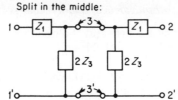

(a2)

Its equivalent lattice:

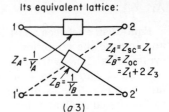

$$Z_A = Z_{sc} = Z_1$$
$$Z_B = Z_{oc} = Z_1 + 2Z_3$$

(a3)

Π network:

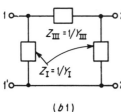

$Z_{III} = 1/Y_{III}$

$Z_I = 1/Y_I$

(b1)

Split in the middle:

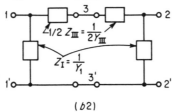

$\frac{1}{2}Z_{III} = \frac{1}{2Y_{III}}$

$Z_I = \frac{1}{Y_I}$

(b2)

Its equivalent lattice (as above) with:

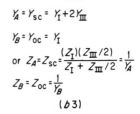

$$Y_A = Y_{sc} = Y_I + 2Y_{III}$$
$$Y_B = Y_{oc} = Y_I$$

or $Z_A = Z_{sc} = \dfrac{(Z_I)(Z_{III}/2)}{Z_I + Z_{III}/2} = \dfrac{1}{Y_A}$

$Z_B = Z_{oc} = \dfrac{1}{Y_B}$

(b3)

Lattice network:

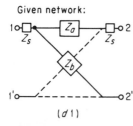

(c1)

Split in the middle:

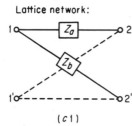

(c2)

Its equivalent lattice (as above) with:

$$Z_A = Z_{sc} = \frac{1}{2}Z_a + \frac{1}{2}Z_a = Z_a$$
$$Z_B = Z_{oc} = \frac{1}{2}Z_b + \frac{1}{2}Z_b = Z_b$$

with reference made to

Fig. 6.6b and c

(c3)

Given network:

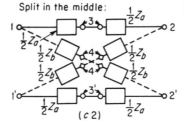

Z_s

(d1)

Split in the middle:

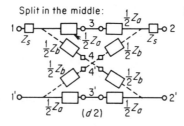

(d2)

Its equivalent lattice (as above) with:

$$Z_A = Z_{sc} = Z_s + \frac{1}{2}Z_a + \frac{1}{2}Z_a$$
$$= Z_s + Z_a$$
$$Z_B = Z_{oc} = Z_s + \frac{1}{2}Z_b + \frac{1}{2}Z_b$$
$$= Z_s + Z_b$$

(d3)

Given network:

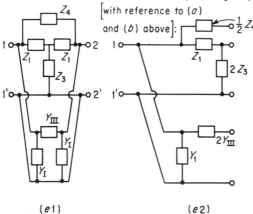

(e1)

Split in the middle, showing only the left half [with reference to (a) and (b) above]:

$\frac{1}{2}Z_4$

Z_1

$2Z_3$

$2Y_{III}$

Y_I

(e2)

Its equivalent lattice (as above) with:

$Z_A = Z_{sc}$ = impedance of 4

parallel elements marked

$Z_4/2$, Z_1, $2Y_{III}$, and Y_I

$$= \frac{1}{\left(\dfrac{Z_4}{2}\right)^{-1} + (Z_1)^{-1} + 2Y_{III} + Y_I}$$

$Z_B = Z_{oc}$ = impedance of 2

parallel elements marked

$Z_1 + 2Z_3$ and Y_I

$$= \frac{1}{(Z_1 + 2Z_3)^{-1} + Y_I}$$

(e3)

FIG. 6.9

to find its equivalent symmetrical Π network in the form of Fig. 6.8b1. According to Art. 6.1B, we only need to substitute the y_{ij} parameters of the lattice in (6.18) into (6.12), where Y_{II} in Fig. 6.4b now becomes another Y_{I} in Fig. 6.8b1. We obtain

Equivalent Π network for a given lattice with notation in Fig. 6.8b:

$$Y_{\mathrm{I}} = Y_B \qquad Y_{\mathrm{III}} = -\tfrac{1}{2}(Y_B - Y_A) \tag{6.32}$$

Given a Π Network, to Find Its Equivalent Lattice. We may find the equivalent lattice of a given symmetrical Π network by (1) substituting the y_{ij} parameters of the Π network in (6.8b) into (6.28) *or* (2) solving for Y_A and Y_B in (6.32), obtaining

Equivalent lattice for a given Π network with notation in Fig. 6.8b:

$$Y_A = Y_{\mathrm{I}} + 2Y_{\mathrm{III}} \qquad Y_B = Y_{\mathrm{I}} \tag{6.33}$$

E. Equivalence between Symmetrical Network and Lattice as Established with the "Half-network" Parameters

We shall use the Z_{oc} and Z_{sc} parameters here. These parameters are called "half-network parameters" in (6.25).

Procedure for finding the equivalent lattice of an arbitrary symmetrical network.† We have already discussed and found a method for obtaining the equivalent lattice of an arbitrary symmetrical network in (6.29). We shall now formalize this method into a procedure for ready application.

Finding the equivalent lattice of a symmetrical network:

Split the given symmetrical network in the middle, obtaining a "half network" as in Fig. 6.7b	(6.34a)
Obtain the open-circuit impedance Z_{oc} of the half network in the manner described in (6.26a) and Fig. 6.7c	(6.34b)
Obtain the short-circuit impedance Z_{sc} of the half network in the manner described in (6.26b) and Fig. 6.7d	(6.34c)
The equivalent lattice now has the form of Fig. 6.7e, where $Z_A = Z_{\mathrm{sc}}$ and $Z_B = Z_{\mathrm{oc}}$	(6.34d)

Illustration 1. Finding the equivalent lattice of a symmetrical T network. We (1) split the symmetrical T network in Fig. 6.9a1 in the middle as in Fig. 6.9a2, (2) obtain $Z_{\mathrm{oc}} = Z_1 + 2Z_3$ according to (6.34b), (3) obtain $Z_{\mathrm{sc}} = Z_1$ according to (6.34c), and (4) find an equivalent lattice as in Fig. 6.9a3.

Our present result is found to check with our earlier result in (6.31) and Fig. 6.8a.

Illustration 2. Finding the equivalent lattice of a symmetrical Π network. For the symmetrical Π network in Fig. 6.9b1, we again follow (6.34), obtaining the equivalent lattice in Fig. 6.9b3.

Our present result checks with our earlier result in (6.33) and Fig. 6.8b.

Illustration 3. Finding the equivalent lattice of a given lattice. We note that the procedure in (6.34) works and yields correct results for symmetrical ladder structures in the two preceding illustrations. We now wish to find out if the procedure in (6.34) also works for lattice and modified-lattice networks.

We shall now apply the procedure in (6.34) to a given lattice and expect that its equivalent lattice (i.e., the result of the procedure) will be identical with the given lattice.

Consider the lattice in Fig. 6.9c1; splitting it in the middle in Fig. 6.9c2 and

† This method is due to Bartlett and is generally known as the *bisection theorem.* See A. C. Bartlett, "The Theory of Electrical Artificial Lines and Filters," p. 28, John Wiley & Sons, Inc., New York, 1930.

following the procedure in (6.34), we obtain the equivalent lattice in Fig. 6.9c3, identical with the given lattice in Fig. 6.9c1.

Illustration 4.   Finding the equivalent lattice of a modified lattice.   We apply the procedure in (6.34) to the modified lattice in Fig. 6.9d1, obtaining the equivalent lattice in Fig. 6.9d3.

Illustration 5.   Finding the equivalent lattice of a bridged-T network in parallel with a Π network.   Figure 6.9e provides an illustration of the procedure.

F. *Identification of Circuit Elements in Equivalent Networks*

Description of problem.   In the procedure and illustrations of finding equivalent networks in preceding sections, we used impedances Z and admittances Y to identify each network branch of the equivalent network.   Actually, we are interested in the equivalent network with identified circuit elements, that is, L's, R's, and C's rather than impedance Z's and admittance Y's.

As remarked in the paragraph preceding Eqs. (6.10), the Z's are the driving-point impedances of some two-terminal networks, and the Y's are the driving-point admittances of some additional two-terminal networks.   These two-terminal networks may be found with special synthesis techniques, and the equivalent network with identified circuit elements obtained.

But are synthesis techniques essential in finding equivalent networks with identified circuit elements?   We shall find answers in the following paragraphs.

Category 1.   *Given a Network, to Find the Equivalent T or Π Network with Identified Circuit Elements.*   For problems of this category, we must use the approach in (6.9) or similar approaches to find the equivalent T network *or* the approach in (6.12) or similar approaches to find the equivalent Π network.   The remarks in the paragraph preceding Eqs. (6.10) are applicable here.

With the exception of some simple cases such as those listed under Category 3 below, it is in general *essential* to use the synthesis approach to obtain the equivalent networks with identified circuit elements.

Category 2.   *Given a Symmetrical Network, to Find the Equivalent Lattice with Circuit Elements Identified.*   It is *not essential* at all to use the synthesis approach for the problems of this category.

We shall discuss in this section how to use the procedure in (6.34) in conjunction with Table 6.1 to obtain solutions of the problems of this category.

Category 3.   *Given a Lattice, to Find the Equivalent Modified Lattice (Whose Special Cases Include Some Particular Symmetrical T Networks, Π Networks, and Ladder Networks) with Identified Circuit Elements.*   Again, it is *not essential* to use the synthesis approach for the problems of this category.

In Art. 6.1G, we shall (1) derive some theorems with the aid of (6.34) and (2) use these theorems in conjunction with Table 6.1 to obtain solutions of the problems of this category.

Finding the equivalent network with identified circuit elements.   If we examine the equivalent lattices of some given networks in Fig. 6.9, column 3, as results of the procedure in (6.34), we note that their Z_A and Z_B network branches all consist in (1) *series connections* (as the "sum of impedances," for example, $Z_B = Z_1 + 2Z_3$) of circuit-element combinations marked with Z's, $2Z$'s, $\frac{1}{2}Z$'s, Y's, $2Y$'s, and $\frac{1}{2}Y$'s, where Z's and Y's represent network branches of the given networks as in Fig. 6.9, column 1, (2) *parallel connections* (as the "sum of admittances," for example, $Y_A = Y_I + 2Y_{III}$) of these circuit-element combinations, and (3) *series-and-then-parallel* (e.g., the parallel combination of the series connection $Z_1 + 2Z_3$ and the element Y_I) or *parallel-and-then-series connections* of these circuit-element combinations.

Table 6.1

1. Circuit elements associated with Z or Y (as $Y = Z^{-1}$)	2. Circuit elements associated with $2Z$ or $Y/2$ $\left[\text{as } Y/2 = (2Z)^{-1}\right]$	3. Circuit elements associated with $Z/2$ or $2Y$ $\left[\text{as } 2Y = (Z/2)^{-1}\right]$
(a1) C	(a2) $\dfrac{C}{2}$	(a3) $2C$
(b1) L	(b2) $2L$	(b3) $\dfrac{1}{2}L$
(c1) R	(c2) $2R$	(c3) $\dfrac{1}{2}R$
(d1) L, C	(d2) $2L$, $\dfrac{C}{2}$	(d3) $\dfrac{1}{2}L$, $2C$
(e1) L, C	(e2) $2L$, $\dfrac{C}{2}$	(e3) $\dfrac{L}{2}$, $2C$
(f1) L_1, R, L_2, C	(f2) $2L_1$, $2R$, $2L_2$, $\dfrac{C}{2}$	(f3) $\dfrac{1}{2}L_1$, $\dfrac{1}{2}R$, $\dfrac{1}{2}L_2$, $2C$
(g1) **Any circuit configuration with:** 1. Inductances $L_1, L_2, \ldots, L_m$ 2. Capacitances $C_1, C_2, \ldots, C_n$ 3. Resistances $R_1, R_2, \ldots, R_K$	(g2) Same circuit configuration with: 1. $2L_1, 2L_2, \ldots, 2L_m$ 2. $C_1/2, C_2/2, \ldots, C_n/2$ 3. $2R_1, 2R_2, \ldots, 2R_K$	(g3) Same circuit configuration with: 1. $L_1/2, L_2/2, \ldots, L_m/2$ 2. $2C_1, 2C_2, \ldots, 2C_n$ 3. $R_1/2, R_2/2, \ldots, R_K/2$

Let us first list all possible circuit-element combinations which may be used as network branches marked Z or Y in the given network in Table 6.1, column 1. It is very easy to work out the corresponding circuit elements for $2Z$, $Y/2$, $Z/2$, and $2Y$, thus completing Table 6.1. For example, $Z = sL + 1/sC$ being the impedance of the circuit-element combination in $(d1)$ of Table 6.1, the impedance of the circuit-element combination $(d2)$ is readily found to be $s(2L) + 1/s(C/2) = 2sL + 2/sC = 2Z$. We may now use Table 6.1 for the circuit elements marked with $2Z$'s, $\frac{1}{2}Z$'s, Y's, and $\frac{1}{2}Y$'s in the equivalent network.

Summarizing, we may use the following procedure to find the equivalent lattice with circuit elements identified for a given symmetrical network:

Finding the equivalent lattice with identified circuit elements for a given symmetrical network:

Follow the procedure in (6.34), obtaining an equivalent lattice whose network branches Z_A and Z_B are represented as various connections of circuit-element combinations marked with Z's, $2Z$'s, $\frac{1}{2}Z$'s, Y's, $2Y$'s, and $\frac{1}{2}Y$'s, where Z's and Y's represent the network branches, with known circuit elements, of the given network   (6.35a)

Identify each circuit-element combination marked with a Z or Y in the given network with an entry in Table 6.1, column 1, and find its corresponding circuit-element combinations as entries in column 2 or 3 of the table for $2Z$, $\frac{1}{2}Y$, $\frac{1}{2}Z$, and $2Y$ (6.35b)

Use the circuit-element combinations for Z's and Y's from the given network, and $2Z$'s, $\frac{1}{2}Y$'s, $\frac{1}{2}Z$'s, and $2Y$'s from Table 6.1 obtained in (6.35b), in the equivalent lattice obtained in (6.35a); we now have an equivalent lattice with identified circuit elements   (6.35c)

Illustration 1. Let us try to find the equivalent lattice with identified circuit elements of the symmetrical T network in Fig. 6.10a1.

Following the procedure in (6.35), we (1) find the equivalent lattice with *un*identified circuit elements in Fig. 6.9a3, (2) identify Z_3 and $2Z_3$ with $(a1)$ and $(a2)$ of Table 6.1, obtaining $C_3/2 = 2$ farads for the element marked $2Z_3$, and (3) obtain the equivalent lattice with identified circuit elements in Fig. 6.10a2.

Illustration 2. For the symmetrical T network in Fig. 6.10b1, we again follow (6.35), with the aid of Table 6.1, to obtain the equivalent lattice with identified circuit elements in Fig. 6.10b2.

Illustration 3. For the symmetrical Π network in Fig. 6.10c1, we again follow (6.35), with the aid of Table 6.1, to obtain the equivalent lattice with identified circuit elements in Fig. 6.10c2.

Illustration 4. For the rather complicated symmetrical network in Fig. 6.10d1, we obtain the equivalent lattice with identified circuit elements in Fig. 6.10d2 by again following (6.35).

G. Generalization of Earlier Results on Equivalence

Theorem A. *For a lattice whose Z_A and Z_B branches have a common series impedance Z_s as in Fig. 6.11a1, we may readily remove Z_s, obtaining a modified lattice in the form of Fig. 6.11a2 as the equivalent network. Z_s may represent the impedance of a single circuit element or a circuit-element combination.*

To prove Theorem A, we need only prove that the two networks in Fig. 6.11a are equivalent. This may be readily accomplished by applying (6.34) to the network in Fig. 6.11a2 and obtaining its equivalent lattice in Fig. 6.11a1. Reference is made to Fig. 6.9d for actually carrying out this procedure.

Illustration A1.   Reduction of a lattice whose Z_A and Z_B branches both have series inductances.   Let us now consider a lattice in the form of Fig. 6.11b1.

For $L_2 \geq L_1$.   For $L_2 \geq L_1$, we may consider that the Z_A and Z_B branches in Fig. 6.11b1 have a common series impedance $Z_s = sL_1$; the larger inductance $L_2 = L_1 + L_2 - L_1 = L_1 + L_b$ is equivalent to two inductances L_1 and L_b in series.   By removing $Z_s = sL_1$, that is, a circuit element L_1 whose impedance is Z_s, according to Theorem A above, we obtain an equivalent modified lattice in the form of Fig. 6.11b2.

For $L_1 \geq L_2$.   We may now consider $Z_s = sL_2$ as the common series impedance of Z_A and Z_B and remove Z_s according to Theorem A above, obtaining an equivalent modified lattice in the form of Fig. 6.11b3.

Remarks.   Note in Fig. 6.11b1 that we have marked N_1 and N_2 as two arbitrary two-terminal networks.   By assigning different N_1 and N_2 networks, we may obtain a number of illustrative examples from this illustration.

Illustration A2.   Reduction of a lattice whose Z_A and Z_B branches both have series capacitances.   Let us now consider a lattice in the form of Fig. 6.11c1.

For $C_2 \geq C_1$.   For $C_2 \geq C_1$ or† $1/sC_2 \leq 1/sC_1$, we may consider that the Z_A and Z_B branches in Fig. 6.11c1 have a common series impedance $Z_s = 1/sC_2$; the smaller capacitance C_1 is equivalent to two capacitances C_2 and C_a in series.   This latter statement implies

Dimension of impedance:

$$\frac{1}{sC_1} = \frac{1}{sC_2} + \frac{1}{sC_a}$$

or

$$C_a = \left(\frac{1}{C_1} - \frac{1}{C_2}\right)^{-1} \tag{6.36}$$

By removing $Z_s = 1/sC_2$, that is, a circuit element C_2 whose impedance is Z_s, according to Theorem A above, we obtain an equivalent modified lattice in the form of Fig. 6.11c2.

For $C_1 \geq C_2$.   We may now consider that $Z_s = 1/sC_1$ is the common series impedance of Z_A and Z_B; the smaller capacitance C_2 is equivalent to two capacitances C_1 and C_b in series, where

$$C_b = \left(\frac{1}{C_2} - \frac{1}{C_1}\right)^{-1} \tag{6.37}$$

By removing $Z_s = 1/sC_1$, that is, a circuit element C_1 whose impedance is Z_s, according to Theorem A above, we obtain an equivalent modified lattice in the form of Fig. 6.11c3.

Remarks.   Again, we may assign different N_1 and N_2 networks in Fig. 6.11c and obtain a number of illustrative examples from the present illustration.

Illustration A3.   Reduction of a lattice whose Z_A and Z_B branches both have series inductances and capacitances.   Let us now consider a lattice in the form of Fig. 6.11d1, where $L_1 \geq L_2$ and $C_1 \geq C_2$.

We may consider that the Z_A and Z_B branches in Fig. 6.11d1 have a common series impedance $Z_s = sL_2 + 1/sC_1$.   By removing Z_s, that is, a series combination of L_2 and C_1 whose impedance is Z_s, according to Theorem A above, we obtain an equivalent modified lattice in the form of Fig. 6.11d2.

---

† Strictly speaking, it is improper to write $1/sC_2 \leq 1/sC_1$.   However, we write it in this form for convenience; it is intended to mean $|1/sC_2| \leq |1/sC_1|$ at real frequencies $s = j\omega$ or $1/\omega C_2 \leq 1/\omega C_1$.

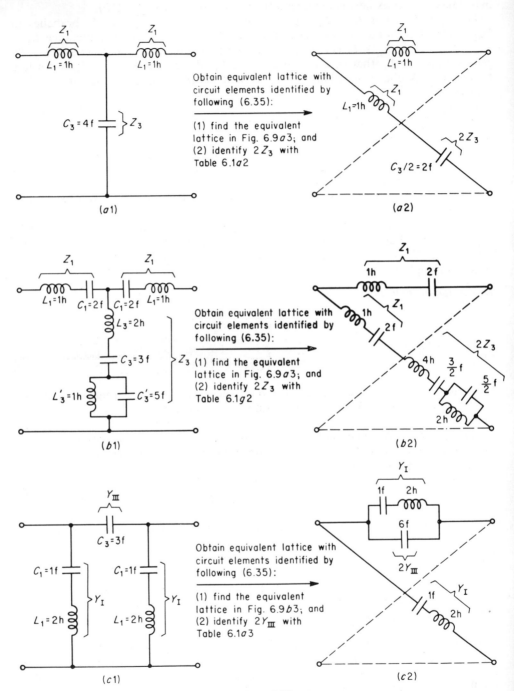

Fig. 6.10

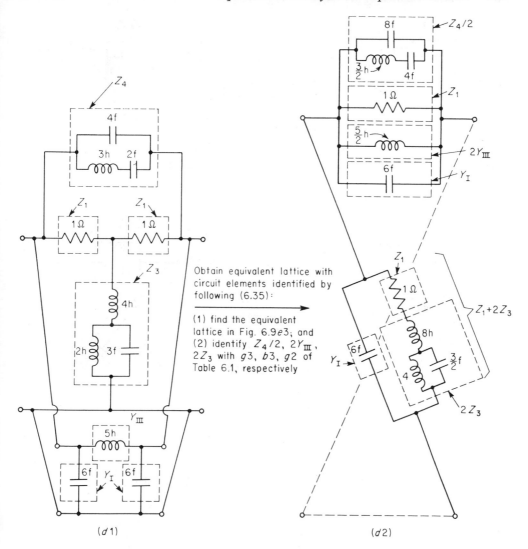

Obtain equivalent lattice with
circuit elements identified by
following (6.35):

(1) find the equivalent
lattice in Fig. 6.9e3; and
(2) identify $Z_4/2$, $2Y_{\rm III}$,
$2Z_3$ with $g3$, $b3$, $g2$ of
Table 6.1, respectively

FIG. 6.10 (*continued*)

The reader may wish to work out this illustration for the other three conditions:
(1) $L_1 \geq L_2$ and $C_2 \geq C_1$, (2) $L_2 \geq L_1$ and $C_1 \geq C_2$, and (3) $L_2 \geq L_1$ and $C_2 \geq C_1$.

Illustration A4.   Reduction of a special lattice to a symmetrical T network.   Let
us consider a lattice in the form of Fig. 6.11e1, where $L_2 \geq L_1$.

We may consider Fig. 6.11e1 as a special case of Fig. 6.11b1 in which the N_1
network is left out as a "short circuit."   Figure 6.11b2, as the result of the application of Theorem A, now does not have the N_1 network; there are two $Z_b = Z_B - Z_s$
branches in parallel.   Combining these two parallel branches, we have the equivalent T network in Fig. 6.11e2.

Again, we may assign different N networks in Fig. 6.11e and obtain a number of
illustrative examples from this illustration.

Illustration A5.   Reduction of another special lattice to a symmetrical T network.
An illustration similar to the preceding one is given in Fig. 6.11f.

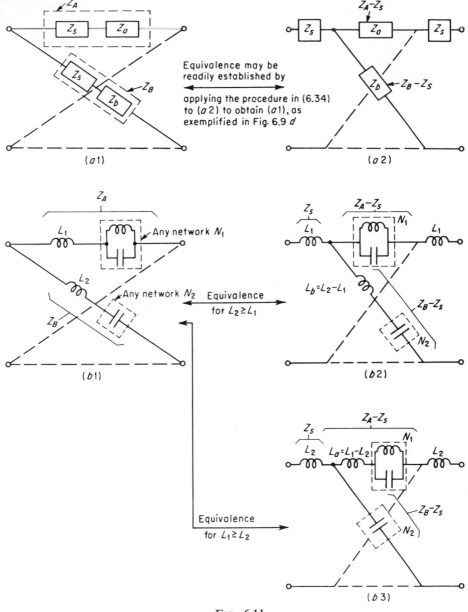

FIG. 6.11

Theorem B. *For a lattice network whose* Y_A *and* Y_B *branches have a common parallel admittance* Y_p *as in Fig. 6.12a1, we may remove* Y_p, *obtaining a modified lattice in the form of Fig. 6.12a2 as the equivalent network.* Z_p *may represent the admittance of a single circuit element or a circuit-element combination.*

To prove Theorem B, we need only prove that the two networks in Fig. 6.12a are equivalent. This may be readily accomplished by applying (6.34) to the network in Fig. 6.12a2 and obtaining its equivalent lattice in Fig. 6.12a1.

Illustration B1.   Reduction of a lattice whose Y_A **and** Y_B **branches both have parallel capacitances.**   Let us now consider a lattice in the form of Fig. 6.12b1.

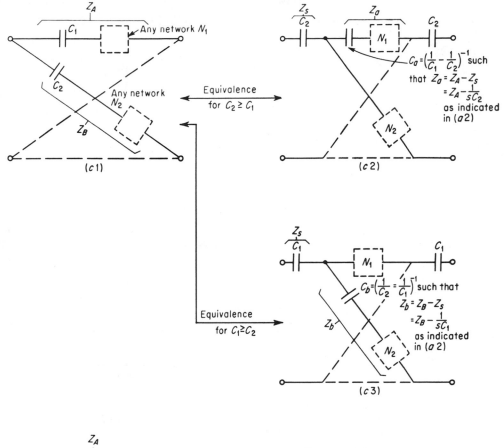

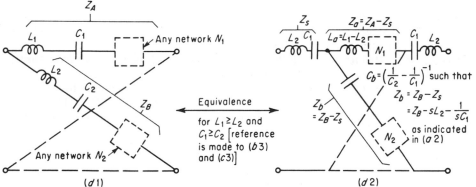

FIG. 6.11 (*continued*)

For $C_2 \geq C_1$. For $C_2 \geq C_1$, we may consider that the Y_A and Y_B branches in Fig. 6.12b1 have a common parallel admittance $Y_p = sC_1$; the larger capacitance $C_2 = C_1 + C_2 - C_1 = C_1 + C_b$ is equivalent to two capacitances C_1 and C_b in parallel. By removing $Y_p = sC_1$, that is, a circuit element C_1 whose admittance is Y_p, according to Theorem B above, we obtain an equivalent modified lattice in the form of Fig. 6.12b2.

For $C_1 \geq C_2$. We may now consider $Y_p = sC_2$ as the common parallel admittance

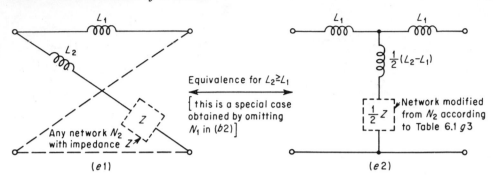

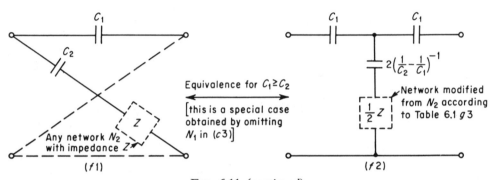

FIG. 6.11 *(continued)*

of Y_A and Y_B and remove Y_p according to Theorem B above, obtaining an equivalent modified lattice in the form of Fig. 6.12*b*3.

Remarks. Note in Fig. 6.12*b*1 that we have marked N_1 and N_2 as two arbitrary two-terminal networks. By assigning different N_1 and N_2 networks, we may obtain a number of illustrative examples from this illustration.

Illustration B2. Reduction of a lattice whose Y_A and Y_B branches both have parallel inductances. Let us consider a lattice in the form of Fig. 6.12*c*1.

For $L_2 \geq L_1$. For $L_2 \geq L_1$ or† $1/sL_2 \leq 1/sL_1$, we may consider that the Y_A and Y_B branches in Fig. 6.12*c*1 have a common parallel admittance $Z_p = 1/sL_2$; the smaller inductance L_1 is equivalent to two inductances L_2 and L_a in parallel. This latter statement implies

Dimension of admittance:

$$\frac{1}{sL_1} = \frac{1}{sL_2} + \frac{1}{sL_a}$$

or

$$L_a = \left(\frac{1}{L_1} - \frac{1}{L_2}\right)^{-1} \tag{6.38}$$

By removing $Y_p = 1/sL_2$, that is, a circuit element L_2 whose admittance is Y_p, according to Theorem B above, we obtain an equivalent modified lattice in the form of Fig. 6.12*c*2.

† Strictly speaking, it is improper to write $1/sL_2 \leq 1/sL_1$. However, we write it in this form for convenience; it is intended to mean $|1/sL_2| \leq |1/sL_1|$ at real frequencies $s = j\omega$ or $1/\omega L_2 \leq 1/\omega L_1$.

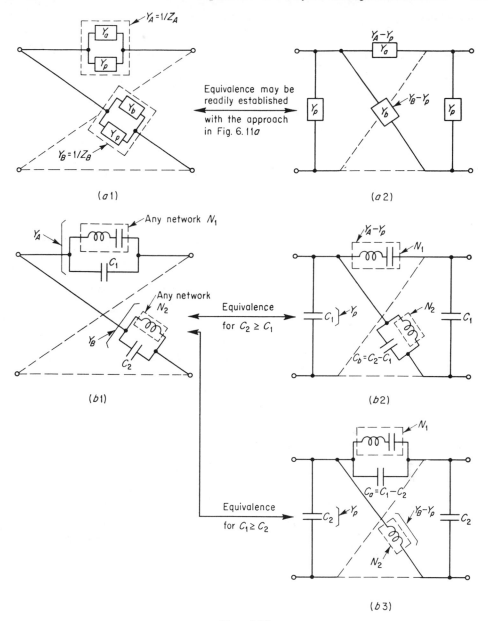

FIG. 6.12

For $L_1 \geq L_2$. We may now consider that $Y_p = 1/sL_1$ is the common parallel admittance of Y_A and Y_B; the smaller inductance L_2 is equivalent to two inductances L_1 and L_b in parallel, where

$$L_b = \left(\frac{1}{L_2} - \frac{1}{L_1} \right)^{-1} \tag{6.39}$$

By removing $Y_p = 1/sL_1$, that is, a circuit element L_1 whose admittance is Y_p, according to Theorem B above, we obtain an equivalent modified lattice in the form of Fig. 6.12c3.

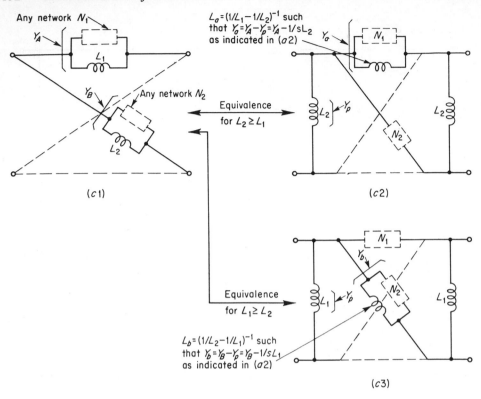

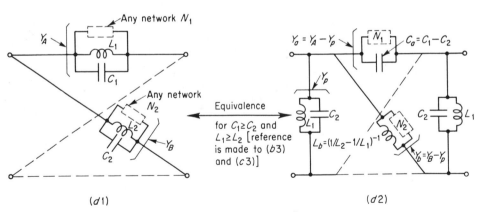

FIG. 6.12 (*continued*)

Remarks. Again, we may assign different N_1 and N_2 networks in Fig. 6.12c and obtain a number of illustrative examples from the present illustration.

Illustration B3.   Reduction of a lattice whose Y_A and Y_B branches both have parallel capacitances and inductances.   Let us now consider a lattice in the form of Fig. 6.12d1, where $C_1 \geq C_2$ and $L_1 \geq L_2$.

We may consider that the Y_A and Y_B branches in Fig. 6.12d1 have a common parallel admittance $Y_p = sC_2 + 1/sL_1$. By removing Y_p, that is, a parallel combination of C_2 and L_1 whose admittance is Y_p, according to Theorem B above, we obtain an equivalent modified lattice in the form of Fig. 6.12d2.

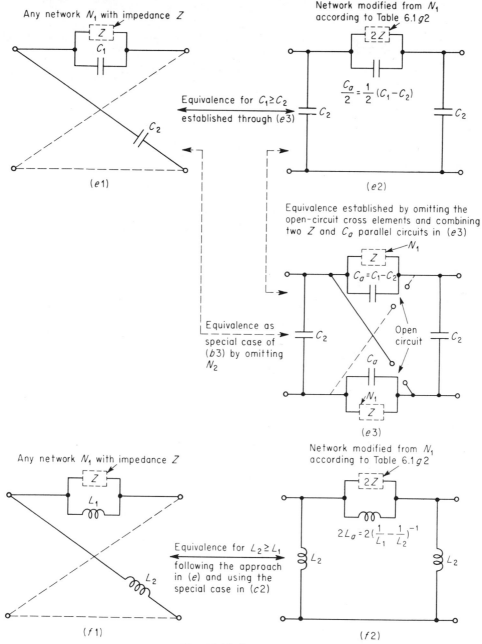

FIG. 6.12 (*continued*)

The reader may wish to work out this illustration under the other three conditions: (1) $C_1 \geq C_2$ and $L_2 \geq L_1$, (2) $C_2 \geq C_1$ and $L_1 \geq L_2$, and (3) $C_2 \geq C_1$ and $L_2 \geq L_1$.

Illustration B4.   Reduction of a special lattice to a symmetrical Π network.   Let us consider a lattice in the form of Fig. 6.12e1, where $C_1 \geq C_2$.

We may consider Fig. 6.12e1 as a special case of Fig. 6.12b1 in which the N_2

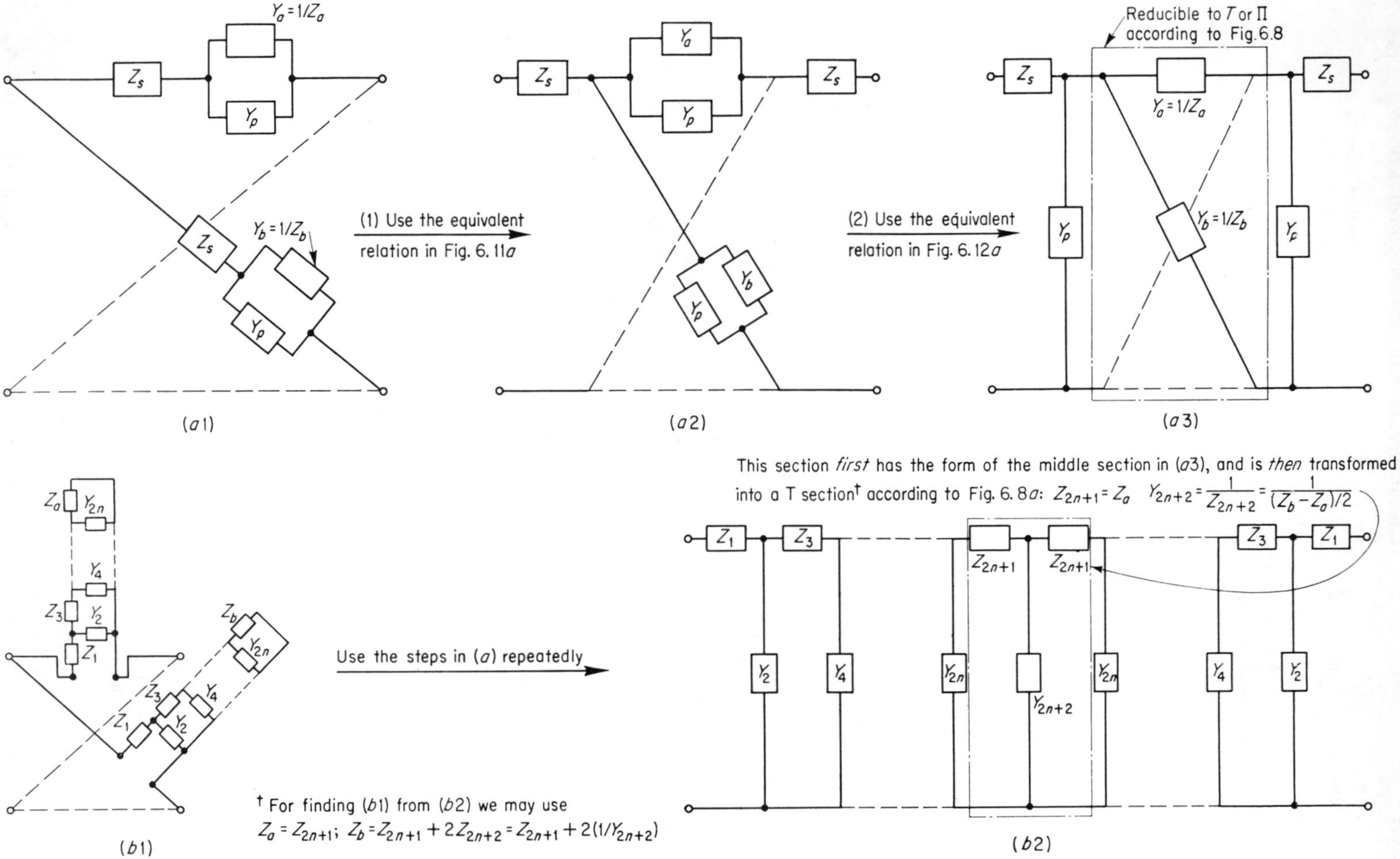

Reducible to T or Π
according to Fig. 6.8

Z_s　Y_p　Z_s

$Y_a = 1/Z_a$　$Y_b = 1/Z_b$

$(a3)$

(2) Use the equivalent
relation in Fig. 6.12a

Z_s　Y_b　Y_p　Z_s

Y_a　Y_p

$(a2)$

(1) Use the equivalent
relation in Fig. 6.11a

$Y_a = 1/Z_a$　Y_p

$Y_b = 1/Z_b$　Z_s　Y_p

Z_s

$(a1)$

This section *first* has the form of the middle section in $(a3)$, and is *then* transformed
into a T section according to Fig. 6.8a: $Z_{2n+1} = Z_a$　$Y_{2n+2} = \dfrac{1}{Z_{2n+2}} = (Z_b - Z_a)/2$

Z_1　Z_3　Z_{2n+1}　Z_{2n+1}

Y_2　Y_4　Y_{2n}　Y_{2n+2}　Y_{2n}

Z_3　Z_1

Y_4　Y_2

$(b2)$

Use the steps in (a) repeatedly

Z_b　Y_{2n}　Y_4　Y_2　Z_1

Z_a　Y_{2n}　Y_4　Y_2　Z_1

Z_3

$(b1)$

† For finding $(b1)$ from $(b2)$ we may use
$Z_a = Z_{2n+1}$; $Z_b = Z_{2n+1} + 2 Z_{2n+2} = Z_{2n+1} + 2(1/Y_{2n+2})$

Fig. 6.13

network is left out as an "open circuit." Figure 6.12b3 without the N_2 network, as the result of the application of Theorem B, is now redrawn in Fig. 6.12e3. With further reduction, we obtain the equivalent Π network in Fig. 6.12e2.

Again, we may assign different N_1 networks in Fig. 6.12e and obtain a number of illustrative examples from this illustration.

Illustration B5. Reduction of another special lattice to a symmetrical Π network. An illustration similar to the preceding one is given in Fig. 6.12f.

Alternate applications of Theorems A and B. We may apply Theorems A and B above alternately to some networks. In the example of the lattice in Fig. 6.13a1, we may first apply Theorem A to remove a series impedance Z_s, and then apply Theorem B to remove a parallel admittance, obtaining the equivalent modified lattice in Fig. 6.13a3. If permissible, we may repeat the earlier steps described above with the aid of Theorems A and B and then reduce the remaining lattice (in the dot-dashed box in Fig. 6.13a3) to an equivalent T or Π network. The lattice in Fig. 6.13a1 would then be reduced to a symmetrical ladder network.

Illustration C. Reduction of a special lattice to a symmetrical ladder. With the alternate application of Theorems A and B suggested above, we may readily reduce the special lattice in Fig. 6.13b1 to the symmetrical ladder in Fig. 6.13b2.

To verify our results, we apply the procedure in (6.34) to the ladder in Fig. 6.13b2 and obtain its equivalent lattice in the form of Fig. 6.13b1.

We have used Y's and Z's to represent various circuit elements or circuit-element combinations. By using *different* circuit elements or circuit-element combinations in place of the blocks marked with Z's and Y's, we may obtain a number of illustrative examples from this illustration.

6.2. Network duality†

A. General Remarks about Network Duality

Remarks about duality in the qualitative (i.e., topological) sense. In Art. 5.7 and Eqs. (5.18), two networks were said to be topologically or qualitatively dual to each other if there were one-to-one correspondences between the following quantities or relations of the two networks:

	Original network (1)	Dual network (2)	
One-to-one correspondences between quantities	Voltage Current Circuit element	Current Voltage Circuit element	(6.40a)
One-to-one correspondences between relations	Loop Node pair Series connection Parallel connection	Node pair Loop Parallel connection Series connection	(6.40b)

[Equations (6.40) may be considered as a rearranged form of (5.18). The topological terms "tree link" and "tree branch" are replaced by the term "circuit element," since tree links and tree branches are actually circuit elements.] "One-to-one correspondence" means that if there are five independent loops in the original network, there must be five independent node pairs in its dual; if there are five loop

---

† Although reference to Art. 5.7 on "network duality in the topological sense" is frequently made here, the reader who omitted Chap. 5 may ignore these references; he will not have difficulty in reading this section (Art. 6.2).

currents in the original network, there must be five node-pair voltages in its dual; if there are 23 circuit elements in the original network, there must be 23 circuit elements in its dual; etc.   These one-to-one correspondences are qualitative relationships; we do not care about the quantitative relationships—for example, the five loop currents in the original network and the five node-pair voltages in its dual network need not be numerically related.

Remarks about duality in the quantitative sense.   We shall now define quantitative duality.   Since the remaining portion of Art. 6.2 will be devoted to quantitative duality, *we shall for brevity use the term "duality" to mean duality in the quantitative sense* unless otherwise indicated.

A network is called (1) a *planar network* if all its branches can be placed in the same plane without any one crossing another or (2) a *nonplanar network* if some of its branches, when placed in the same plane, cross each other.   If each edge is considered as a network branch, Fig. 5.2*a*1 or *a*2 depicts a planar network, while Fig. 5.6 depicts some nonplanar networks.

Two networks are said to be quantitatively dual to each other if

Network duality (definition):

> They maintain the one-to-one correspondences in Eqs. (6.40)   (6.41*a*)

> The mathematical system which describes the behavior of the original system and relates the quantities in column 1 of (6.40a) also describes the behavior of its dual system and relates the quantities in column 2 of (6.40a)   (6.41*b*)

We now pose this question: *Do dual networks which satisfy definition (6.41) exist?* The answer is "yes" for planar networks.   Condition (6.41*a*) may be readily satisfied for the dual networks obtained with the procedure to be introduced in Art. 6.2D; condition (6.41*b*) may be satisfied by (1) further classifying the circuit elements, e.g., as inductances, resistances, and capacitances, (2) assigning values to these circuit elements as L's, R's, and C's or their reciprocals, Γ's, G's, and D's, and (3) establishing numerical relations between corresponding quantities of the two networks in (6.40), as we shall do in subsequent sections (Art. 6.2B and C).

B. Simple Illustrations Used to Establish Network Duality—A One-loop and a One-node Network

Let us assume that the one-node network (namely, a network with one independent node) in Fig. 6.14*a*2 or *b*2 is the dual of the one-loop network in Fig. 6.14*a*1 or *b*1, obtained with the procedure to be introduced in Art. 6.2D, and that the condition in (6.41*a*) is already satisfied by these two networks.   We shall now try to establish the condition in (6.41*b*) for these two networks.

A one-loop network.   It is obvious that we may use the differential equation

Describing one-loop network behavior in Fig. 6.14*a*1:

$$L\frac{di_1}{dt} + Ri_i + D\int i_1\, dt = e_1(t) \tag{6.42}$$

to describe the behavior of the one-loop network in Fig. 6.14*a*1 in terms of instantaneous voltage $e(t)$ and current $i(t)$.

The one-loop network in Fig. 6.14*b*1 is identical with Fig. 6.14*a*1, except that the voltage and current are now represented in complex amplitudes E and I.   We may

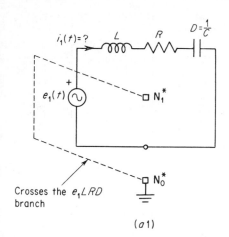

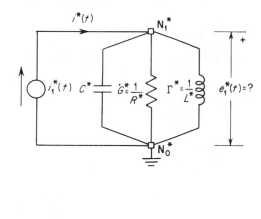

Crosses the e_1LRD
branch

(a1)   (a2)

May be considered as a 2-terminal network with   May be considered as a 2-terminal network with

$$Z_D = Z_D(s) = \frac{E_1}{I_1} = Ls + R + D\frac{1}{s}$$

$$Y_0^* = Y_0^*(s) = \frac{I_1^*}{E_1^*} = C^*s + G^* + \Gamma^*\left(\frac{1}{s}\right)$$

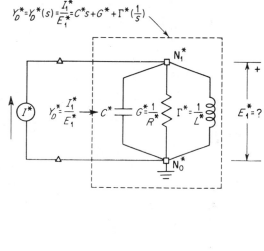

Crosses the E_1LRD
branch

(b1)   (b2)

FIG. 6.14

use the algebraic equation

Describing one-loop network behavior in Fig. 6.14b1:

$$\left(sL + R + \frac{D}{s}\right)I_1 = E_1 \qquad s = j\omega \qquad (6.43)$$

or
$$Z_D(s) = \frac{E_1}{I_1} = sL + R + \frac{D}{s} \qquad D = \frac{1}{C} \qquad (6.44)$$

to describe its behavior in terms of the voltage E_1 and current I_1 in complex amplitudes.

A one-node network. It is again obvious that we may use the differential equation

Describing one-node network behavior in Fig. 6.14a2:

$$C^*\frac{de_1^*}{dt} + G^*e_1^* + \Gamma^*\int e_1^* \, dt = i_1^*(t) \qquad (6.45)$$

Table 6.2

Original network, i.e., given network (1)	Dual or reciprocal network (2)	Numerical relations for finding reciprocal-w.r.t.-k network (3)	Numerical relations for finding dual or reciprocal network—same as column 3 for $k = 1$ (4)
(a1) Voltage e (or E)	(a2) Current i^* (or I^*)	(a3) $i^* = \dfrac{e}{k} \left(\text{or } I^* = \dfrac{E}{k} \right)$	(a4) $i^* = e$ (or $I^* = E$)
(b1) Current i (or I)	(b2) Voltage e^* (or E^*)	(b3) $e^* = ki$ (or $E^* = kI$)	(b4) $e^* = i$ (or $E^* = I$)
(c1) Inductance $L \left(\text{or } \Gamma = \dfrac{1}{L} \right)$	(c2) Capacitance $C^* \left(\text{or } D^* = \dfrac{1}{C^*} \right)$	(c3) $C^* = \dfrac{L}{k^2} \left(\text{or } D^* = k^2 \Gamma \right)$	(c4) $C^* = L$ (or $D^* = \Gamma$)
(d1) Capacitance $C \left(\text{or } D = \dfrac{1}{C} \right)$	(d2) Inductance $L^* \left(\text{or } \Gamma^* = \dfrac{1}{L^*} \right)$	(d3) $L^* = k^2 C \left(\text{or } \Gamma^* = \dfrac{D}{k^2} \right)$	(d4) $L^* = C$ (or $\Gamma^* = D$)
(e1) Resistance $R \left(\text{or } G = \dfrac{1}{R} \right)$	(e2) Conductance $G^* \left(\text{or } R^* = \dfrac{1}{G^*} \right)$	(e3) $G^* = \dfrac{R}{k^2} \left(\text{or } R^* = k^2 G \right)$	(e4) $G^* = R \left(\text{or } R^* = G = \dfrac{1}{R} \right)$
(f1) Loop	(f2) Node pair		
(g1) Node pair	(g2) Loop		
(h1) Series connection	(h2) Parallel connection		
(i1) Parallel connection	(i2) Series connection		

158

to describe the behavior of the one-node network in Fig. 6.14a2 in terms of instantaneous current $i_1^*(t)$ and voltage $e_1^*(t)$.

The one-node network in Fig. 6.14b2 is identical with Fig. 6.14b1, except for the use of voltage and current in complex amplitudes. We may use the algebraic equation

Describing one-node network behavior in Fig. 6.14b2:

$$\left(sC^* + G^* + \frac{\Gamma^*}{s}\right)E_1^* = I_1^* \qquad s = j\omega \tag{6.46}$$

or

$$Y_D(s) = \frac{E_1^*}{I_1^*} = sC^* + G^* + \frac{\Gamma^*}{s} \qquad \Gamma^* = \frac{1}{L^*} \tag{6.47}$$

to describe its behavior in terms of the current I_1^* and voltage E_1^* in complex amplitudes.

Mathematical systems. Let us consider a differential equation of the form

Differential equation:

$$a\frac{d}{dt}[x(t)] + bx(t) + c\int x(t)\,dt = y(t) \tag{6.48}$$

and an algebraic equation of the form

Algebraic equation:

$$\left(as + b + \frac{c}{s}\right)X = Y \tag{6.49}$$

Comparing (6.48) with (6.42) and (6.45), we note that (6.48) may be used to represent *both* (6.42) and (6.45), provided we impose the following numerical relations: $i^* = e$, $e^* = i$, $C^* = L$, $G^* = R$, and $\Gamma^* = D$ (that is, $1/L^* = 1/C$, or $L^* = C$). The above conditions satisfy (6.41b) for duality for the two networks in Fig. 6.14a. These numerical relations are listed in Table 6.2, column 4, to be used in finding the dual of a given network.

Now, comparing (6.49) with (6.43) and (6.46), we also note that the algebraic equation (6.49) may be used to represent *both* (6.43) and (6.46), provided we impose, in addition to the above, the following numerical relations: $I^* = E$ and $E^* = I$. The additional numerical relations are also tabulated in Table 6.2, column 4.

C. Additional Illustrations to Establish Duality—A Two-loop and a Two-node Network

Again, let us assume that the two-node network in Fig. 6.15b is the dual of the two-loop network in Fig. 6.15a, obtained with the procedure to be introduced in Art. 6.2D, and that the condition in (6.41a) is already satisfied by these two networks. We shall now try to establish condition (6.41b) for these two networks.

Mathematical system. Let us consider a system of two simultaneous linear differential equations of the form

Two differential equations:

$$a_3\frac{dx_1}{dt} + (b_1 + b_3)x_1 + c_1\int x_1\,dt - \left(a_3\frac{dx_2}{dt} + b_3x_2\right) = y_1$$

$$-\left(a_3\frac{dx_1}{dt} + b_3x_1\right) + (a_2 + a_3)\frac{dx_2}{dt} + (b_2 + b_3)x_2 + c_2\int x_2\,dt = y_2 \tag{6.50}$$

where x_1 and x_2 stand for $x_1(t)$ and $x_2(t)$.

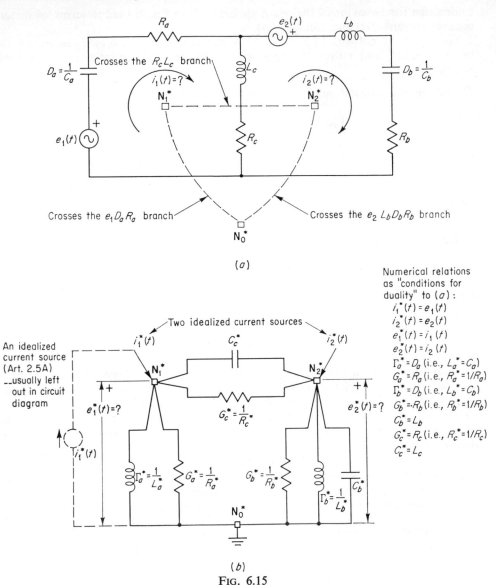

(a)

Numerical relations
as "conditions for
duality" to (a):

$i_1^*(t) = e_1(t)$
$i_2^*(t) = e_2(t)$
$e_1^*(t) = i_1(t)$
$e_2^*(t) = i_2(t)$
$\Gamma_a^* = D_a$ (i.e., $L_a^* = C_a$)
$G_a^* = R_a$ (i.e., $R_a^* = 1/R_a$)
$\Gamma_b^* = D_b$ (i.e., $L_b^* = C_b$)
$G_b^* = R_b$ (i.e., $R_b^* = 1/R_b$)
$C_b^* = L_b$
$G_c^* = R_c$ (i.e., $R_c^* = 1/R_c$)
$C_c^* = L_c$

(b)

FIG. 6.15

A two-loop network. The system of two differential equations obtained by substituting

Conditions for (6.50) to describe two-loop network behavior in Fig. 6.15a:

$$x_1 = i_1 \qquad x_2 = i_2 \qquad y_1 = e_1 \qquad y_2 = e_2$$
$$a_2 = L_b \qquad a_3 = L_c$$
$$b_1 = R_a \qquad b_2 = R_b \qquad b_3 = R_c \tag{6.51a}$$
$$c_1 = D_a \qquad c_2 = D_b$$

into (6.50) may easily be verified to be the equations describing the behavior of the two-loop network in Fig. 6.15a.

A two-node network. Similarly, the system of two differential equations obtained by substituting

Conditions for (6.50) *to describe two-node network behavior in Fig. 6.15b:*

$$
\begin{array}{llll}
x_1 = e_1^* & x_2 = e_2^* & y_1 = i_1^* & y_2 = i_2^* \\
a_2 = C_b^* & a_3 = C_c^* & & \\
b_1 = G_a^* & b_2 = G_b^* & b_3 = G_c^* & \\
c_1 = \Gamma_a^* & c_2 = \Gamma_b^* & &
\end{array}
\tag{6.51b}
$$

into (6.50) may easily be verified to be the equations describing the behavior of the two-node network in Fig. 6.15b.

Numerical relations for duality. In order to satisfy condition (6.41b) for duality for the two networks in Fig. 6.15, we must equate (6.51a) with (6.51b) and obtain a set of numerical relations as indicated in Fig. 6.15b. These numerical relations are similar to those obtained in the earlier illustrations (Art. 6.2B) and are tabulated in Table 6.2, column 4, for later use.

D. Procedure for Finding the Dual Network

To find the dual of a given network in the quantitative sense, we proceed as follows:

Step 1. *Mark a point in each loop of the original network, designating it as a node* N_k^* *of the dual network; mark a point exterior to the original network, designating it as the reference node* N_0^* *of the dual network.*

For example, let us use the two-loop network in Fig. 6.15a as the original network. We mark nodes N_0^*, N_1^*, and N_2^*.

Step 2. *Connect two nodes* N_i^* *and* N_j^* *as obtained in Step 1 above with a dashed line, crossing a network branch of the original network. This dashed line indicates that there exists a "corresponding" network branch of the dual network connecting the nodes* N_i^* *and* N_j^*.

Three such dashed lines are drawn in Fig. 6.15a.

To simplify the statement in the next step, let us introduce the following symbols for the description of networks or network branches in symbolic form:

Symbols	*Their meanings*	
$x_1 x_2$ (or x_1-x_2)	Series connection of x_1 and x_2	(6.52)
$y_1 \parallel y_2$	Parallel connection of y_1 and y_2	

For example, $m_1 m_2 \cdots m_h$ is the symbolic form for a network branch consisting of circuit elements $m_1, m_2, \ldots, m_h$ in series; $n_1^* \parallel n_2^* \parallel \cdots \parallel n_h^*$, of circuit elements $n_1^*, n_2^*, \ldots, n_h^*$ in parallel. Similarly, $m_1(m_2 \parallel m_3)m_4$ represents a series connection of (1) m_1, (2) a parallel combination of m_2 and m_3, and (3) m_4; $n_1^* \parallel n_2^* n_3^* \parallel n_4^*$, a parallel connection of (1) n_1^*, (2) a series combination of n_2^* and n_3^*, and (3) n_4^*.

Step 3. *For each* $m_1 m_2 \cdots m_{h-1} m_h$ *branch of the original network, the dual network has a corresponding* $n_1^* \parallel n_2^* \cdots \parallel n_{h-1}^* \parallel n_h^*$ *branch; for each* m_i *identified with an entry in Table* 6.2, *column* 1, n_i *is the corresponding entry in column* 2; $n_i^* = m_i$ *for* $i = 1, 2, \ldots, h$ *as prescribed in column* 4.

For example, the original network has an $e_1 D_a R_a$ branch crossed by the dashed line $N_0^* N_1^*$ in Fig. 6.15a; the dual network has a corresponding $i_1^* \parallel \Gamma_a^* \parallel G_a^*$ branch depicted in Fig. 6.15b, where $i_1^* = e_1$, $\Gamma_a^* = D_a$ (or $L_a^* = C_a$), and $G_a^* = R_a$ (or $R_a^* = 1/R_a$) are prescribed in Table 6.2, column 4. Similarly, corresponding to the

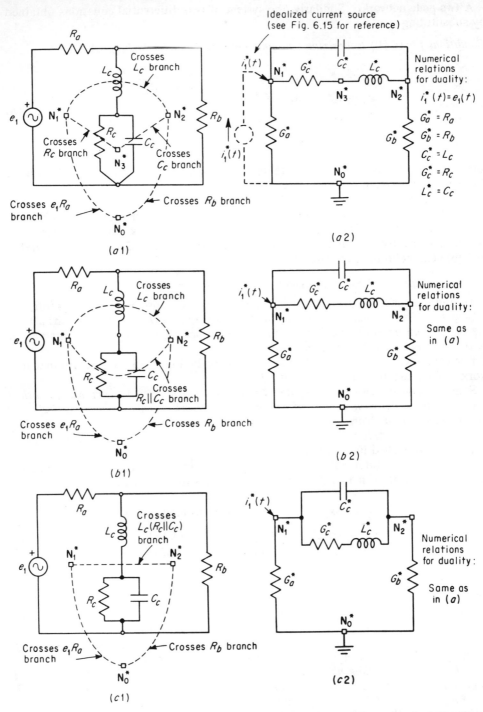

FIG. 6.16   (a) L_c, R_c, and C_c considered as three separate network branches in (a1); (b) L_c and $R_c \parallel C_c$ considered as two separate network branches in (b1); (c) $L_c(R_c \parallel C_c)$ considered as a single network branch in (c1).

$R_c L_c$ branch and the $e_b L_b D_b R_b$ branch of the original network in Fig. 6.15a, the dual network has a $G_c^* \parallel C_c^*$ branch and an $i_2^* \parallel C_b^* \parallel \Gamma_b^* \parallel G_b^*$ branch, as in Fig. 6.15b, where $G_c^* = R_c$, $C_c^* = L_c$, and $i_2^* = e_2$, $C_b^* = L_b$, $\Gamma_b^* = D_b$, $G_b^* = R_b$. We now have in Fig. 6.15b the complete dual of the network in Fig. 6.15a.

Remarks about the Modification of Step 3. In Step 3, we assumed that a network branch consists of circuit elements in series *or* a single circuit element as a special case. If we allow ourselves to choose a network branch as a "series-parallel combination" of circuit elements, Step 3 is still applicable with slight modification: (1) replace each series connection in the original network with a parallel connection in the dual and (2) replace each parallel connection in the original network with a series connection in the dual.

For example, for an $m_1(m_2 \parallel m_3)m_4$ branch in the original network, the dual network has a corresponding $n_1^* \parallel (n_2^* n_3^*) \parallel n_4^*$ branch; $n_1^* = m_1$, $n_2^* = m_2$, $n_3^* = m_3$, and $n_4^* = m_4$ numerically.

Justification of the above procedure. Two networks are dual in the quantitative sense if they satisfy conditions (6.41). But how do we know that the procedure for finding the dual network is correct and justified? Let us check the result of this procedure against conditions (6.41).

Throughout the above procedure we have maintained the *one-to-one correspondences* between the original and dual networks (e.g., loop versus node pair,† circuit elements L, R, D versus Γ^*, G^*, C^*, voltage e versus i^*, series connection versus parallel connection, etc.) as tabulated in (6.40). Condition (6.41a) is therefore satisfied.

In Art. 6.2B and C, we established that the numerical relations, as prescribed in Table 6.2, column 4, must be maintained between corresponding circuit elements of two networks in order to satisfy (6.41b) for duality. Since the above procedure makes use of these numerical relations, condition (6.41b) is satisfied.

We have now justified the procedure and are certain that the result is the dual of the original network.

Remarks about the procedure. In the above procedure and its associated illustration in Fig. 6.15, we assumed that a network branch in the original network corresponds to

A network branch:

$$\text{Any single } e, i, R \text{ (or } G\text{), } L \text{ (or } \Gamma\text{), or } C \text{ (or } D\text{) element} \qquad (6.53a)$$

or   Any *series* combination of e's, i's, R's (or G's), L's (or Γ's), and/or C's (or D's)   (6.53b)

It is true that we usually define the network branches of any given network in these two ways. However, we may add a third interpretation of a network branch,

A network branch:

$$\text{Any } series\text{-}parallel \text{ combination of } e\text{'s, } i\text{'s, } R\text{'s, } L\text{'s, and/or } C\text{'s} \qquad (6.53c)$$

and the above procedure, with slight modification, is also applicable. Let us now look into the following illustrations:

Illustration 1. For the network in Fig. 6.16a1, we shall consider L_c, R_c, and C_c as *three separate network branches.* We now have a three-loop network. Following the above procedure, we have the dual in Fig. 6.16a2.

† *For each loop* $\mathbf{M}_k$ *of the original network, there exists a node pair* $\mathbf{N}_k^* \mathbf{N}_0^*$ *of the dual network, where* $\mathbf{N}_k^*$ *is determined in Step 1 in one-to-one correspondence with the loop* $\mathbf{M}_k$, *and* $\mathbf{N}_0^*$ *is the "reference node" or "ground node."*

Illustration 2.   For the network in Fig. 6.16b1, which is the *same* network as in Fig. 6.16a1, we shall consider L_c and $R_c \parallel C_c$ as *two separate network branches.* We now have a two-loop network. Following the above procedure with the indicated modification, we have the dual in Fig. 6.16b2.

Illustration 3.   For the network in Fig. 6.16c1, which is the *same* network as in Fig. 6.16a1 and b1, we shall consider $L_c(R_c \parallel C_c)$ as *a single network branch.* Again we have a two-loop network. Following the above procedure with the indicated modification, we obtain the dual in Fig. 6.16c2.

A Summarizing Remark.   Comparing the results of the above illustrations in Fig. 6.16a2, b2, and c2, we see that all three are the same dual network. We may therefore make the following remark: *For a given network, we may define network branches in any of the three interpretations in* (6.53) *and obtain a unique dual network with the above procedure and its modification.*

Illustration A.   We may readily apply the procedure given at the beginning of Art. 6.2D to the network in Fig. 6.14a1, obtaining the dual network in Fig. 6.14a2 with the following numerical relations:

$$i_1^*(t) = e_1(t) \qquad e_1^*(t) = i_1(t)$$
$$C^* = L \qquad G^* = R \qquad \Gamma^* = C \tag{6.54}$$

Illustration B.   We may apply the procedure at the beginning of Art. 6.2D to the network in Fig. 6.17a1, obtaining the dual network in Fig. 6.17a2 with circuit values obtained through numerical relations (for example, $R_b = 3$ implies $G_b^* = 1/R_b^* = 3$ or $R_b^* = \frac{1}{3}$ through the numerical relation $G_b^* = R_b$, etc.).

E. Additional Illustrations and Remark about a Property Implied by Duality

Illustration A′.   We may readily apply the procedure given at the beginning of Art. 6.2D to the network in Fig. 6.14b1, obtaining the dual network in Fig. 6.14b2 with the following numerical relations:

$$I_1^* = E_1 \qquad E_1^* = I_1 \tag{6.55}$$

and
$$C^* = L \qquad G^* = R \qquad \Gamma^* = D \tag{6.56}$$

Now, let us consider the two-terminal network in Fig. 6.14b1, i.e., the "original network" *minus* the voltage source E_1, whose driving-point impedance is

$$Z_D = Z_D(s) = \frac{E_1}{I_1}$$

and the two-terminal network in Fig. 6.14b2, i.e., the "dual network" minus the current source I_1^*, whose driving-point admittance is $Y_D^* = Y_D^*(s) = I_1^*/E_1^*$. From (6.55), we have the relation

$$Y_D^*(s) = Z_D(s) \tag{6.57}$$

In the present simple illustration, (6.57) is further supported by the exact expressions for $Z_D(s)$ and $Y_D^*(s)$ in (6.44) and (6.47) under condition (6.56).

It is only fitting and proper for us to ask this question: *Can duality as a relation between two general networks having voltage and/or current sources be modified and used as a relation between 2 two-terminal networks?*   Before we answer this question, let us look into a more general illustration.

Illustration B′.   In Illustration B above, we established duality between the two networks in Fig. 6.17a with the following numerical relations:

$$I_1^* = E_1 \qquad E_1^* = I_1 \tag{6.58}$$

and
$$G_a^* = R_a = 1 \qquad G_b^* = R_b = 3 \qquad L_c^* = C_c = 2 \qquad \cdots \tag{6.59}$$

Now, let us redraw Fig. 6.17a as Fig. 6.17b. For the driving-point impedance $Z_D = Z_D(s) = E_1/I_1$ of the two-terminal network in Fig. 6.17b1 and the driving-point admittance $Y_D^* = Y_D^*(s) = I_1^*/E_1^*$ of the two-terminal network in Fig. 6.17b2, (6.58) implies

Dual networks minus sources as two-terminal networks in Fig. 6.17b:

$$Y_D^*(s) = Z_D(s) \tag{6.60}$$

Two two-terminal networks with the relation in (6.60) are called reciprocal networks. Reciprocal networks will be studied in Art. 6.3.

Remark. The above discussion suggests that *we may use a modified version of the procedure for finding the dual network in Art. 6.2D to find the reciprocal network of a given two-terminal network.* This modified procedure will be given in Art. 6.3B.

6.3. Reciprocal networks

A. Description of Reciprocal Networks

Reciprocal-w.r.t.-k networks. A two-terminal network **A** with a driving-point impedance $Z_D(s) = 1/Y_D(s)$ and a two-terminal network **B** with a driving-point impedance $Z_D^*(s) = 1/Y_D^*(s)$, as depicted in Fig. 6.18a, are said to be *reciprocal with respect to k* if

Reciprocal-w.r.t-k networks:

$$Z_D(s)Z_D^*(s) = k^2 \tag{6.61a}$$

or $\qquad Z_D^*(s) = k^2 Y_D(s) \qquad$ or $\qquad Y_D^*(s) = \dfrac{Z_D(s)}{k^2} \qquad$ (6.61b)

where k is a real, positive constant. If **A** is the original network, **B** is its reciprocal-w.r.t.-k network, and vice versa.

Reciprocal networks. When 2 two-terminal networks **A** and **B**, as depicted in Fig. 6.18a, are reciprocal with respect to k, and $k = 1$, which implies

Reciprocal networks:

$$Z_D(s)Z_D^*(s) = 1 \tag{6.62a}$$

or $\qquad Z_D^*(s) = Y_D(s) \qquad$ or $\qquad Y_D^*(s) = Z_D(s) \qquad$ (6.62b)

the networks are usually referred to simply as two reciprocal networks. If **A** is the original network, **B** is its reciprocal network, and vice versa.

We shall use the term "reciprocal networks" to mean two networks related in the manner of (6.62) unless otherwise indicated.

B. Finding the Reciprocal Network

Finding the reciprocal of a general network. The remark at the end of Art. 6.2E, with the aid of Fig. 6.17b, suggests the procedure for finding the reciprocal network of a general network. This procedure is now described in Fig. 6.18b:

Finding the reciprocal of a general two-terminal network:

$$\text{Follow Steps 1, 2, and 3 in Fig. 6.18}b \tag{6.63}$$

Illustration 1. Let us find the reciprocal network of the two-terminal network on the right of 11′ in Fig. 6.17a1.

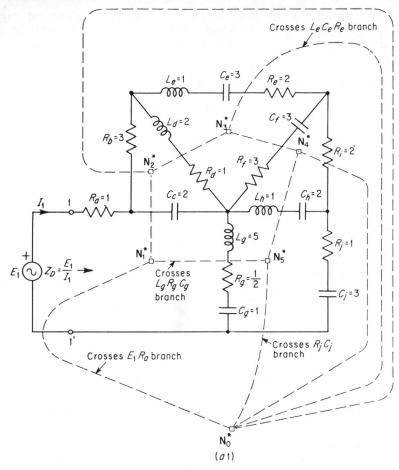

Fig. 6.17

According to the procedure in (6.63) and Fig. 6.18*b*, we (1) add a voltage source E_1 in Fig. 6.17*a*1, (2) use the procedure in Art. 6.2D to find the dual network in Fig. 6.17*a*2, and (3) leave out the current source I_1^*, obtaining the reciprocal network on the right of 11′ in Fig. 6.17*a*2.

Illustration 2. Let us find the reciprocal network of the two-terminal *RC* network on the right of 11′ in Fig. 6.19*a* consisting only of resistances and capacitances as circuit elements.

According to the procedure in (6.63) and Fig. 6.18*b*, we (1) add a voltage source E_1 in Fig. 6.19*a*, (2) use the procedure in Art. 6.2D to find the dual network in Fig. 6.19*b*, whose circuit values are numerically related to those in the given network in Fig. 6.19*a* and indicated in the figure:

$$R_1^* = \frac{1}{R_1} \quad (\text{as } G_1^* = R_1) \qquad R_3^* = \frac{1}{R_3} \qquad R_5^* = \frac{1}{R_5} \qquad R_7^* = \frac{1}{R_7} \qquad (6.64)$$

$$L_2^* = C_2 \qquad\qquad\qquad\qquad L_4^* = C_4 \qquad L_6^* = C_6 \qquad L_8^* = C_8$$

and (3) leave out the current source I_1^*, obtaining the reciprocal *RL* network on the right of 11′ in Fig. 6.19*b*.

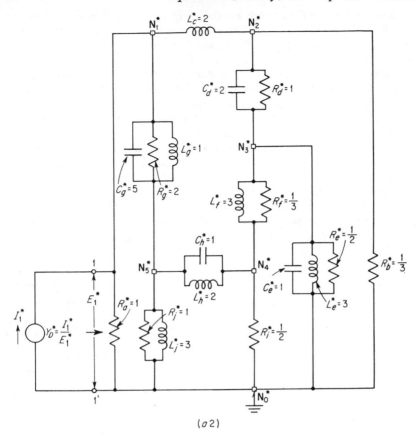

(a2)

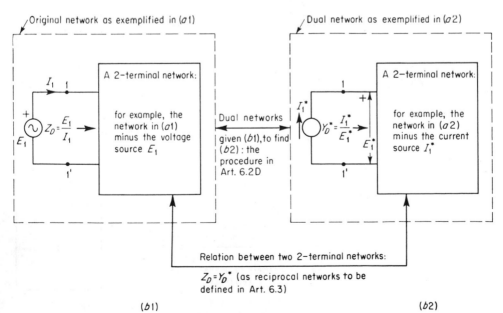

Original network as exemplified in (a1)

Dual network as exemplified in (a2)

A 2-terminal network:

for example, the network in (a1) minus the voltage source E_1

A 2-terminal network:

for example, the network in (a2) minus the current source I_1^*

Dual networks given (b1), to find (b2): the procedure in Art. 6.2D

Relation between two 2-terminal networks:

$Z_D = Y_D^*$ (as reciprocal networks to be defined in Art. 6.3)

(b1)   (b2)

FIG. 6.17 (*continued*)

We note here that the *RC* network on the right of 11′ in Fig. 6.19*a* has the *RL* network on the right of 11′ in Fig. 6.19*b* as its reciprocal network. In general, we shall find that (1) *the reciprocal of an RC network is always an RL network and* (2) *the reciprocal of an RL network is always an RC network*.

Some remarks about the general procedure in (6.63). As stated earlier, the procedure in (6.63) may be used to find the reciprocal of a general network which, for example, may be (1) a series-parallel network, (2) a ladder network, or (3) a non-series-parallel and nonladder network. But is it always necessary to use this procedure for networks of all three categories?

It is easy to recognize that both the series-parallel networks and the ladder networks are connected in an orderly series-parallel fashion; this is not true for the other types of networks. Since (1) the procedure in (6.63) utilizes the one-to-one correspondences established through duality between columns 1 and 2 of Table 6.2 and (2) "series-to-parallel" and "parallel-to-series" are among these one-to-one correspondences, we immediately suspect that *simplified versions of (6.63) as the procedures for finding the reciprocals of* (1) *a series-parallel network and* (2) *a ladder network*

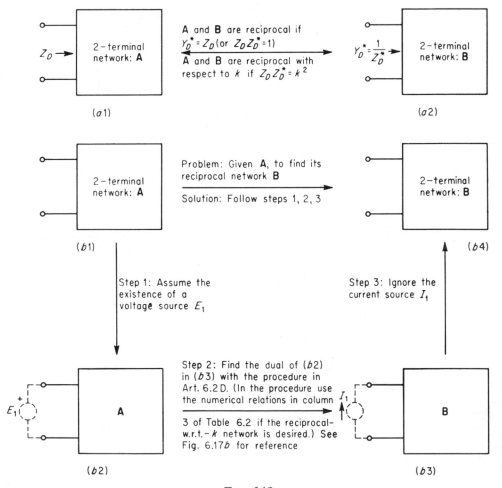

FIG. 6.18

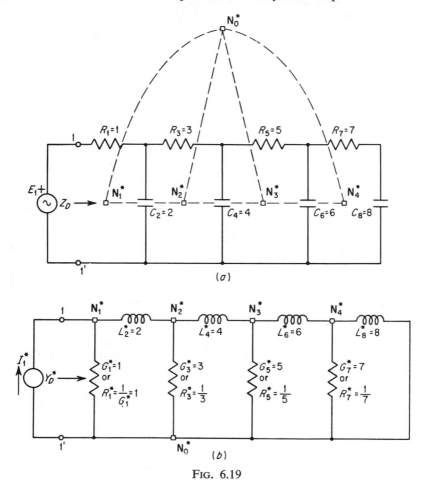

FIG. 6.19

may be readily obtained by allowing (1) *each series connection in the original network to be changed to a parallel connection and* (2) *each parallel connection to be changed to a series connection.* These new procedures will be formalized and described in subsequent paragraphs.

Finding the reciprocal of a series-parallel network. To find the reciprocal of an original series-parallel network, we need proceed as follows:

Finding the reciprocal of a series-parallel network:

> *Find a reciprocal network structure such that, for any set of circuit elements (or network branches) connected in series in the original network structure, "corresponding" circuit elements (or network branches) in the reciprocal structure are connected in parallel, and vice versa*   (6.65a)

> *For inductances L_i, resistances R_j, and capacitances C_h in the original network, use capacitances C_i^*, conductances G_j^* (or resistances $R_j^* = 1/G_j^*$), and inductances L_h^* as respective corresponding circuit elements in the reciprocal network*   (6.65b)

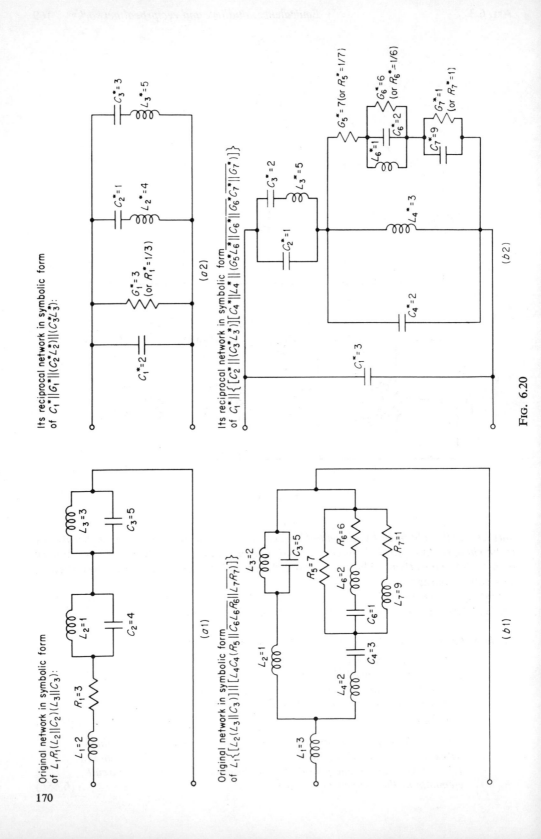

Original network in symbolic form
of $L_1 R_1 (L_2 || C_2) (L_3 || C_3)$:

(*a*1)

Its reciprocal network in symbolic form
of $C_1^* || G_1^* || (C_2^* L_2^*) || (C_3^* L_3^*)$:

(*a*2)

Original network in symbolic form
of $L_1 \{ [L_2 (L_3 || C_3)] || [L_4 C_4 (R_5 || C_6 L_6 R_6 || \overline{L_7 R_7})] \}$

(*b*1)

Its reciprocal network in symbolic form
of $C_1^* || \{ [C_2^* || (C_3^* L_3^*)] [C_4^* || L_4^* || (G_5^* L_6^* || C_6 || G_6^* C_7^* || G_7^*)] \}$

(*b*2)

Fig. 6.20

170

The circuit values of the reciprocal network may be computed with the numerical relations

$$C_i^* = \frac{L_i}{k^2} \qquad\qquad k = 1$$

$$G_j^* = \frac{R_j}{k^2} \qquad R_j^* = \frac{k^2}{R_j} \qquad k = 1$$

$$L_h^* = k^2 C_h \qquad\qquad k = 1$$

for all possible i, j, and h $\hspace{8cm}$ (6.65c)

An alternative form of (6.65) will be given in (6.68).

Illustration 3.   Let us find the reciprocal network of the series-parallel network in Fig. 6.20a1.

The original network structure in Fig. 6.20a1 consists of

Original network structure in Fig. 6.20a1:

Four network branches L_1, R_1, $L_2 \parallel C_2$ (that is, a parallel combination of L_2 and C_2), and $L_3 \parallel C_3$ in series $\hspace{3cm}$ (6.66a)

According to (6.65a) and (6.65b), the reciprocal network structure must consist of

Reciprocal network structure in Fig. 6.20a2:

Four network branches C_1^*, G_1^*, $C_2^* L_2^*$ (that is, a series combination
of C_2^* and L_2^*), and $C_3^* L_3^*$ in parallel $\hspace{3cm}$ (6.66b)

as in Fig. 6.20a2.   Imposing the numerical relations in (6.65c), we obtain the reciprocal network together with the circuit values in Fig. 6.20a2.

Remarks.   In general, we need not describe the original and reciprocal network structures in statements as we did in (6.66).   We merely examine the original network structure in Fig. 6.20a1 and sketch its reciprocal network structure without circuit values in Fig. 6.20a2.   We then determine the circuit values with the aid of (6.65c).

However, if we decide to describe the network structures, e.g., for complicated series-parallel networks, we may use the symbolic forms discussed earlier instead of the statements in (6.66).

Symbolic Form of a Series-Parallel Network.   With the symbols defined in (6.52), we may now conveniently use the following symbolic forms:

Symbolic form of network in Fig. 6.20a1:

$$L_1 R_1 (L_2 \parallel C_2)(L_3 \parallel C_3) \equiv \text{network answering description of (6.66a)} \quad (6.67a)$$

Symbolic form of network in Fig. 6.20a2:

$$C_1^* \parallel G_1^* \parallel (C_2^* L_2^*) \parallel (C_3^* L_3) \equiv \text{network answering description of (6.66b)} \quad (6.67b)$$

Comparing (6.67b) with (6.67a) as the symbolic forms of two reciprocal series-parallel networks, we may rewrite (6.65) in an alternative form:

Finding the reciprocal of a series-parallel network—an alternative form of (6.65):

Represent the original network in symbolic form $\hspace{3cm}$ (6.68a)

*Identify the symbols and elements of this form with the entries in the
first column below, and replace them with the corresponding entries*

in the second column to obtain the symbolic form of the reciprocal network: (6.68b)

Symbol " - "   Symbol " ∥ "
Symbol " ∥ "   Symbol " - "
Inductances L_i Capacitances C_i^*
Resistances R_j Conductances G_j^*
Capacitances C_h Inductances L_h^*

With circuit values determined according to (6.65c), obtain the reciprocal network   (6.68c)

Illustration 4.   Let us find the reciprocal network of the series-parallel network in Fig. 6.20b1.

Suppose we follow the procedure in (6.65). For $L_1 = 3$ in series with the rest of the original network, we have a corresponding C_1^* in parallel with the rest of the reciprocal network according to (6.65a) and (6.65b); $C_1^* = L_1 = 3$ according to (6.65c). Similarly, we may obtain other circuit elements; the reciprocal network, thus obtained, is shown in Fig. 6.20b2.

If, instead, we follow the procedure in (6.68), we write the symbolic form of the original network, as shown in Fig. 6.20b1, modify it into the symbolic form (also shown in the figure) of the reciprocal network according to (6.68b), and obtain the reciprocal network with circuit values in Fig. 6.20b2 with the aid of (6.68c).

Finding the reciprocal of a ladder network.   We have already discussed how to simplify the general network procedure in (6.63) into a procedure for finding the reciprocal of a ladder network.

We shall now formalize and describe this procedure.

Finding the reciprocal of a ladder network:

Identify the original ladder network with the ladder structure in Fig. 6.21a1 or b1; if it is identified with Fig. 6.21a1, its reciprocal network structure has the form of Fig. 6.21a2; if identified with Fig. 6.21b1, then it has the form of Fig. 6.21b2   (6.69a)

For each branch B_i consisting of a single circuit element, identify the circuit element with an entry in the first column below; the corresponding entry in the second column represents the corresponding branch B_i^* of the reciprocal network

Inductances L_i Capacitances C_i^*
Resistances R_j Conductances G_j^*
Capacitances C_h Inductances L_h^* (6.69b)

For each branch B_i which is a series-parallel network itself, find the reciprocal series-parallel network with the aid of (6.65) or (6.68) and use it as the corresponding branch B_i^* of the reciprocal network   (6.69c)

The circuit values of the reciprocal network may be computed with the following numerical relations for all possible i, j, and h:

$$C_i^* = \frac{L_i}{k^2} \qquad\qquad k = 1$$

$$G_j^* = \frac{R_j}{k^2} \qquad R_j^* = \frac{k^2}{R_j} \qquad k = 1 \qquad (6.69d)$$

$$L_h^* = k^2 C_h \qquad\qquad k = 1$$

Original ladder network:

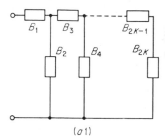

(*a*1)

For each network branch B_i which is a series–parallel network itself with impedance Z_i find its corresponding branch B_i^* as its reciprocal series–parallel network whose admittance is $Y_i^* = Z_i$ according to (6.65)

Its reciprocal ladder network:

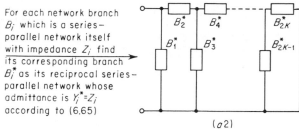

(*a*2)

Original ladder network:

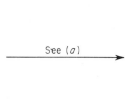

(*b*1)

See (*a*)

Its reciprocal ladder network:

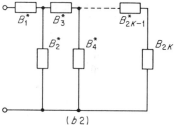

(*b*2)

FIG. 6.21

Illustration 5. Let us now use (6.69) to find the reciprocal of the *RC* ladder network on the right of 11′ in Fig. 6.19*a*.

We first identify the original ladder network in Fig. 6.19*a* with Fig. 6.21*a*1, knowing that it has a reciprocal network structure in Fig. 6.21*a*2. Identifying the circuit elements as suggested in (6.69*b*) and (6.69*d*), we have the reciprocal network with circuit values on the right of 11′ in Fig. 6.19*b*.

This checks with our earlier result in Illustration 2 associated with Eq. (6.64), which is identical to the present illustration but solved by a different procedure.

Illustration 6. Let us now use (6.69) to find the reciprocal of the ladder network in Fig. 6.22*a*.

We first identify the original ladder network in Fig. 6.22*a* with Fig. 6.21*a*1, knowing that it has a reciprocal network structure in Fig. 6.21*a*2.

Since each branch in Fig. 6.22*a* is a series-parallel network itself, we must follow (6.69*c*) instead of (6.69*b*). For example, the B_1^* branch in the reciprocal network in Fig. 6.22*b* is the reciprocal of the B_1 branch in the original network in Fig. 6.22*a*, the B_2^* branch is the reciprocal of the B_2 branch, etc. With circuit values appropriately computed according to (6.69*d*), we now have the reciprocal network in Fig. 6.22*b*.

C. Finding the Reciprocal-w.r.t.-k Network

Comparison with reciprocal network and remarks. Let us compare the reciprocal and reciprocal-w.r.t.-*k* networks of a network with driving-point admittance $Y_D(s)$. According to (6.62*b*) and (6.61*b*), we have

For the reciprocal network:

$$Z_D^*(s) = Y_D(s) \qquad (6.70a)$$

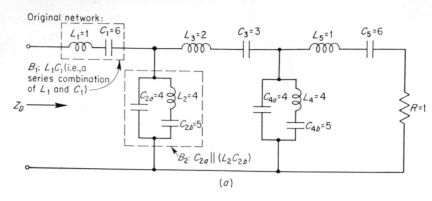

(a)

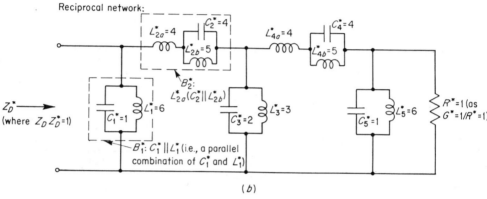

(b)

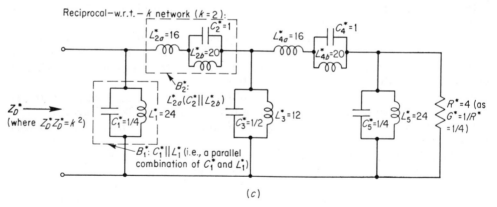

(c)

FIG. 6.22

For the reciprocal-w.r.t.-k network:

$$Z_D^*(s) = k^2 Y_D(s) = k^2 \times \text{same function as above} \qquad (6.70b)$$

This means that, *for a given network* **A**, *the driving-point impedances of its recipro-cal network* **B** *and reciprocal-w.r.t.-k network* **C** *differ only by a constant* k^2, *and* networks **B** and **C** are potentially equivalent networks according to (6.3). *Knowing the reciprocal network* **B**, *we may readily find the reciprocal-w.r.t.-k network* **C** *by modification with some numerical relations.* For example, we may replace (1) each circuit element such as L^*, R^*, or $D^* = 1/C^*$ which is proportional† to an impedance in dimension in **B** with a similar element of "modified" magnitude such as $L^*_{(k)} = k^2 L^*$, $R^*_{(k)} = k^2 R^*$, or $D^*_{(k)} = k^2 L^*$ and (2) each circuit element such as $\Gamma^* = 1/L^*$, $G^* = 1/R^*$, or C^* which is inversely proportional to an impedance in dimension in **B** with a similar element of modified magnitude such as $\Gamma^*_{(k)} = \Gamma^*/k^2$, $G^*_{(k)} = G^*/k^2$, or $C^*_{(k)} = C^*/k^2$.

As the result of the above discussion, we are able to obtain the procedures for finding the reciprocal-w.r.t.-k network of a given network by modifying procedures (6.63), (6.65), (6.68), and (6.69) for finding the reciprocal network. The modifications only involve changes in numerical relations. These procedures are as follows:

Finding the reciprocal-w.r.t.-k network:

> For a general network as the original network, follow the procedure in (6.63) or Fig. 6.18b, using the numerical relations in Table 6.2, column 3 (instead of column 4) (6.71a)

> For a series-parallel network as the original network, follow the procedure in (6.65) or (6.68), using the given k (instead of $k = 1$) in the numerical relations (6.71b)

> For a ladder network as the original network, follow the procedure in (6.69), using the given k (instead of $k = 1$) in the numerical relations (6.71c)

Illustration 7. Let us find the reciprocal-w.r.t.-k network for the network in Fig. 6.22a, $k = 2$. Since the original network is a ladder, we shall follow the procedure in (6.71c) or (6.69) for $k = 2$.

We first identify the original ladder network in Fig. 6.22a with Fig. 6.21$a1$, knowing that it has a reciprocal network structure in Fig. 6.21$a2$.

Since each branch in Fig. 6.22a is a series-parallel network itself, we must follow (6.69c). For example, the B_1^* branch in the reciprocal-w.r.t-k network in Fig. 6.22c is the reciprocal (with respect to $k = 2$) of the B_1 branch; the B_2^* branch is the reciprocal (with respect to $k = 2$) of the B_2 branch; etc. With circuit values appropriately computed for $k = 2$ according to (6.69d), we now have the reciprocal network in Fig. 6.22c.

D. *Some Additional Remarks about Reciprocal Networks*

Network synthesis with reciprocal-network techniques. In Illustrations 2 and 5 in Art. 6.3B, we demonstrated that (1) the reciprocal of an RC network is always an RL network, (2) the reciprocal of an RL network is always an RC network, and (3) given one network, we may always find the other as its reciprocal with the procedures in (6.63), (6.65), (6.68), or (6.69).

Suppose we are given the driving-point admittance, say

$$Y_{\hat{D}}^*(s) = \text{given network function } W(s) \text{ in the form of (3.13)} \qquad (6.72)$$

of an RL network which is unknown to us, and we wish to find this network. In the language of network synthesis, we wish to "synthesize $Y_{\hat{D}}^*(s)$ with an RL network."

---

† For example, the impedances of an inductance L^*, a resistance R^*, and a reciprocal capacitance D^* are, respectively, $Z_L^* = sL^*$, $Z_R^* = R^*$, and $Z_D^* = D^*/s$; it is obvious that L^*, R^*, and D^* are *proportional* to their impedances. On the other hand, the impedances of a reciprocal inductance Γ^*, a conductance G^*, and a capacitance C^* are, respectively, $Z_\Gamma^* = s/\Gamma^*$, $Z_G^* = 1/G^*$, and $Z_C^* = 1/sC^*$; Γ^*, G^*, and C^* are *inversely proportional* to their impedances.

This problem may be solved with several different approaches; for example,

Problem and direct approach:

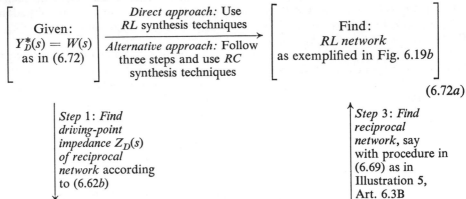

$$(6.72a)$$

Alternative approach with reciprocal-network techniques:

$$(6.72b)$$

The alternative approach in (6.72*b*) is based upon the facts that (1) *RL* and *RC* networks are reciprocal networks and (2) the original network is the reciprocal of its own reciprocal network. The latter statement is reflected in Steps 1 and 3; each of these two steps finds a reciprocal.

The problem described in (6.72*a*) may, of course, be solved with the direct approach: Use *RL* synthesis techniques. But what if we do not know any *RL* synthesis techniques? We may still solve the problem with the alternative approach in (6.72). This means that *we may solve an RL synthesis problem without knowing any RL synthesis techniques, but with the aid of reciprocal-network relations*. This is an illustration of network synthesis with "reciprocal-network techniques"; these techniques are applicable to other problems of network synthesis.

Reciprocal networks in filters. Let us consider two simple reciprocal networks:

Network **A**:   A series combination of C_1 and L_1

Network **B**:   A parallel combination of L_1^* and C_1^* $$(6.73)$$

where $$L_1^* = C_1 \qquad C_1^* = L_1 \qquad\qquad (6.73a)$$

Network **A** is actually a series *resonant* circuit with $f_0 = 1/\sqrt{L_1 C_1}$ as its resonant frequency; it presents no impedance to any signal of frequency f_0 and lets the signal pass freely. Network **B** is actually a parallel resonant, i.e., *antiresonant*, circuit with $f_0^* = 1/\sqrt{L_1^* C_1^*}$ as its resonant frequency, where $f_0^* = f_0$ according to (6.73*a*); it presents infinite impedance to and stops any signal of frequency $f_0 = f_0^*$. This illustrates in a simple manner the fact that *if a network lets a signal of a certain frequency pass freely, its reciprocal network stops it, and vice versa*.

Through the same kind of reasoning, we find that (1) the reciprocal of a low-pass filter (one which lets signals of low frequencies pass freely and attenuates or eliminates signals of high frequencies) is a high-pass filter, and vice versa, and (2) the reciprocal of a bandpass filter (one which passes signals of frequencies f within a frequency band, say $f_1 \leq f \leq f_2$) is a band-elimination filter, and vice versa.

Here we note that the reciprocal relations between networks are useful in the investigation and comparison of filters.

Some remarks about reciprocal-w.r.t.-k and reciprocal networks.   Let us consider a network **A** with driving-point impedance $Z_D(s)$ and another network **B** with driving-point impedance $Z_D^*(s)$, reciprocal with respect to k.   According to (6.61a),

Reciprocal-w.r.t.-k networks **A** *and* **B**:

$$Z_D(s)Z_D^*(s) = k^2 \tag{6.74}$$

This may be rearranged into

$$\frac{Z_D(s)}{k}\frac{Z_D^*(s)}{k} = 1$$

or

$$\bar{Z}_D(s)\bar{Z}_D^*(s) = 1 \tag{6.75}$$

where $\bar{Z}_D(s) = Z_D(s)/k$ and $\bar{Z}_D^*(s) = Z_D^*(s)/k$ are the *normalized* driving-point impedances (Art. 3.4) of the two networks.   We note that (6.75) has the form of (6.62a) for reciprocal networks.

The above discussion has elucidated one point: *If two networks are reciprocal with respect to k, their normalized versions, with k as the normalizing quantity, are reciprocal networks, and vice versa.*

PROBLEMS

6.1. Refer to the four-terminal network in Fig. P 2.6 whose parameters y_{ij} and z_{ij} have already been obtained in Prob. 4.12.

 (*a*) Obtain an equivalent T network, physical or nonphysical, in the form of Fig. 6.4a.
 (*b*) Obtain an equivalent Π network, physical or nonphysical, in the form of Fig. 6.4b.
 (*c*) Check the result in (*b*) against the result in (*a*) with the aid of Eqs. (6.14) or (6.15).

6.2. Given: The symmetrical networks in Fig. P 6.2.
Find the equivalent lattice for each.

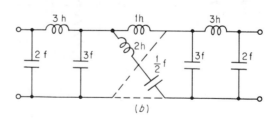

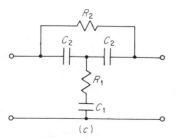 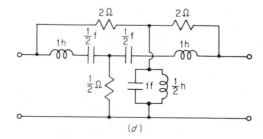

FIG. P 6.2

6.3. Given: The lattice in Fig. P 6.3.
Find its equivalent T network.

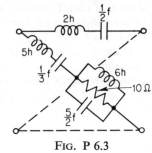

FIG. P 6.3

6.4. Given: The lattice in Fig. P 6.4.
Find an equivalent network in unbalanced form.

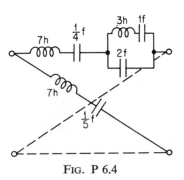

FIG. P 6.4

6.5. Given: The network in Fig. P 6.5.
Find its dual.

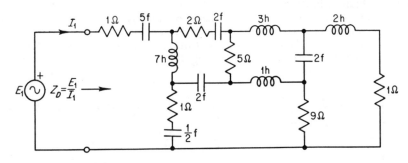

FIG. P 6.5

6.6. Given: $R_1 \parallel \{[C_2(L_3 \parallel R_3)] \parallel [(\overline{C_4L_4R_4} \parallel \overline{L_5R_5})L_6C_6]\}$ as the symbolic representation of a network, and $R_1 = 2$ ohms, $C_2 = 3$ farads, $L_3 = 7$ henrys, $R_3 = 6$, $C_4 = \frac{5}{2}$, $L_4 = 5$, $R_4 = \frac{7}{3}$, $L_5 = 8$, $R_5 = \frac{1}{3}$, $L_6 = \frac{11}{2}$, $C_6 = 1$.
(*a*) Represent the network with a circuit diagram.
(*b*) Obtain its reciprocal network.
(*c*) Obtain its reciprocal-w.r.t.-k network for $k = 2$.

6.7. Consider the network in Fig. 6.22c as the original network (and ignore all the asterisks in the figure).
(*a*) Obtain its reciprocal network.
(*b*) Obtain its reciprocal-w.r.t.-k network for $k = 3$.

part **C** Frequency analysis of excitation and response

In Part C we study network responses in the domain of the frequency ω. The Fourier series, Fourier integral, and Fourier transform are the mathematical tools we shall use. The review of the Fourier series is primarily intended to provide uniform notation and terminology.

The Fourier transform is used here as a tool in the study of transient responses. But why do we use it, in view of the fact that the Laplace transform, which will be introduced later, is a standard tool for transient study? The Laplace-transform approach always requires a knowledge of the network function, that is, $G(s)$, and under certain conditions we have no way of obtaining it. However, we may treat the network as a black box, measure its network characteristics $G_0(\omega)$ and $\theta(\omega)$, and use the Fourier-transform approach to obtain its transient responses.

7 Fourier series

7.1. Description of terms

A. Repeating Waveform

Definitions. A repeating function $e(t)$ is defined as a function of the time t which repeats its functional value indefinitely at a fixed time interval T; that is,

$$e(t) = e(t + nT) \qquad n = 0, \pm 1, \pm 2, \ldots \tag{7.1}$$

A repeating function is also called a *periodic function*. The time interval T is called the *period* of the function.

The waveform of a repeating function is called a repeating waveform. A portion of the waveform covering a complete period T is called a *cycle*. The number of cycles per second of a waveform is called its *frequency* or fundamental frequency. It is obvious that the frequency f_0 in cycles per second and the period T are related as follows:

$$f_0 = \frac{1}{T} \tag{7.2}$$

The angular frequency ω_0 in radians per second is then

$$\omega_0 = 2\pi f_0 = \frac{2\pi}{T} \tag{7.3}$$

which, for brevity, is called the frequency.

Illustration 1. A repeating function

$$e(t) = 1 \cos \omega_0 t \tag{7.4}$$

has a waveform as in Fig. 7.1a or b. The solid portion of either waveform in Fig. 7.1 represents a complete cycle. In Fig. 7.1a, we choose the interval $[0, T]$ as a complete cycle. The interval $[-T/2, +T/2]$ is a complete cycle in Fig. 7.1b.

We may also consider ωt, instead of t alone, in radians, as our independent variable. This means that we must change the scale of the horizontal axis in Fig. 7.1b to obtain, with the aid of (7.3), the representation in Fig. 7.1c.

Equation (7.4) is a sinusoidal function. A sinusoidal function is either a sine or a cosine function and is the simplest kind of repeating function.

Illustration 2. The repeating functions $e_1(t) = \cos \omega t$ and $e_2(t) = \frac{1}{9} \cos 3\omega t$ are indicated in Fig. 7.2. Their sum

$$e(t) = 1 \cos \omega_0 t + \tfrac{1}{9} \cos 3\omega_0 t \tag{7.5}$$

181

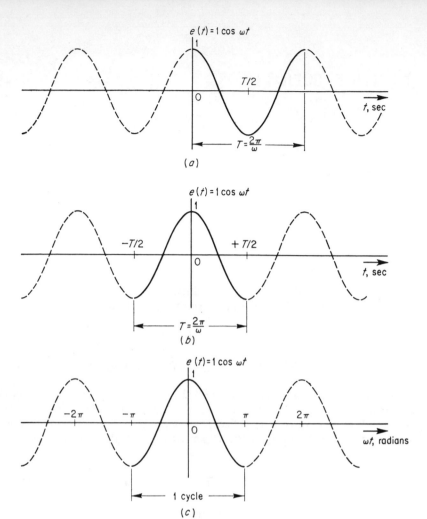

$e(t) = 1 \cos \omega t$

T/2

t, sec

$T = \dfrac{2\pi}{\omega}$

(a)

$e(t) = 1 \cos \omega t$

$-T/2$ $+ T/2$

t, sec

$T = \dfrac{2\pi}{\omega}$

(b)

$e(t) = 1 \cos \omega t$

-2π $-\pi$ π 2π

ωt, radians

1 cycle

(c)

FIG. 7.1

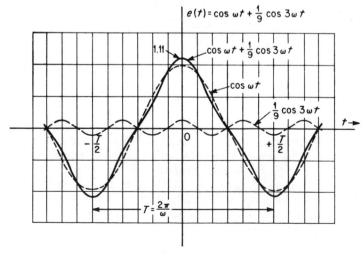

$e(t) = \cos \omega t + \dfrac{1}{9} \cos 3\omega t$

1.11 $\cos \omega t + \dfrac{1}{9} \cos 3\omega t$

$\cos \omega t$

$\dfrac{1}{9} \cos 3\omega t$

$t \rightarrow$

$-\dfrac{T}{2}$ $+\dfrac{T}{2}$

$T = \dfrac{2\pi}{\omega}$

FIG. 7.2

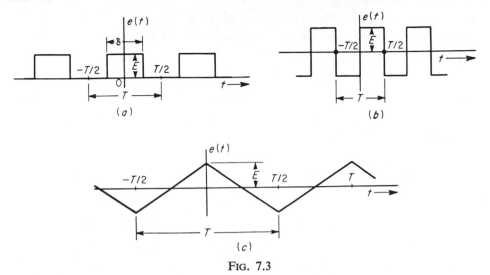

FIG. 7.3

is also a repeating function and is shown in Fig. 7.2.   We may say that the repeating function (7.5) has two components: (1) a component of frequency ω_0 and magnitude 1 and (2) a component of frequency $3\omega_0$ and magnitude $\frac{1}{9}$.

Other illustrations.   Additional illustrations of repeating waveforms are included in Fig. 7.3.

B. *Nonrepeating Waveform*

In contrast to the "repeating function" and "repeating waveform," we have "nonrepeating function" and "nonrepeating waveform." These terms are self-explanatory.   Illustrations are included in Fig. 7.4.

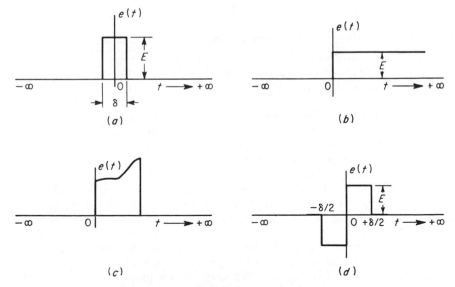

FIG. 7.4

C. Time and Frequency Domains—Some Simple Illustrations

Representations in the time domain.   Suppose $e_1(t)$ and $e_2(t)$ represent two electric signals, either voltages or currents.   Let

$$e_1(t) = 1 \cos \omega_0 t \tag{7.6a}$$

and

$$e_2(t) = 1 \cos \omega_0 t + \tfrac{1}{9} \cos 3\omega_0 t \tag{7.6b}$$

These repeating functions have already been studied in the illustrations.   Their representations are reproduced in Fig. 7.5a and b.   We note that for each of these

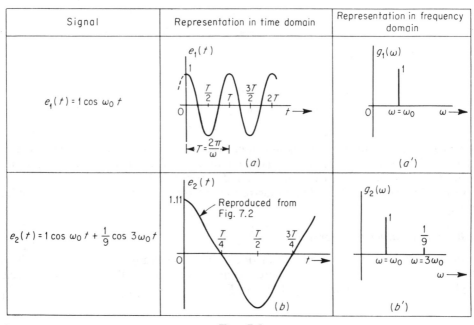

Signal	Representation in time domain	Representation in frequency domain
$e_1(t) = 1 \cos \omega_0 t$	(a)	(a')
$e_2(t) = 1 \cos \omega_0 t + \frac{1}{9} \cos 3\omega_0 t$	(b)	(b')

FIG. 7.5

representations, there is a functional value associated with each fixed value of the *time parameter t* [for example, $e_1(t) = 1$ at $t = 0$, $e_1(t) = 1/\sqrt{2}$ at $t = T/8$, and so on]; each representation completely describes the behavior of its signal.   We shall call the graphs in Fig. 7.5a and b the representations of the signals in (7.6) in the *time domain*.

Representations in the frequency domain.   To describe $e_1(t)$ and $e_2(t)$ in (7.6) in the English language, we may say that $e_1(t)$ has only one component in the form of a cosine function having frequency ω_0 and magnitude 1, and that $e_2(t)$ has two components in the form of cosine functions, one having frequency ω_0 and magnitude 1, and the other having frequency $3\omega_0$ and magnitude $\frac{1}{9}$.   It is obvious that they can be graphically represented in Fig. 7.5a' and b'.   Here we have, for each of the representations, a functional value representing the component magnitude associated with each fixed value of the *frequency* ω [for example, $g_1(\omega) = 1$ at $\omega = \omega_0$ and $g_1(\omega) = 0$ at $\omega \neq \omega_0$; $g_2(\omega) = 1$ at $\omega = \omega_0$, $g_2(\omega) = \frac{1}{9}$ at $\omega = 3\omega_0$, and $g_2(\omega) = 0$ at $\omega \neq \omega_0$ and $\omega \neq 3\omega_0$]; each representation, with the understanding that each component is a cosine function in our present simple illustrations, completely describes the behavior of its signal.   We shall call the graphs in Fig. 7.5a' and b' the representations of the signals (7.6) in the *frequency domain*.

Remarks.   To help define the term "frequency domain," we have used some very simple illustrations with two simple *repeating* functions $e_1(t)$ and $e_2(t)$ in (7.6).   However, we shall find later in this chapter that the concept of the frequency domain is most important in problems involving nonrepeating functions.

7.2. Fourier series in trigonometric form

A. Standard Form

We shall find that a repeating function $e(t)$ can usually be represented as a Fourier series in a standard form:

Fourier series in trigonometric form:

$$e(t) = \frac{A_0}{2} + \sum_{n=1}^{\infty} A_n \cos n\omega_0 t + \sum_{n=1}^{\infty} B_n \sin n\omega_0 t$$

$$= \frac{A_0}{2} + A_1 \cos \omega_0 t + A_2 \cos 2\omega_0 t + A_3 \cos 3\omega_0 t + \cdots + B_1 \sin \omega_0 t$$

$$+ B_2 \sin 2\omega_0 t + B_3 \sin 3\omega_0 t + \cdots \tag{7.7}$$

We may consider that the repeating function $e(t)$ in Fig. 7.2 has a Fourier series (7.5) with only two terms.   Identifying (7.5) with (7.7), we have $A_0 = 0$, $A_1 = 1$, $A_2 = 0$, $A_3 = \frac{1}{9}$, $A_4 = A_5 = \cdots = 0$, and $B_1 = B_2 = B_3 = \cdots = 0$.

B. Conditions for Representing a Repeating Function with a Fourier Series

Conditions.   If a repeating function $e(t)$ has (1) a finite number of points of discontinuity and (2) a finite number of maxima and minima in the interval $-T/2 \leq t \leq T/2$, it can be represented by a Fourier series in the form of (7.7).

Definitions and illustrations.   The term *discontinuity* is used to describe the situation in which $e(t_0)$ has a finite jump at some point $t = t_0$.   Analytically, this means that the two limiting values of $e(t)$, as t approaches t_0 from the right-hand and left-hand sides, exist but are unequal; i.e.,

$$\lim_{\varepsilon \to 0} e(t_0 + \varepsilon) \neq \lim_{\varepsilon \to 0} e(t_0 - \varepsilon) \tag{7.8a}$$

or, in abbreviation,

$$e(t_0^+) \neq e(t_0^-) \tag{7.8b}$$

For illustration, we have a finite jump at $t = t_1$ in Fig. 7.6a; the unequal limits are $e(t_1^+) = 3$ and $e(t_1^-) = 4$.   Therefore, we have a discontinuity at $t = t_1$.   We find that $e(t)$ in Fig. 7.6a has six discontinuities at $t = -t_3, -t_2, -t_1, t_1, t_2,$ and t_3 in the interval $-T/2 \leq t \leq T/2$.   We also observe that the function $e(t)$ in Fig. 7.6b has one discontinuity at $t = 0$ in the interval $-T/2 \leq t \leq T/2$.

A function $e(t)$ is said to have a *maximum* at $t = t_0$ if

$$e(t_0) - e(t_0 + \varepsilon) > 0 \tag{7.9a}$$

and

$$e(t_0) - e(t_0 - \varepsilon) > 0 \tag{7.9b}$$

for all sufficiently small positive values of ε.   A function $e(t)$ is said to have a *minimum* at $t = t_0'$ if

$$e(t_0') - e(t_0' + \varepsilon) < 0 \tag{7.10a}$$

and

$$e(t_0') - e(t_0' - \varepsilon) < 0 \tag{7.10b}$$

for all sufficiently small positive values of ε.   We now know that $e(t)$ in Fig. 7.7a has nine maxima at $-t_4, -t_3, -t_2, -t_1, t_a, t_b, t_c, t_d,$ and t_e and nine minima at $-t_e$, $-t_d, -t_c, -t_b, -t_a, t_1, t_2, t_3,$ and t_4.

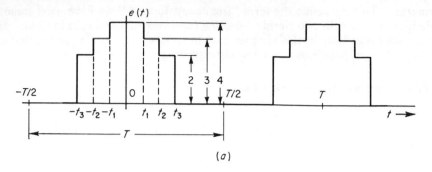

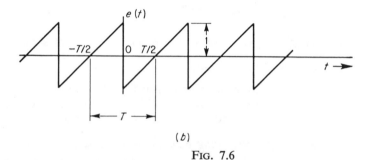

Fig. 7.6

It is obvious that the functions in Figs. 7.6 and 7.7a are representable by Fourier series in the form of (7.7), as they satisfy the conditions stated at the beginning of Art. 7.2B.

Illustration. *A repeating function having infinitely many maxima and minima* in the interval $-T/2 \leq t \leq T/2$ (for $T = 4$) is shown in Fig. 7.7b and described by

$$e(t) = \begin{cases} -(t+2)\sin\dfrac{\pi}{t+2} & -2 \leq t < -1 & (7.11a) \\[2ex] t\sin\dfrac{\pi}{t} & -1 \leq t \leq +1 & (7.11b) \\[2ex] -(t-2)\sin\dfrac{\pi}{t-2} & +1 < t \leq +2 & (7.11c) \end{cases}$$

We shall find that† there are infinitely many maxima and minima of $e(t)$ in the neighborhoods of $t = -2$, 0, and $+2$. This repeating function undoubtedly cannot be represented by a Fourier series in the form of (7.7).

7.3. Evaluation of the coefficients in a Fourier series in trigonometric form

Our problem here can be described as follows:

Given: A waveform or a repeating function $e(t)$ describing this waveform.

Find a Fourier series in the form of (7.7):

$$e(t) = \frac{A_0}{2} + A_1 \cos \omega_0 t + A_2 \cos 2\omega_0 t + A_3 \cos 3\omega_0 t + \cdots$$
$$+ B_1 \sin \omega_0 t + B_2 \sin 2\omega_0 t + B_3 \sin 3\omega_0 t + \cdots \quad (7.12)$$

† See F. S. Woods, "Advanced Calculus," p. 6, Ginn and Company, Boston, 1934.

To find this Fourier series is actually to evaluate its coefficients A_0 and A_n and B_n for $n = 1, 2, \ldots$, since $\omega_0 = 2\pi/T$ is known.

A. Procedure

Evaluation of A_0. We shall integrate (7.12) over t for a complete cycle from $t = 0$ to $t = T = 2\pi/\omega_0$ (or from $t = -T/2 = -\pi/\omega_0$ to $t = T/2 = \pi/\omega_0$):

$$\int_0^{2\pi/\omega_0} e(t)\, dt = \int_0^{2\pi/\omega_0} \left(\frac{A_0}{2}\, dt + A_1 \cos \omega_0 t\, dt + A_2 \cos 2\omega_0 t\, dt + \cdots \right.$$
$$\left. + B_1 \sin \omega_0 t\, dt + B_2 \sin 2\omega_0 t\, dt + \cdots \right)\, dt$$
$$= \int_0^{2\pi/\omega_0} \frac{A_0}{2}\, dt + 0 + 0 + \cdots + 0 + 0 + \cdots \qquad (7.13a)$$

$$\int_0^{2\pi/\omega_0} e(t)\, dt = \frac{A_0}{2} \frac{2\pi}{\omega_0} \qquad (7.13b)$$

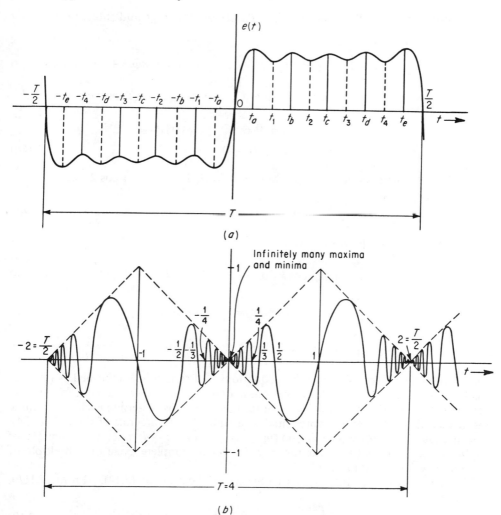

(a)

(b)

FIG. 7.7

Equation (7.13a) results from

$$\int_0^{2\pi/\omega_0} \cos k\omega_0 t \, dt = \int_0^{2\pi/\omega_0} \sin k\omega_0 t \, dt = 0 \qquad k - 1, 2, 3, \ldots \qquad (7.14a)$$

or, with $x = \omega_0 t$,

$$\int_0^{2\pi} \cos kx \, dx = \int_0^{2\pi} \sin kx \, dx = 0 \qquad k = 1, 2, 3, \ldots \qquad (7.14b)$$

Equations (7.14) may be intuitively explained as follows: The area under a sinusoidal wave, either a cosine function or a sine function, vanishes for a complete cycle or a multiple of complete cycles. This means that the positive area above the horizontal axis equals the negative area below the axis, and they cancel out.
From (7.13b), we have

$$A_0 = \frac{\omega_0}{\pi} \int_0^{2\pi/\omega_0} e(t) \, dt \qquad (7.15)$$

Evaluation of A_n. We shall multiply (7.12) by $\cos n\omega_0 t$ and integrate it over t from $t = 0$ to $t = 2\pi/\omega_0$:

$$\int_0^{2\pi/\omega_0} e(t) \cos n\omega_0 t \, dt = \int_0^{2\pi/\omega_0} \left(\frac{A_0}{2} \cos n\omega_0 t + A_1 \cos \omega_0 t \cos n\omega_0 t + \cdots + A_n \right.$$

$$\left. \times \cos n\omega_0 t \cos n\omega_0 t + \cdots + B_1 \sin \omega_0 t \cos n\omega_0 t + \cdots \right) dt$$

$$= 0 + 0 + \cdots + 0 + \int_0^{2\pi/\omega_0} A_n \cos n\omega_0 t$$

$$\times \cos n\omega_0 t \, dt + 0 + 0 + \cdots \qquad (7.16a)$$

$$\int_0^{2\pi/\omega_0} e(t) \cos n\omega_0 t \, dt = A_n \int_0^{2\pi/\omega_0} (\cos n\omega_0 t)^2 \, dt = A_n \int_0^{2\pi/\omega_0} (\tfrac{1}{2} + \tfrac{1}{2} \cos 2n\omega_0 t) \, dt$$

$$= \frac{A_n}{2} \frac{2\pi}{\omega_0} + 0 \qquad (7.16b)$$

Equation (7.16a) results from

$$\int_0^{2\pi} \sin mx \cos kx \, dx = 0 \qquad m \neq k \qquad (7.17a)$$

$$\int_0^{2\pi} \cos mx \cos kx \, dx = 0 \qquad m \neq k \qquad (7.17b)$$

and

$$\int_0^{2\pi} \sin mx \sin kx \, dx = 0 \qquad m \neq k \qquad (7.17c)$$

for all integral values of m and k. Equations (7.17) may be established as follows: Each of the integrands $\sin mx \cos kx$, $\cos mx \cos kx$, and $\sin mx \sin kx$, for $m \neq k$, can be represented as a sum of two sine terms or two cosine terms; each of the three integrals (7.17) can then be represented as a sum of two integrals of the type (7.14). For example, $\sin mx \cos kx = [\sin (m + k)x + \cos (m - k)x]/2$; the integrals of $\sin (m + k)x$ and $\cos (m - k)x$ for $m \neq k$ over a complete cycle or a multiple of complete cycles will vanish.
The zero term in (7.16b) results from the application of (7.14). From (7.16b), we have

$$A_n = \frac{\omega_0}{\pi} \int_0^{2\pi/\omega_0} e(t) \cos n\omega_0 t \, dt \qquad n = 1, 2, \ldots \qquad (7.18)$$

Evaluation of B_n. We shall multiply (7.12) by sin $n\omega_0 t$ and integrate it over t from $t = 0$ to $t = 2\pi/\omega_0$. Following a procedure similar to the above, with the aid of (7.17), we find

$$B_n = \frac{\omega_0}{\pi} \int_0^{2\pi/\omega_0} e(t) \sin n\omega_0 t \, dt \qquad n = 1, 2, \ldots \tag{7.19}$$

Summary. The coefficients of a Fourier series, in the trigonometric form (7.7), representing a given $e(t)$ may be computed from

Fourier coefficients (for Fourier series in trigonometric form):

$$A_0 = \frac{\omega_0}{\pi} \int_0^{2\pi/\omega_0} e(t) \, dt \tag{7.20a}$$

$$A_n = \frac{\omega_0}{\pi} \int_0^{2\pi/\omega_0} e(t) \cos n\omega_0 t \, dt \qquad n = 1, 2, \ldots \tag{7.20b}$$

$$B_n = \frac{\omega_0}{\pi} \int_0^{2\pi/\omega_0} e(t) \sin n\omega_0 t \, dt \qquad n = 1, 2, \ldots \tag{7.20c}$$

These integrals may be evaluated in the interval from $t = -T/2 = -\pi/\omega_0$ to $t = T/2 = \pi/\omega_0$ instead of the interval from $t = 0$ to $t = 2\pi/\omega_0$.

B. Illustrative Examples

Illustration 1. We shall now try to find the Fourier series of the repeating function $e(t)$ in Fig. 7.3a which can be described as

$$e(t) = \begin{cases} 0 & -\dfrac{T}{2} \le t < -\dfrac{\delta}{2} \\ E & -\dfrac{\delta}{2} \le t \le \dfrac{\delta}{2} \\ 0 & \dfrac{\delta}{2} < t \le \dfrac{T}{2} \end{cases} \tag{7.21}$$

Using Eqs. (7.20), we find

$$A_0 = \frac{\omega_0}{\pi} \int_{-T/2}^{T/2} e(t) \, dt = \frac{\omega_0}{\pi} \int_{-\pi/\omega_0}^{\pi/\omega_0} e(t) \, dt$$

$$= \frac{\omega_0}{\pi} \left(\int_{-\pi/\omega_0}^{-\delta/2} 0 \, dt + \int_{-\delta/2}^{\delta/2} E \, dt + \int_{\delta/2}^{\pi/\omega} 0 \, dt \right) = E \frac{\omega_0 \delta}{\pi} \tag{7.22a}$$

$$A_n = \frac{\omega_0}{\pi} \left(0 + \int_{-\delta/2}^{\delta/2} E \cos n\omega_0 t \, dt + 0 \right)$$

$$= \frac{E \sin n\omega_0 t}{n\pi} \bigg|_{t=-\delta/2}^{t=\delta/2} = E \frac{2 \sin (n\omega_0 \delta/2)}{n\pi} \tag{7.22b}$$

and

$$B_n = \frac{\omega_0}{\pi} \left(0 + \int_{-\delta/2}^{\delta/2} E \sin n\omega_0 t \, dt + 0 \right)$$

$$= E \frac{-\cos n\omega_0 t}{n\pi} \bigg|_{t=-\delta/2}^{t=\delta/2} = 0 \tag{7.22c}$$

The Fourier series of $e(t)$ in (7.21) now has the form

$$e(t) = \frac{2E}{\pi} \left[\frac{1}{2} \frac{\omega_0 \delta}{2} + \frac{\sin (\omega_0 \delta/2)}{1} \cos \omega_0 t \right.$$

$$\left. + \frac{\sin (2\omega_0 \delta/2)}{2} \cos 2\omega_0 t + \frac{\sin (3\omega_0 \delta/2)}{3} \cos 3\omega_0 t + \cdots \right] \quad (7.22d)$$

where E, ω_0, and δ are usually given quantities.

Other illustrations. Using Eqs. (7.20), we may likewise find, for the waveform in Fig. 7.3b, a Fourier series of the form

$$e(t) = \frac{4E}{\pi} \left(\sin \omega_0 t + \frac{1}{3} \sin 3\omega_0 t + \frac{1}{5} \sin 5\omega_0 t + \cdots \right) \quad (7.23)$$

and, for the waveform in Fig. 7.3c, a Fourier series of the form

$$e(t) = \frac{8E}{\pi^2} \left(\cos \omega_0 t + \frac{1}{9} \cos 3\omega_0 t + \frac{1}{25} \cos 5\omega_0 t + \cdots \right) \quad (7.24)$$

7.4. Fourier series in complex form

A. Standard Form

A repeating function $e(t)$, subjected to the conditions discussed in Art. 7.2B, can be represented by a Fourier series in a new standard form:

Fourier series in complex form:

$$e(t) = \sum_{n=-\infty}^{+\infty} C_n e^{jn\omega_0 t}$$

$$= C_0 + C_1 e^{j\omega_0 t} + C_2 e^{j2\omega_0 t} + \cdots + C_{-1} e^{-j\omega_0 t} + C_{-2} e^{-j2\omega_0 t} + \cdots \quad (7.25)$$

where C_n for any n is a complex quantity. We shall show in Art. 7.5 that the two forms (7.7) and (7.25) of a Fourier series are consistent and that we may use either form to represent a repeating function.

B. Evaluation of the Coefficients in a Fourier Series in Complex Form

We wish to find a Fourier series in the form of (7.25) for a given waveform or a repeating function $e(t)$ which describes it. To find this Fourier series is actually to evaluate the coefficients C_n for any n.

Evaluation of C_0. We shall integrate (7.25) over t for a complete cycle, say from $t = 0$ to $t = T = 2\pi/\omega_0$ (or from $t = -T/2 = -\pi/\omega_0$ to $t = T/2 = \pi/\omega_0$):

$$\int_0^{2\pi/\omega_0} e(t) \, dt = \int_0^{2\pi/\omega_0} (C_0 \, dt + C_1 e^{j\omega_0 t} \, dt + C_2 e^{j2\omega_0 t} \, dt + \cdots + C_{-1} e^{-j\omega_0 t} \, dt$$

$$+ C_{-2} e^{-j2\omega_0 t} \, dt + \cdots)$$

$$= \int_0^{2\pi/\omega_0} C_0 \, dt + 0 + 0 + \cdots + 0 + 0 + \cdots \quad (7.26a)$$

$$\int_0^{2\pi/\omega_0} e(t) \, dt = C_0 \frac{2\pi}{\omega_0} \quad (7.26b)$$

Equation (7.26a) results from

$$\int_0^{2\pi/\omega_0} e^{jk\omega_0 t} \, dt = \int_0^{2\pi/\omega_0} (\cos k\omega_0 t + j \sin k\omega_0 t) \, dt$$

$$= \int_0^{2\pi/\omega_0} \cos k\omega_0 t \, dt + j \int_0^{2\pi/\omega_0} \sin k\omega_0 t \, dt$$

$$= 0 + j0 = 0 \quad k = \pm 1, \pm 2, \ldots \quad (7.27)$$

which is established with the aid of (7.14).   From (7.26b) we have

$$C_0 = \frac{\omega_0}{2\pi} \int_0^{2\pi/\omega_0} e(t)\, dt \tag{7.28}$$

Evaluation of C_n.   We shall multiply (7.25) by $e^{-jn\omega_0 t}$ and integrate it over t from $t = 0$ to $t = 2\pi/\omega_0$:

$$\int_0^{2\pi/\omega_0} e(t)\, e^{-jn\omega_0 t}\, dt = \int_0^{2\pi/\omega_0} (C_0 e^{-jn\omega_0 t} + C_1 e^{-j(n-1)\omega_0 t} + \cdots + C_{n-1} e^{-j\omega_0 t}$$

$$+ C_n + C_{n+1} e^{j\omega_0 t} + \cdots + C_{-1} e^{-j(n+1)\omega_0 t}$$

$$+ C_{-2} e^{-j(n+2)\omega_0 t} + \cdots)\, dt$$

$$= 0 + 0 + \cdots + 0 + \int_0^{2\pi/\omega_0} C_n\, dt + 0 + 0 + \cdots \tag{7.29a}$$

$$\int_0^{2\pi/\omega_0} e(t)\, e^{-jn\omega_0 t}\, dt = C_n \frac{2\pi}{\omega_0} \tag{7.29b}$$

Equation (7.29a) results from (7.27).   Combining (7.28) and (7.29b), we may state that the coefficients of a Fourier series representing a given function $e(t)$ in complex form (7.25) may be computed from

Fourier coefficient (or Fourier series transform):

$$C_n = \frac{\omega_0}{2\pi} \int_0^{2\pi/\omega_0} e(t) e^{-jn\omega_0 t}\, dt \qquad n = 0, \pm 1, \pm 2, \ldots \tag{7.30}$$

where C_n is a complex quantity.   We shall call C_n the *complex amplitude* of the frequency component (with frequency $\omega = n\omega_0$) of the wave described by the function $e(t)$.   If we write (7.30) in the form

$$C_n = |C_n|\, e^{j\phi_n} \tag{7.31}$$

the absolute value $|C_n|$ represents the magnitude of the $n\omega_0$ frequency component, and the exponent ϕ_n in radians represents the *phase* angle of this component. C_n, as defined in (7.30), is called the *Fourier series transform* of $e(t)$.

Illustration 1.[†]   Suppose we have a repeating wave $e(t)$ as in Fig. 7.8a, and we wish to represent it as a Fourier series in the form of (7.25).   Since

$$e(t) = \begin{cases} 0 & -\dfrac{T}{2} \le t < -\dfrac{\delta}{2} \\[2mm] E & -\dfrac{\delta}{2} \le t \le \dfrac{\delta}{2} \\[2mm] 0 & \dfrac{\delta}{2} < t \le T \end{cases}$$

† Suppose, instead, that we choose the point A in Fig. 7.8a to be the "zero" time, that is, $t = 0$.   We shall find that $|C_n|$ thus computed is the same as obtained in this illustration. This means that, *for the same waveform $e(t)$, a shift of time axis will not affect the computed value of $|C_n|$ which represents the magnitude of the $n\omega_0$ frequency component.*   To study the magnitudes of the frequency components of $e(t)$, we often choose the time axis such that (1) $e(t)$ is an even function or has an even symmetry with respect to the chosen time axis as in Fig. 7.8a—then the computed C_n is a real quantity, and $|C_n|$ can readily be found—or (2) $e(t)$ is an odd function or has symmetry with respect to the origin associated with this chosen time axis as in Fig. 7.7a—then the computed C_n is a purely imaginary quantity, say $C_n = jk_n$, and $|C_n|$ can easily be obtained.

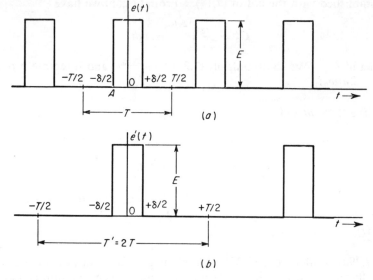

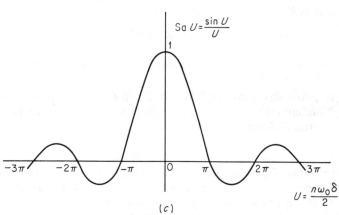

Fig. 7.8

Eq. (7.30) becomes

$$C_n = \frac{\omega_0}{2\pi} \int_{-T/2}^{T/2} e(t)e^{-jn\omega_0 t}\, dt = \frac{\omega_0}{2\pi} \int_{-\pi/\omega_0}^{\pi/\omega_0} e(t)\, e^{-jn\omega_0 t}\, dt$$

$$= \frac{\omega_0}{2\pi}\left(\int_{-\pi/\omega_0}^{-\delta/2} + \int_{-\delta/2}^{\delta/2} + \int_{\delta/2}^{\pi/\omega_0} \right) e(t)e^{-jn\omega_0 t}\, dt$$

$$= \frac{\omega_0}{2\pi}\left(0 + \int_{-\delta/2}^{\delta/2} Ee^{-jn\omega_0 t}\, dt + 0 \right) = \frac{E\omega_0}{2\pi} \left. \frac{e^{-jn\omega_0 t}}{-jn\omega_0} \right|_{t=-\delta/2}^{t=\delta/2}$$

$$= \frac{E}{\pi n} \frac{-e^{-j(n\omega_0\delta/2)} + e^{j(n\omega_0\delta/2)}}{2j}$$

$$= \frac{E}{\pi n} \sin \frac{n\omega_0\delta}{2} \qquad (7.32)$$

or

$$C_n = \frac{E\delta}{T} \operatorname{Sa} U = \frac{E\delta}{T} \frac{\sin U}{U} \qquad (7.32a)$$

where

$$U = \frac{n\omega_0\delta}{2} \qquad (7.32b)$$

and $T = 2\pi/\omega_0$. Sa $U = (\sin U)/U$ is the *sampling function* of the variable U and is shown in Fig. 7.8c. Substituting (7.32a) into (7.25) for $n = 0, 1, 2, \ldots$, we have the Fourier series representing the wave in Fig. 7.8a.

We now wish to find a *graphical representation* of C_n in (7.32a), which is the complex amplitude of the frequency components (with frequency $\omega = n\omega_0$) of the wave $e(t)$ as given in Fig. 7.8a. We change the scales of the axes in Fig. 7.8c to $\omega = n\omega_0 = 2U/\delta$ along the horizontal axis and $C_n = (E\delta/T)$ Sa $(n\omega_0\delta/2)$ along the vertical axis to obtain Fig. 7.9a. The heights of the vertical lines $C_0, C_1, C_2, \ldots$ in Fig. 7.9a are computed with (7.32a), with the integral values $0, 1, 2, \ldots$ for n, and represent the *complex amplitude*† of each frequency component; their *envelope* is described by

$$C_n = \frac{E\delta}{T}\frac{\sin U}{U} = \frac{E\delta}{T}\frac{\sin (\omega\delta/2)}{\omega\delta/2} \tag{7.33}$$

where the frequency ω is treated as a continuous variable.

For $E = 3$, $\delta = \frac{1}{3}$, and $T = 1$, we shall find $C_3 = 0$, as in Fig. 7.9a. We say that $\omega = 3\omega_0$ is the first *crossover frequency* of the repeating rectangular pulse with fundamental frequency $\omega_0 = 2\pi/T$, since the components C_2 and C_4 with frequencies on both sides of $\omega = 3\omega_0$ are completely (i.e., 180°) out of phase with each other. We may also call $\omega = 6\omega_0$ and $\omega = 9\omega_0$, respectively, the second and third crossover frequencies of the rectangular pulse.

For any combination of δ and T, we may find the first crossover frequency $\omega = n_0\omega_0$ by use of the smallest value of n (which we designate as n_0) such that $C_n = 0$ in (7.32). This obviously requires $U = n_0\omega_0\delta/2 = \pi$, that is,

$$\frac{n_0(2\pi/T)\delta}{2} = \pi \quad \text{or} \quad n_0 = \frac{T}{\delta} \tag{7.34}$$

We may therefore make the following statement: The first crossover frequency of a repeating rectangular pulse with period T and pulse width δ is $n_0\omega_0$ in radians per second, where n_0 is prescribed by (7.34).

For clarity in the subsequent discussion and the illustrations that lead to the derivation of the Fourier integral, we shall consider $n_0 = T/\delta$ as an integer by using a T which is a multiple of δ. However, $n_0 = T/\delta$ does not necessarily have to be an integer. If $\omega = n\omega_0$ is considered as a continuous variable, $\omega = n_0\omega_0$ is the value of ω at which the envelope of the frequency components crosses the ω axis, as illustrated in Fig. 7.9a.

C. Some Remarks about Fourier Series in Complex Form

Relations between pulse spacing and frequency components. Consider the wave $e'(t)$ in Fig. 7.8b with a period $T' = 2T$, where T is the period of the wave $e(t)$ in Fig. 7.8a. We wish to compare the frequency components of these two waves. It is obvious that (7.32) applies to both waves except for notation. We shall find that the imposed condition and its consequences are as shown in Table 7.1.

† For this particular example, the frequency components are either in phase or completely (i.e., 180°) out of phase at the instant $t = 0$. The positive quantities $C_0, C_1, C_2, C_3 = 0$, $C_6 = 0, C_7, \ldots$ are all in phase; the negative quantities $C_4, C_5, C_8, \ldots$ are completely out of phase with C_0. For illustration, $C_0 = 1$ is a vector $C_0 = 1 \underline{/0°}$ with a *zero phase angle*, and $C_4 = -0.207$ is a vector $C_4 = (0.207)\underline{/\pi} = (0.207)\underline{/180°}$ with a 180° *phase angle;* they are obviously out of phase.

As another example, with $C_n = |C_n| e^{j\phi_n} = |C_n| \underline{/\phi_n}$, where the phase angles ϕ_n are *not* all 0° or 180°, we cannot plot C_n versus ω as we did in Fig. 7.9a. To represent C_n as a function of ω graphically, we need two separate graphs: $|C_n|$ versus ω and ϕ_n versus ω.

It is now easy to see that if the period is tripled, (1) the d-c or reference amplitude is reduced to *one-third* its original value, (2) there are *three times as many* frequency components before the first crossover frequency, and (3) the fundamental frequency is *divided by three*.

With an inquisitive mind, we now wish to know: *What happens if the period*

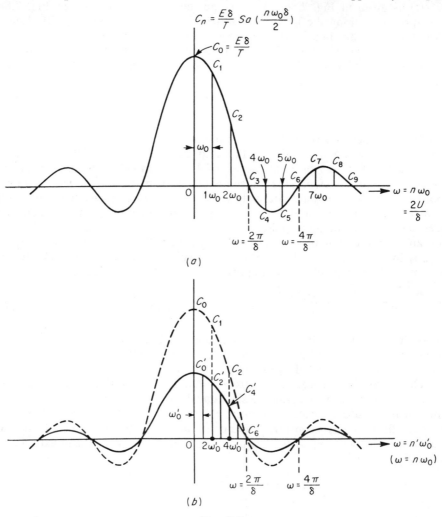

FIG. 7.9

approaches infinity, that is, $T' \to \infty$? According to the above arguments, we shall find

$$C_0' \to 0 \qquad n_0' \to \infty \qquad \omega_0' \to 0 \qquad (7.35)$$

This means that for a nonrepeating pulse as our limiting situation, e.g., with $T' \to \infty$ in Fig. 7.8b, (1) the d-c or reference amplitude is reduced to an *infinitesimally small* or zero value, (2) there are *infinitely many* frequency components before the first crossover frequency, and (3) the fundamental frequency or the frequency spacing between components becomes *infinitesimally small*. Items 2 and 3 imply that we have a continuous spectrum, rather than a spectrum of discrete quantities, for the frequency components. We shall call this a *continuous frequency spectrum*. But how can we handle a situation with an infinitesimally small reference amplitude C_0', where all other amplitudes C_n' are smaller than C_0' as indicated in Fig. 7.9b? We shall postpone this discussion until Art. 8.1A.

Time and frequency domains. $e(t)$, either as a given function describing a waveform or as a Fourier series in the form of (7.25), is a function of the time variable t.

Table 7.1

	Wave $e(t)$ in Fig. 7.8a	Wave $e'(t)$ in Fig. 7.8b	Observed relations
Condition.........	T	$T' = 2T$	1. The period is *doubled*
Consequences ...	$C_0 = \dfrac{E\delta}{T}$	$C_0' = \dfrac{E\delta}{T'} = \dfrac{1}{2}C_0$	2. The amplitude of the d-c or reference component is now *halved*; see Fig. 7.9b
	$n_0 = \dfrac{T}{\delta}$	$n_0' = \dfrac{T'}{\delta} = 2n_0$	3. There are now *twice as many* frequency components in the frequency range from direct current to the first crossover frequency; see Fig. 7.9b for a specific illustration with $n_0 = 3$ and $n_0' = 6$
	$\omega_0 = \dfrac{2\pi}{T}$	$\omega_0' = \dfrac{2\pi}{T'} = \dfrac{\omega_0}{2}$	4. The fundamental frequency is now *halved*

We say that $e(t)$ is defined in the *time domain*, for it has a functional value associated with each fixed value of the time t. For illustration, $e(t)$ in Fig. 7.8a is defined in the time domain.

C_n, as the Fourier series transform of $e(t)$ in the form of (7.30), is a function of the discrete frequencies $\omega = n\omega_0$ for $n = 0, 1, 2, \ldots$. We say that C_n is defined in the *frequency domain*, for it has a functional value associated with each fixed value of the frequency $\omega = n\omega_0$; for example, the functional value of C_n is computed with (7.30) for the frequencies $\omega = n\omega_0$ having only integral values of n, and is zero for all other frequencies. For illustration, C_n in Fig. 7.9a is defined in the frequency domain.

It is obvious that there is a one-to-one correspondence between the representations of a wave in the time and frequency domains:

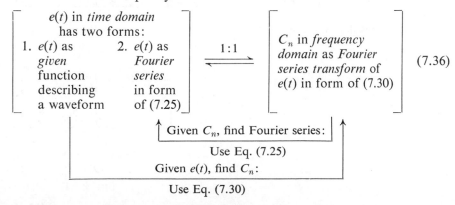

7.5. Relation between the two forms of Fourier series

It is obvious that the Fourier series in the complex form (7.25),

$$e(t) = C_0 + C_1 e^{j\omega_0 t} + C_2 e^{j\omega_0 t} + \cdots + C_{-1} e^{-j\omega_0 t} + C_{-2} e^{-j2\omega_0 t} + \cdots \quad (7.37a)$$

is reducible to the Fourier series in the trigonometric form (7.7),

$$e(t) = \frac{A_0}{2} + A_1 \cos \omega_0 t + A_2 \cos 2\omega_0 t + \cdots + B_1 \sin \omega_0 t + B_2 \sin 2\omega_0 t + \cdots \quad (7.37b)$$

if we can make

$$C_n e^{jn\omega_0 t} + C_{-n} e^{-jn\omega_0 t} = A_n \cos n\omega_0 t + B_n \sin n\omega_0 t \quad (7.38)$$

and

$$C_0 = \frac{A_0}{2} \quad (7.39a)$$

Equation (7.38) holds if

$$C_n = \frac{A_n - jB_n}{2} \quad (7.39b)$$

and

$$C_{-n} = \frac{A_n + jB_n}{2} \quad (7.39c)$$

Substituting (7.39b), (7.39c), and $e^{\pm jn\omega_0 t} = \cos n\omega_0 t \pm j \sin n\omega_0 t$ into the left-hand side of Eq. (7.38), we find that it equals the right-hand side of Eq. (7.38); Eq. (7.38) is then established. We may therefore make the following statement: The two forms of Fourier series in (7.37) are *identical* under conditions (7.39).

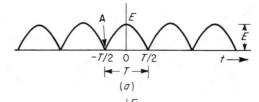

(a)

PROBLEMS

7.1. Obtain the Fourier series in trigonometric form for the following waveforms:

(a) The full-wave rectified cosine waveform in Fig. P 7.1a.

(b) The half-wave rectified cosine waveform in Fig. P 7.1b.

(c) The sawtooth waveform in Fig. P 7.1c.

(d) The triangular waveform in Fig. P 7.1d.

(b)

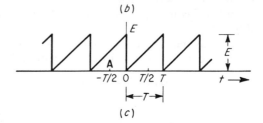

(c)

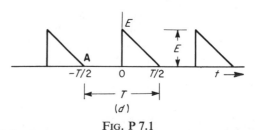

(d)

FIG. P 7.1

7.2. Designate point **A** as the new reference zero time $t = 0$ (instead of point 0 as indicated) for each waveform in Fig. P 7.1.   Repeat Prob. 7.1.

7.3. (*a*) Obtain the Fourier series in complex form for the waveform in Fig. P 7.1*a*.   Plot either $|C_n|$ versus n or $|C_n|$ versus $\omega = n\omega_0$, where $\omega_0 = 2\pi/T$ and C_n is the Fourier coefficient.

(*b*) Obtain the Fourier series in complex form for the *same* waveform, but with point **A** as the new reference zero time $t = 0$ (instead of point 0 as indicated) in Fig. P 7.1*a*.   Plot either $|C_n|$ versus n or $|C_n|$ versus $\omega = n\omega_0$, where $\omega_0 = 2\pi/T$.

Compare the $|C_n|$ plots in (*a*) and (*b*), and note that a shift of time axis does not affect the computed value of $|C_n|$ which represents the magnitude of the $n\omega_0$ frequency component of the wave.

7.4. Repeat Prob. 7.3 for the waveform in Fig. P 7.1*b*.

7.5. Repeat Prob. 7.3 for the waveform in Fig. P 7.1*c*.

7.6. (*a*) Obtain the Fourier series in complex form for the waveform in Fig. P 7.1*d*; represent its Fourier coefficient in the form $C_n = |C_n|\, e^{j\phi_n}$ as indicated in (7.31).

(*b*) Plot either $|C_n|$ versus n or $|C_n|$ versus $\omega = n\omega_0$, where $\omega_0 = 2\pi/T$; sketch its *envelope*, i.e., a continuous curve on which the vertical lines representing $|C_0|$, $|C_1|$, $|C_2|$, . . . terminate.

(*c*) Plot either ϕ_n versus n or ϕ_n versus $\omega = n\omega_0$, where $\omega_0 = 2\pi/T$; sketch its *envelope*.

8 Applications of Fourier series and Fourier integral in frequency analysis

8.1. Fourier integral as a generalized form of Fourier series

A. *Process of Generalization*

We have already studied the relations between pulse spacing and frequency components in Art. 7.4C. We know that, for $T \rightarrow \infty$ and constant pulse width δ for the wave in Fig. 7.8a, we have

$$C_0 \rightarrow 0 \qquad n \rightarrow \infty \qquad \omega_0 \rightarrow 0 \tag{8.1}$$

This means that the representations for frequency components in Fig. 7.9a must be modified. We have infinitely many frequency components (for $n_0 \rightarrow \infty$) before the first crossover at $\omega = 2\pi/\delta$; that is, we have a *continuous frequency spectrum*. But how are we going to represent C_n, where $|C_n| < C_0$ for any n, and $C_0 \rightarrow 0$? Since we are interested only in the relative magnitudes of the frequency components, why do we not investigate the limit of C_n/ω_0 for both $\omega_0 \rightarrow 0$ and $C_n \rightarrow 0$ as the consequence of $T \rightarrow \infty$ and (8.1)? The Fourier series transform (7.30) and the Fourier series (7.25) may now be written in the forms

$$\frac{C_n}{\omega_0} = \frac{1}{2\pi} \int_{-T/2}^{T/2} e(t) e^{-jn\omega_0 t} \, dt \tag{8.2a}$$

$$e(t) = \sum_{n=-\infty}^{+\infty} \frac{C_n}{\omega_0} e^{jn\omega_0 t} \omega_0 = \sum_{n=-\infty}^{+\infty} \frac{C_n}{\omega_0} e^{jn\omega_0 t} [n\omega_0 - (n-1)\omega_0]$$

$$= \sum_{n=-\infty}^{+\infty} \frac{C_n}{\omega_0} e^{jn\omega_0 t} \Delta(n\omega_0) \tag{8.2b}$$

where $\Delta(n\omega_0)$ is the incremental change in the quantity $n\omega_0$.

B. *Fourier Integral and Fourier Transform in the Complex Forms*

When $T \rightarrow \infty$ in Fig. 7.8a, we actually have a *nonrepeating function* as depicted in Fig. 8.1a for our analysis.

Fourier-intergal and Fourier-transform representations of the first kind. For $T \rightarrow \infty$ and its implied relations $\omega_0 \rightarrow 0$ and $C_n \rightarrow 0$, we define $\omega = n\omega_0$ and

$$g(\omega) = \lim_{\omega_0 \rightarrow 0} \frac{C_n}{\omega_0}$$

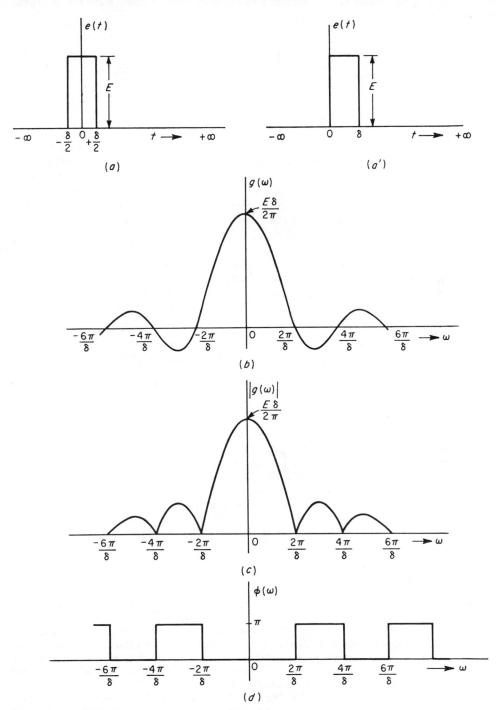

FIG. 8.1

Replacing $n\omega_0$ by ω and taking the limit as $\omega_0 \to 0$, we find that (8.2*b*) has the form of an integral:†

Fourier integral:‡

$$e(t) = \int_{-\infty}^{+\infty} g(\omega)e^{j\omega t}\, d\omega \qquad (8.3a)$$

Equation (8.2*a*) becomes

Fourier transform:§

$$g(\omega) = \frac{1}{2\pi} \int_{-\infty}^{+\infty} e(t)\, e^{-j\omega t}\, dt \qquad (8.3b)$$

We shall call (8.3*a*) the *Fourier integral*, and (8.3*b*) the *Fourier transform* (or the Fourier integral transform), in the complex forms associated with a nonrepeating wave.

Given a waveform described by $e(t)$, we can find its Fourier transform $g(\omega)$ with the aid of (8.3*b*), which represents the *complex amplitude* on a relative basis of any frequency component in $e(t)$. $g(\omega)$ is a continuous distribution or spectrum of the frequency components of $e(t)$. We may write (8.3*b*) in the form

$$g(\omega) = |g(\omega)|\, e^{j\phi(\omega)} \qquad (8.4)$$

where $|g(\omega)|$ represents the distribution of relative *magnitudes*, and $\phi(\omega)$ the distribution of *phase* angles, of the frequency components.

Given a Fourier transform $g(\omega)$, we can find its wave representation or Fourier integral $e(t)$ with the aid of (8.3*a*). A one-to-one correspondence between $e(t)$ and $g(\omega)$ is obvious:

$$\begin{bmatrix} e(t) \text{ in } \textit{time domain} \\ \text{represented by (8.3}a\text{)} \end{bmatrix} \overset{1:1}{\rightleftharpoons} \begin{bmatrix} g(\omega) \text{ in } \textit{frequency domain} \\ \text{represented by (8.3}b\text{)} \end{bmatrix} \qquad (8.5)$$

Illustration 1. For the nonrepeating function $e(t)$ in Fig. 8.1*a*, we find, with the aid of (8.3*b*), the Fourier transform

$$g(\omega) = \frac{1}{2\pi}\left(\int_{-\infty}^{-\delta/2} + \int_{-\delta/2}^{\delta/2} + \int_{\delta/2}^{+\infty} \right) e(t)e^{-j\omega t}\, dt$$

$$= 0 + \frac{1}{2\pi} \int_{-\delta/2}^{\delta/2} E e^{-j\omega t}\, dt + 0$$

$$= \frac{E}{2\pi} \int_{-\delta/2}^{\delta/2} (\cos \omega t - j \sin \omega t)\, dt$$

$$= \frac{E\delta}{2\pi} \frac{\sin(\omega\delta/2)}{\omega\delta/2} \qquad (8.6)$$

† We may define an integral in this manner: $\displaystyle\int_{x_a}^{x_b} f(x)\, dx = \lim_{n\to\infty} \sum_{i=1}^{n} f(x_i)\, \Delta x_i$, where the range of integration x_b to x_a is divided into n parts, and the largest Δx_i approaches zero as $n \to \infty$.

‡ Definition varies among authors. Equations (8.3*a*) and (8.3*b*) are generalized, respectively, from the Fourier series in (7.25) and the Fourier coefficient (or Fourier series transform) in (7.30); they are called, respectively, the Fourier integral and the Fourier transform of the function $e(t)$. Some authors call (8.3*b*) the Fourier integral as well as the Fourier transform, and call (8.3*a*) the inverse Fourier transform.

§ In addition to the approach of evaluating the integral in (8.3*b*), we may also obtain the Fourier transform $g(\omega)$ of a time function $f(t)$ or $e(t)$, often more conveniently, with the aid of (1) a Fourier-transform table or (2) a Laplace-transform table (e.g. Table 11.2), with $F(s) = \mathscr{L}[f(t)]$ and $g(\omega) = (1/2\pi)F(j\omega)$, provided that (1) $f(t) = 0$ for $t < 0$ and (2) $g(\omega)$ exists. The existence of the Fourier transform will be discussed in Art. 11.2.

which has a continuous distribution as indicated in Fig. 8.1*b*. The magnitude $|g(\omega)|$ and phase angle $\phi(\omega)$ of $g(\omega)$, as defined in (8.4), are depicted in Fig. 8.1*c* and *d*.

Illustration 2. For the nonrepeating function $f(t) = e(t)$ in Fig. 7.4*d*, we find, with the aid of (8.3*b*), the Fourier transform

$$g(\omega) = \frac{1}{2\pi}\left(\int_{-\infty}^{-\delta/2} + \int_{-\delta/2}^{0} + \int_{0}^{\delta/2} + \int_{\delta/2}^{+\infty}\right) e(t)e^{-j\omega t}\,dt$$

$$= 0 + \frac{1}{2\pi}\left(\int_{-\delta/2}^{0} -Ee^{-j\omega t}\,dt + \int_{0}^{\delta/2} Ee^{-j\omega t}\,dt\right) + 0$$

$$= \frac{E}{j2\pi\omega}[2 - (e^{j\omega\delta/2} + e^{-j\omega\delta/2})] = \frac{E}{j2\pi\omega}\left(2 - 2\cos\frac{\omega\delta}{2}\right)$$

$$= j\left(\frac{-2E}{\pi\omega}\right)\sin^2\frac{\omega\delta}{4} \tag{8.7}$$

Fourier-integral and Fourier-transform representations of the second kind. In deriving the Fourier-integral and Fourier-transform representations (8.3) of the first kind, we let $\omega = n\omega_0$ and defined $g(\omega) = \lim_{\omega_0 \to 0} (C_n/\omega_0)$. The reasons for defining $g(\omega)$ are: (1) Both $\omega_0 \to 0$ and $C_n \to 0$ for $T \to \infty$ and (2) we are interested in finding a function of ω to represent the relative magnitudes of the frequency components. Since we only wish to represent the frequency components on a *relative* basis, we may define $g_*(\omega) = \lim_{f_0 \to 0} (C_n/f_0) = \lim_{\omega_0 \to 0} (2\pi C_n/\omega_0)$. Modifying (8.2) accordingly, we find that, instead of (8.3), we have

$$e(t) = \frac{1}{2\pi}\int_{-\infty}^{+\infty} g_*(\omega)e^{j\omega t}\,d\omega \tag{8.8a}$$

$$g_*(\omega) = \int_{-\infty}^{+\infty} e(t)\,e^{-j\omega t}\,dt \tag{8.8b}$$

We shall call (8.8*a*) and (8.8*b*), respectively, the *Fourier integral* and *Fourier transform* of the *second kind* in contrast to (8.3), which may be said to be of the first kind. It is obvious that

$$g_*(\omega) = 2\pi g(\omega) \tag{8.9}$$

where $g(\omega)$ and $g_*(\omega)$ are the Fourier transforms of the first and second kinds.

One may use the Fourier integral and transform of either kind consistently, without using the other. However, different textbooks and references may contain different representations, some using the first kind, and some the second kind. The reader must be aware of both, but must use one kind consistently for the problems of frequency analysis. Equation (8.9) enables us to change a Fourier transform from one kind to the other.

In this book, we shall consistently use the Fourier integral and transform of the *first* kind as defined in (8.3) for all applications in frequency analysis. However, we shall use those of the second kind in the derivation of the Laplace transform to be discussed in Chap. 11; this is in line with common practice and the accepted form of the Laplace transform.

C. Even and Odd Functions

Even function. A function $F(x)$ is said to be an even function of the variable x if

$$F(-x) = F(x) \tag{8.10a}$$

It is obvious that an even function $F(x)$ has *even symmetry* with respect to the vertical $x = 0$ axis in its graphical representation. Even functions of the time variable t can be found in Figs. 7.3a and c, 7.4a, 7.6a, 7.7b, and 7.8a and b; even functions of the variable frequency ω can be found in Fig. 7.9a and b and Eq. (8.6).

Odd function.   A function $G(x)$ is said to be an odd function of the variable x if

$$G(-x) = -G(x) \tag{8.10b}$$

It is obvious that an odd function $G(x)$ has symmetry with respect to the origin, i.e., *point symmetry*, in its graphical representation. Odd functions of the time variable t can be found in Figs. 7.3b, 7.4d, 7.6b, and 7.7a; an illustration of an odd function of the variable frequency ω is provided by Eq. (8.7).

Even and odd relations between $e(t)$ and its Fourier transform.   We have demonstrated in the illustrations in Art. 8.1B associated with Eqs. (8.6) and (8.7) that:

1. The Fourier transform of a nonrepeating function $e(t)$ which is an even function of the time t is a *real* and *even* function of the frequency ω.

2. The Fourier transform of a nonrepeating function which is an odd function of the time t is a *purely imaginary* and *odd* function of the frequency ω.

Although we have tested them only twice, we shall find that these statements are true for any nonrepeating function $e(t)$.

8.2. Problems of frequency analysis

A. Frequency Spectrum of a Waveform

We have already discussed how to find the frequency spectrum of a waveform. Only some summarizing remarks will be given here.

Repeating function.   We can find the Fourier coefficient C_n of a repeating function $e(t)$ with the aid of (7.30).

If C_n is complex, we may represent it in the form of (7.31) and then plot two graphs: $|C_n|$ versus ω and ϕ_n versus ω for the discrete frequencies $\omega = n\omega_0$ for $n = 0, 1, 2, \ldots$. The graph of $|C_n|$ versus ω may be called the *frequency spectrum* of a repeating function $e(t)$.

If C_n is real, we may plot C_n versus ω for the discrete frequencies $\omega = n\omega_0$ for $n = 0, 1, 2, \ldots$. For example, Illustration 1 in Art. 7.4B, which is identified with a repeating function $e(t)$ as depicted in Fig. 7.8a, has the C_n versus ω graph in Fig. 7.9a. A C_n versus ω graph is sometimes also called a frequency spectrum of a repeating function. However, the term *frequency spectrum* more frequently refers to a $|C_n|$ versus ω graph. A $|C_n|$ versus ω graph for $e(t)$ in Fig. 7.8a will be a modified version of Fig. 7.9a in which the vertical lines with negative loops as their envelope (for example, C_4, C_5; C_8, C_9; C_{12}, C_{13}; etc.) are moved above the ω axis.

Nonrepeating function.   We can find the Fourier transform $g(\omega)$ of a nonrepeating function $e(t)$ with the aid of (8.3). $g(\omega)$ is also called the spectrum function of $e(t)$.

From the discussion in Art. 8.1C, we find: For even $e(t)$, $g(\omega)$ is real and even; for odd $e(t)$, $g(\omega)$ is purely imaginary and odd; for $e(t)$ neither odd nor even, $g(\omega)$ is complex (i.e., neither real nor purely imaginary) and neither even nor odd.

We may represent a complex $g(\omega)$ in the form of (8.4) and then plot two graphs: $|g(\omega)|$ versus ω and $\phi(\omega)$ versus ω. The graph of $|g(\omega)|$ versus ω is called the *frequency spectrum* of a nonrepeating function $e(t)$.

If $g(\omega)$ is real, we may plot a $g(\omega)$ versus ω graph. For example, in Illustration 1 in Art. 8.1B, the nonrepeating function $e(t)$ in Fig. 8.1a is shown to have the $g(\omega)$ versus ω graph in Fig. 8.1b. A $g(\omega)$ versus ω graph is sometimes called a frequency spectrum of a nonrepeating function. However, the term *frequency spectrum* more frequently refers to a $|g(\omega)|$ versus ω graph. A $|g(\omega)|$ versus ω graph for $e(t)$ in

Fig. 8.1*a* is given in Fig. 8.1*c*. Considering $g(\omega)$ as $|g(\omega)|e^{j\phi(\omega)}$ as in (8.4), we find the $\phi(\omega)$ versus ω graph in Fig. 8.1*d* for $e(t)$.

Choice of time axis and its effect on the frequency spectrum. For the nonrepeating function $e(t)$ in Fig. 8.1*a*, we have obtained $g(\omega)$ in (8.6); thus

$$|g(\omega)| = \frac{E\delta}{2\pi}\left|\frac{\sin(\omega\delta/2)}{\omega\delta/2}\right| \tag{8.11a}$$

Its frequency spectrum, i.e., the $|g(\omega)|$ versus ω graph, is depicted in Fig. 8.1*c*.

For the same waveform with the *time axis shifted* as indicated in Fig. 8.1*a'*, we find

$$g(\omega) = \frac{1}{2\pi}\left(\int_{-\infty}^{0} + \int_{0}^{\delta} + \int_{\delta}^{+\infty}\right)e(t)e^{-j\omega t}\,dt$$

$$= 0 + \frac{1}{2\pi}\int_{0}^{\delta} Ee^{-j\omega t}\,dt + 0 = e^{-j(\omega\delta/2)}\frac{E\delta}{2\pi}\frac{\sin(\omega\delta/2)}{\omega\delta/2} \tag{8.11b}$$

Since $|e^{-j\theta}| = |\cos\theta - j\sin\theta| = \sqrt{\cos^2\theta + \sin^2\theta} = 1$ for any θ, (8.11*b*) implies

$$|g(\omega)| = \frac{E\delta}{2\pi}\left|\frac{\sin(\omega\delta/2)}{\omega\delta/2}\right| \tag{8.11c}$$

Equations (8.11*a*) and (8.11*c*) are identical. Other illustrations will yield similar results. We may therefore state: *For a given waveform $e(t)$, the frequency spectrum, i.e., the $|g(\omega)|$ versus ω graph, remains the same no matter which time instant is chosen to be the "zero" time (that is, $t = 0$).* For this reason, we may choose our time axis arbitrarily in studying the relative magnitudes of the frequency components of a signal $e(t)$ having a given waveform. It is often desirable, if possible, to choose the time axis such that (1) $e(t)$ is an even function—$g(\omega)$ is then real and even, and $|g(\omega)|$ can readily be found—or (2) $e(t)$ is an odd function—$g(\omega)$ is then purely imaginary and odd, and $|g(\omega)|$ can easily be computed.

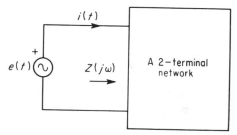

Fig. 8.2

B. *Response of a Two-terminal Network*

Description of problem. We shall postpone our study of the transient response of a two-terminal network until Chap. 12; we shall study here the steady-state response $i(t)$ of a linear two-terminal network with a (driving-point) impedance $Z(j\omega)$, as depicted in Fig. 8.2, subject to a voltage excitation $e(t)$ which is a repeating function of t.

Illustration. A *sinusoidal excitation* $e_n(t)$ with frequency $\omega = n\omega_0$ may be represented in the form of Eqs. (2.7):

Excitation:

$$e_n(t) = E_n e^{jn\omega_0 t} \tag{8.12a}$$

with the understanding that it represents the real part of $E_n e^{jn\omega_0 t}$, or

$$e_n(t) = \mathrm{Re}\,(E_n e^{jn\omega_0 t}) \tag{8.12a'}$$

where E_n is usually a complex quantity in the form $E_n = |E_n| e^{j\phi_n} = |E_n| \underline{/\phi_n}$. It is obvious that $e_n(t)$ may also be represented as

Excitation in alternative form:

$$e_n(t) = A_n \cos n\omega_0 t + B_n \sin n\omega_0 t \tag{8.12b}$$

$$e_n(t) = |E_n| \cos (n\omega_0 t + \phi_n) \tag{8.12b'}$$

where

$$|E_n| = \sqrt{A_n^2 + B_n^2} \qquad \phi_n = \tan^{-1}\left(-\frac{B_n}{A_n}\right) \tag{8.13a}$$

and

$$A_n = |E_n| \cos \phi_n \qquad B_n = -|E_n| \sin \phi_n \tag{8.13b}$$

Again, $e(t)$ may be represented in the form

Excitation in another alternative form:

$$e_n(t) = C_n e^{jn\omega_0 t} + C_{-n} e^{-jn\omega_0} \tag{8.12c}$$

where

$$E_n = 2C_n \tag{8.13c}$$

and C_{-n} is the conjugate of C_n.

As a simple illustration, we may try $C_n = 1 + j1$, $C_{-1} = 1 - j1$, and $E_n = 2C_n = 2 + j2$ in (8.12a') and (8.12c). We find that both equations are equal to

$$2(\cos n\omega_0 t - \sin n\omega_0 t)$$

and therefore are *equal to* each other.

Suppose the excitation $e(t)$ is given in one of the forms (8.12a), (8.12b), and (8.12c), and we wish to find its response $i(t)$. Through relations (8.13), we can always represent the excitation in the form of (8.12a):

Excitation:

$$e(t) = e_n(t) = E_n e^{jn\omega_0 t} \tag{8.14}$$

Using the relation similar to Eqs. (2.7), we have

Response:

$$i(t) = i_n(t) = I_n e^{jn\omega_0 t} \tag{8.15a}$$

with the understanding that it represents the real part of $I_n e^{jn\omega_0 t}$, or

$$i(t) = i_n(t) = \text{Re}\,(I_n e^{jn\omega_0 t}) \tag{8.15a'}$$

where

$$I_n = \frac{E_n}{Z(j\omega)} = \frac{E_n}{Z(jn\omega_0)} \tag{8.16}$$

and I_n is usually a complex quantity and can be represented in the form

$$I_n = |I_n| e^{j\phi'_n} = |I_n| \underline{/\phi'_n}$$

Just as the excitation $e(t)$ has three forms of representation, the response $i(t)$ has three forms. In addition to (8.15a), we have

Response in alternative form:

$$i(t) = i_n(t) = A'_n \cos n\omega_0 t + B'_n \sin n\omega_0 t \tag{8.15b}$$

$$i(t) = |I_n| \cos (n\omega_0 t + \phi'_n) \tag{8.15b'}$$

where

$$|I_n| = \sqrt{(A'_n)^2 + (B'_n)^2} \qquad \phi'_n = \tan^{-1}\left(-\frac{B'_n}{A'_n}\right) \tag{8.17a}$$

and

$$A'_n = |I_n| \cos \phi'_n \qquad B'_n = -|I_n| \sin \phi'_n \tag{8.17b}$$

We may also represent $i(t)$ in the form

Response in another alternative form:

$$i(t) = i_n(t) = C'_n e^{jn\omega_0 t} + C'_{-n} e^{-jn\omega_0} \tag{8.15c}$$

where
$$I_n = 2C'_n \tag{8.17c}$$

is a relation similar to (8.13c), and C'_{-n} is the conjugate of C_n.

Response $i(t)$ of a two-terminal network subject to a sinusoidal excitation. Summarizing the above discussion, the problem

$$
\begin{bmatrix}
\text{Given a sinusoidal} \\
\text{excitation } e(t) \text{ in one of} \\
\text{three forms in (8.12)}
\end{bmatrix}
\rightarrow
\begin{bmatrix}
\text{Find steady-state} \\
\text{response } i(t) \text{ in one of} \\
\text{three forms in (8.15)}
\end{bmatrix}
\tag{8.18}
$$

for a two-terminal network may be solved in the following manner: (1) convert an excitation $e(t)$ given in any form of (8.12) into the form of (8.12a) or (8.12a') using relations (8.13) and (2) find the response $i(t)$ in the form of (8.15a) or (8.15a') with the aid of relation (8.16); then, if the problem requires that the response be represented in the form of (8.15b) or (8.15c), use relations (8.17) in converting (8.15a) into the desired form. More specifically, the method of solution may be described as follows:

[$e(t)$ in form (8.12b) or (8.12b')]   [$i(t)$ in form (8.15b) or (8.15b')]

Use (8.13a) ↓   Use (8.17b) ↑

[$e(t)$ in form (8.12a) or (8.12a')] $\xrightarrow[\text{(8.16)}]{\text{Use}}$ [$i(t)$ in form (8.15a) or (8.15a')]   (8.19)

Use (8.13c) ↑   Use (8.17c) ↓

[$e(t)$ in form (8.12c)]   [$i(t)$ in form (8.15c)]

Response $i(t)$ of a two-terminal network subject to a given excitation $e(t)$. A given excitation $e(t)$, a repeating function but not sinusoidal, is applied to a linear two-terminal network. We wish to investigate the steady-state response $i(t)$ of the network.

Because the network is linear, the superposition theorem applies here. This means that, if we represent the excitation as $e(t) = e_0 + e_1(t) + e_2(t) + \cdots$, we may find the response as $i(t) = i_0 + i_1(t) + i_2(t) + \cdots$, where i_0, $i_1(t)$, $i_2(t)$, ... are the respective component responses due to the component excitations e_0, $e_1(t)$, $e_2(t)$, ... Finding $i_n(t)$ for each n from a given $e_n(t)$ is a problem similar to the above illustration, with the method of solution outlined in (8.19). This suggests the following *procedure* in finding the response $i(t)$:

1. Represent the given $e(t)$ by a Fourier series in the form of (7.25):

$$e(t) = e_0 + e_1(t) + e_2(t) + e_3(t) + \cdots \tag{8.20}$$

where
$$e_0 = C_0$$
$$e_n(t) = C_n e^{jn\omega_0 t} + C_{-n} e^{-jn\omega_0 t} \qquad n = 1, 2, \ldots \tag{8.20a}$$

If $e(t)$ is already given as a Fourier series in the form of (7.7), convert it into the form of (7.25) with relations (7.39).

2. Represent each component excitation $e_n(t)$ in the form of (8.12a) with the aid of (8.13c):

$$e_0 = E_0$$
$$e_n(t) = E_n e^{jn\omega_0 t} \qquad n = 1, 2, \ldots \tag{8.21}$$

where
$$E_0 = C_0$$
$$E_n = 2C_n \qquad n = 1, 2, \ldots \tag{8.21a}$$

3. Find the component response $i_n(t)$ for each component excitation $e_n(t)$ in (8.21) with the aid of (8.16). As in (8.15a), we now have

$$i_0 = I_0 \qquad i_n(t) = I_n e^{jn\omega_0 t} \tag{8.22}$$

where
$$I_0 = \frac{E_0}{Z(j0)} = \frac{C_0}{Z(j0)}$$

$$I_n = \frac{E_n}{Z(jn\omega_0)} = \frac{2C_n}{Z(jn\omega_0)} \qquad n = 1, 2, \ldots \tag{8.22a}$$

4. If the problem requires that the response $i(t) = i_0 + i_1(t) + i_2(t) + \cdots$ be represented by a Fourier series of the form of (7.25), find, with the aid of (8.17c) and (8.15c),

$$i(t) = C_0' + C_1' e^{j\omega_0 t} + C_2' e^{j2\omega_0 t} + \cdots$$
$$+ C_{-1}' e^{-j\omega_0 t} + C_{-2}' e^{-j2\omega_0 t} + \cdots \tag{8.23}$$

where
$$C_0' = I_0 = \frac{C_0}{Z(j0)}$$

$$C_n' = \frac{1}{2} I_n = \frac{C_n}{Z(jn\omega_0)} \qquad n = 1, 2, \ldots \tag{8.23a}$$

$$C_{-n}' = \text{conjugate of } C_n'$$

4'. If the problem requires that the response $i(t) = i_0 + i_1(t) + i_2(t) + \cdots$ be represented by a Fourier series of the form of (7.7), find, with the aid of (8.17b) and (8.15b),

$$i(t) = \frac{A_0'}{2} + A_1' \cos \omega_0 t + A_2' \cos 2\omega_0 t + \cdots$$
$$+ B_1' \sin \omega_0 t + B_2' \sin 2\omega_0 t + \cdots \tag{8.24}$$

with
$$A_0' = 2I_0 = \frac{2C_0}{Z(j0)}$$

$$A_n' = |I_n| \cos \phi_n \tag{8.24a}$$
$$B_n' = -|I_n| \sin \phi_n$$

where
$$I_n = |I_n| e^{j\phi_n} = \frac{2C_n}{Z(jn\omega_0)} \tag{8.24b}$$

$|I_n|$ and ϕ_n in (8.24a) are obtained from (8.24b):

$$|I_n| = \left| \frac{2C_n}{Z(jn\omega_0)} \right| \qquad \text{and} \qquad \phi_n = \tan^{-1} \frac{b_n}{a_n}$$

where $2C_n/Z(jn\omega_0) = a_n + jb_n$.

C. Response of a Four-terminal Network

Description of problem. Suppose we have a voltage excitation $e_1(t)$ as input to a linear four-terminal network as in Fig. 8.3a. We wish to investigate the response $e_2(t)$.

Transmission characteristic of a four-terminal network. We have described $G(s)$ in Art. 3.5C as the transfer voltage-ratio function of a four-terminal network. This is a transfer function which will be discussed in more detail and used a great deal in

Chap. 18. At present, we shall be satisfied to use $G(j\omega)$, that is, $G(s)$ at the real frequencies $s = j\omega$, which is represented in (3.39) as

$$G(j\omega) = G_0(\omega)e^{-j\theta(\omega)} \qquad (8.25)$$

We shall call $G(j\omega)$ or $G_0(\omega)e^{-j\theta(\omega)}$ the *transmission characteristic* or *complex gain* of a four-terminal network, $G_0(\omega)$ its *gain characteristic* (or absolute gain characteristic), and $\theta(\omega)$ its *phase characteristic*. At a fixed frequency ω, $G_0(\omega)$ represents the *ratio* of the magnitude of the ω frequency component in the output to that in the input: $\theta(\omega)$ represents the phase angle with which the ω frequency component in the output *lags* that in the input. If $G_0(\omega) > 1$, we have amplification or gain; if $G_0(\omega) < 1$,

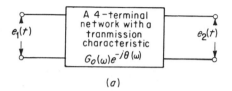

(a)

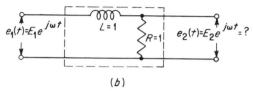

(b)

FIG. 8.3

attenuation or loss. If $\theta(\omega)$ is positive, a phase delay (also a time delay) is introduced by the network; if $\theta(\omega)$ is negative, a phase advance is introduced.

We shall use the simple circuit with single sinusoidal excitation in Fig. 8.3b for an almost trivial illustration. For excitation $e_1(t) = E_1 e^{j\omega t}$, we wish to know the voltage $e_2(t)$ across the resistor R. We have an equivalent four-terminal network. It is obvious that

$$G(s) = \frac{E_2}{E_1} = \frac{1}{s+1}$$

$$G(j\omega) = \frac{1}{1+j\omega}\frac{1-j\omega}{1-j\omega} = \frac{1}{1+\omega^2} - j\frac{\omega}{1+\omega^2} \qquad (8.26)$$

and with the aid of (3.40)

$$G_0(\omega) = \sqrt{\left(\frac{1}{1+\omega^2}\right)^2 + \left(\frac{\omega}{1+\omega^2}\right)^2} = \frac{1}{\sqrt{1+\omega^2}} \qquad (8.26a)$$

and

$$\theta(\omega) = -\tan^{-1}\frac{-\omega/(1+\omega^2)}{1/(1+\omega^2)} = \tan^{-1}\omega \qquad (8.26b)$$

The gain and phase characteristics of the network arrangement in Fig. 8.3b are given in Fig. 8.4a and b. We note that the gain characteristic $G_0(\omega) = |G(j\omega)|$ is an *even* function of ω; the phase characteristic $\theta(\omega)$, an odd function. $G_0(\omega)$ and $\theta(\omega)$ as given in Fig. 8.4a and b are the transmission characteristics of a *low-pass* network.

We have included the *negative-frequency* region, that is, $-\infty < \omega \leq 0$, in the representations of the transmission characteristics in Fig. 8.4a and b. The inclusion of the negative-frequency region is for *mathematical expediency*. For example, a signal with a frequency $\omega = n\omega_0$,

$$e(t) = E_n \cos(n\omega_0 t + \phi_n) = (E_n \cos \phi_n) \cos n\omega_0 t + (-E_n \sin \phi_n) \sin n\omega_0 t$$
$$= A_n \cos n\omega_0 t + B_n \sin n\omega_0 t \qquad (8.27a)$$

may be represented as

$$e(t) = C_n e^{jn\omega_0 t} + C_{-n} e^{-jn\omega_0 t} = C_n e^{j\omega t} + C_{-n} e^{-j\omega t} \qquad (8.27b)$$

subject to conditions (7.39). We may consider that this sinusoidal signal $e(t) = E_n \cos(\omega t + \phi_n)$ has two components: $C_n e^{j\omega t}$ with a positive frequency ω, and $C_{-n} e^{j(-\omega)t}$ with a negative frequency $-\omega$.   If we have an excitation $e(t)$ in the form of (8.27b), it is convenient to use the transmission characteristics defined over both the positive and negative regions of the frequency axis.   The negative-frequency region is also called the *fictitious*-frequency region, for negative frequencies exist only in mathematical equations such as (8.27b) and not in reality—for example, the negative-frequency component $C_{-n} e^{-j\omega t}$ combines with the positive-frequency component $C_n e^{j\omega t}$ to give the actual signal $e(t) = E_n \cos(\omega t + \phi_n)$ with positive frequency.

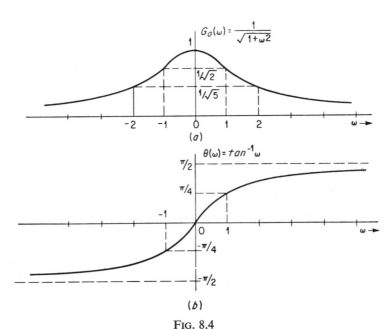

FIG. 8.4

Idealized transmission characteristics of a low-pass network.   We often use a low-pass network to eliminate the high-frequency components of a signal; we call such a network a low-pass filter.   It is often desirable for the filter to have a sharp cutoff frequency ω_c in its gain characteristic, as in Fig. 8.5a.   As an approximation to the odd-function phase characteristic $\theta(\omega)$ in Fig. 8.4b, and for easy mathematical manipulation in finding the network response, we shall assume the ideal form of the phase characteristic in Fig. 8.5b.   We now have two *idealized* transmission characteristics for a low-pass network, displayed in Fig. 8.5a and b and analytically represented by

$$G_0(\omega) = \begin{cases} K & -\omega_c \leq \omega \leq \omega_c \\ 0 & \omega < -\omega_c, \, \omega_c < \omega \end{cases} \tag{8.28a}$$

and
$$\theta(\omega) = \omega t_d \tag{8.28b}$$

where ω_c is the cutoff frequency, and t_d is the time delay introduced by the network. We shall discuss the time delay in Art. 9.10.

Idealized transmission characteristics cannot be realized with physical networks, but are approximations to the transmission characteristics of some physical networks.

Response $e_2(t)$ subject to a repeating-function excitation $e_1(t)$. Suppose $e_1(t)$ is sinusoidal, say

$$e_1(t) = E_1 e^{j\omega t} \tag{8.29}$$

with the understanding, as in (2.7), that the actual excitation is the real part of $E_1 e^{j\omega t}$; that is,

$$e_1(t) = \operatorname{Re}\,(E_1 e^{j\omega t}) \tag{8.29a}$$

The response $e_2(t)$ in Fig. 8.3a is merely

$$e_2(t) = E_2 e^{j\omega t} \tag{8.30}$$

with the understanding that the actual response is the real part of $E_2 e^{j\omega t}$; that is,

$$e_2(t) = \operatorname{Re}\,(E_2 e^{j\omega t}) \tag{8.30a}$$

where

$$E_2 = E_1 G(j\omega) = E_1 G_0(\omega) e^{-j\theta(\omega)} \tag{8.31}$$

and $G(j\omega) = G_0 e^{-j\theta(\omega)}$ is the transmission characteristic of the network.

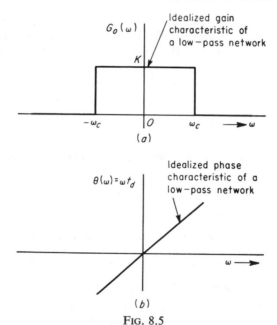

FIG. 8.5

We now suppose that the excitation $e_1(t)$ is a repeating function, but not sinusoidal. We (1) represent $e_1(t)$ as a Fourier series, (2) treat each component in this Fourier series as an excitation and find its response as above, and (3) add all these component responses to obtain the composite response $e_2(t)$. This procedure is similar to that for a two-terminal network as described in Art. 8.2B.

Response $e_2(t)$ subject to a nonrepeating function $e_1(t)$ as excitation. We may find the Fourier transform of the excitation $e_1(t)$ in the form of (8.3b),

$$g_1(\omega) = \frac{1}{2\pi} \int_{-\infty}^{+\infty} e_1(t) e^{-j\omega t}\, dt \tag{8.32}$$

which represents the complex amplitudes of the frequency components of the excitation $e_1(t)$ on a relative basis. Since the transmission characteristic $G(j\omega) = G_0(\omega) e^{-j\theta(\omega)}$ relates the relative complex amplitude of each frequency component in the response to that in the excitation, we have

$$g_2(\omega) = g_1(\omega) G(j\omega) = g_1(\omega) G_0(\omega) e^{-j\theta(\omega)} \tag{8.33a}$$

which is the Fourier transform of the response $e_2(t)$.   To find the response, we substitute (8.33a) into (8.3a):

$$e_2(t) = \int_{-\infty}^{+\infty} g_2(\omega)e^{j\omega t}\,d\omega = \int_{-\infty}^{+\infty} g_1(\omega)G_0(\omega)e^{-j\theta(\omega)}e^{j\omega t}\,d\omega \qquad (8.33b)$$

Summarizing the above procedure, we have

$$\text{Time domain:} \quad \left[\begin{array}{c}\text{Given excitation } e_1(t) \\ \text{in Fig. 8.3a}\end{array}\right] \xrightarrow{\text{Problem}} \left[\text{Find response } e_2(t)\right]$$

$$\left\downarrow\begin{array}{l}\text{Step 1:} \\ \text{Use (8.32)}\end{array}\right. \qquad\qquad\qquad \left\uparrow\begin{array}{l}\text{Step 3:} \\ \text{Use (8.33b)}\end{array}\right. \quad (8.34)$$

$$\text{Frequency domain:} \quad \left[\begin{array}{c}\text{Fourier transform of} \\ \text{excitation } g_1(\omega)\end{array}\right] \xrightarrow[\text{Use (8.33a)}]{\text{Step 2:}} \left[\begin{array}{c}\text{Fourier transform} \\ \text{of response } g_2(\omega)\end{array}\right]$$

For illustration, let us consider a low-pass network with idealized *transmission characteristics* as in Fig. 8.5a and b.   For an excitation $e_1(t)$ having a Fourier transform $g_1(\omega)$ as represented in (8.32), the Fourier transform of the response is found to be

$$g_2(\omega) = \begin{cases} g_1(\omega)Ke^{-j\omega t_d} & -\omega_c \le \omega \le \omega_c \\ 0 & \omega < -\omega_c, \; \omega_c < \omega \end{cases} \qquad (8.35a)$$

The response $e_2(t)$ will then have the form

$$e_2(t) = \int_{-\infty}^{+\infty} g_2(\omega)e^{j\omega t}\,d\omega = \int_{-\omega_c}^{\omega_c} g_1(\omega)Ke^{-j\omega t_d}e^{j\omega t}\,d\omega$$

$$= K\int_{-\omega_c}^{\omega_c} g_1(\omega)e^{j\omega(t-t_d)}\,d\omega \qquad (8.35b)$$

8.3. A summary of the frequency analysis of a rectangular pulse

We summarize some of our earlier results here for future reference.

A. *Fourier Series of a Repeating Rectangular Pulse*

A repeating rectangular pulse $e(t)$ of the shape indicated in Fig. 7.8a has a Fourier series in the trigonometric form (7.7) with coefficients A_n and B_n described by (7.22).

This same repeating pulse $e(t)$ also has a Fourier series in the complex form (7.25) with coefficient C_n described by (7.32).   Also known as the Fourier series transform and expressible in the form of (7.31), C_n represents the complex amplitude of each frequency component of $e(t)$ and is illustrated in Fig. 7.9a for a value of $T/\delta = 3$ in Fig. 7.8a.

B. *Fourier Transform of a Nonrepeating Rectangular Pulse*

The Fourier transform $g(\omega)$ in complex form for the nonrepeating rectangular pulse $e(t)$ in Fig. 8.1a is represented by (8.6) and shown in Fig. 8.1b.

$g(\omega)$, expressible in the form of (8.4), indicates the relative complex amplitude of each frequency component of $e(t)$.

The Fourier transforms $a(\omega)$ and $b(\omega)$ in trigonometric form for a nonrepeating function will be discussed in Arts. 9.8 and 9.9.   We shall find that Fourier transforms in trigonometric form are better adapted for use in problems involving bandpass networks with modulated signals than for use in the low-pass-network problems we have been treating.

PROBLEMS

8.1. Obtain the Fourier transform of the nonrepeating waveform in Fig. P 8.1.

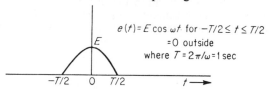

$e(t) = E \cos \omega t$ for $-T/2 \leq t \leq T/2$
$= 0$ outside
where $T = 2\pi/\omega = 1$ sec

FIG. P 8.1

8.2. Obtain the Fourier transform of the non-repeating waveform in Fig. P 8.2.

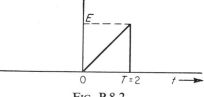

FIG. P 8.2

8.3. (*a*) Obtain the Fourier transform $g(\omega)$ of the nonrepeating waveform in Fig. P 8.3; represent it in the form $g(\omega) = |g(\omega)| e^{j\phi(\omega)}$, as indicated in (8.4). (*b*) Plot $|g(\omega)|$ versus ω. (*c*) Plot $\phi(\omega)$ versus ω.

Note that (1) the nonrepeating waveform in Fig. P 8.3 is a single cycle of the repeating waveform in Fig. P 7.1*d* and (2) the $|g(\omega)|$ and $\phi(\omega)$ curves of the nonrepeating waveform obtained here are similar in shape to the envelopes of $|C_n|$ and ϕ_n for the repeating waveform obtained in Prob. 7.6.

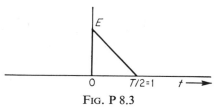

FIG. P 8.3

8.4. Given: The two-terminal network in Fig. P 8.4*b* subject to the sawtooth voltage excitation $e(t)$ in Fig. P 8.4*a*.

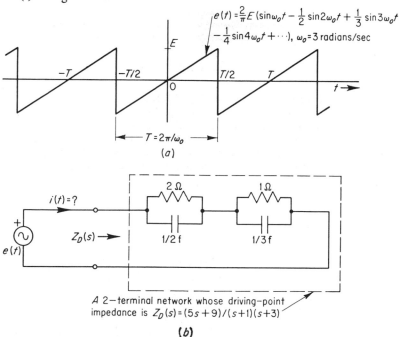

$e(t) = \frac{2}{\pi}E(\sin\omega_o t - \frac{1}{2}\sin 2\omega_o t + \frac{1}{3}\sin 3\omega_o t$
$- \frac{1}{4}\sin 4\omega_o t + \cdots)$, $\omega_o = 3$ radians/sec

$T = 2\pi/\omega_o$

(*a*)

A 2-terminal network whose driving-point
impedance is $Z_D(s) = (5s + 9)/(s+1)(s+3)$

(*b*)

FIG. P 8.4

Find the current response $i(t)$.   REFERENCE: See the procedure associated with Eqs. (8.20) through (8.24) in Art. 8.2B.

8.5. Given: The four-terminal network in Fig. P 8.5b subject to the voltage excitation $e_A(t)$, a half-wave rectified cosine waveform in Fig. P 8.5a.

Find the voltage excitation $e_B(t)$.   Employ the same procedure as in Prob. 8.4 except for notations which require use of $e_A(t)$, $e_B(t)$, and $1/G(s)$ in place of $e(t)$, $i(t)$, and $Z(s)$.

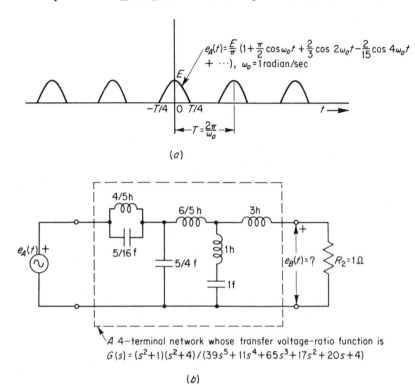

$$e_A(t) = \frac{E}{\pi}\left(1 + \frac{\pi}{2}\cos\omega_o t + \frac{2}{3}\cos 2\omega_o t - \frac{2}{15}\cos 4\omega_o t + \cdots\right), \quad \omega_o = 1\ \text{radian/sec}$$

$-T/4 \quad 0 \quad T/4$

$T = \frac{2\pi}{\omega_o}$

(*a*)

4/5h

6/5 h   3h

$e_A(t) +$

5/16 f

5/4 f   1h

1f

$|e_B(t)| = ?$ $R_2 = 1\Omega$

A 4–terminal network whose transfer voltage-ratio function is
$$G(s) = (s^2+1)(s^2+4)/(39s^5 + 11s^4 + 65s^3 + 17s^2 + 20s + 4)$$

(*b*)

FIG. P 8.5

8.6. Repeat Prob. 8.4 for the excitation in Fig. P 8.5a.

8.7. Repeat Prob. 8.5 for the excitation in Fig. P 8.4a.

8.8. Given: A four-terminal network having the idealized transmission characteristics (1) $G_0(\omega)$ as in Fig. 8.5a with $K = 1$ and $\omega_c \to \infty$ and (2) $\theta(\omega) = \omega t_d$ as in Fig. 8.5b.

Show that, for an arbitrary excitation $e_1(t) = f(t)$, the network response is $e_2(t) = f(t - t_d)$. In other words, the response has the same waveform as the excitation, but is delayed for a time interval t_d sec.

9 Study of network responses with the Fourier transform

9.1. Response of an idealized low-pass four-terminal network subject to a unit-step excitation

A. Description of Problem

A four-terminal network, say an amplifier or a passive network, is usually rated according to its steady-state and transient performances. To determine the transient performance of a network, a unit-step function as depicted in Fig. 9.1a,

$$u(t) = \begin{cases} 1 & t \geq 0 \\ 0 & t < 0 \end{cases} \tag{9.1}$$

or a step function, which is a unit-step function multiplied by a constant, is often used as the excitation $e_1(t)$ to the network, as indicated in Fig. 9.1b. The response $e_2(t)$ due to the step-function excitation is usually studied with particular reference to:

1. *The rise transient response and its rise time.* The definition of *rise time* varies among authors. It may be defined as the time required for the transient to reach nine-tenths of its maximum value, e.g., the time interval OF in Fig. 9.1c.

2. *The persistence of the response or "staying power."* The persistence of the response may be measured by the decay time, which in turn can be defined as the time required for the transient to decay from the maximum to one-tenth of this value. For example, the time interval CG in Fig. 9.1c is the decay time. The larger the decay time, the better the staying power of the response.

The study of transient performance is particularly important for video amplifiers and pulse and switching circuits.

We shall find in Art. 9.4 that the steady-state and transient performances of a network are closely related. Knowing the transient response of a network subject to a step-function excitation, we can predict the steady-state response subject to a sinusoidal excitation.

Problem under investigation. We shall investigate the response $e_2(t)$ of a four-terminal low-pass network having idealized transmission characteristics as indicated in Fig. 8.5a and b subject to a unit-step excitation $e_1(t) = u(t)$. Let us assume $K = 1$ in Fig. 8.5a. This means that the network will pass freely frequencies $\omega \leq \omega_c$ and cut out all $\omega > \omega_c$. The d-c component in the excitation is identified with $\omega = 0$ and therefore will appear with its original magnitude in the response.

The response $e_2(t)$ in Fig. 9.1c decayed because it lacked a d-c component. The network transmission characteristic $G_0(\omega)$ must have the relation $G_0(0) = 0$ and must eliminate the d-c component in the response.

For our present problem, we have a transmission characteristic $G_0(\omega) = 1$ for $-\omega_c \leq \omega \leq \omega_c$. This means that the d-c component in the excitation $e_1(t)$ will

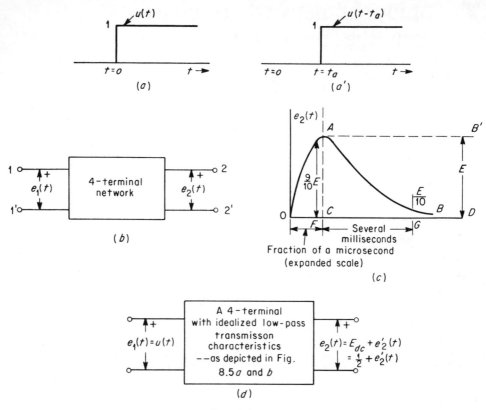

FIG. 9.1

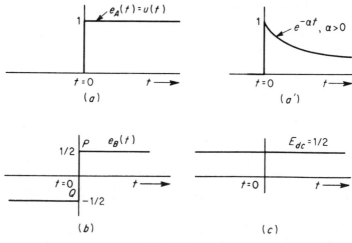

FIG. 9.2

appear in the response $e_2(t)$ with the original magnitude. Therefore, the response $e_2(t)$ will "stay up" and will follow the general shape of OAB' in Fig. 9.1c. We have no decay transient for the test of "staying power," but only a *rise transient*, to study. We shall investigate the rise transient for its (1) shape, i.e., waveform, (2) rise time, and (3) time delay as introduced by the four-terminal network.

A remark about the d-c component of a signal $e(t)$ **and the Fourier transform** $g(\omega)$ **of this signal.** From earlier discussions, we know that (1) we may find the Fourier transform or spectrum function $g(\omega)$ of a given signal function $e(t)$ with the aid of (8.3b) and (2) we may derive the signal function $e(t)$ from the Fourier transform $g(\omega)$ with the aid of (8.3a).

Let us assume $e_A(t) = u(t)$ as in Fig. 9.2a and find its Fourier transform $g(\omega)$ with the aid of (8.3b). If we use this $g(\omega)$ in (8.3a), we shall find with appropriate limiting processes, instead of $e_A(t)$, a new signal function $e_B(t)$ having an approximate representation as depicted in Fig. 9.2b. It is obvious that

$$e_A(t) = e_B(t) + E_{dc} = e_B(t) + \tfrac{1}{2} \tag{9.2}$$

where $E_{dc} = \tfrac{1}{2}$ (Fig. 9.2c) is the d-c component in $e_A(t)$. The Fourier transform $g(\omega)$ apparently does *not* include the d-c component in the signal function $e(t)$. In a network problem solved by Fourier transforms, we must treat the d-c component separately.

A remark about our present problem. We shall investigate the response $e_2(t)$ of a four-terminal network having idealized characteristics as depicted in Fig. 8.5a and b subject to a unit-step excitation $e_1(t) = u(t)$. According to the above remark, we must treat the d-c component separately. The d-c component in the excitation $e_1(t) = u(t)$ is obviously $\tfrac{1}{2}$ (say in volts) at any instant (including the negative time axis) as depicted in Fig. 9.2c; the d-c component in the response $e_2(t)$ for a transmission characteristic $G_0(\omega) = 1$ for $-\omega_c \le \omega \le \omega_c$ must be $E_{dc} = 1 \times \tfrac{1}{2} = \tfrac{1}{2}$. The response must then be

$$e_2(t) = E_{dc} + e_2'(t) = \tfrac{1}{2} + e_2'(t) \tag{9.3}$$

where $e_2'(t)$ is the a-c response subject to the excitation $e_1(t)$ as indicated in Fig. 9.1. $e_2'(t)$ can be obtained with the procedure in (8.34).

B. Procedure for Finding the Response Subject to a Unit-step Excitation

We shall find the response for the problem described above and in Fig. 9.1d using the procedure in (8.34).

Fourier transform of a unit-step excitation. Strictly speaking, the Fourier transform of a unit-step excitation does not exist [this will be discussed in an illustration associated with Eq. (11.16a)]. We shall use a limiting process to get around this difficulty for the time being and introduce the Laplace transform in Art. 11.3 as a generalization of the Fourier transform to take care of many functions whose Fourier transforms do not exist.

The assumption that a unit-step excitation is an exponential excitation $e^{-\alpha t}$ with extremely small $\alpha > 0$, that is, a limiting case, should be good enough for *practical* circuit applications.

Let us now consider a unit-step function as the limit of an exponential function as depicted in Fig. 9.2a', i.e.,

$$e_1(t) = u(t) = \begin{cases} \lim\limits_{\alpha \to 0} e^{-\alpha t} & \alpha > 0, t \ge 0 \\ 0 & t < 0 \end{cases} \tag{9.4a}$$

and then find its Fourier transform with the aid of (8.3*b*) and a limiting process:

$$g_1(\omega) = \frac{1}{2\pi} \int_{-\infty}^{\infty} e_1(t) e^{-j\omega t} \, dt = \frac{1}{2\pi} \left(\int_{-\infty}^{0} + \int_{0}^{\infty} \right)$$

$$= 0 + \lim_{\alpha \to 0} \frac{1}{2\pi} \int_{0}^{\infty} e^{-\alpha t} e^{-j\omega t} \, dt$$

$$= \lim_{\alpha \to 0} \frac{1}{2\pi} \frac{1}{\alpha + j\omega} = \frac{1}{2\pi} \frac{1}{j\omega} \tag{9.4b}$$

Fourier transform of the response. Using (8.35*a*) and the prescribed transmission characteristics for $K = 1$ in Fig. 8.5*a* and *b*, we have

$$g_2(\omega) = \begin{cases} \dfrac{1}{2\pi} \dfrac{1}{j\omega} (1 e^{-j\omega t_d}) & -\omega_c \le \omega \le \omega_c \\[2mm] 0 & \omega < -\omega_c, \ \omega_c < \omega \end{cases} \tag{9.5a}$$

Network response. The response has the form [Eq. (9.3)]

$$e_2(t) = \tfrac{1}{2} + e_2'(t) \tag{9.5b}$$

and $e_2'(t)$ may be obtained with the aid of (8.35*b*).

$$e_2(t) = \frac{1}{2} + \int_{-\omega_c}^{\omega_c} \frac{1}{2\pi} \frac{1}{j\omega} e^{j\omega(t-t_d)} \, d\omega$$

$$= \frac{1}{2} + \frac{1}{2\pi} \int_{-\omega_c}^{\omega_c} \frac{1}{j\omega} [\cos \omega(t - t_d) + j \sin \omega(t - t_d)] \, d\omega \tag{9.6a}$$

$$e_2(t) = \frac{1}{2} + 0 + \frac{1}{2\pi} \int_{-\omega_c}^{\omega_c} \frac{\sin \omega(t - t_d)}{\omega} \, d\omega \dagger$$

$$= \frac{1}{2} + 0 + \frac{2}{2\pi} \int_{0}^{\omega_c} \frac{\sin \omega(t - t_d)}{\omega} \, d\omega \ddagger \tag{9.6b}$$

Letting

$$U = \omega(t - t_d)$$

$$x = U \big|_{\omega = \omega_c} = \omega_c(t - t_d) \tag{9.7a}$$

and

$$\frac{d\omega}{\omega} = \frac{dU/(t - t_d)}{U/(t - t_d)} = \frac{dU}{U} \tag{9.7b}$$

we may rewrite (9.6*b*) as

$$e_2(t) = \frac{1}{2} + \frac{1}{\pi} \int_{0}^{x} \frac{\sin U}{U} \, dU = \frac{1}{2} + \frac{1}{\pi} \text{Si } x \tag{9.6c}$$

$$e_2(t) = \frac{1}{2} + \frac{1}{\pi} \text{Si } [\omega_c(t - t_d)] \tag{9.6d}$$

---

† $G(\omega) = \cos \omega(t - t_d)/j\omega$ is an *odd* function of ω according to definition (8.10*b*), and $\int_{-\omega_c}^{\omega_c} G(\omega) \, d\omega = 0$. For reference, see $\int_{-t_a}^{t_a} f(t) \, dt = 0$ as the area under the curve in Fig. 7.7*a* between the limits $-t_a$ and t_a.

‡ $F(\omega) = \sin \omega(t - t_d)/\omega$ is an *even* function of ω according to definition (8.10*a*), and $\int_{-\omega_c}^{\omega_c} F(\omega) \, d\omega = 2 \int_{0}^{\omega_c} F(\omega) \, d\omega$. For reference, see $\int_{-\omega_c}^{\omega_c} g(\omega) \, d\omega = 2 \int_{0}^{\omega_c} g(\omega) \, d\omega$ as the area under the curve in Fig. 8.4*a* between the limits $-\omega_c$ and ω_c for any ω_c.

where Si x is the *sine integral* of x, defined as the integral of a sampling function Sa $U = (\sin U)/U$:

$$\text{Si } x = \int_0^x \frac{\sin U}{U}\, dU \tag{9.7c}$$

To plot the response $e_2(t)$, it is only necessary to use Eq. (9.6d) and a table of sine integrals.† A typical response is given in Fig. 9.3d.

Response waveform. To study the response $e_2(t)$ as represented in (9.6d), we may (1) plot the sampling function Sa U in Fig. 9.3a, (2) plot the sine integral Si x in Fig. 9.3b with Si x_1 equal to the area under the Sa U curve in Fig. 9.3a from $U = 0$ to $U = x_1$ for any value of x_1, Si x being defined in (9.7c), and (3) change the scales along both axes to obtain the horizontal axis and add $\frac{1}{2}$ to the vertical representation, obtaining the response $e_2(t)$ in Fig. 9.3d.

Comparing the response $e_2(t)$ in Fig. 9.3d with the unit-step excitation in Fig. 9.1a, we note that:

1. A time delay t_d in seconds is introduced in the response.
2. A time interval is required for the buildup of the transient response.
3. Overshoots or oscillations are introduced in the response.

These three phenomena are introduced by the four-terminal network having idealized transmission characteristics as depicted in Fig. 8.5a and b.

C. Buildup Time of the Response

The buildup time of the transient response $e_2(t)$ as indicated in Fig. 9.3d is the time required for the transient to proceed from F to G, that is, from its zero value to its steady-state value.

Let us reproduce the transient response $e_2(t)$ in Fig. 9.4, draw a straight line $F'AG'$ tangent to A, and construct a right triangle $F'H'G'$. The time interval t_B, the "length" of side $F'H'$ of the triangle, is an approximation of the buildup time. We now wish to find t_B.

The slope $1/t_B$ is also the derivative $d[e_2(t)]/dt$ at $t = t_d$ (i.e., at A in Fig. 9.4). With reference to (9.7), we have

$$\frac{1}{t_B} = \frac{d}{dt}\,[e_2(t)]_{t=t_d} = \frac{d}{dt}\left(\frac{1}{2} + \frac{1}{\pi}\,\text{Si } x\right)_{t=t_d} \tag{9.8a}$$

$$\frac{1}{t_B} = \frac{1}{\pi}\,\frac{d(\text{Si } x)}{dx}\bigg|_{t=t_d}\,\frac{dx}{dt}\bigg|_{t=t_d} = \frac{1}{\pi}\,(1)(\omega_c) \tag{9.8b}$$

Equation (9.8b) results from

$$\frac{d}{dx}\Big(\text{Si } x\Big)_{\substack{t=t_d \\ x=\omega_c(t-t_d)}} = \frac{d}{dx}\left(\int_0^x \frac{\sin U}{U}\, dU\right)_{\substack{t=t_d \\ U=\omega(t-t_d),\,\omega=\omega_c}}$$

$$= \frac{\sin U}{U}\bigg|_{U=0} = 1 \tag{9.9a}$$

$$\frac{dx}{dt} = \frac{d}{dt}\,[\omega_c(t - t_d)] = \omega_c \tag{9.9b}$$

From (9.8), we find the *buildup time*,

$$t_B = \frac{\pi}{\omega_c} = \frac{\pi}{2\pi f_c} = \frac{1}{2f_c} \tag{9.10}$$

† See E. Jahnke and F. Emde, "Tables of Functions," Dover Publications, Inc., New York, 1945, for such a table.

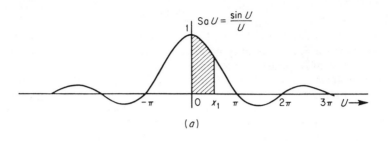

(a)

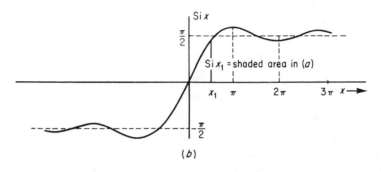

(b)

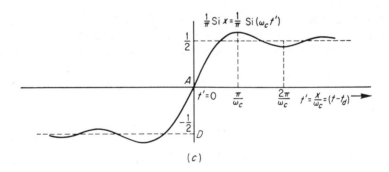

(c)

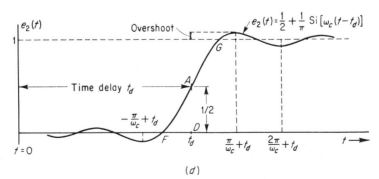

(d)

FIG. 9.3

where ω_c is the cutoff frequency in radians per second, and f_c in cycles per second, of the idealized low-pass transmission characteristic as depicted in Fig. 8.5a.

As an illustration, a buildup time of 1 msec is expected for a cutoff frequency of 500 cps from (9.10). Since (9.10) was derived with a low-pass network with idealized transmission characteristics, it is only an approximate equation for application to actual physical networks.

D. Remarks about the Response of a Network Subject to a Given Excitation

We have demonstrated above that, for a unit-step-function excitation $e_1(t) = u(t)$ to a four-terminal low-pass network with idealized transmission characteristics, the response $e_2(t)$ in Fig. 9.4 is usually regarded as a transient response. The unit-step excitation is not a repeating function as defined in (7.1). We may in general consider the network response subject to a nonrepeating function as a *transient response*.

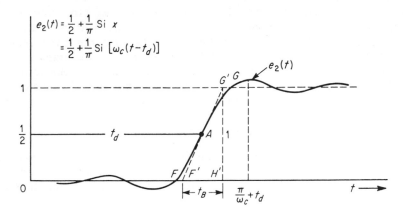

$$e_2(t) = \frac{1}{2} + \frac{1}{\pi} \, \text{Si} \; x$$

$$= \frac{1}{2} + \frac{1}{\pi} \, \text{Si} \; [\omega_c(t - t_d)]$$

Fig. 9.4

Finding the response of a two-terminal network subject to a given excitation. If the excitation is a repeating function, we may find the steady-state response according to the procedure in Art. 8.2B. If the excitation is a nonrepeating function, we may find the transient response using Laplace-transform methods to be discussed in Chaps. 12 and 13.

Finding the response of a four-terminal network subject to a repeating excitation. For a repeating function as excitation, the steady-state response may be found according to the procedure in Art. 8.2C.

Finding the transient response of a four-terminal network subject to a nonrepeating excitation. There are two approaches to this problem, depending upon how the four-terminal network is characterized.

If the transfer function $G(s)$ of the network is known, we may use the Laplace-transform method, as discussed in Chaps. 12 and 13, to find the transient response.

If the transmission characteristics of the network in the form of the gain characteristic $G_0(\omega)$ and the phase characteristic $\theta(\omega)$ are available, the method of Fourier transforms as described in (8.34) and demonstrated in Art. 9.1B may be used in the determination of the transient response. The transfer function $G(s)$ and the transmission characteristics $G_0(\omega)$ and $\theta(\omega)$ are related in (3.39). Knowing $G(s)$, we can readily find $G_0(\omega)$ and $\theta(\omega)$. But the converse is not true. For a network (1) having a complicated network configuration or a large number of circuit elements, (2) containing distributed circuit elements such as transmission lines or significant wiring capacitances, or (3) whose circuit diagram is unavailable, $G(s)$ is difficult to determine, while $G_0(\omega)$ and $\theta(\omega)$ are easy to measure and can be readily plotted as graphs. With $G_0(\omega)$ and $\theta(\omega)$ available, the transient response may readily be obtained.

If $G_0(\omega)$ and $\theta(\omega)$ are available in graphical form, we may approximate them as functions of ω. For example, we may consider $G_0(\omega)$ as three linear segments, for the positive frequencies, and let $G_0(\omega) = f_1(\omega)$ for $0 \le \omega \le \omega_1$, $G_0(\omega) = f_2(\omega)$ for $\omega_1 < \omega \le \omega_2$, and $G_0(\omega) = f_3(\omega)$ for $\omega_2 < \omega < \infty$, where $f_1(\omega)$, $f_2(\omega)$, and $f_3(\omega)$ are three equations for straight lines [for example, $f_1(\omega) = m_1\omega + b_1$]. Since $G_0(\omega)$ is an even function of ω, we may easily include the negative frequencies. Equation (8.33b) may then be used in the evaluation of the transient response.

Knowing the gain characteristic $G_0(\omega)$, but not knowing the phase characteristic $\theta(\omega)$, we may find the approximate waveform of the transient response. We note in our illustration in Art. 9.1B that a "linear" phase characteristic $\theta(\omega) = \omega t_d$ (Fig. 8.5b) introduces a time delay t_d into the transient response $e_2(t)$ to a unit-step excitation (Fig. 9.4). For any nonrepeating excitation, we may then use a transmission characteristic $G(j\omega) = G_0(\omega)e^{-j\theta(\omega)} = G_0(\omega)$, where $G_0(\omega)$ is the given gain characteristic and $\theta(\omega) \equiv 0$ is assumed, and follow (8.34) to find the transient response without time delay as $\theta(\omega) = \omega t_d \equiv 0$ and $t_d \equiv 0$. The transient response thus obtained has the approximate waveform of the true response, with some error introduced due to the "nonlinearity" of the phase characteristic.

9.2. Rectangular pulse as an algebraic sum of two step functions

The superposition theorem applies to linear networks. If an excitation is a sum of two signals, the response of a linear network is the sum of the two responses due to the two signals. It is obvious that we may (1) decompose a given excitation into two

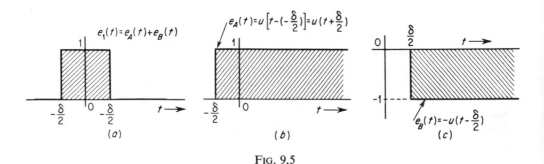

FIG. 9.5

signals, $e_A(t) + e_B(t)$, (2) find the response of the network due to $e_A(t)$, (3) find the response due to $e_B(t)$, and (4) add these individual responses.

A.   Rectangular Pulse as an Excitation to an Idealized Low-pass Network

Excitation as a superposition of two unit-step functions. Suppose we wish to find the response of a four-terminal low-pass network having idealized transmission characteristics as depicted in Fig. 8.5a and b subject to a rectangular-pulse excitation with unit magnitude as indicated in Fig. 9.5a. According to the above discussion, we may decompose $e_1(t)$ (Fig. 9.5) into

$$e_1(t) = e_A(t) + e_B(t) \tag{9.11}$$

where

$$e_A(t) = u\left[t - \left(-\frac{\delta}{2}\right)\right] = u\left(t + \frac{\delta}{2}\right) \tag{9.11a}$$

$$e_B(t) = -u\left(t - \frac{\delta}{2}\right) \tag{9.11b}$$

and $u(t - t_a)$ is defined as follows: $u(t - t_a) = 0$ for $t < t_a$ and $u(t - t_a) = 1$ for $t \geq t_a$, as depicted in Fig. 9.1a'. The response $e_2(t)$ to the excitation $e_1(t)$ is then the sum of the responses to the excitations $e_A(t)$ and $e_B(t)$.

Component responses. We have found the response to a unit-step excitation $u(t)$ in (9.6d). $e_A(t)$ and $e_B(t)$ are also unit-step functions, and we may modify (9.6d) to find their responses.

For the excitation

$$e_A(t) = u\left(t + \frac{\delta}{2}\right)$$

$$= u(t') \qquad \text{for } t' = t + \frac{\delta}{2} \tag{9.11a'}$$

the response, according to (9.6d), is

$$e_{2A}(t) = \frac{1}{2} + \frac{1}{\pi}\,\text{Si}\,[\omega_c(t' - t_d)] \tag{9.12a}$$

$$e_{2A}(t) = \frac{1}{2} + \frac{1}{\pi}\,\text{Si}\left[\omega_c\left(t - t_d + \frac{\delta}{2}\right)\right] \tag{9.12a'}$$

For the excitation

$$e_B(t) = -u\left(t - \frac{\delta}{2}\right)$$

$$= -u(t'') \qquad \text{for } t'' = t - \frac{\delta}{2} \tag{9.11b'}$$

the response, according to (9.6d), is

$$e_{2B}(t) = -\left\{\frac{1}{2} + \frac{1}{\pi}\,\text{Si}\,[\omega_c(t'' - t_d)]\right\} \tag{9.12b}$$

$$e_{2B}(t) = -\frac{1}{2} - \frac{1}{\pi}\,\text{Si}\left[\omega_c\left(t - t_d - \frac{\delta}{2}\right)\right] \tag{9.12b'}$$

Network response. Combining (9.12a') and (9.12b'), we find the network response subject to the excitation $e_1(t)$ as described in (9.11):

$$e_2(t) = e_{2A}(t) + e_{2B}(t)$$

$$= \frac{1}{\pi}\left\{\text{Si}\left[\omega_c\left(t - t_d + \frac{\delta}{2}\right)\right] - \text{Si}\left[\omega_c\left(t - t_d - \frac{\delta}{2}\right)\right]\right\} \tag{9.13}$$

Constructing $e_{2A}(t)$ in Fig. 9.6a from (9.12a) or (9.12a') in the same way that Fig. 9.3d is constructed with the aid of a table of sine integrals, and similarly constructing $e_{2B}(t)$ from (9.12b) or (9.12b'), we combine them to obtain the *graphical representation* of the response $e_2(t)$ in Fig. 9.6b.

Both excitation $e_1(t)$ and response $e_2(t)$ are included in Fig. 9.6b, and a delay t_d in seconds is indicated. For waveform comparison, we often ignore the time delay t_d and put one waveform on the other, as in Fig. 9.6c. From (9.10), we note that the higher the cutoff frequency ω_c, i.e., the broader the bandwidth of the network, the smaller the buildup time t_B, and the sharper the rising portions of the waveforms in Figs. 9.4 and 9.6c.

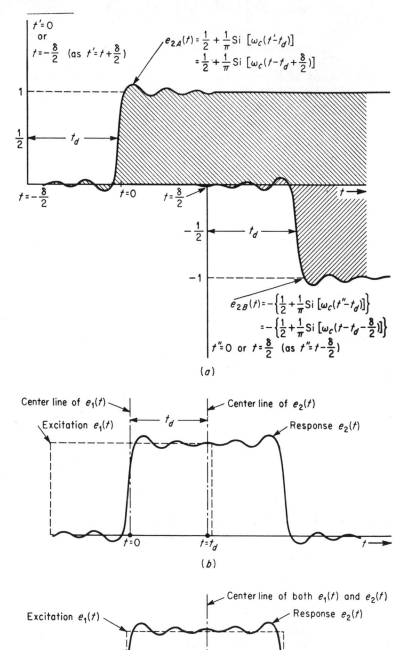

$$t' = 0$$
or
$$t = -\frac{\delta}{2} \quad \left(\text{as } t' = t + \frac{\delta}{2}\right)$$

$$e_{2A}(t) = \frac{1}{2} + \frac{1}{\pi} \text{Si} \left[\omega_c(t' - t_d)\right]$$
$$= \frac{1}{2} + \frac{1}{\pi} \text{Si} \left[\omega_c(t - t_d + \frac{\delta}{2})\right]$$

$$t = -\frac{\delta}{2} \qquad t = 0 \qquad t = \frac{\delta}{2}$$

$$e_{2B}(t) = -\left\{\frac{1}{2} + \frac{1}{\pi} \text{Si} \left[\omega_c(t'' - t_d)\right]\right\}$$
$$= -\left\{\frac{1}{2} + \frac{1}{\pi} \text{Si} \left[\omega_c(t - t_d - \frac{\delta}{2})\right]\right\}$$
$$t'' = 0 \text{ or } t = \frac{\delta}{2} \quad \left(\text{as } t'' = t - \frac{\delta}{2}\right)$$

(a)

Center line of $e_1(t)$ — Center line of $e_2(t)$

Excitation $e_1(t)$ Response $e_2(t)$

$$t = 0 \qquad t = t_d$$

(b)

Center line of both $e_1(t)$ and $e_2(t)$

Excitation $e_1(t)$ Response $e_2(t)$

(c)

Fig. 9.6

For idealized transmission characteristics with an infinite bandwidth, that is, $\omega_o \to \infty$ in Fig. 8.5a, the excitation $e_1(t)$ and response $e_2(t)$ have almost identical waveforms, except for the delay t_d in seconds and the overshoots. All the overshoots will concentrate at the sharp edge of the pulse with zero area under the "overshoot

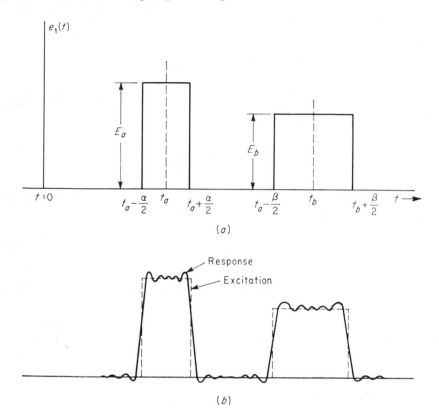

(a)

(b)

FIG. 9.7

loops." Note that $\pi/\omega_c \to 0$, $2\pi/\omega_c \to 0$, $3\pi/\omega \to 0, \ldots$, for $\omega_c \to \infty$ in Fig. 9.3d, and all overshoots will concentrate at $t' = t_d$, with zero area under the degenerate "overshoot loops."

B. Further Illustrations

Suppose we wish to find the response of a four-terminal low-pass network with idealized transmission characteristics as in Fig. 8.5a and b to an excitation consisting of two rectangular pulses as depicted in Fig. 9.7a. The excitation is

$$e_1(t) = E_a \left\{ u\left[t - \left(t_a - \frac{\alpha}{2} \right) \right] - u\left[t - \left(t_a + \frac{\alpha}{2} \right) \right] \right\}$$

$$+ E_b \left\{ u\left[t - \left(t_b - \frac{\beta}{2} \right) \right] - u\left[t - \left(t_b + \frac{\beta}{2} \right) \right] \right\} \quad (9.14)$$

We may write an expression for the response to each pulse, similar to (9.13) except for magnitude and time reference. For the first pulse, we should modify (9.13) with (1) a factor E_a for the magnitude, (2) t replaced by $t + t_a$, since we had $t = 0$ as time reference in Fig. 9.5, and have $t = t_a$ now in Fig. 9.7a, and (3) δ replaced by

α for notation. Similar modifications should be made on (9.13) for the response to the second pulse. The network response of the excitation $e_1(t)$ as depicted in Fig. 9.7a is now the sum of the responses to the two pulses:

$$e_2(t) = \frac{E_a}{\pi}\left\{\text{Si}\left[\omega_c\left(t + t_a - t_d + \frac{\alpha}{2}\right)\right] - \text{Si}\left[\omega_c\left(t + t_a - t_d - \frac{\alpha}{2}\right)\right]\right\}$$

$$+ \frac{E_b}{\pi}\left\{\text{Si}\left[\omega_c\left(t + t_b - t_d + \frac{\beta}{2}\right)\right] - \text{Si}\left[\omega_c\left(t + t_b - t_d - \frac{\beta}{2}\right)\right]\right\} \quad (9.15)$$

Using a table of sine integrals, we may plot (9.15). A sketch of a typical response is shown in Fig. 9.7b. The waveforms of both excitation and response, ignoring the time delay, are placed together in the same graph for comparison.

9.3. Unit-impulse function as a derivative of the unit-step function

A. *Unit-impulse Function and Fourier Transform*

Illustration. Suppose that we charge a capacitor to $C = 1$ farad with a current $i(t)$ as in Fig. 9.8a; we then have the following relations:

$$e(t) = \frac{1}{C}\int i(t)\, dt = \int i(t)\, dt = \text{integral of } i(t) \quad (9.16a)$$

$$i(t) = C\frac{de(t)}{dt} = \frac{de(t)}{dt} = \text{derivative of } e(t) \quad (9.16b)$$

Let us assume, as a special case, that a rectangular pulse $i(t)$ as depicted in Fig. 9.8b is used to charge the capacitor C. The voltage $e(t)$ across C is obviously

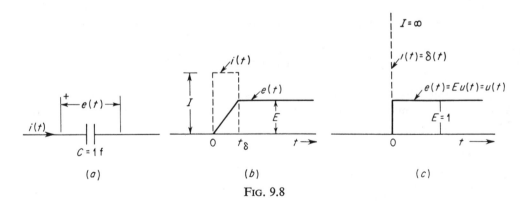

(a)   (b)   (c)

Fig. 9.8

also as indicated in Fig. 9.8b. From (9.16), the following relations are obviously true:

$$E = \frac{1}{C}It_\delta = It_\delta \quad (9.17a)$$

$$I = C\frac{E}{t_\delta} = \frac{E}{t_\delta} \quad (9.17b)$$

Unit-impulse function. A unit-impulse function $\delta(t)$ representing a current is defined as a rectangular current pulse with magnitude $I \to \infty$ and width $t_\delta \to 0$

which will charge a 1-farad capacitor to a voltage $E = 1$ volt with a charge $Q = E/C = 1/1 = 1$ coulomb. In other words, a unit-impulse (current) function $\delta(t)$ is a rectangular pulse identified with

Magnitude:	$I \rightarrow \infty$	
Duration:	$t_\delta \rightarrow 0$	(9.18)
Product:	$It_\delta \rightarrow 1$	

A unit-impulse function $\delta(t)$ is shown in Fig. 9.8c. If Fig. 9.8c is considered as the limiting case of Fig. 9.8b, (9.16) still holds. For $e(t) = u(t)$ as a unit-step function, and $i(t) = \delta(t)$ as a unit-impulse function, we now have

$$u(t) = \int \delta(t)\, dt = \text{integral of } \delta(t) \tag{9.19a}$$

$$\delta(t) = \frac{d}{dt}\, u(t) = \text{derivative of } u(t) \tag{9.19b}$$

Fourier transform of a unit-impulse function. Since a unit-impulse function $\delta(t)$ is a limiting case of a rectangular pulse, we shall first find the Fourier transform of a rectangular pulse as depicted in Fig. 9.8b, and then find its limit under conditions (9.18). Modifying (8.6) for the Fourier transform of our rectangular pulse and taking the limit, we find the Fourier transform of a unit-impulse function $\delta(t)$:

$$g_\delta(\omega) = \lim_{\substack{t_\delta \to 0 \\ I \to \infty}} \frac{It_\delta}{2\pi} \frac{\sin(\omega t_\delta/2)}{\omega t_\delta/2} = \frac{1}{2\pi} 1 = \frac{1}{2\pi} \tag{9.20a}$$

The Fourier transform of a unit-step function $u(t)$ was obtained in (9.4b) as

$$g_u(\omega) = \frac{1}{2\pi}\frac{1}{j\omega} \tag{9.20b}$$

and we note that

$$g_u(\omega) = \frac{g_\delta(\omega)}{j\omega} \tag{9.21}$$

B. Integral-and-Derivative Relations

Spectrum functions of the unit-step and unit-impulse functions. From (9.19) through (9.21), we note some relations between the unit-step function $u(t)$ and the unit-impulse function $\delta(t)$:

Time domain:

To find $\delta(t)$, take derivative:
$$\delta(t) = \frac{du(t)}{dt}$$

$[u(t)] \xrightarrow{\hspace{3cm}} [\delta(t)]$

To find $u(t)$, take integral:
$$u(t) = \int \delta(t)\, dt$$

$(8.3) \hspace{5cm} (8.3) \hspace{3cm} (9.22)$

To find $g_\delta(\omega)$, multiply by $j\omega$:
$$g_\delta(\omega) = j\omega g_u(\omega)$$

$\begin{bmatrix} g_u(\omega) = \text{Fourier} \\ \text{transform of } u(t) \end{bmatrix} \xrightarrow{\hspace{2cm}} \begin{bmatrix} g_\delta(\omega) = \text{Fourier} \\ \text{transform of } \delta(t) \end{bmatrix}$

To find $g_u(\omega)$, divide by $j\omega$:

Frequency domain:
$$g_u(\omega) = \frac{g_\delta(\omega)}{j\omega}$$

The Fourier transform $g(\omega)$ of a signal function $e(t)$ is also the spectrum function representing the complex amplitudes of the frequency components of the signal, as indicated in the discussion associated with Eq. (8.4).   We have illustrated above that $u(t)$ and $\delta(t)$, forming an integral-and-derivative relation themselves, have spectrum functions $g_u(\omega)$ and $g_\delta(\omega)$ which are related by a factor $j\omega$. Knowing $g_u(\omega)$, we can find $g_\delta(\omega)$ by multiplying $g_u(\omega)$ by $j\omega$; knowing $g_\delta(\omega)$, we can find $g_u(\omega)$ by dividing $g_\delta(\omega)$ by $j\omega$.

Spectrum function of a signal function which is the derivative of another signal function.   We shall find that the relations in (9.22) can also be true for other signal functions, provided their spectrum functions as the "Fourier transforms of the signal functions" exist.   We shall study the existence of the Fourier transform later in Art. 11.2.   For example, if a signal function $e_d(t)$ is the derivative of another signal function $e_i(t)$, that is,

$$e_d(t) = \frac{d}{dt}\, e_i(t) \qquad (9.23a)$$

and if the spectrum function of $e_i(t)$,

$$g_i(\omega) = \frac{1}{2\pi} \int_{-\infty}^{+\infty} e_i(t) e^{-j\omega t}\, dt \qquad (9.24)$$

is known, say evaluated from a known $e_i(t)$ with (9.24), we can find the spectrum function $g_d(\omega)$ of the derivative $e_d(t)$ by multiplying $g_i(\omega)$ by $j\omega$; that is,

$$g_d(\omega) = j\omega g_i(\omega) \qquad (9.23b)$$

Spectrum function of a signal function which is the integral of another signal function. Again, this is an interpretation of (9.22) for signals other than unit-step and unit-impulse functions.   If a signal function $e_i(t)$ is the integral of another signal function $e_d(t)$, that is,

$$e_i(t) = \int e_d(t)\, dt \qquad (9.25a)$$

and if the spectrum function of $e_d(t)$,

$$g_d(\omega) = \frac{1}{2\pi} \int_{-\infty}^{+\infty} e_d(t)\, e^{-j\omega t}\, dt \qquad (9.26)$$

is known, say evaluated from a known $e_d(t)$ with (9.26), we can find the spectrum function $g_i(\omega)$ of the integral $e_i(t)$ by dividing $g_d(\omega)$ by $j\omega$; that is,

$$g_i(\omega) = \frac{g_d(\omega)}{j\omega} \qquad (9.25b)$$

Remarks.   Summarizing the above, we find in general that, for a given signal function $e(t)$ and its spectrum function $g(\omega)$,

1. The spectrum function of the derivative of $e(t)$ is $j\omega g(\omega)$.
2. The spectrum function of the integral of $e(t)$ is $g(\omega)/j\omega$.

The spectrum function of a signal represents the complex amplitudes of the frequency components of the signal.

When we study the Laplace transforms of a signal function and its derivative and integral in Chap. 11, we shall see that† these two statements are true.   Because of the physical importance of the spectrum function, this section (Art. 9.3B) is included to aid the reader in understanding the problem of frequency analysis.

---

† By choosing a signal function which is zero in its negative-time region and letting $s = j\omega$ in its Laplace transform, we find its Fourier transform (8.8b) of the second kind.   The Fourier transforms or spectrum functions of a signal and its integral and derivative, thus obtained, will be found to satisfy (9.23b) and (9.25b).

9.4. Square-wave testing—a link between the transient and steady-state responses

A. Description of Problem

Suppose we use a unit-step function $u(t)$ as excitation for a four-terminal network and display its transient response on a cathode-ray oscilloscope. With this transient response *known*, let us look into the following questions:

Question 1. *Can we predict the magnitude and relative phase of the steady-state response of this network to a sinusoidal excitation of unit magnitude at frequency ω_a?*

Yes. The known transient response of the four-terminal network subject to a unit-step excitation provides enough information for us to compute

$$E_a/\underline{\phi_a} = \text{steady-state response of network subject to sinusoidal excitation}$$
$$\text{of unit magnitude} \qquad (9.27)$$

which will be discussed in Art. 9.4B and C.

Question 2. *Can we predict the gain characteristic $G_0(\omega)$ of the network as defined in (3.39)?*

Yes. By definition,

$$G_0(\omega_a) = \frac{\text{magnitude of steady-state } \textit{response}}{\text{subject to sinusoidal excitation of unit magnitude at } \omega_a} = \frac{E_a}{1} = E_a \qquad (9.28)$$

where E_a is a quantity described in (9.27) and computed with the procedure to be discussed in Art. 9.4C. We may repeat this procedure for a large number of frequencies ω_b, ω_c, ... and obtain $G_0(\omega_b)$, $G_0(\omega_c)$, ... Obviously, we may construct a graph depicting the gain characteristic $G_0(\omega)$.

Question 3. *Can we predict the phase characteristic $\theta(\omega)$ of the network as defined in (3.39)?*

We would have some difficulty finding the *exact* phase characteristic $\theta(\omega)$ as defined in (3.39), but can readily determine a *relative* phase characteristic $\theta'(\omega) = \theta(\omega) - \theta_k$, where θ_k is a constant but unknown phase angle.

The phase shift between two network responses at ω_a and ω_b can be computed with *either* exact phase characteristic $\theta(\omega)$ *or* relative phase characteristic $\theta'(\omega)$ as $\theta'(\omega_a) - \theta'(\omega_b) = \theta(\omega_a) - \theta_k - [\theta(\omega_b) - \theta_k] = \theta(\omega_a) - \theta(\omega_b)$.

To obtain the relative phase characteristic $\theta'(\omega)$, we (1) compute ϕ_a for the frequency ω_a as in (9.27), (2) compute ϕ_b, ϕ_c, ... for a large number of frequencies ω_b, ω_c, ..., and (3) plot $-\phi_a$, $-\phi_b$, $-\phi_c$, ... at the frequencies ω_a, ω_b, ω_c, ... This graph depicts the relative phase characteristic $\theta'(\omega)$ for the reasons given below.

$E_a/\underline{\phi_a}$ in (9.27) is the steady-state response with magnitude E_a and relative phase ϕ_a subject to a sinusoidal excitation $1/\underline{0°}$ at ω_a. Assume that $\phi_a - \theta_k$ is the absolute phase of the response at ω_a. We then have an excitation $1/\underline{0°}$, a response $E_a/\underline{\phi_a} - \theta_k$, and a gain $G(j\omega_a) = (E_a/\underline{\phi_a} - \theta_k)/(1/\underline{0}) = E_a/\underline{\phi_a} - \theta_k = E_a e^{j(\phi_a - \theta_k)}$. Identifying this $G(j\omega_a)$ with $G_0(\omega_a)e^{-j\theta(\omega_a)}$ as defined in (3.39), we find that $\phi_a - \theta_k = -\theta(\omega_a)$, or $\theta(\omega_a) - \theta_k = -\phi_a$. For $\theta'(\omega) = \theta(\omega) - \theta_k$, we construct the $\theta'(\omega)$ graph, plotting $-\phi_a$, $-\phi_b$, ... at the frequencies ω_a, ω_b, ...

Question 4. *How can we conveniently display a network response subject to a unit-step excitation on a cathode-ray oscilloscope and keep track of its time scale accurately?*

We can conveniently use the leading edge of a repeating rectangular pulse of unit height and suitable width (Fig. 9.9a) as an approximate unit-step excitation, and

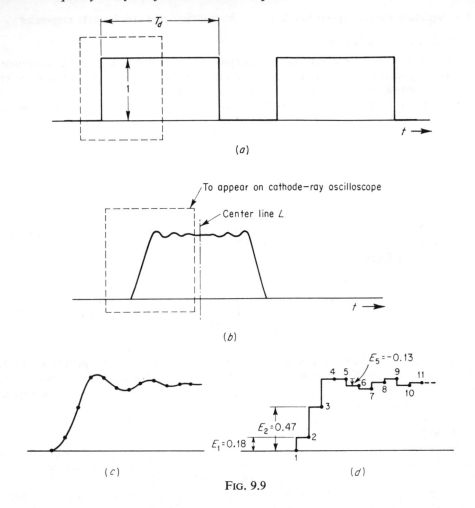

FIG. 9.9

study the response on a cathode-ray oscilloscope as demonstrated in Fig. 9.9*b*. The width T_d in Fig. 9.9*a* must be *large* enough so that the center of the response will represent a steady-state d-c signal free of ripples, as indicated near the center line *L* in Fig. 9.9*b*.

To keep track of the time scale accurately, we may mark time intervals with "timing dots" on the cathode-ray oscilloscope screen as in Fig. 9.9*c* by modulating the cathode-ray beam with a standard signal having a frequency f_s cps. This may be accomplished by connecting a signal generator to the grid of a cathode-ray oscilloscope through a capacitor which isolates their d-c potentials. The standard frequency $\omega_s = 2\pi f_s$ must be much *higher* than the frequencies ω_a, ω_b, ω_c, ... at which we wish to compute the gain and relative phase of the network; the discussion in Art. 9.4B will make clear why this is necessary.

B. Underlying Principle of Square-wave Testing†

Comparison of the frequency components of two step functions starting at the same instant. Suppose we wish to compare the component of frequency ω_a in the step

† A. V. Bedford and G. L. Fredendall, Analysis, Synthesis, and Evaluation of the Transient Response of Television Apparatus, *Proc. IRE*, October, 1942, pp. 440–457.

function $e_A(t) = Eu(t)$ with that in $e'_A(t) = E'u(t)$, both starting at $t = 0$, as depicted in Fig. 9.10a and a'.

The spectrum function or Fourier transform of a unit-step function $u(t)$ has been worked out in (9.4b). We need only modify this result with the factors E and E' for our problem. The spectrum function for $e_A(t) = Eu(t)$ is then

$$g_A(\omega) = \frac{E}{2\pi}\frac{1}{j\omega} \tag{9.29a}$$

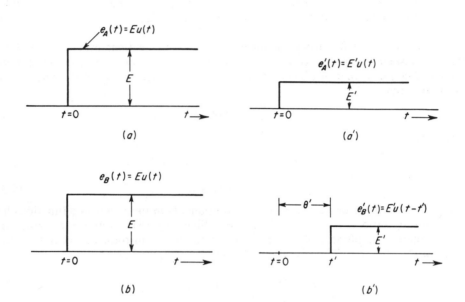

Fig. 9.10

and the spectrum function for $e'_A(t) = E'u(t)$ is

$$g'_A(\omega) = \frac{E'}{2\pi} \frac{1}{j\omega} \tag{9.29b}$$

Comparing the ω_a components in $e_A(t)$ and $e'_A(t)$, we find, with the aid of (9.29), that

$$\frac{\omega_a \text{ component in } e_A(t) = Eu(t)}{\omega_a \text{ component in } e'_A(t) = E'u(t)} = \frac{g_A(\omega_a)}{g'_A(\omega_a)} = \frac{E}{E'} \tag{9.30}$$

This means that the ω_a components in $e_A(t)$ and $e'_A(t)$ as depicted in Fig. 9.10a and a' have a magnitude ratio E/E' and are in phase; that is, $E/E' = |E/E'| e^{j0°}$ is a real quantity.

Comparison of the frequency components of two step functions which do not start at the same instant. Suppose we wish to compare the ω_a component in the step function $e_B(t) = Eu(t)$ with that in $e'_B(t) = E'u(t - t')$ as depicted in Fig. 9.10b and b'. Let us assume that

$$f_a = \frac{\omega_a}{2\pi} = 2{,}000 \text{ cps} \tag{9.31a}$$

with a *period*

$$T_a = \frac{1}{f_a} = 500 \times 10^{-6} \text{ sec} \tag{9.31b}$$

$$t' = 50 \times 10^{-6} \text{ sec} \tag{9.31c}$$

If $t' = 0$ as in the previous case, the ω_a components in these two step functions have a magnitude ratio E/E' and are in phase. Since $e'_B(t)$ starts at $t = t'$ rather than $t = 0$, there is a phase shift θ' in its ω_a component, introduced by a time-delay interval $t' - 0 = t'$. The phase shift θ' may be computed as

$$\theta' = 360 \frac{t'}{T_a} = 360 \frac{\omega_a}{2\pi} t' \quad \text{deg} \tag{9.32}$$

If the time-delay interval t' is equal to the period T_a, i.e., a *complete cycle* of the ω_a component, θ' should be 360°. Equation (9.32) is therefore obvious.

For our present problem,

$$\theta' = 360 \frac{50 \times 10^{-6}}{500 \times 10^{-6}} = 36° \tag{9.32a}$$

We shall find that the ω_a components in $e'_B(t)$ and $e_B(t)$ still have the same magnitude ratio E/E'.

Corresponding to (9.30), we now have

$$\frac{\omega_a \text{ component in } e_B(t) = Eu(t)}{\omega_a \text{ component in } e'_B(t) = E'u(t - t')} = \frac{E\underline{/0°}}{E'\underline{/\theta'}} = \frac{E}{E'e^{j\theta'}} \tag{9.33}$$

Summarizing the above discussions, we may state: *The ω_a components in $e_B(t)$ and $e'_B(t)$, as depicted in Fig. 9.10b and b', have a magnitude ratio E/E' and a phase difference θ' as prescribed by (9.32)*.

Transient response as a summation of step functions. Suppose the transient response $e_2(t)$ of a network subject to a unit-step excitation is that in Fig. 9.10c. We may represent this response in a new manner as follows:

1. We mark this response with "timing dots" which are spaced t_0 sec apart and label these dots with numerals. If the response $e_2(t)$ is displayed on a cathode-ray oscilloscope, these "timing dots" may be marked with a modulating signal as described in Question 4, Art. 9.4A.

2. We construct the step functions $E_1 u(t - t_1)$, $E_2 u(t - t_2)$, ... A step function $E_i u(t - t_i)$ starts at the ith timing dot, where E_i is a measure of the vertical distance from the ith timing dot to the $(i + 1)$st. For example, the step function $E_1 u(t - t_1)$ starting at the timing dot 1 is represented by the shaded area in Fig. 9.10c; E_1 is a positive quantity, say $E_1 = 0.1$. The other shaded area represents the step function $E_{14} u(t - t_{14})$ starting at the timing dot 14; E_{14} is a *negative* quantity, say $E_{14} = -0.05$, since timing dot 15 is *below* dot 14.

3. We add the step functions in (2). For a sufficiently large number of timing dots, this gives us the transient response $e_2(t)$ of the network subject to a unit-step excitation. With reference to Fig. 9.10c, we write

$$e_2(t) = \sum_{i=1}^{\infty} E_i u(t - t_i)$$
$$= E_1 u(t - t_1) + E_2 u(t - t_2) + E_3 u(t - t_3) + \cdots \qquad (9.34)$$

Steady-state response at the frequency ω_a computed from a known transient response. Let us assume that the magnitude of the transient response $e_2(t)$ subject to a unit-step excitation approaches 1 for $t \to \infty$. This assumption is made to facilitate the computation in our illustration. If the magnitude is K, and $K \neq 1$, we multiply the result of our computation by K. We further assume that this known transient response $e_2(t)$ as depicted in Fig. 9.10c has already been marked with timing dots and approximated as a summation of step functions as described in (9.34).

If the response $e_2(t)$ is displayed on a cathode-ray oscilloscope, we can always adjust the gain of the oscilloscope to make it appear to approach 1 in magnitude for $t \to \infty$. The procedure of computation in Art. 9.4C can, therefore, be directly applied. We may then adjust our results by an appropriate factor.

We now wish to predict, i.e., to compute from the known transient response $e_2(t)$ in Fig. 9.10c, the steady-state response of this network subject to a sinusoidal excitation of unit magnitude at frequency ω_a. We may proceed as follows:

1. The transient response $e_2(t)$ as depicted in Fig. 9.10c is a summation of step functions $E_1 u(t - t_1)$, $E_2 u(t - t_2)$, ...

2. Comparing the ω_a components in the step function $E_1 u(t - t_1)$ and the unit-step excitation, we derive a relation similar to (9.33):

$$\frac{\begin{array}{c}\omega_a \text{ component in step function } E_1 u(t - t_1) \\ \text{in transient response } e_2(t)\end{array}}{\omega_a \text{ component in unit-step excitation}} = \frac{E_1}{1} \qquad (9.35a)$$

3. Comparing the ω_a components in the step function $E_2 u(t - t_2)$ and the unit-step excitation, we derive a relation similar to (9.33):

$$\frac{\begin{array}{c}\omega_a \text{ component in step function } E_2 u(t - t_2) \\ \text{in transient response } e_2(t)\end{array}}{\omega_a \text{ component in unit-step excitation}} = \frac{E_2 / \theta_{1,2}}{1} \qquad (9.35b)$$

where $\theta_{1,2}$ (Fig. 9.10c) is a phase shift introduced by a time-delay interval

$$t_{1,2} = t_2 - t_1 = t_0$$

4. Comparing the ω_a components in the step function $E_i(t - t_i)$ and the unit-step excitation, we derive a relation similar to (9.33):

$$\frac{\begin{array}{c}\omega_a \text{ component in step function } E_i u(t - t_i) \\ \text{in transient response } e_2(t)\end{array}}{\omega_a \text{ component in unit-step excitation}} = \frac{E_i / \theta_{1,i}}{1} \qquad (9.35c)$$

5. Summing (9.35a), (9.35b), and then (9.35c) for $i = 3, 4, \ldots$, we have

$$\frac{\omega_a \text{ component in transient response } e_2(t)}{\text{subject to unit-step excitation}} \Big/ \text{} = E_1 + E_2 \underline{/\theta_{1,2}} + E_3 \underline{/\theta_{1,3}} + \cdots$$

$$\omega_a \text{ component in unit-step excitation}$$

$$= E_1 + E_2 e^{j\theta_{1,2}} + E_3 e^{j\theta_{1,3}} + \cdots \quad (9.36)$$

6. The ratio (9.36) of the ω_a components in the transient response $e_2(t)$ and its unit-step excitation will be the same, for the same network, as the ratio of the steady-state response E_a/ϕ_a to its sinusoidal excitation $1/0°$ of unit magnitude for the same network. Since $E_a/\phi_a/1/0° = E_a/\phi_a = E_a e^{j\phi_a}$, (9.36) also represents

$$E_a e^{j\phi_a} = E_1 + E_2 e^{j\theta_{1,2}} + E_3{}^{j\theta_{1,3}} + \cdots$$

$$= E_1 + E_2(\cos\theta_{1,2} + j\sin\theta_{1,2}) + E_3(\cos\theta_{1,3} + j\sin\theta_{1,3}) + \cdots \quad (9.37a)$$

$$E_a e^{j\phi_a} = E_1 + E_2\cos\theta_{1,2} + E_3\cos\theta_{1,3} + \cdots + j(E_2\sin\theta_{1,2} + E_3\sin\theta_{1,3} + \cdots)$$

$$= P_A + jQ_A \quad (9.37b)$$

It is obvious that the *magnitude E_a* and *relative phase ϕ_a* of the steady-state response E_a/ϕ_a of the network subject to a sinusoidal excitation $1/0°$ at the frequency ω_a, as represented above, may be computed as

$$E_a = \sqrt{P_A{}^2 + Q_A{}^2} \quad (9.37c)$$

$$\phi_a = \tan^{-1}\frac{Q_A}{P_A} \quad (9.37d)$$

where P_A and Q_A are defined in (9.37b) and computed from quantities E_i and $\theta_{1,i}$ obtainable from the (*known*) transient response $e_2(t)$ subject to a unit-step excitation as in Fig. 9.10c.

C. Illustration: Procedure and Computation

Problem.   The transient response of a network subject to a unit-step excitation is *known* and displayed on a cathode-ray oscilloscope with a magnitude approaching 1 for $t \to \infty$. To keep track of the time scale, we have marked this response with "timing dots" (Fig. 9.9c) by modulating the cathode-ray beam with a standard signal of frequency

$$f_s = 20,000 \text{ cps} \quad (9.38a)$$

This means that each time interval between two consecutive "timing dots" is

$$t_0 = T_s = \frac{1}{f_s} = 50 \times 10^{-6} \text{ sec} \quad (9.38b)$$

We now wish to predict the magnitude and relative phase of the steady-state response of this network subject to a sinusoidal excitation of unit magnitude at a frequency

$$f_a = 2,000 \text{ cps} \quad (9.39)$$

or $\omega_a = 2\pi f_a$ in radians per second.

Step 1.   *Find the time interval $t_{1,i}$ between timing dots 1 and i.*   With reference to Fig. 9.10c for notation, we find

$$t_{1,i} = (i-1)t_0 = (i-1)\frac{1}{f_s} \quad (9.40)$$

$$t_{1,i} = (i-1)50 \times 10^{-6} \text{ sec} \quad (9.40a)$$

where f_s is the frequency of the standard signal used to modulate the cathode-ray beam and mark the timing dots.

Step 2. *Find the phase shift $\theta_{1,i}$ introduced by the time interval $t_{1,i}$.* With reference to Fig. 9.10c and Eq. (9.32), we find

$$\theta_{1,i} = 360 f_a t_{1,i} = 360(i - 1)\frac{f_a}{f_s} \tag{9.41a}$$

$$\theta_{1,i} = 36(i - 1) \quad \text{deg} \tag{9.41b}$$

Step 3. *Construct steps beginning with each timing dot as in Fig. 9.9d. Record the magnitude E_i of each step until E_i is negligible in comparison with E_1.*

Step 4. *Tabulate the magnitude E_i of each step and $E_i(\cos \theta_{1,i} + j \sin \theta_{1,i})$, where $\theta_{1,i}$ is defined in (9.41), for every i. The sum $\Sigma E_i(\cos \theta_{1,i} + j \sin \theta_{1,i})$ for all i is the steady-state response E_a / ϕ_a of the network subject to a sinusoidal excitation $1 / 0°$ at frequency f_a cps or $\omega_a = 2\pi f_a$ rad/sec. E_a is the magnitude, and ϕ_a the relative phase, of this response.* Using $\theta_{1,i} = 36(i - 1)$ deg in (9.41b) and the recorded values of E_i in Step 3, we find

$$E_a / \phi_a = 0.744 + j0.600 = 0.955 / 38.9° \tag{9.42}$$

with the aid of Table 9.1.

Table 9.1

Step i	Magnitude E_i	$E_i(\cos \theta_{1,i} + j \sin \theta_{1,i})$
1	0.18	$0.180 + j0$
2	0.47	$0.380 + j0.276$
3	0.45	$0.139 + j0.428$
4	0.00	$0.000 + j0.000$
5	−0.13	$0.105 - j0.076$
6	−0.04	$0.040 + j0.000$
7	0.09	$-0.073 - j0.053$
8	0.05	$-0.015 - j0.048$
9	−0.05	$-0.028 + j0.085$
10	0.02	$0.016 - j0.012$
11	0.00	$0.000 + j0.000$
Sum.....	....	$0.744 + j0.600$

Remark. To find the gain characteristic $G_0(\omega)$ and the relative-phase characteristic $\theta'(\omega)$ for this network, follow the procedures discussed in Questions 2 and 3 in Art. 9.4A.

D. Some Remarks about the Transient and Steady-state Responses of a Linear Low-pass Four-terminal Network

Finding the steady-state response (or the steady-state characteristics) of a network from its transient response. This is what we have discussed in Art. 9.4B and C and remarked on in Art. 9.4A. From the *known* transient response of a network subject to a unit-step excitation, we can determine the steady-state response E_a / ϕ_a subject to a sinusoidal excitation $1 / 0°$ at any arbitrary frequency ω_a.

Knowing the steady-state responses E_a / ϕ_a, E_b / ϕ_b, E_c / ϕ_c, ... at a large number of frequencies ω_a, ω_b, ω_c, ..., we also know the gain characteristic $G_0(\omega)$ and the relative phase characteristic $\theta'(\omega) = \theta(\omega) - \theta_k$ of the network, as remarked on in

Questions 2 and 3 in Art. 9.4A. $G_0(\omega)$ and $\theta(\omega)$ [or $\theta'(\omega)$] are often called the *steady-state characteristics* or *frequency characteristics* of the network.

Finding the transient response of a network from its steady-state characteristics (or its steady-state responses at a large number of frequencies).   As remarked above, if we *know* the steady-state responses at a large number of frequencies, we also know $G_0(\omega)$ and $\theta'(\omega) = \theta(\omega) - \theta_k$. The phase characteristic $\theta(\omega)$ must be an odd function of ω, and, for the low-pass network we are treating, $\theta(\omega) = 0$ for $\omega = 0$. This means that $\theta_k = \theta(0) - \theta'(0) = 0 - \theta'(0) = -\theta'(0)$ is determined, and $\theta(\omega) = \theta'(\omega) + \theta_k$ is now a known expression, say in the form of a graph. We now have both the gain characteristic $G_0(\omega)$ and the phase characteristic $\theta(\omega)$ as *known* expressions.

With $G_0(\omega)$ and $\theta(\omega)$ available, the transient response of the network subject to a unit-step excitation may be readily obtained by the procedure described in Art. 9.1B.

If we are interested *only* in the approximate waveform of the transient response subject to a unit-step excitation and do not care about the time delay t_d, we may use the available $G_0(\omega)$ and assume $\theta(\omega) = 0$ in following the procedure in Art. 9.1B. Reference is made to the last paragraphs in Art. 9.1D for justification.

Relations between the transient and steady-state responses of a linear low-pass four-terminal network.   Summarizing the above discussions, we find, for a given linear low-pass four-terminal network,

$$\begin{bmatrix} A. \text{ Transient response} \\ \text{subject to unit-step} \\ \text{excitation} \end{bmatrix} \xrightleftharpoons[\substack{\text{To find } A, \text{ use procedure} \\ \text{in Art. 9.1B}}]{\substack{\text{To find } B, \text{ use procedure} \\ \text{in Art. 9.4C}}} \begin{bmatrix} B. \text{ Steady-state characteristics} \\ G_0(\omega) \text{ and } \theta(\omega) \text{ or steady-state} \\ \text{responses at all frequencies} \end{bmatrix}$$

$$(9.43)$$

The square-wave testing described in this section (Art. 9.4) provides a link between the transient and steady-state responses of a linear low-pass four-terminal network.

9.5. Some theoretical response waveforms

A. Some Typical Response Waveforms

We have tabulated in Fig. 9.11(2a) and (3a) the results of Arts. 9.1B and 9.2A for the responses of a network with the transmission characteristics depicted in Fig. 8.5a and b or 9.11a subject to a unit-step excitation and a rectangular-pulse excitation.

Following procedure (8.34) as in Art. 9.1B, we may find the responses of networks with other theoretical transmission characteristics $G_0(\omega)$ and $\theta(\omega)$ and add them to Fig. 9.11.

B. Some Remarks

From the responses in Fig. 9.11, we note:

1. We have assumed a linear phase characteristic $\theta(\omega) = \omega t_d$ for all these illustrations; this $\theta(\omega)$ is responsible for a delay of t_d sec in all the responses.

2. "Overshoots" or "oscillations" exist in Fig. 9.11(2a) and (3a), but not in Fig. 9.11(2d) and (3d). We are led to believe that these "overshoots" or "oscillations" are introduced by the sharp cutoff of the gain characteristic $G_0(\omega)$ as exhibited in Fig. 9.11a.

3. Letting $\theta(\omega) = 0$ (that is, $t_d = 0$) in Fig. 9.11b, we find that the response is identical with the excitation throughout column b. This means that the four-terminal network is nothing but two shorting wires, one between terminals 1 and 2, and the other between 1' and 2'.

9.6. Responses of two related excitations

We shall now study, in Fig. 9.11, the responses of two related excitations.

A. Property of Superposition

As we have demonstrated in Fig. 9.5, a rectangular-pulse excitation $e_1(t)$ as depicted in Fig. 9.11(3) is equal to the algebraic sum

$$e_1(t) = u(t - t_1) - u(t - t_2) \tag{9.44}$$

where　　　　　$u(t - t_1) =$ unit-step function as depicted in
Fig. 9.11(2) but shifted *left* by a
time interval $|t_1| = |-\delta/2| = \delta/2$ 　　　(9.44a)

$u(t - t_2) =$ unit-step function as depicted in
Fig. 9.11(2) but shifted *right* by a
time interval $|t_2| = |\delta/2| = \delta/2$ 　　　(9.44b)

Comparing the responses in Fig. 9.11(2a) with (3a), (2b) with (3b), (2c) with (3c), and (2d) with (3d), we see that any response $e_2(t)$ among those in Fig. 9.11(3a), (3b), (3c), and (3d) is equal to the algebraic sum

$$e_2(t) = e_{2L}(t) - e_{2R}(t) \tag{9.45}$$

where　　　　　$e_{2L}(t) =$ response of $u(t - t_1)$, i.e., response
as depicted in Fig. 9.11(2a) [or (2b),
(2c), or (2d)] shifted *left* by a time
interval $|t_1| = |-\delta/2| = \delta/2$ 　　　(9.45a)

$e_{2R}(t) =$ response of $u(t - t_2)$, i.e., response
as depicted in Fig. 9.11(2a) [or (2b),
(2c), or (2d)] shifted *right* by a
time interval $|t_2| = |\delta/2| = \delta/2$ 　　　(9.45b)

Summarizing the above, we may state: *If*

$$e_1(t) = e_{1A}(t) + e_{1B}(t) \tag{9.46a}$$

is the excitation of a linear four-terminal network, its response must have the form

$$e_2(t) = e_{2A}(t) + 2_{2B}(t) \tag{9.46b}$$

where $e_{2A}(t)$ and $e_{2B}(t)$ are the respective responses of this network subject to excitations $e_{1A}(t)$ and $e_{1B}(t)$.

B. Integral-and-Derivative Relationship between Two Excitations

Now we shall study the relationship between the responses of a linear low-pass four-terminal network subject to two excitations having an integral-and-derivative relationship.

Integral-and-derivative relationship between responses as implied conditions. The unit-step excitation $u(t)$ and the unit-impulse excitation $\delta(t)$, as depicted in Fig. 9.11(2) and (1), have the integral-and-derivative relationship stated in (9.19). We now wish to investigate the responses of a system subjected to these functions as excitations.

For the network transmission characteristics exhibited in Fig. 9.11a, we observe that the response to $u(t)$ [Fig. 9.11(2a)] and the response to $\delta(t)$ [Fig. 9.11(1a)] also have an integral-and-derivative relationship. Note that y_1 at $t = t_1$ in Fig. 9.11(2a) equals the shaded area under the response waveform from $t = 0$ to $t = t_1$ in Fig.

Network trans

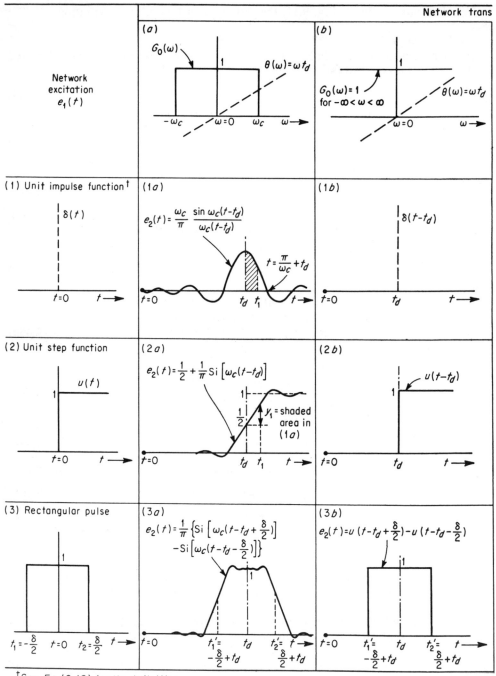

(1) Unit impulse function †

(2) Unit step function

(3) Rectangular pulse

†See Eq.(9.18) for its definition.

FIG.

mission characteristics

(c)

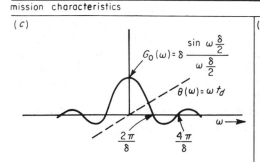

$$G_0(\omega) = \delta\,\frac{\sin\omega\frac{\delta}{2}}{\omega\frac{\delta}{2}}$$

$$\theta(\omega) = \omega t_d$$

$$\frac{2\pi}{\delta} \qquad \frac{4\pi}{\delta}$$

(d)

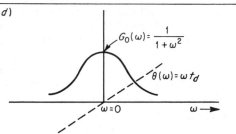

$$G_0(\omega) = \frac{1}{1+\omega^2}$$

$$\theta(\omega) = \omega t_d$$

$$\omega = 0$$

(1c)

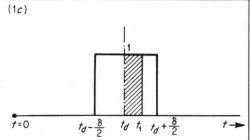

$$t=0 \qquad t_d - \frac{\delta}{2} \quad t_d \ \ t_1 \ \ t_d + \frac{\delta}{2}$$

(1d)

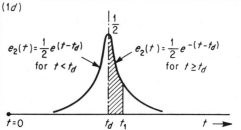

$$e_2(t) = \frac{1}{2}e^{(t-t_d)}$$
$$\text{for } t < t_d$$

$$e_2(t) = \frac{1}{2}e^{-(t-t_d)}$$
$$\text{for } t \geq t_d$$

$$t=0 \qquad t_d \ \ t_1$$

(2c)

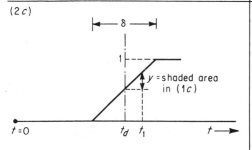

$$\leftarrow \delta \rightarrow$$

$$y = \text{shaded area in } (1c)$$

$$t=0 \qquad t_d \ \ t_1$$

(2d)

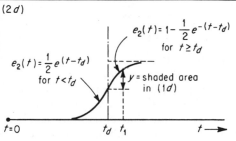

$$e_2(t) = 1 - \frac{1}{2}e^{-(t-t_d)}$$
$$\text{for } t \geq t_d$$

$$e_2(t) = \frac{1}{2}e^{(t-t_d)}$$
$$\text{for } t < t_d$$

$$y = \text{shaded area in } (1d)$$

$$t=0 \qquad t_d \ \ t_1$$

(3c)

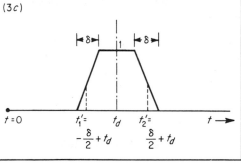

$$\leftarrow\delta\rightarrow \quad \leftarrow\delta\rightarrow$$

$$t=0 \qquad t_1' = \qquad t_d \quad t_2' =$$
$$-\frac{\delta}{2}+t_d \qquad \frac{\delta}{2}+t_d$$

(3d)

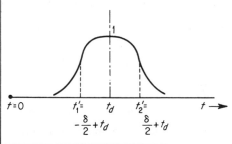

$$t=0 \qquad t_1' = \qquad t_d \quad t_2' =$$
$$-\frac{\delta}{2}+t_d \qquad \frac{\delta}{2}+t_d$$

9.11

9.11(1*a*). This implies that the response waveform in Fig. 9.11(2*a*) is equal to the *integral* of the response waveform in Fig. 9.11(1*a*) plus a constant of integration which equals $\frac{1}{2}$, and that the latter is the *derivative* of the former.

Comparing all the responses in Fig. 9.11(2*b*) to (2*d*) with the respective responses in Fig. 9.11(1*b*) to (1*d*), we see that an integral-and-derivative relationship exists.

We are now led to believe that *if an integral-and-derivative relationship exists between two excitations to a linear low-pass four-terminal network, this same relationship exists between their responses.* This property can be readily understood with the aid of the Laplace transform, which will be studied in Chaps. 11 through 13.

Spectrum functions of two excitations and their responses when the excitations have an integral-and-derivative relationship. If an excitation $e_{1d}(t)$ is the derivative of another excitation $e_{1i}(t)$, that is,

Excitations:
$$e_{1d}(t) = \frac{d}{dt} e_{1i}(t) \tag{9.47a}$$

their respective spectrum functions $g_{1d}(\omega)$ and $g_{1i}(\omega)$, according to (9.23), are related by

Excitation spectra:
$$g_{1d}(\omega) = j\omega g_{1i}(\omega) \tag{9.47b}$$

Let $e_{2d}(t)$ and $e_{2i}(t)$ be, respectively, the responses of a linear low-pass four-terminal network subject to the excitations $e_{1d}(t)$ and $e_{1i}(t)$. Equation (9.47*a*) now implies

Responses:
$$e_{2d}(t) = \frac{d}{dt} e_{2i}(t) \tag{9.48a}$$

Since $g_{2d}(\omega)$ and $g_{2i}(\omega)$ are the respective spectrum functions of the responses $e_{2d}(t)$ and $e_{2i}(t)$, (9.23) also implies

Response spectra:
$$g_{2d}(\omega) = (j\omega)g_{2i}(\omega) \tag{9.48b}$$

This means that *if we are given an excitation $e_{1i}(t)$ to a linear low-pass four-terminal network and the spectrum function $g_{2i}(\omega)$ of its response, we can immediately determine, with (9.48b), the spectrum function $g_{2d}(\omega)$ of the response of another excitation $e_{1d}(t)$ which is the derivative of $e_{1i}(t)$.*

We also note that $e_{1i}(t)$ and $e_{2i}(t)$ are the integrals of $e_{1d}(t)$ and $e_{2d}(t)$, and Eqs. (9.47*b*) and (9.48*b*) are also the relations existing between their spectrum functions.

9.7. Remarks about the application of Fourier integrals and Fourier transforms in the complex forms to bandpass network problems

We shall show here that the Fourier integral and Fourier transform in the complex forms are not necessarily the best tools for handling bandpass network problems; then we shall introduce the Fourier integral and Fourier transform in the trigonometric forms in Art. 9.8. The reader may *omit* this section (Art. 9.7) and proceed directly to Art. 9.8.

A. Fourier Transform of a Modulated Pulse

Representations of a modulated pulse. We may represent the modulated pulse with rectangular envelope in Fig. 9.12*a* as

$$e_1(t) = \begin{cases} E \cos \omega_0 t & -\dfrac{\delta}{2} \le t \le \dfrac{\delta}{2} \\[2mm] 0 & t < -\dfrac{\delta}{2}, \ \dfrac{\delta}{2} < t \end{cases} \tag{9.49a}$$

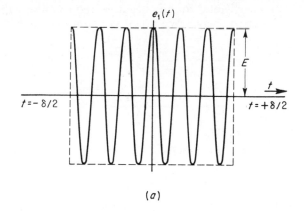

(a)

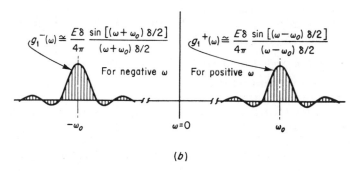

(b)

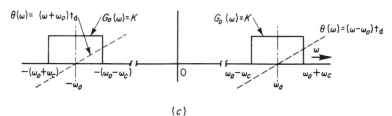

(c)

FIG. 9.12

or as

$$e_1(t) = \begin{cases} \dfrac{E(e^{j\omega_0 t} + e^{-j\omega_0 t})}{2} & -\dfrac{\delta}{2} \le t \le \dfrac{\delta}{2} \\[2ex] 0 & t < -\dfrac{\delta}{2}, \ \ \dfrac{\delta}{2} < t \end{cases} \qquad (9.49b)$$

Fourier transform in the complex form. Substituting (9.49b) into (8.3b), we find the Fourier transform $g_1(\omega)$ of $e_1(t)$:

$$g_1(\omega) = \frac{E\delta}{4\pi} \frac{\sin\left[(\omega - \omega_0)\delta/2\right]}{(\omega - \omega_0)\delta/2} + \frac{E\delta}{4\pi} \frac{\sin\left[(\omega + \omega_0)\delta/2\right]}{(\omega + \omega_0)\delta/2} \qquad (9.50)$$

In general, the carrier frequency, $f_0 = \omega_0/2\pi$ in cycles per second or ω_0 in radians per second, is very large. Under this condition, we shall find that the first term on the right-hand side of (9.50) is negligible† for any negative frequency, and the second term negligible for any positive frequency.   We now have, approximately,

$$g_1{}^+(\omega) \cong \frac{E\delta}{4\pi} \frac{\sin\,[(\omega - \omega_0)\delta/2]}{(\omega - \omega_0)\delta/2} \qquad \omega > 0 \qquad\qquad (9.50a)$$

$$g_1{}^-(\omega) \cong \frac{E\delta}{4\pi} \frac{\sin\,[(\omega + \omega_0)\delta/2]}{(\omega + \omega_0)\delta/2} \qquad \omega < 0 \qquad\qquad (9.50b)$$

which is depicted in Fig. 9.12b.

Some remarks about negative frequencies.   The negative-frequency region,

$$-\infty < \omega \leq 0$$

is used here for mathematical expediency, as remarked earlier in the discussion associated with Eqs. (8.27).   The negative-frequency components do not exist in reality.   The negative-frequency spectrum is a mirror image of the positive-frequency spectrum, as is evident in Fig. 9.12b.

B. Bandpass Network Subject to a Modulated-pulse Excitation

Idealized transmission characteristics.   The spectrum of an unmodulated rectangular pulse is a sampling function centered at $\omega = 0$, as depicted in Fig. 8.1b. The spectrum of a modulated pulse is a sampling function centered at $\omega = \omega_0$; its mirror image is another sampling function centered at $\omega = -\omega_0$ in the negative region, as depicted in Fig. 9.12b.

In the study of the responses of a low-pass network subject to unmodulated excitations in Arts. 9.1 and 9.2, we used the idealized transmission characteristics centered at $\omega = 0$ as depicted in Fig. 8.5a and b.   For a spectrum of a modulated pulse centered at ω_0 as in Fig. 9.12b, we obviously need a bandpass network with passband also centered at ω_0.   We shall use the idealized transmission characteristics

$$G_0(\omega) = \begin{cases} K & \omega_0 - \omega_c \leq \omega \leq \omega_0 + \omega_c \\ 0 & \text{other } (+) \text{ frequencies} \end{cases} \qquad\qquad (9.51a)$$

$$\theta(\omega) = (\omega - \omega_0)t_d \qquad \text{for all } (+) \text{ frequencies} \qquad\qquad (9.51b)$$

in the positive-frequency region as depicted in Fig. 9.12c.   Transmission characteristics (9.51) will pass the frequency components in $g_1{}^+(\omega)$ as described by (9.50a) between $\omega_0 - \omega_c \leq \omega \leq \omega_0 + \omega_c$ in the positive-frequency region.   The symmetrical images of (9.51),

$$G_0(\omega) = \begin{cases} K & \text{for } -(\omega_0 + \omega_c) \leq \omega \leq -(\omega_0 - \omega_c) \\ 0 & \text{for other } (-) \text{ frequencies} \end{cases} \qquad\qquad (9.52a)$$

$$\theta(\omega) = (\omega + \omega_0)t_d \qquad \text{for all } (-) \text{ frequencies} \qquad\qquad (9.52b)$$

in the negative-frequency region, also depicted in Fig. 9.12c, will pass the frequency components in $g_1{}^-(\omega)$ as described by (9.50b) between $-\omega_0 + \omega_c \leq \omega \leq -(\omega_0 - \omega_c)$.

Response of an idealized bandpass network subject to a modulated-pulse excitation. Let the excitation $e_1(t)$ and its Fourier transform $g_1(\omega)$ be respectively represented by (9.49) and (9.50) and depicted in Fig. 9.12a and b.   Let the bandpass network have the idealized transmission characteristics represented by (9.51) and (9.52) and depicted

† Note that this term has a (numerically) large denominator and is therefore negligible.

in Fig. 9.12*c*.   To find the response $e_2(t)$, procedure (8.34) is still applicable.   Using (8.33*b*), and with reference to Fig. 9.12*b* and *c*, we have

$$e_2(t) = \int_{-\infty}^{+\infty} g_1(\omega) G_0(\omega) e^{-j\theta(\omega)} e^{j\omega t} \, d\omega$$

$$e_2(t) = \left(\int_{-\infty}^{-(\omega_0 + \omega_c)} + \int_{-(\omega_0 + \omega_c)}^{-(\omega_0 - \omega_c)} + \int_{-(\omega_0 - \omega_c)}^{0} + \int_{0}^{\omega_0 - \omega_c} + \int_{\omega_0 - \omega_c}^{\omega_0 + \omega_c} + \int_{\omega_0 + \omega_c}^{\infty} \right)$$

$$\times \, g_1(\omega) G_0(\omega) e^{-j\theta(\omega)} e^{j\omega t} \, d\omega$$

$$= 0 + \int_{-(\omega_0 + \omega_c)}^{-(\omega_0 - \omega_c)} g_1^{-}(\omega) K e^{-j(\omega + \omega_0) t_d} e^{j\omega t} \, d\omega + 0 + 0$$

$$+ \int_{\omega_0 - \omega_c}^{\omega_0 + \omega_c} g_1^{+}(\omega) K e^{-j(\omega - \omega_0) t_d} e^{j\omega t} \, d\omega + 0 \quad (9.53)$$

where $g_1^{-}(\omega)$ and $g_1^{+}(\omega)$ are defined in (9.50).

   Remarks.   It is easy to recognize that the response of a bandpass network subject to a modulated pulse is laborious to evaluate in the form of (9.53).   Equation (9.53) is obtained with the procedure described in (8.34), where $e_1(t)$, $e_2(t)$, and $g_1(\omega)$, $g_2(\omega)$ are Fourier integrals and Fourier transforms in the *complex forms* as defined in (8.3).

   In using the complex forms, we must treat both the positive and the negative frequencies, even though the negative frequencies do not exist in reality, but are only introduced for mathematical expediency.   We may evaluate the response $e_2(t)$ of a low-pass network subject to unmodulated excitation $e_1(t)$ as an integral with only *one* single continuous range of integration [Eq. (8.35*b*)].   For a bandpass network subject to a modulated excitation $e_1(t)$, we must evaluate $e_2(t)$ as an integral with *two* separate continuous ranges of integration, one in the negative-frequency region, and another in the positive-frequency region [Eq. (9.53)].   The procedure for finding a response described in (8.34), using Fourier integrals and Fourier transforms in the *complex forms*, is therefore handy for a low-pass network problem with an unmodulated excitation; it is cumbersome for a bandpass network problem with a modulated excitation because of the necessity of evaluating an integral over *two* separate ranges.

   We shall introduce, in Art. 9.8, the Fourier integral and Fourier transform in the *trigonometric forms*, which are defined in the *positive-frequency region* only.   Finding the response $e_2(t)$ of a bandpass network subject to a modulated excitation is much easier using Fourier integrals and Fourier transforms in the trigonometric forms. It requires the evaluation of an integral for *one* continuous range in the positive-frequency region.

9.8. Fourier integral and Fourier transform in the trigonometric forms; their applications to bandpass network problems

   We have remarked above that the complex forms of the Fourier integral and Fourier transform are not the most desirable forms to be used in bandpass network problems. We shall now introduce the trigonometric forms.

   A review of the Fourier series in trigonometric form.   A repeating function $e(t)$, satisfying the conditions prescribed in Art. 7.2B, may be represented as a Fourier series

$$e(t) = \frac{A_0}{2} + \sum_{n=1}^{\infty} (A_n \cos n\omega_0 t + B_n \sin n\omega_0 t) \quad (9.54)$$

The Fourier coefficients, i.e., the coefficients of (9.54), may be computed from (7.20) or

$$A_n = \frac{\omega_0}{\pi} \int_0^{2\pi/\omega_0} e(t) \cos n\omega_0 t \, dt \qquad n = 0, 1, 2, \ldots \tag{9.55a}$$

$$B_n = \frac{\omega_0}{\pi} \int_0^{2\pi/\omega_0} e(t) \sin n\omega_0 t \, dt \qquad n = 1, 2, \ldots \tag{9.55b}$$

Fourier integral and Fourier transform in trigonometric forms. We generalized the Fourier series $e(t)$ and Fourier coefficient C_n in the complex forms into the Fourier integral and Fourier transform in the complex forms in Art. 8.1. Considering a nonrepeating function as the limiting case of a repeating function with period $T \to \infty$, we found that, for $T \to \infty$, the fundamental frequency $\omega_0 \to 0$, where $f_0 = \omega_0/2\pi = 1/T$, and the Fourier coefficient $C_n \to 0$. Letting $\omega = n\omega_0$ and defining $g(\omega) = \lim_{\omega_0 \to 0} (C_n/\omega_0)$, we obtained the Fourier integral and Fourier transform in the complex forms in (8.3).

Let us again consider a nonrepeating function as the limiting case of a repeating function with period $T \to \infty$. For $T \to \infty$, we again find $\omega_0 \to 0$ and the Fourier coefficients $A_n \to 0$ and $B_n \to 0$, where A_n and B_n are prescribed in (9.55). Letting $\omega = n\omega_0$ and defining $a(\omega) = \lim_{\omega_0 \to 0} (A_n/\omega_0)$ and $b(\omega) = \lim_{\omega_0 \to 0} (B_n/\omega_0)$ as we defined $g(\omega) = \lim_{\omega_0 \to 0} (C_n/\omega_0)$ in Art. 8.1, we convert (9.54) into

$$e(t) = \int_0^\infty a(\omega) \cos \omega t \, d\omega + \int_0^\infty b(\omega) \sin \omega t \, d\omega \tag{9.56}$$

and (9.55) into

$$a(\omega) = \frac{1}{\pi} \int_{-\infty}^{+\infty} e(t) \cos \omega t \, dt \tag{9.57a}$$

$$b(\omega) = \frac{1}{\pi} \int_{-\infty}^{+\infty} e(t) \sin \omega t \, dt \tag{9.57b}$$

We shall call (9.56) the *Fourier integral*, and (9.57) the *Fourier transforms* (or the Fourier integral transforms), in the trigonometric forms associated with a non-repeating wave.

Remarks about the Fourier transforms in the trigonometric forms. In the complex form, the Fourier transform $g(\omega)$ of a wave $e(t)$ is the spectrum function representing the complex amplitude of any frequency component in $e(t)$, as remarked in the discussion associated with Eq. (8.4).

It takes *two* real numbers a and b to represent *one* complex number $C = a + jb$. The frequency components of a signal $e(t)$ can be adequately represented by *one* complex spectrum function $g(\omega)$, or by *two* real spectrum functions[†] $a(\omega)$ and $b(\omega)$ in quadrature (i.e., 90° out of phase). We shall call $a(\omega)$ and $b(\omega)$ the *compone nt spectrum functions*.

Response of a bandpass network. Let us assume that the passband of the network is from $\omega = \omega_1$ to $\omega = \omega_2$ and that the transmission characteristics are $G_0(\omega)$ and $\theta(\omega)$ as defined in (3.39). By definition, $G_0(\omega) = 0$ outside the passband. For an excitation $e_1(t)$, we have the Fourier transforms or component-spectrum functions

$$a_1(\omega) = \frac{1}{\pi} \int_{-\infty}^{+\infty} e_1(t) \cos \omega t \, dt \tag{9.58a}$$

$$b_1(\omega) = \frac{1}{\pi} \int_{-\infty}^{+\infty} e_1(t) \sin \omega t \, dt \tag{9.58b}$$

[†] The ω_1 component in $e(t)$ may be determined from $a(\omega)$ and $b(\omega)$. Its magnitude is $\sqrt{[a(\omega_1)]^2 + [b(\omega_1)]^2}$; its phase is $\theta = \tan^{-1}[b(\omega_1)/a(\omega_1)]$.

After we modify the magnitudes of $a_1(\omega)$ and $b_1(\omega)$ with $G_0(\omega)$ and introduce a phase shift $\theta(\omega)$ for each of these two components, we shall use a relation similar to (9.56) to obtain the network response:

$$e_2(t) = \int_{\omega_1}^{\omega_2} \{a_1(\omega)G_0(\omega)\} \cos [\omega t - \theta(\omega)] \, d\omega$$

$$+ \int_{\omega_1}^{\omega_2} \{b_1(\omega)G_0(\omega)\} \cos [\omega t - \theta(\omega)] \, d\omega \quad (9.59)$$

We note the modification of the magnitudes in braces and the introduction of the phase shift in brackets. Since $G_0(\omega) = 0$ outside the passband, the integrals in (9.59) are evaluated only between the limits of the passband.

9.9. Illustration: a bandpass network with idealized transmission characteristics subject to a modulated-pulse excitation

A. Finding the Response

A *modulated pulse* as depicted in Fig. 9.12a and represented by

$$e_1(t) = \begin{cases} E \cos \omega_0 t & -\dfrac{\delta}{2} \leq t \leq \dfrac{\delta}{2} \\[2mm] 0 & t < -\dfrac{\delta}{2}, \dfrac{\delta}{2} < t \end{cases} \quad (9.60)$$

is used as excitation to an idealized bandpass network. We assume the carrier frequency is

$$\omega_0 = \text{a very large frequency} \quad (9.60a)$$

The *idealized transmission characteristics* of the bandpass network are

$$G_0(\omega) = \begin{cases} K & \omega_1 \leq \omega \leq \omega_2, \; \omega_1 = \omega_0 - \omega_c, \; \omega_2 = \omega_0 + \omega_c \\ 0 & \omega < \omega_1, \; \omega_2 < \omega \end{cases} \quad (9.61a)$$

$$\theta(\omega) = (\omega - \omega_0)t_d \quad (9.61b)$$

as depicted in the positive-frequency region in Fig. 9.12c.

The *network response* $e_2(t)$ may be obtained by first finding $a_1(\omega)$ and $b_1(\omega)$ with the aid of (9.58),

$$a_1(\omega) = \frac{1}{\pi} \int_{-\delta/2}^{\delta/2} E \cos \omega_0 t \cos \omega t \, dt$$

$$= \frac{E}{2\pi} \int_{-\delta/2}^{\delta/2} [\cos (\omega - \omega_0)t + \cos (\omega + \omega_0)t] \, dt$$

$$= \frac{E}{\pi} \left\{ \frac{\sin [(\omega - \omega_0)\delta/2]}{\omega - \omega_0} + \frac{\sin [(\omega + \omega_0)\delta/2]}{\omega + \omega_0} \right\} \quad (9.62a)$$

$$a_1(\omega) \cong \frac{E}{\pi} \frac{\sin [(\omega - \omega_0)\delta/2]}{\omega - \omega_0} \quad (9.62a')$$

where the second term in (9.62a) is obviously negligible in comparison with the first term under assumption (9.60a), and

$$b_1(\omega) = \frac{1}{\pi} \int_{-\delta/2}^{\delta/2} E \cos \omega_0 \sin \omega t \, dt$$

$$= \frac{E}{\pi} \int_{-\delta/2}^{\delta/2} [\sin (\omega - \omega_0)t + \sin (\omega + \omega_0)t] \, dt = 0 \quad (9.62b)$$

and then substituting (9.61) and (9.62) into (9.59):

$$e_2(t) = \int_{\omega_0-\omega_c}^{\omega_0+\omega_c} \frac{E}{\pi} \frac{\sin\left[(\omega-\omega_0)\delta/2\right]}{\omega-\omega_0} K \cos\left[\omega t - (\omega-\omega_0)t_d\right] d\omega + 0 \quad (9.63a)$$

Equation (9.63a) can be manipulated into†

$$e_2(t) = \frac{EK}{2\pi} \cos\omega_0 t \left(\int_{-\omega_c(\delta/2+t-t_d)}^{\omega_c(\delta/2+t-t_d)} \frac{\sin U_1}{U_1} dU_1 + \int_{-\omega_c(\delta/2-t+t_d)}^{\omega_c(\delta/2-t+t_d)} \frac{\sin U_2}{U_2} dU_2 \right) \quad (9.63b)$$

$$e_2(t) = \frac{EK}{2\pi} \cos\omega_0 t \left(2\int_{0}^{\omega_c(\delta/2+t-t_d)} \frac{\sin U_1}{U_1} dU_1 + 2\int_{0}^{\omega_c(\delta/2-t+t_d)} \frac{\sin U_2}{U_2} dU_2 \right)^{\ddagger} \quad (9.63c)$$

$$e_2(t) = \frac{EK}{\pi} \cos\omega_0 t \left\{ \mathrm{Si}\left[\omega_c\left(t-t_d+\frac{\delta}{2}\right)\right] + \mathrm{Si}\left[-\omega_c\left(t-t_d-\frac{\delta}{2}\right)\right] \right\} \quad (9.63d)$$

We therefore have the response§

$$e_2(t) = \frac{EK}{\pi} \left\{ \mathrm{Si}\left[\omega_c\left(t-t_d+\frac{\delta}{2}\right)\right] - \mathrm{Si}\left[\omega_c\left(t-t_d-\frac{\delta}{2}\right)\right] \right\} \cos\omega_0 t \quad (9.64)$$

B. Some Remarks

For an unmodulated rectangular pulse [Fig. 9.11(3)] as excitation to an idealized low-pass network, the response is represented by (9.13) and depicted in Fig. 9.13a, which is reproduced from Fig. 9.11(3a).

For a modulated pulse with a carrier frequency ω_0 and a rectangular envelope (Fig. 9.12a) as excitation to an idealized bandpass network with passband centered at ω_0, the response is represented by (9.64) and depicted in Fig. 9.13b.

Obviously, the envelope of the modulated response is identical with the unmodulated response.

9.10. Remarks about the time delay in a network

A. Some Illustrations of Time Delays in Networks

Illustration 1.   Signal of a single frequency as excitation to a four-terminal network.
Let us apply sinusoidal excitation

Excitation: $\qquad e_1(t) = |E_1| \sin\omega_0 t$ $\qquad\qquad\qquad\qquad\qquad$ (9.65a)

$\qquad\qquad\qquad\quad e_1(t) = \mathrm{Im}\,(E_1 e^{j\omega_0 t}) \qquad E_1 = |E_1|e^{j0} = |E_1|$ $\qquad$ (9.65b)

to the four-terminal linear network in Fig. 9.14b.   We may readily obtain the response

$$e_2(t) = |E_2| \sin(\omega_0 t - \theta) \qquad\qquad (9.65c)$$

where $\theta = \theta(\omega_0)$, and $\theta(\omega) = -\underline{/G(j\omega)}$ is the *phase characteristic* of the network. Since $\theta = \theta(\omega_0)$ is a constant for fixed ω_0, we may rewrite (9.65c) in the form

Response: $\qquad\qquad e_2(t) = |E_2| \sin\omega_0(t - t_d)$ $\qquad\qquad\qquad$ (9.65d)

---

† We first change variables in (9.63a) to make it a function of $\Omega = \omega - \omega_0$ instead of a function of ω; then we let $U_1 = \Omega(\delta/2 + t - t_d)$ and $U_2 = \Omega(\delta/2 - t + t_d)$ to obtain (9.63b). For verification, (9.63b) is readily reducible to (9.63a).

‡ $\int_{-x}^{x} [(\sin U)/U]\,dU = 2\int_{0}^{x} [(\sin U)/U]\,dU$ because $(\sin U)/U$ is an even function of U [see the second footnote associated with Eq. (9.6b)].   See (9.7c) for the definition of Si x.

§ $\mathrm{Si}(-x) = -\mathrm{Si}\,x$.   Note that Si x is an odd function of x in Fig. 9.3b.

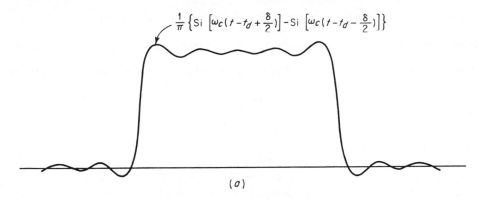

$$\frac{1}{\pi}\left\{\mathrm{Si}\left[\omega_c\left(t-t_d+\frac{\delta}{2}\right)\right]-\mathrm{Si}\left[\omega_c\left(t-t_d-\frac{\delta}{2}\right)\right]\right\}$$

(a)

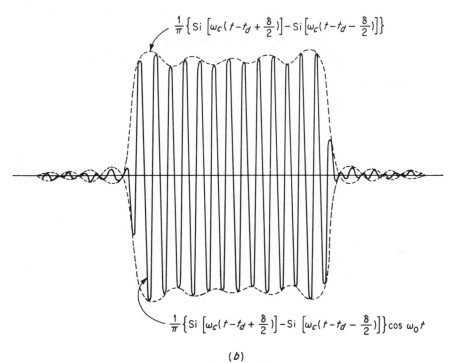

$$\frac{1}{\pi}\left\{\mathrm{Si}\left[\omega_c\left(t-t_d+\frac{\delta}{2}\right)\right]-\mathrm{Si}\left[\omega_c\left(t-t_d-\frac{\delta}{2}\right)\right]\right\}$$

$$\frac{1}{\pi}\left\{\mathrm{Si}\left[\omega_c\left(t-t_d+\frac{\delta}{2}\right)\right]-\mathrm{Si}\left[\omega_c\left(t-t_d-\frac{\delta}{2}\right)\right]\right\}\cos\omega_0 t$$

(b)

Fig. 9.13

where the delay is

Delay:
$$t_d = \left[\frac{\theta(\omega)}{\omega}\right]_{\omega=\omega_0} \tag{9.65e}$$

By plotting (9.65a) and (9.65d) in Fig. 9.14a and comparing them, we see that t_d in (9.65e) represents the "time lag" or "time delay" of the response $e_2(t)$ with respect to the excitation $e_1(t)$.

Illustration 2. Signal of a single frequency as excitation to a two-terminal network. As in the preceding illustration, we apply a sinusoidal excitation

Excitation:
$$e(t) = |E|\sin\omega_0 t \tag{9.66a}$$

to the two-terminal linear network in Fig. 9.15*b* and obtain the response

Response: $\qquad i(t) = |I| \sin (\omega_0 t - \theta) = |I| \sin \omega_0 (t - t_d)$ $\qquad$ (9.66*b*)

where $\theta = \theta(\omega_0)$, and $\theta(\omega) = -\underline{/Y(j\omega)}$ is the *phase characteristic* of the network. Its delay is

Delay: $\qquad t_d = \left[\dfrac{\theta(\omega)}{\omega} \right]_{\omega = \omega_0}$ $\qquad$ (9.66*c*)

By plotting (9.66*a*) and (9.66*b*) in Fig. 9.15*a* and comparing them, we see that t_d in (9.66*c*) represents the "time delay" of the response.

Illustration 3.   Signal consisting in a group of frequencies as excitation to a four-terminal low-pass network with idealized transmission characteristics. Let us summarize here the illustration in Art. 9.1.   For the network in Fig. 9.16*b* with the

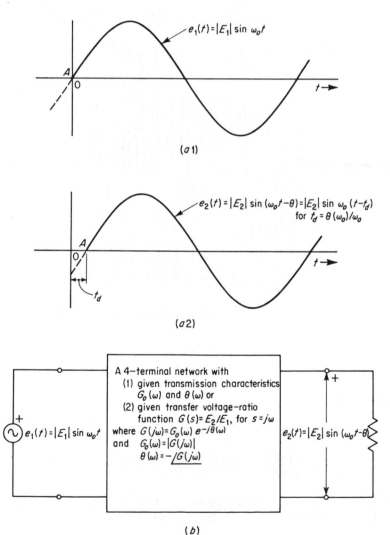

(*a*1)

(*a*2)

(*b*)

FIG. 9.14

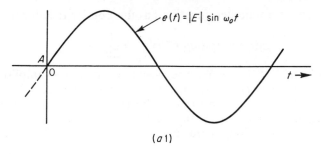

(*a*1)

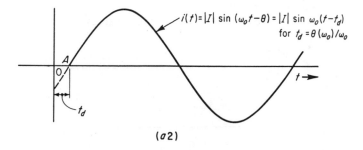

(*a*2)

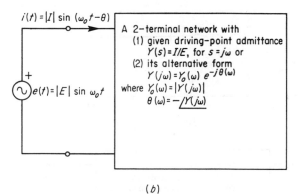

(*b*)

FIG. 9.15

idealized transmission characteristics $G_0(\omega) = K$ for $-\omega_c \leq \omega \leq \omega_c$ and

Idealized phase characteristic in Fig. 9.16c:

$$\theta(\omega) = \omega t_d \qquad (9.67a)$$

as depicted in Fig. 9.16c, the response $e_2(t)$ subject to the unit-step excitation $e_1(t)$ in Fig. 9.16*a*1 is now depicted in Fig. 9.16*a*2. The excitation and response waveforms are not identical; the distortion is caused by the finite bandwidth of $G_0(\omega)$ in Fig. 9.16c. Comparing $e_2(t)$ with $e_1(t)$ in Fig. 9.16*a*, we see that we may logically call t_d the "time delay" of the response. For $\theta(\omega) = \omega t_d$ in (9.67a), we may obtain t_d as

Delay: $$t_d = \left[\frac{d}{d\omega}\theta(\omega)\right]_{\omega=\omega_0=0} \qquad (9.67b)$$

Both $e_1(t)$ and $e_2(t)$ are found to have a group of significant frequency components in the neighborhood of $\omega = \omega_0 = 0$. We shall justify this statement as follows:

The excitation $e_1(t)$ as a unit-step function has the Fourier transform

$$g_1(\omega) = |g_1(\omega)|\, e^{-j\phi_1(\omega)} = \frac{1}{2\pi}\frac{1}{j\omega} \tag{9.68}$$

according to (9.4b) and (8.4); (9.68) represents the complex amplitudes of the frequency components in $e_1(t)$. It is, therefore, obvious that $e_1(t)$ has a group of significant frequency components in the neighborhood of $\omega = \omega_0 = 0$ in the sense that its dominating components are in the vicinity of $\omega = \omega_0 = 0$.

The response $e_2(t)$ has the Fourier transform

$$g_2(\omega) = \begin{cases} \dfrac{1}{2\pi}\dfrac{1}{j\omega}\, Ke^{-j\omega t_d} & -\omega_c \le \omega \le \omega_c \tag{9.69a} \\[2mm] 0 & \text{other values of } \omega \tag{9.69b} \end{cases}$$

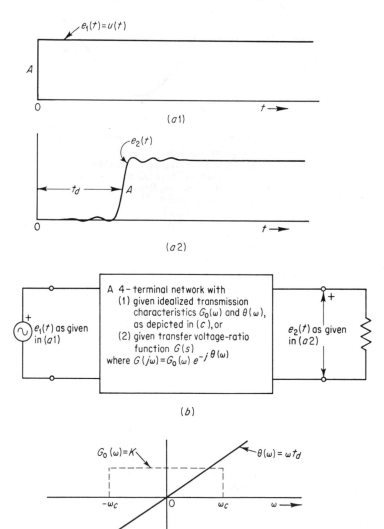

Fig. 9.16

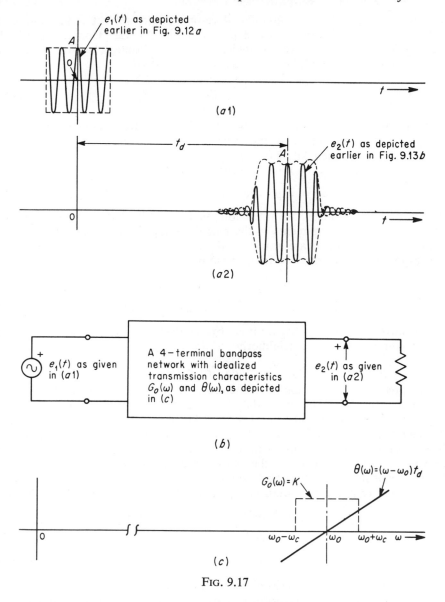

FIG. 9.17

representing the complex amplitudes of the frequency components in $e_2(t)$. Again it is obvious that $e_2(t)$ has a group of significant frequency components in the neighborhood of $\omega = \omega_0 = 0$.

Illustration 4. Signal consisting in a group of frequencies as excitation to a four-terminal bandpass network with idealized transmission characteristics. Let us summarize here the illustration in Art. 9.9. For the bandpass network in Fig. 9.17b with the idealized transmission characteristics $G_0(\omega) = K$ for $\omega_0 - \omega_c \leq \omega \leq \omega_0 + \omega_c$ and

Idealized phase characteristic in Fig. 9.17c:

$$\theta(\omega) = (\omega - \omega_0)t_d \qquad\qquad (9.70a)$$

as depicted in Fig. 9.17c, the modulated response $e_2(t)$ subject to the modulated excitation $e_1(t)$ in Fig. 9.17a1 is now depicted in Fig. 9.17a2. Comparing $e_2(t)$ and $e_1(t)$ in Fig. 9.17a, we see that we may logically call t_d the "time delay" of the response. For $\theta(\omega) = (\omega - \omega_0)t_d$ in (9.70a), we may obtain t_d as

$$Delay: \qquad t_d = \left[\frac{d}{d\omega}\,\theta(\omega)\right]_{\omega=\omega_0} \qquad (9.70b)$$

Both $e_1(t)$ and $e_2(t)$, as modulated signals with carrier frequency ω_0, are found to have a group of significant frequency components in the neighborhood† of $\omega = \omega_0$. We shall justify this statement as follows:

The excitation $e_1(t)$ has the Fourier transform

$$g_1^+(\omega) = \text{expression and graph in Fig. 9.12}b \qquad (9.71)$$

for the positive frequencies. It is obvious in Fig. 9.12b that $e_1(t)$ has a group of significant frequency components in the neighborhood of $\omega = \omega_0$ in the sense that its dominating components are in the vicinity of $\omega = \omega_0$.

The response $e_2(t)$ has the Fourier transform

$$g_2^+(\omega) = \begin{cases} g_1^+(\omega)Ke^{-j(\omega-\omega_0)t_d} & \omega_0 - \omega_c \le \omega \le \omega_0 + \omega_c \qquad (9.72a) \\ 0 & \text{other values of } \omega \qquad (9.72b) \end{cases}$$

for the positive frequencies. Again it is obvious that $e_2(t)$ has a group of significant frequency components in the neighborhood of $\omega = \omega_0$.

B. Two Definitions of Delay: Phase and Group Delays

In the preceding illustrations we encountered signals that were (1) individual frequencies in the forms of sinusoidal signals and (2) groups of frequencies. We also obtained the various relations between the phase characteristic $\theta(\omega)$ and the time delay t_d in (9.65e), (9.66c), (9.67b), and (9.70b) for these illustrations. We shall now formalize these relations into two definitions of time delay, after we have first given a precise description of the phase characteristic $\theta(\omega)$.

Description of the phase characteristic $\theta(\omega)$. Using $N(s)$ to represent any network function of the response/excitation type‡ of a given network, we may readily write

$$N(j\omega) = N_0(\omega)e^{-j\theta(\omega)} = N_0(\omega)\underline{/-\theta(\omega)} \qquad (9.73)$$

where

$$N_0(\omega) = |N(j\omega)| \qquad (9.74a)$$

$$\theta(\omega) = -\underline{/N(j\omega)} \qquad (9.74b)$$

and $\theta(\omega)$ is the "phase characteristic" of the network.

This network function $N(s)$ may be (1) any of the transfer functions $G(s) = E_2/E_1$, $Y_T(s) = I_2/E_1$, $Z_T(s) = E_2/I_1$, or $A(s) = I_2/I_1$ of a four-terminal network or (2) a driving-point function $Y(s) = I_1/E_1$ or $Z(s) = E_1/I_1$ of a two-terminal network. In Art. 9.10A, we used only $G(s)$ and $Y(s)$ in the illustrations.

† The negative-frequency components in the neighborhood of $\omega = -\omega_0$ are merely the mirror images of the positive-frequency components and need not be considered if the Fourier transform in the trigonometric form, instead of in the complex form, is used. Reference is made to Arts. 9.7 and 9.8.

‡ We have already defined some transfer functions of the response/excitation type for four-terminal networks in Art. 3.5C. For two-terminal networks, the network function of the response/excitation type is (1) a driving-point admittance $Y(s) = I/E$ if we use a voltage excitation and a current response or (2) a driving-point impedance $Z(s) = E/I$ if we use a current excitation and a voltage response.

Phase delay.   The phase delay of a network is defined by†

Phase delay: $$t_d = \tau_p(\omega_0) = \left[\frac{\theta(\omega)}{\omega}\right]_{\omega=\omega_0} \tag{9.75}$$

It measures the delay of the individual frequency ω_0 in passing through the network. We shall elaborate on the interpretation of "phase delay" in Art. 9.10C.

Group delay.   The group delay of a network is defined by†

Group delay: $$t_d = \tau_g(\omega_0) = \left[\frac{d}{d\omega}\,\theta(\omega)\right]_{\omega=\omega_0} \tag{9.76}$$

It measures the delay of a group of frequencies in the neighborhood (i.e., vicinity) of the frequency ω_0 in passing through the network if all the significant components among the group of frequencies have approximately the same delay.

We shall elaborate on the interpretation of "group delay" in Art. 9.10D.

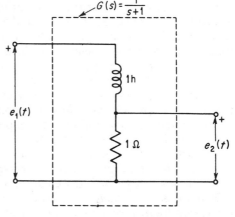

FIG. 9.18

C. Remarks about the Phase Delay

We have defined the "phase delay" of a network in (9.75) and interpreted it as the delay of the individual frequency ω_0. We now elaborate on this interpretation with the following remarks:

Remark 1.   *The phase delay, as defined in (9.75), measures the delay of a sinusoidal signal of frequency ω_0 in passing through the network.*   Reference is made to Illustrations 1 and 2 in Art. 9.10A.

Remark 2.   *The phase delay also measures the delay of the ω_0 component of an arbitrary signal in passing through the network.*   The arbitrary signal, as the excitation to the network, may consist in a group of frequency components; for example, it may be a unit-step function, a single pulse, a pulse train, etc.

Remark 3.   *For a network having an idealized linear phase characteristic $\theta(\omega) = \omega t_d$, the phase delay is the same for all frequencies.*   Since $t_d = \theta(\omega)/\omega$ is a constant independent of the frequency ω, this remark is obvious.

Numerical Illustration A (for the phase delay).   For the trivial four-terminal voltage-divider network in Fig. 9.18, the transfer voltage-ratio function $G(s) = 1/(1 + s)$ may be readily represented in the form $G(j\omega) = G_0(\omega)e^{-j\theta(\omega)} = (1/\sqrt{1 + \omega^2})\,e^{-j\,\tan^{-1}\omega}$; its phase characteristic is, therefore,

$$\theta(\omega) = \tan^{-1}\omega \tag{9.77a}$$

Let us find its phase delay at $\omega_0 = 1$ rad/sec.

According to (9.75), the phase delay at $\omega_0 = 1$ is

$$t_d = \tau_p(\omega_0) = \left.\frac{\tan^{-1}\omega_0}{\omega_0}\right|_{\omega_0=1} = \frac{\pi/4}{1} = \frac{\pi}{4}\,\text{sec} \tag{9.77b}$$

† Since ω_0 in (9.75) and (9.76) is merely a dummy variable representing an "interested" frequency, we may use ω in its place and write (9.75) and (9.76) in the forms (1) $t_d = \tau_g(\omega) = \theta(\omega)/\omega$ and (2) $t_d = \tau_g(\omega) = d\theta(\omega)/d\omega$.

D. Remarks about the Group Delay

We have defined the "group delay" of a network in (9.76) and interpreted it as the delay of a group of frequencies whose delays are nearly equal. We shall now elaborate this interpretation with the following remarks:

Remark 1. *The definition of the group delay in (9.76) is meaningful only when all significant components among the group of frequencies have approximately the same delay and ω_0 in (9.76) is a representative frequency of this group.*

If all the frequency components of an arbitrary excitation have exactly the same delay t_d in passing through the network, the response consisting in all these uniformly "delayed" frequency components must also have a delay t_d with respect to the excitation.

We have just described an idealized case in which all the frequencies have the same delay. What if these frequencies do not have the same delay? Let us consider the two following situations:

1. If the delay is about the same for all significant frequency components and the network has an adequate bandwidth, the response waveform resembles the excitation waveform; if ω_0 is a representative frequency chosen from among the significant frequencies, the group delay as defined in (9.76) represents the approximate delay of the response with respect to the excitation.

2. If the delays for the significant frequency components are very much nonuniform, the response waveform may be so distorted from the excitation waveform that they defy any logical means of comparison to determine the delay of the response. In this situation, the definition of group delay in (9.76) is meaningless.

Remark 1 is, therefore, justified.

Remark 2. *We should always choose a representative frequency ω_0 from the group of frequencies such that the significant frequency components are in its neighborhood.*

We have already justified Remark 2 in the discussion following Remark 1.

Remark 3. *For many low-pass networks, it is appropriate to choose $\omega_0 = 0$ as the representative frequency to use in computing the group delay with (9.76).*

In Illustration 3 of Art. 9.10A, we demonstrated the method for obtaining the delay for a group of frequencies with (9.67b), which is consistent with the definition of group delay in (9.76). However, an idealized linear phase characteristic $\theta(\omega) = \omega t_d$ as depicted in Fig. 9.19a1 or 9.16c was used in the illustration, and $d\theta/d\omega = t_d$ was a constant. In general, a typical $\theta(\omega)$ as depicted in Fig. 9.19a2 is not linear.

Remark 4. *For many bandpass networks with modulated signals, it is appropriate to choose the carrier frequency ω_0 as the representative frequency to use in computing the group delay with (9.76).*

In Illustration 4 of Art. 9.10A, we demonstrated the method for obtaining the delay for a group of frequencies in the neighborhood of ω_0 with (9.70b), which is consistent with the definition of group delay in (9.76). However, an idealized linear characteristic $\theta(\omega) = (\omega - \omega_0)t_d$ as depicted in Fig. 9.19b1 or 9.17c was used in the illustration, and $d\theta/d\omega = t_d$ was a constant. In general, a typical $\theta(\omega)$ as depicted in Fig. 9.19b2 is not linear.

Remark 5. *The group delay as defined in (9.76) is a more appropriate measure of the "delay" performance of a delay line or any network which handles signals consisting in groups of frequencies than is the phase delay defined in (9.75).*

Because of the nature of the signals being handled, it is obviously more appropriate to use the group delay than the phase delay.

Remark 6. *An ideal delay line has a transfer voltage-ratio function*

For ideal delay line: $\qquad\qquad G(s) = Ke^{-st_d}$ $\qquad\qquad$ (9.78)

and transmission characteristics

For ideal delay line:
$$G_0(\omega) = |G(j\omega)| = K$$
$$\theta(\omega) = -\underline{/G(j\omega)} = \omega t_d \tag{9.79}$$

A network having a response† $e_2(t) = u(t - t_d)f(t - t_d)$, identical to the excitation $e_1(t) = u(t)f(t)$ in waveform but lagging the excitation by a time interval t_d, is called an "ideal" delay line. The transfer voltage-ratio function of such a network can be found, with the aid of the Laplace transform,‡ to be

$$G(s) = \frac{E_2(s)}{E_1(s)} = \frac{\mathscr{L}[e_2(t)]}{\mathscr{L}[e_1(t)]} = \frac{\mathscr{L}[u(t - t_d)f(t - t_d)]}{\mathscr{L}[u(t)f(t)]} = \frac{e^{-st_d}F(s)}{F(s)} = e^{-st_d}$$

With gain constant K,

$$G(s) = \frac{E_2(s)}{E_1(s)} = \frac{\mathscr{L}[Ku(t - t_d)f(t - t_d)]}{\mathscr{L}[u(t)f(t)]} = Ke^{-st_d}$$

which is identical to (9.78).

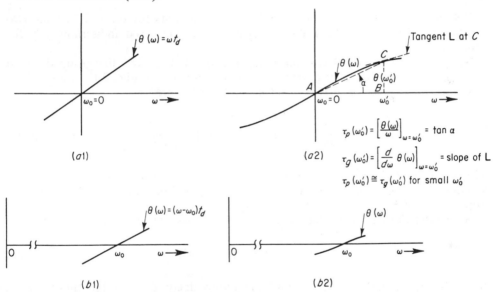

FIG. 9.19   (*a*) For low-pass networks; (*b*) for bandpass networks.

Applying the procedure described in (9.73) and (9.74), we obtain the transmission characteristic of an ideal delay line [Eq. (9.79)], depicted in Fig. 9.11*b*. Note that the responses in Fig. 9.11(1*b*), (2*b*), and (3*b*) are identical with the respective excitations in Fig. 9.11(1), (2), and (3) in waveform, but lag them by a time interval t_d.

Remark 7. *For the typical phase characteristic $\theta(\omega)$ in Fig. 9.19a2 for a low-pass network, the phase delay§ $\tau_p = [\theta(\omega)/\omega]_{\omega = \omega_0}$, and the group delay $\tau_g = [d\theta(\omega)/d\omega]_{\omega = \omega_0}$, are analogous to the d-c (or static) resistance¶ R_A and the a-c (dynamic) resistance r_A*

† Compare $e_1(t) = u(t)f(t)$ and $e_2(t) = u(t - t_d)f(t - t_d)$ with the waveforms in Fig. 11.3*b* and *d*; note that $e_1(t)$ and $e_2(t)$ have identical waveforms except for the delay t_d.

‡ The Laplace transform will be studied in Chaps. 11 to 13.   The transfer function given here can readily be obtained by applying property 4 in Table 11.3.

§ ω_0' (instead of ω_0) is used to avoid confusion with $\omega_0 = 0$ in an earlier illustration.

¶ For a discussion on the static and dynamic resistances see, for example, J. D. Ryder, "Engineering Electronics," pp. 32–33, McGraw-Hill Book Company, Inc., New York, 1957. Actually, the d-c conductance $G_A = (i/v)_{v = v_A}$ (where $G_A = 1/R_A$) and the a-c conductance $g_A = (di/dv)_{v = v_A}$ (where $g_A = 1/r_A$), rather than R_A and r_A themselves, are the quantities analogous to the phase delay $\tau_p = (\theta/\omega)_{\omega = \omega_0}$ and the group delay $\tau_g = (d\theta/d\omega)_{\omega = \omega_0}$.

of a nonlinear element, e.g., a diode.   The phase and group delays are approximately the same; i.e.,

$$\tau_p \cong \tau_g \qquad (9.80)$$

for small ω_0' or ω_0 in (9.75) and (9.76).

For nonlinear voltage-current relations, if we have a fixed voltage, i.e., an "individual" voltage, the d-c resistance is used; if we have a voltage varying about a fixed value v_0, that is, a "group" of voltages in the neighborhood of v_0, the a-c resistance is used.

For nonlinear phase relations, if we have a fixed frequency, i.e., an "individual" frequency, the phase delay is used; if we have a frequency varying about a fixed value ω_0, that is, a "group" of frequencies in the neighborhood of ω_0, the group delay is used.

It is hoped that this analogy will aid the reader in understanding phase and group delays.

Relation (9.80) is obvious in Fig. 9.19a2 and accounts for the fact that the two definitions of delay in (9.75) and (9.76) are sometimes used indiscriminately for small ω_0' or ω_0.

Numerical Illustration B (for the group delay).   Let us find the group delay at $\omega_0 = 0$ for the trivial four-terminal low-pass network in Fig. 9.18 whose phase characteristic is given in (9.77a).   According to (9.76), we have

$$t_d = \tau_g(\omega_0) = \left[\frac{d}{d\omega}(\tan^{-1}\omega)\right]_{\omega=\omega_0=0} = \left(\frac{1}{1+\omega^2}\right)_{\omega=\omega_0=0} = 1 \text{ sec} \qquad (9.81)$$

This means that, for an excitation such as a step function (or any other signal whose significant frequency components are in the neighborhood of $\omega_0 = 0$), there is an approximate delay $t_d = 1$ sec in the response.

Numerical Illustration C (for the group delay).   Assuming a phase characteristic

$$\theta(\omega) = \tan^{-1}(\omega - 100) \qquad (9.82a)$$

for a bandpass network, let us find the group delay at $\omega_0 = 100$ (normalized). According to (9.76), we have

$$t_d = \tau_g(\omega_0) = \left\{\frac{d}{d\omega}[\tan^{-1}(\omega - 100)]\right\}_{\omega=\omega_0=100} = \frac{1}{1+(\omega-100)^2}\bigg|_{\omega=\omega_0=100} = 1 \text{ sec}$$
$$(9.82b)$$

This means that, for an excitation whose significant frequency components are in the neighborhood of $\omega_0 = 100$, e.g., a modulated pulse as represented in (9.60) and Fig. 9.17a1, there is an approximate delay $t_d = 1$ sec in the response (Fig. 9.17a2).

PROBLEMS

9.1. Given: A four-terminal network having the idealized transmission characteristics (1) $G_0(\omega)$ as depicted in Fig. 8.5 with $K = 1$ and $\omega_c = 4\pi \times 10^5$ (that is, $\omega_c = 2\pi f_c$, and $f_c = 2 \times 10^5$ cps) and (2) $\theta(\omega) = \omega t_d$, with $t_d = 40$ μsec.

(a) Plot the response $e_2(t)$ subject to a unit-step excitation $e_1(t) = u(t)$ as depicted in Fig. 9.2a.   Use Jahnke and Emde or similar tables.

(b) Determine the buildup time t_B.

9.2. Repeat Prob. 9.1*a* for the square-topped pulse excitation in Fig. P 9.2. SUGGESTION: Choose any convenient zero-time reference (for $t = 0$); use and modify the result of Prob. 9.1*a* whenever possible in the solution of Probs. 9.2 through 9.4.

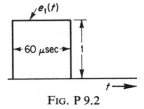

FIG. P 9.2

9.3. Repeat Prob. 9.1*a* for the two-pulse excitation in Fig. P 9.3.

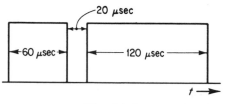

FIG. P 9.3

9.4. Repeat Prob. 9.1*a* for the excitation in Fig. P 9.4.

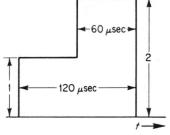

FIG. P 9.4

9.5. The transient response of a four-terminal network subject to a unit-step excitation is displayed on a cathode-ray oscilloscope and plotted to scale in Fig. P 9.5. The "timing dots" are obtained by modulating the cathode-ray beam with a standard signal of frequency $f_s = 12,000$ cps. Predict the magnitude and relative phase of the steady-state response of this network subject to a sinusoidal excitation of unit magnitude and frequency $f_a = 1,000$ cps.

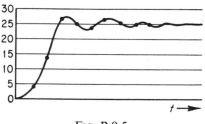

FIG. P 9.5

9.6. Given: A four-terminal network with transmission characteristics as in Fig. 9.11*a*.
Find the response to a unit-impulse excitation $e_1(t) = \delta(t)$, and check your result with Fig. 9.11(1*a*).

9.7. Given: A four-terminal network with transmission characteristics as in Fig. 9.11*c*.
Find the response subject to a unit-impulse excitation $e_1(t) = \delta(t)$, and check your result with Fig. 9.11(1*c*).

9.8. (*a*) A certain four-terminal linear network with *unknown* transmission characteristics has the response depicted in Fig. 9.11(3*a*) when subject to the rectangular-pulse excitation in Fig. 9.11(3). Can we predict the network response subject to the excitation in Fig. P 9.8, the derivative of the signal in Fig. 9.11(3)? If the answer is "yes," make an approximate sketch of this "predicted" response, and discuss how this sketch is obtained. REMARK: The transmission characteristics are actually depicted in Fig. 9.11*a*. Assume that this network is merely a black box so that its transmission characteristics are *unknown*.

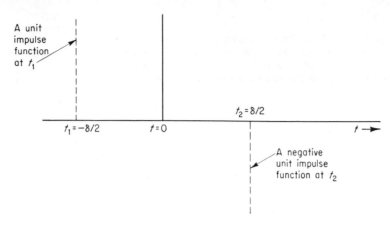

FIG. P 9.8

(*b*) If this network is known to have the response in Fig. 9.11(1*a*) when subject to the unit-impulse excitation in Fig. 9.11(1), can we predict the network response subject to the excitation in Fig. P 9.8? If the answer is "yes," make an approximate sketch of this "predicted" response, and discuss how this sketch is obtained.

Compare the results of (*a*) and (*b*).

9.9. Given: A bandpass network whose transmission characteristics are described by Eqs. (9.51).

Find the response $e_2(t)$ subject to the modulated excitation

$$e_1(t) = \begin{cases} E \cos \omega_0 t & t_a - \dfrac{\alpha}{2} \le t \le t_a + \dfrac{\alpha}{2}, \ t_b - \dfrac{\beta}{2} \le t \le t_b + \dfrac{\beta}{2} \\ 0 & \text{other values of } t \end{cases}$$

9.10. Given: A low-pass network with the transfer voltage-ratio function

$$G(s) = \frac{4s^2 + 1}{10s^3 + 5s^2 + 3s + 1}$$

(*a*) What is the phase delay of this network at $\omega_0 = 1$ rad/sec?
(*b*) What is the group delay of this network at $\omega_0 = 0$?

10 Graphical method for obtaining transfer network characteristics

10.1. Ruler-protractor method

We confine our study here to the evaluation of gain (or attenuation) and phase characteristics, although the ruler-protractor method is also applicable to the evaluation of their derivatives.†

A. Description of Problem

As remarked in Art. 1.1, one of the problems of network analysis is to find a network characteristic from a given network function. This network characteristic is often desired in the form of a graph.

For instance, we may have an amplifier with a known transfer voltage-ratio function $G(s)$ and wish to find its associated network characteristics, say the gain characteristic $G_0(\omega)$ and the phase characteristic $\theta(\omega)$ as defined in (3.39), as of two graphs.

Method of numerical computation. We may compute $G_0(\omega)$ and $\theta(\omega)$ with the aid of (3.40) for each value of the frequency ω and plot these graphs point by point. For a good representation, we must choose *many* discrete values of the frequency ω at which to compute $G_0(\omega)$ and $\theta(\omega)$. The numerical computation is laborious and time-consuming.

A graphical method. But is it possible to obtain the network characteristics, for example, $G_0(\omega)$ and $\theta(\omega)$, from a given network function, for example, $G(s)$, without resorting to the tedious process of computing the value of each network characteristic at each frequency? The answer is "yes." We may use a graphical method, employing a ruler to measure the length of a vector, and a protractor to measure its phase angle. This ruler-protractor method will yield our discrete characteristics after some simple algebraic operations are performed on the measured quantities, which are real and not complex numbers.

B. Some Simple Vector Operations

We review here some of the simple vector operations to justify the procedure of the ruler-protractor method.

$s - p_i$ **or** $s - r_i$ **as a vector.** In addition to representing a point in a complex plane, a complex number, say $a_1 + jb_1$, may represent a vector in a complex plane. For instance, $a_1 + jb_1 = -2 + j2$ in Fig. 10.1*b* may represent a vector **ON** or $p_1 = P_1\underline{/\gamma_1}$, where the length of the vector is $P_1 = \sqrt{a_1{}^2 + b_1{}^2} = \sqrt{8}$, and the phase angle of the vector with respect to the horizontal reference in the counterclockwise direction is $\gamma_1 = \tan^{-1}(2/-2) = 135°$. Similarly, **OM** or $s = 0 + j\omega_a = \omega_a\underline{/90°}$

---

† For example, see E. G. Gilbert, A Vector Method for the Evaluation of Derivatives of Phase, Gain and Attenuation, *Proc. IRE*, vol. 47, no. 1, p. 85, January, 1959.

represents another vector in the s plane (where $s = \sigma + j\omega$), as depicted in Fig. 10.1a.

p_i, being a complex number and representing a pole of a network function in the s plane, may then represent a vector from the origin to the pole in the s plane. This has been demonstrated in Fig. 10.1b. Similarly, r_i, being a complex number and representing a zero of a network function in the s plane, may then represent a vector from the origin to the zero in the s plane.

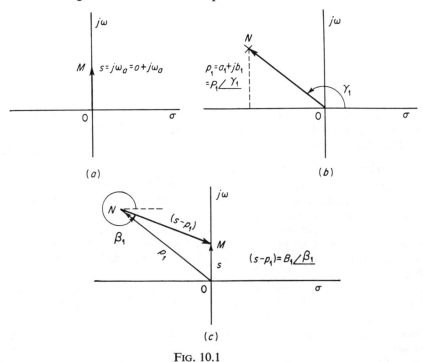

FIG. 10.1

$s - p_i$ depicts a vector from a pole $p_i = a_i + jb_i$ to a point s. $j\omega_a - p_i$, as a special case of $s - p_i$, is a vector $B_i/\underline{\beta_i}$ from p_i to $s = j\omega_a$, which is depicted for $i = 1$ in Fig. 10.1c. The length $B_i = |s - p_i|$ and the phase β_i of this vector can be measured, respectively, with a ruler and a protractor.

Similarly, $s - r_i = A_i/\underline{\alpha_i}$ is a vector from a zero r_i to a point $s = j\omega_a$ on the real-frequency axis. The length (i.e., magnitude) $A_i = |s - r_i|$ and the phase α_i of this vector can also be measured, respectively, with a ruler and a protractor.

Vector multiplication and division. For a given set of vectors, say

$$A_1/\underline{\alpha_1}, A_2/\underline{\alpha_2}, \ldots, A_m/\underline{\alpha_m} \qquad B_1/\underline{\beta_1}, B_2/\underline{\beta_2}, \ldots, B_n/\underline{\beta_n}$$

we find

$$\frac{A_1/\underline{\alpha_1} A_2/\underline{\alpha_2} \cdots A_m/\underline{\alpha_m}}{B_1/\underline{\beta_1} B_2/\underline{\beta_2} \cdots B_n/\underline{\beta_n}}$$

$$= \frac{A_1 A_2 \cdots A_m}{B_1 B_2 \cdots B_n} /\underline{\alpha_1 + \alpha_2 + \cdots + \alpha_m - \beta_1 - \beta_2 - \cdots - \beta_n} \qquad (10.1)$$

This means that the new vector in (10.1) has a magnitude equal to the algebraic product of the magnitudes of the individual vectors in the form

$$A_1 A_2 \cdots A_m B_1^{-1} B_2^{-1} \cdots B_n^{-1}$$

and a phase angle equal to the algebraic sum of their phase angles in the form $\alpha_1 + \alpha_2 + \cdots + \alpha_m - \beta_1 - \beta_2 - \cdots - \beta_n$.

Identification with network function. To avoid unwieldy numbers in our manipulations, we shall use a normalized transfer voltage-ratio function:

$$G(s) = \frac{(s - r_1)(s - r_2) \cdots (s - r_m)}{(s - p_1)(s - p_2) \cdots (s - p_n)} \tag{10.2}$$

The actual (unnormalized) transfer voltage-ratio function can be readily obtained as†

$$\begin{bmatrix} \text{Actual } transfer \\ \text{voltage-ratio} \\ \text{function} \end{bmatrix} = \begin{bmatrix} \text{normalized} \\ \text{form (10.2)} \end{bmatrix} \times \begin{bmatrix} \text{normalizing} \\ \text{quantity } K \end{bmatrix} = KG(s) \tag{10.2a}$$

We have remarked above that both $s - p_i$ and $s - r_i$ are vectors as in Fig. 10.1c for $s - p_i$, where p_i and r_i are, respectively, a pole and a zero of a network function in the s plane.   Letting

$$s - r_i = A_i \underline{/\alpha_i} = |s - r_i| \underline{/\alpha_i} \qquad i = 1, 2, \ldots, m \tag{10.2b}$$

$$s - p_i = B_i \underline{/\beta_i} = |s - p_i| \underline{/\beta_i} \qquad i = 1, 2, \ldots, n \tag{10.2c}$$

we may rewrite the network function (10.2) in the form of (10.1), where Eqs. (10.2b) and (10.2c) provide the identity for each vector.   For $s = j\omega$, we may identify $G(s)$ in (10.2) with $G(j\omega) = G_0(\omega)e^{-j\theta(\omega)}$ in (3.39), finding

$$G_0(\omega) = \frac{A_1 A_2 \cdots A_m}{B_1 B_2 \cdots B_n} = \frac{|s - r_1| \, |s - r_2| \cdots |s - r_m|}{|s - p_1| \, |s - p_2| \cdots |s - p_n|} \Bigg|_{s=j\omega}$$

$$= \frac{|j\omega - r_1| \, |j\omega - r_2| \cdots |j\omega - r_m|}{|j\omega - p_1| \, |j\omega - p_2| \cdots |j\omega - p_n|} \tag{10.3a}$$

and

$$\theta(\omega) = -(\alpha_1 + \alpha_2 + \cdots + \alpha_m - \beta_1 - \beta_2 - \cdots - \beta_n) \tag{10.3b}$$

We must keep in mind the fact that the network characteristics $G_0(\omega)$ and $\theta(\omega)$ in (10.3) are obtained from a normalized network function $G(s)$ in (10.2) and are therefore relative (i.e., normalized) network characteristics.   The actual gain characteristic, as suggested by (10.2a), is

$$\begin{bmatrix} \text{Actual } gain \\ \text{characteristic} \end{bmatrix} = \begin{bmatrix} \text{normalized} \\ \text{form in (10.3a)} \end{bmatrix} \times \begin{bmatrix} \text{normalizing} \\ \text{quantity } K \\ \text{in (10.2a)} \end{bmatrix} = KG_0(\omega) \tag{10.3a'}$$

and the actual phase characteristic is that‡ indicated by (10.3b).

---

† The zeros r_i and poles p_i in (10.2) will then have numerical values of medium magnitude. See Eq. (3.23) and the remarks immediately following.   Also note that the normalized network function equals the actual network function divided by the normalizing quantity K, and $K = W(0)$ in the example of (3.23).

‡ Let $\mathbf{G}(s)$ and $G(s)$ be, respectively, the actual and the normalized forms of a transfer voltage-ratio function; let $\mathbf{G}(j\boldsymbol{\omega}) = \mathbf{G}_0(\boldsymbol{\omega})e^{-j\theta(\boldsymbol{\omega})}$ and $G(j\omega) = G_0(\omega)e^{-j\theta(\omega)}$.   According to (10.2a) and (10.3a'), $\mathbf{G}(s) = KG(s)$ and $\mathbf{G}_0(\boldsymbol{\omega}) = KG_0(\omega)$, implying $\boldsymbol{\theta}(\boldsymbol{\omega}) = \theta(\omega)$ as indicated in this statement, which is *true* for both $K > 0$ and $K < 0$.

For $K > 0$, $\mathbf{G}(j\boldsymbol{\omega}) = \mathbf{G}_0(\boldsymbol{\omega})e^{-j\theta(\boldsymbol{\omega})} = KG_0(\omega)e^{-j\theta(\omega)} = |KG_0(\omega)| \, e^{-j\theta(\omega)}$ has $\mathbf{G}_0(\boldsymbol{\omega}) = KG_0(\omega)$ as its gain characteristic and $\boldsymbol{\theta}(\boldsymbol{\omega}) = \theta(\omega)$ as its phase characteristic.   For $K < 0$, $K = -|K| = |K| \, e^{-j\pi}$, $\mathbf{G}(j\boldsymbol{\omega}) = \mathbf{G}_0(\boldsymbol{\omega})e^{-j\theta(\boldsymbol{\omega})} = KG_0(\omega)e^{-j\theta(\omega)} = |K| \, G_0(\omega)e^{-j[\theta(\omega) + \pi]}$, we have *two* interpretations: (1) $\mathbf{G}(j\boldsymbol{\omega})$ has $\mathbf{G}_0(\boldsymbol{\omega}) = KG_0(\omega)$ as its gain characteristic and $\boldsymbol{\theta}(\boldsymbol{\omega}) = \theta(\omega)$ as its phase characteristic, *as in the above statement*, or (2) $\mathbf{G}(j\boldsymbol{\omega})$ has $\mathbf{G}_0(j\boldsymbol{\omega}) = |K| \, G_0(\omega)$ as its gain characteristic and $\boldsymbol{\theta}(\boldsymbol{\omega}) = \theta(\omega) + \pi$ as its phase characteristic.

Remarks about network characteristics.   To find the network characteristics, say $G_0(\omega)$ and $\theta(\omega)$, from a given network function, say $G(s)$, we must find the values of $G_0(\omega)$ and $\theta(\omega)$ at many discrete values of the frequency ω and plot them as graphs. We may, for an arbitrary frequency ω_a, find the value of $G_0(\omega_a)$ by (1) measuring the lengths of the vectors $s - p_i$ for $i = 1, 2, \ldots, n$, namely, for each i, the vector from the pole p_i to the point $s = j\omega_a$ on the real-frequency axis, (2) measuring the lengths of the vectors $s - r_i$ for $i = 1, 2, \ldots, m$, namely, for each i, the vector from the zero r_i to the point $s = j\omega_a$ on the real-frequency axis, and (3) then finding their algebraic product with the aid of (10.3a).   Similarly, we may find the value of $\theta(\omega_a)$ by measuring the phase angles of the vectors $s - p_i$ for $i = 1, 2, \ldots, n$, and $s - r_i$ for $i = 1, 2, \ldots, m$, and then finding the algebraic sum with the aid of (10.3b).   We may then repeat this process for other frequencies.

C. *Procedure of the Ruler-Protractor Method*

This procedure is only a summary of our discussion in the preceding section.   We shall use, for illustration, the shunt-compensated video amplifier in Fig. 3.5 and its normalized voltage-gain function

$$G(s) = \frac{s - r_1}{(s - p_1)(s - p_2)} \tag{10.4}$$

as indicated in (3.26b); we shall find its gain characteristic $G_0(\omega)$ and phase characteristic $\theta(\omega)$ as defined in (3.39).   We shall proceed as follows:

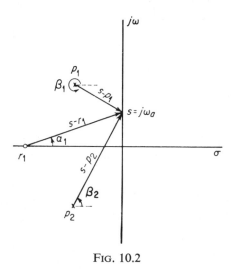

FIG. 10.2

Step 1.   Construct a pole-and-zero plot of the network function $G(s)$ as depicted in Fig. 10.2.   For an arbitrary frequency ω_a, construct vectors from each zero r_i of $G(s)$ to the point $s = j\omega_a$, and from each pole p_i of $G(s)$ to the point $s = j\omega_a$.

Step 2.   Measure, for each vector $s - r_i$, the length $A_i = |j\omega_a - r_i|$ and phase angle α_i; also measure, for each vector $s - p_i$, the length $B_i = |j\omega_a - p_i|$ and phase angle β_i.

Step 3.   Using the above-measured quantities, find the values of $G_0(\omega_a)$ and $\theta(\omega_a)$ with the aid of (10.3).

Step 4.   Repeat the above steps for ω_b, ω_c, . . . (for as many points as necessary in order to plot smooth curves in Fig. 10.3) and then plot the "$G_0(\omega)$ versus ω" and "$\theta(\omega)$ versus ω" graphs as in Fig. 10.3.

D. *Remarks about the Ruler-Protractor Method*

To avoid confusion, we shall change notation, using $\mathbf{t}_d$ as the actual unnormalized phase delay, t_d as the normalized phase delay, $\boldsymbol{\omega}$ instead of ω_0 in (9.75) as the actual frequency, ω_0 as the normalizing frequency, and $\omega = \boldsymbol{\omega}/\omega_0$ as the normalized frequency.

Time delay as a network characteristic.   We defined the phase delay of a network in (9.75):

Actual phase delay: $\qquad\qquad\qquad \mathbf{t}_d = \tau_p(\boldsymbol{\omega}) = \dfrac{\theta}{\boldsymbol{\omega}} \tag{10.5a}$

where θ is the phase characteristic of the network.

To normalize the delay t_d in terms of the normalized frequency $\boldsymbol{\omega}$, where $\omega = \boldsymbol{\omega}/\omega_0$ or $\boldsymbol{\omega} = \omega\omega_0$, let us (1) choose $T_0 = 2\pi/\omega_0$ as the normalizing time, i.e., a reference quantity with the dimension of time, (2) substitute $\boldsymbol{\omega} = \omega\omega_0$ into (10.5a), and (3) define the normalized delay to be

Normalized phase delay:

$$\boldsymbol{t_d} = \frac{t_d}{T_0} = \frac{\text{Eq. (10.5a)}}{T_0} = \frac{\theta/\boldsymbol{\omega}}{T_0} = \frac{\theta/\omega\omega_0}{2\pi/\omega_0} = \frac{\theta}{2\pi\omega} \tag{10.5b}$$

This means that if we know $\theta(\omega)$, we can easily find t_d, and vice versa, with the aid of (10.5b). The ruler-protractor method, which enables us to plot a "$\theta(\omega)$ versus ω" graph, now indirectly permits us to construct a "t_d versus ω" graph which may be called a *normalized time-delay characteristic* of the network. For example, we may use the phase characteristic $\theta(\omega)$ in Fig. 10.3b to compute $t_d = \theta(\omega)/2\pi\omega$ for each value of ω and then plot t_d versus ω.

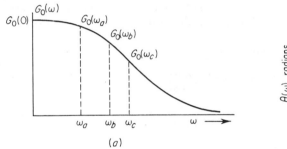 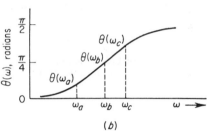

FIG. 10.3   (a) Gain characteristic $G_0(\omega)$; (b) phase characteristic $\theta(\omega)$.

Steady-state response of a network for a sinusoidal input of unit magnitude. The ruler-protractor method discussed in this chapter is a graphical method for finding the characteristics of a given network. With known network characteristics $G_0(\omega)$ and $\theta(\omega)$, we can readily predict the steady-state response of a network for a sinusoidal input of unit magnitude.

For illustration, assume that a network has a sinusoidal input of complex magnitude $E_1 = 1e^{j0°} = 1$ volt and frequency $\omega_a = 2\pi \times 10^4$ rad/sec or $f_a = 10^4$ cps, and that the values of its network characteristics at ω_a are $G_0(\omega_a) = 2$ and $\theta(\omega_a) = 30°$. The steady-state response of the network is therefore

$$E_2 = |E_2|\, e^{j\phi_2} = |E_1|G_0(\omega_a)e^{j(\phi_1 - \theta)}$$
$$= [1 \times G_0(\omega_a)]e^{j(0° - \theta)}$$
$$= G_0(\omega_a)e^{-j\theta} = 2e^{-j30°} \tag{10.6}$$

Since the values of the network characteristics $G_0(\omega)$ and $\theta(\omega)$ are obtained in the ruler-protractor method, we may regard the ruler-protractor method as described above as a graphical method for determining the steady-state sinusoidal response of a network for a sinusoidal input of unit magnitude.

Transient response of a network for a unit-step-function input. Is there another version of the above-described ruler-protractor method which serves as a graphical method for determining the transient response of a network for a unit-step-function input, i.e., an input of 1 volt (direct current) suddenly applied at the instant $t = 0$? The answer is "yes." We shall remark on this method in Art. 13.2D.

10.2. Remarks about the experimental version of the ruler-protractor method using an electrolytic tank

Since a network function and a complex potential function (of line charges) have the same form,† they are said to be "analogous" to each other. This concept of analogy enables us to solve many network problems as equivalent potential problems, known as "potential analog problems."

For example, suppose we wish to determine the gain characteristic $G_0(\omega)$ of a given $G(s)$. Through the concept of analogy we may use a circular tank, filled with electrolytic solution, which has two sets of electrodes of opposite polarities simulating the poles p_i and zeros r_i of the network function $G(s)$. We need two electrodes of the same polarity to simulate p_1 and p_2, and one electrode of opposite polarity to simulate r_1, at locations corresponding to the pole-and-zero plot in Fig. 10.2 for the network function $G(s)$ in (10.4). To find the value of the network characteristic $G_0(\omega)$ at a specific frequency ω_a, we need only measure the potential at the point corresponding to $s = j\omega_a$ in the tank. Determining the network characteristic for the entire frequency range, i.e., $\omega = 0$ to $\omega = \infty$, is therefore only a matter of measuring the potential distribution along the $j\omega$ axis in the tank.

PROBLEMS

10.1. The normalized gain, i.e., normalized transfer voltage-ratio function, of the shunt-compensated video amplifier in Fig. 3.5 is given in (3.26b) as

$$G(s) = \frac{s - r_1}{(s - p_1)(s - p_2)}$$

where $\qquad r_1 = \frac{-1}{Q} \qquad p_1, p_2 = -\frac{1}{2Q} \pm j\frac{1}{2Q}\sqrt{4Q - 1} \qquad Q = \frac{L}{R^2 C}$

For $G(j\omega) = G_0(j\omega)e^{-j\theta(\omega)}$, $G_0(\omega)$ is the *relative gain*, i.e., normalized "absolute" gain, $\theta(\omega)$ is the *relative phase*, and ω is the *normalized frequency*. Letting $R = 10^4$ ohms and $C = 20 \mu\mu f$ and assigning an arbitrary value to Q, use the ruler-protractor method to compute $G_0(\omega)$ and $\theta(\omega)$ at different values of the normalized frequency ω; then

(a) Plot four $G_0(\omega)$ versus ω curves for $Q = 0, 0.1, 0.5,$ and 1 on a sheet of semilog paper. The different values of the parameter Q correspond to the different values of the inductance L used for compensation; for $L = 0$ (that is, $Q = 0$), the video amplifier is uncompensated. From these curves, we may usually choose a value of L (or Q) for optimum compensation.

(b) Plot four $\theta(\omega)$ versus ω curves for $Q = 0, 0.1, 0.5,$ and 1 on another sheet of semilog paper.

10.2. (a) Defining the normalized time delay t_d as in (10.5b) and choosing

$$T_0 = \frac{2\pi}{\omega_0} = \frac{2\pi}{\text{normalizing frequency in (3.25b)}}$$

plot four t_d versus ω curves for $Q = 0, 0.1, 0.5,$ and 1 for the video amplifier in Prob. 10.1, ω being the normalized frequency.

(b) Let $R = 10^4$ ohms and $C = 20 \mu\mu f$ in the video amplifier in Fig. 3.5. Find the unnormalized delay t_d at the unnormalized frequency $\omega = 4 \times 10^6$ rad/sec for $L = 2$ mh, using the curves obtained in (a). SUGGESTION: Compute the normalizing quantities ω_0 and T_0 first to facilitate the processes of normalization and denormalization.

(c) Repeat (b) for $L = 0$.

† For example, see the author's "Linear Network Design and Synthesis," chaps. 22 and 23, in press. A study of the principles and procedures underlying the electrolytic-tank technique for network analysis and synthesis is included in these two chapters.

10.3. Given: The insertion voltage-ratio function for a modern filter of the Butterworth type as defined in (3.43),

$$e^\theta = (s - r_0)(s - r_1)(s - \bar{r}_1)(s - r_2)(s - \bar{r}_2)$$

with zeros depicted in Fig. P 10.3.

(a) At the real frequencies $s = j\omega$, where ω is the normalized frequency, $e^\theta = e^\alpha e^{j\beta}$, where e^α is the *insertion voltage-ratio characteristic*, and β is the *insertion phase characteristic*. Plot e^α and β versus the normalized frequency ω with the aid of the ruler-protractor method. Note that e^α and β correspond to $G_0(\omega)$ and $-\theta(\omega)$ in Prob. 10.1.

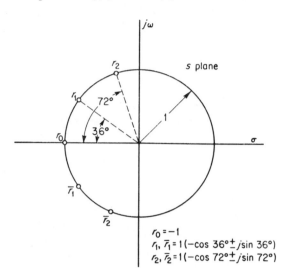

$$r_0 = -1$$
$$r_1, \bar{r}_1 = 1(-\cos 36° \pm j \sin 36°)$$
$$r_2, \bar{r}_2 = 1(-\cos 72° \pm j \sin 72°)$$

FIG. P 10.3

(b) The insertion voltage-ratio characteristic e^α is usually not a rational function of ω. For expediency in mathematical manipulation, we often prefer using the *insertion power characteristic* defined as

$$e^{2\alpha} = (e^\alpha)^2 = |e^\theta|^2_{s=j\omega}$$

Plot $e^{2\alpha}$ versus ω by modifying the result of (a).

(c) Plot the *insertion loss*

$$\alpha = \alpha(\omega) = \ln e^\alpha = \ln |e^\theta|_{s=j\omega}$$

in nepers (1 neper = 8.686 db) versus ω by modifying the result of (a).

part **D** Study of network responses using Laplace-transformation methods

In Part D we study network responses in the domain of the complex frequency $s = \sigma + j\omega$. The Laplace transform is the mathematical tool used in this study.

No previous knowledge of the Laplace transform is needed for this part of the text. The Laplace transform is introduced with a rigorous mathematical foundation and studied in detail with its extensive applications. The reader whose primary interest lies in applications may omit Arts. 11.2 and 11.3A on the mathematical foundation and use the material in the text strictly for applications.

The Laplace-transform approach in the study of network responses also leads to the establishment of the so-called "fundamental criterion for stability," which is the foundation of all stability criteria. Some of these criteria will be studied later in the text.

Laplace transformation as
applied to elementary functions
and operations

11.1. The concept of transform

A. Simple Illustration

One-to-one correspondence between a given number and its logarithm. It is a simple and well-known fact that, given a real, positive number a, we can easily find its logarithm, $A = \log_{10} a$, from a *table of logarithms;* knowing A, we can determine its antilogarithm a from the same table or a *table of antilogarithms.* For example, $a = 152.3$ implies $A = 2.1827$, and vice versa. It is obvious that there is a one-to-one correspondence between a given number and its logarithm:

$$\text{[Given number } a] \xrightleftharpoons{1:1} \text{[Logarithm } A = \log_{10} a]$$

Calculation of numbers made simple with logarithms. Suppose we are to evaluate

$$y = \left[\frac{(87.13)^{\frac{1}{2}}(5.174)}{(1.072)^7}\right]^{\frac{1}{3}} \tag{11.1}$$

We obviously must perform some complicated operations such as extracting roots, finding high powers, and multiplication and division of long numbers on

$$a = 87.13 \qquad b = 5.174 \qquad c = 1.072 \tag{11.1a}$$

However, this problem may be made simple with logarithms in the manner shown on top of page 268.

Remarks about the logarithm as a transform. If we regard the logarithm of a number as its transform, which may be called the "logarithmic transform," we see that a given problem (11.2a) has an equivalent problem (11.2b) in terms of the transforms, and that the equivalent problem is less difficult to solve. The solution of (11.2a) is simply the *inverse transform* or antilogarithm of the solution of (11.2b).

B. Some Remarks about Transforms

Types of transforms. The above is an illustration of perhaps the simplest and most commonly used transform we can think of. Depending upon the nature of the problem, we choose a particular type of transform to use.

For instance, suppose we are interested in finding the response $e_2(t)$ of a linear four-terminal network with *given* transmission characteristics $G_0(\omega)$ and $\theta(\omega)$ subject to a given excitation $e_1(t)$. The Fourier transform is used for such a problem, as

Given problem and solution:

$$\left[\begin{array}{c} y = \left(\dfrac{a^{\frac{1}{2}}b}{c^7}\right)^{\frac{1}{3}} \\[2mm] \text{where } a, b, c \text{ are as} \\ \text{specified in (11.1}a) \end{array}\right] \xrightarrow[\text{as described above}]{\text{Complicated operations}} \left[\; y = 3.096 \;\right]$$

$$(11.2a)$$

Finding logarithms
(i.e., finding *transforms*)
$A = \log_{10} a = 1.94017$
$B = \log_{10} b = 0.71382$
$C = \log_{10} c = 0.03019$
from a table

Finding antilogarithm
(i.e., finding *inverse transform*)
$y = \log_{10}^{-1} Y$
$\quad = \log_{10}^{-1} 0.49084$
from a table

Equivalent problem and solution (in transforms):

$$\left[\begin{array}{l} \log_{10} y = \frac{1}{3}(\frac{1}{2}\log_{10} a + \log_{10} b \\ \qquad - 7\log_{10} c) \\ \quad = \frac{1}{3}[\frac{1}{2}(1.94017) + 0.71382 \\ \qquad -7(0.03019)] \end{array}\right] \xrightarrow[\substack{\text{(Performing simple} \\ \text{operations on } \textit{transforms})}]{\substack{\textit{Simple operations} \text{ such as} \\ +, -, \text{ and } \times \text{ with} \\ \text{fractions or integers}}} \left[\begin{array}{l} Y = \log_{10} y \\ \quad = 0.49084 \end{array}\right]$$

$$(11.2b)$$

described in (8.34). This is no longer a transform of a number as in the simple illustration above, but a transform of a function of time: $g_1(\omega)$ in (8.34) is the Fourier transform of $e_1(t)$.

When a physical system as described by a *given* linear differential equation or a system of differential equations is under investigation, the Laplace transform, to be discussed in detail in this chapter, is often used.

Purpose of using transforms. As illustrated in (11.2), a transform indeed "transforms" a *difficult* problem into a simpler one.

Procedure in the solution of a problem using transforms. We (1) find the transforms of all the functions (or numbers) associated with the given problem, (2) formulate and solve the equivalent problem in transforms, and (3) find the inverse transform of the solution of the equivalent problem, which is then the solution of the given problem. Equations (11.2) provide a simple illustration.

One-to-one correspondence between a given function (or number) and its transform. A transform must be well defined in the sense that, for a given function (or number), there is a unique transform, and vice versa. This condition is essential to obtaining a unique solution for a given problem.

Let us hypothetically assume the contrary. Suppose that $Y = \log_{10} y_1$ and $Y = \log_{10} y_2$, for $y_1 \neq y_2$. For Y calculated in (11.2b), should y_1 or should y_2 be our solution in (11.2a)? We have no way of knowing which is correct.

We shall *not* use any transform which is not well defined in the above sense. The logarithm (or "logarithmic transform"), the Fourier transform, and the Laplace transform are all well defined.

11.2. Remarks about the existence of the Fourier transform

A. Convergence of Improper Integral

Improper integrals. For a function $f(t)$ continuous in the interval $t_a \leq t < \infty$, we have an improper integral

Type I:
$$\int_{t_a}^{\infty} f(t)\, dt \qquad\qquad (11.3)$$

and, for a function continuous in the interval $-\infty < t \le t_b$, we have an improper integral

Type II:
$$\int_{-\infty}^{t_b} f(t)\, dt \tag{11.3a}$$

Definition of convergence.   An improper integral (11.3) converges if

$$\lim_{R \to \infty} \int_{t_a}^{R} f(t)\, dt = A \tag{11.4}$$

In this case, A is the value of the integral (11.3).

The integral (11.3) is said to diverge if it does not converge.

Notation.   When the integrand $f(t)$ is positive, we sometimes use

$$\int_{t_a}^{\infty} f(t)\, dt < \infty \tag{11.5a}$$

to indicate that the integral (11.3) converges, and

$$\int_{t_a}^{\infty} f(t)\, dt = \infty \tag{11.5b}$$

to indicate that the integral (11.3) diverges.

Remarks about uniform convergence.   We shall now consider integrals of the type

$$\int_{t_a}^{\infty} f(\omega, t)\, dt \tag{11.6}$$

Let us suppose that this integral converges for each fixed ω in the interval $\omega_1 \le \omega \le \omega_2$ and has the value $F(\omega)$.   Set

$$S_R(\omega) = \int_{t_a}^{R} f(\omega, t)\, dt \tag{11.6a}$$

We shall now define uniform convergence as follows: The integral (11.6) *converges uniformly* to $F(\omega)$ in the interval $\omega_1 \le \omega \le \omega_2$ *if*, corresponding to an arbitrary $\varepsilon_0 > 0$, there is a number R_0, independent of ω in $\omega_1 \le \omega \le \omega_2$, such that when $R > R_0$,

$$|F(\omega) - S_R(\omega)| < \varepsilon_0 \qquad \omega_1 \le \omega \le \omega_2 \tag{11.7a}$$

When the integral (11.6) converges uniformly to $F(\omega)$, we write

$$F(\omega) = \int_{t_a}^{\infty} f(\omega, t)\, dt \tag{11.7b}$$

The Weierstrass M test.   If $f(\omega, t)$ and $M(t)$ have a finite number of discontinuities in the intervals $t_a \le t < \infty$ and $\omega_1 \le \omega \le \omega_2$,

$$|f(\omega, t)| \le M(t) \qquad t_a \le t < \infty,\ \omega_1 \le \omega \le \omega_2 \tag{11.8a}$$

and
$$\int_{t_a}^{\infty} M(t)\, dt < \infty \tag{11.8b}$$

then the integral (11.6) converges uniformly to $F(\omega)$ in $\omega_1 \le \omega \le \omega_2$; that is,

$$F(\omega) = \int_{t_a}^{\infty} f(\omega, t)\, dt \tag{11.9}$$

To justify this Weierstrass M test, we compare (11.6a) with (11.7b) to find

$$|F(\omega) - S_R(\omega)| \le \int_{R}^{\infty} |f(\omega, t)|\, dt \le \int_{R}^{\infty} M(t)\, dt$$

Since the last integral is independent of ω in $\omega_1 \leq \omega \leq \omega_2$ and tends to zero as R tends to infinity, the result is immediate.

B. Bilateral and Unilateral Fourier Transforms

Bilateral Fourier transform as a sum of two improper integrals. The Fourier transform (8.8b) is called a *bi*lateral Fourier transform because it is an integral

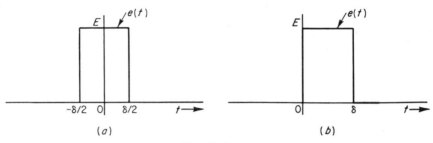

FIG. 11.1

whose range of integration covers both the negative-frequency and the positive-frequency regions.

Let $g(\omega)$ replace $g_*(\omega)$ in (8.8b), and rewrite it as

$$g(\omega) = \int_{-\infty}^{\infty} e(t)e^{-j\omega t}\, dt$$

$$= \int_{-\infty}^{0} e(t)e^{-j\omega t}\, dt + \int_{0}^{\infty} e(t)\, e^{-j\omega t}\, dt \qquad (11.10)$$

We note here that the bilateral Fourier transform is actually a sum of two improper integrals of the types (11.3) and (11.3a).

Remarks about the choice of time axis. When using the bilateral Fourier transform (8.3b) or (8.8b) for frequency analyses as in Chaps. 7 through 9, we try to *choose* a reference time axis such that the signal function $e(t)$ is either an even function of t, an odd function, or the sum of an even function and an odd function. This results in a simpler representation of the Fourier transform $g(\omega)$ as discussed in Art. 8.1C. For example, the choice of the time axis in Fig. 11.1a is preferred if we wish to find the bilateral Fourier transform in the simplest possible form for the signal depicted. No matter what reference time axis we choose, the Fourier transforms provide us with the same essential information: (1) the relative magnitude of each frequency component and (2) the relative phase of each frequency component.

We may choose any reference time axis for a given signal and compute its Fourier transform. We may represent a signal in the shape of a rectangular pulse with magnitude E and duration δ as

$$e(t) = \begin{cases} 0 & t < -\dfrac{\delta}{2} \\[2mm] E & -\dfrac{\delta}{2} \leq t \leq \dfrac{\delta}{2} \\[2mm] 0 & \dfrac{\delta}{2} < t \end{cases} \qquad (11.11)$$

with time axis as in Fig. 11.1a, *or as*

For negative time: $\qquad\qquad e(t) = 0 \qquad\qquad t < 0$ $\qquad\qquad\qquad$ (11.12a)

For positive time: $\qquad\qquad e(t) = \begin{cases} E & 0 \le t \le \delta \\ 0 & \delta < t \end{cases}$ $\qquad\qquad\qquad$ (11.12b)

with time axis as in Fig. 11.1b.

We can always choose the reference time axis for a given physical signal such that (11.12a) is true. We shall say that this signal function $e(t)$ is defined only for *positive* time (that is, $t \ge 0$).

Unilateral Fourier transform. If we use a signal function $e(t)$ defined for both positive time and negative time, for example, $e(t)$ in Eq. (11.11), and if we use the bilateral Fourier transform in (11.10), we have two improper integrals to cope with. Improper integrals are often a source of trouble, as they may diverge.

If we use a signal function defined only for positive time, for example, $e(t)$ in Eqs. (11.12), and if we use (11.10) to find its Fourier transform, we have only one improper integral to cope with. The first integral in (11.10) vanishes as $e(t) = 0$ for $t < 0$.

For a signal function $e(t)$ defined only for positive time, i.e., one for which $e(t) = 0$ for $t < 0$, we may define the Fourier transform to be

$$g(\omega) = \int_0^\infty e(t) e^{-j\omega t}\, dt \qquad\qquad (11.13)$$

This is called a *uni*lateral Fourier transform because it is an integral whose range of integration covers only the *positive-time* region.

Remarks. From now on, we shall assume that a given signal function $e(t)$ always starts at $t = 0$ or at a positive time $t = t_1 > 0$, and

$$e(t) = 0 \qquad t < 0$$

A Fourier transform will then be a unilateral Fourier transform as defined in (11.13).

C. Convergence of the (Unilateral) Fourier Transform

For a given signal function $e(t)$, we wish to investigate whether the improper integral

$$\int_0^\infty e(t) e^{-j\omega t}\, dt$$

converges uniformly to $g(\omega)$. If this integral does not converge at all, we say that the Fourier transform of $e(t)$ does not exist.

Application of the Weierstrass M test. We let

$$f(\omega, t) = e(t) e^{-j\omega t} \qquad 0 \le t < \infty, 0 \le \omega < \infty$$

which implies

$$|f(\omega, t)| = |e(t) e^{-j\omega t}| = |e(t)| \qquad 0 \le t < \infty, 0 \le \omega < \infty$$

as the result of $|e^{-j\omega t}| = |\cos \omega t - j \sin \omega t| = (\cos^2 \omega t + \sin^2 \omega t)^{\frac{1}{2}} = 1$, and choose $M(t)$ in (11.8a) to be $\qquad M(t) = |e(t)| \qquad 0 \le t < \infty$

Interpreting (11.9) and (11.8b) with the present notation, we may state: The Fourier transform

$$g(\omega) = \int_0^\infty e(t) e^{-j\omega t}\, dt$$

exists if

Condition for existence of Fourier transform:

$$\int_0^\infty |e(t)|\, dt < \infty \qquad\qquad (11.14)$$

Illustration 1.   For a rectangular-pulse function as depicted in Fig. 11.1*b*,

$$e(t) = \begin{cases} 1 & 0 \le t \le \delta \\ 0 & t < 0, t > \delta \end{cases} \tag{11.15a}$$

or

$$e(t) = u(t) - u(t - \delta) \tag{11.15a'}$$

it is easy to verify that

$$\int_0^\infty |e(t)|\, dt = \delta < \infty$$

That is, condition (11.14) is satisfied, and the Fourier transform of (11.15*a*) exists. Using (11.13), we find

$$g(\omega) = \int_0^\delta (1)\, e^{-j\omega t}\, dt = \frac{e^{-j\omega t}}{-j\omega}\Big|_{t=0}^{t=\delta} = \frac{1 - e^{-j\omega\delta}}{j\omega} \tag{11.15b}$$

Illustration 2.   For a unit-step function

$$e(t) = u(t) = \begin{cases} 1 & 0 \le t \\ 0 & t < 0 \end{cases} \tag{11.16a}$$

we can easily see that

$$\int_0^\infty |e(t)|\, dt = \infty$$

That is, condition (11.14) is not satisfied, and the Fourier transform of (11.16*a*) does not exist.

However, for practical circuit applications, it often suffices to consider a unit-step function as an exponential function

$$e(t) = e^{-\alpha t} \qquad \alpha > 0$$

with extremely small α, that is, a limiting case with $\alpha \to 0$.   In this case, the Fourier transform can be evaluated, for example, in Eq. (9.4*b*).

Illustration 3.   For a runaway d-c transient

$$e(t) = 1e^{\alpha t} \qquad \alpha > 0 \tag{11.17a}$$

as described in Table 3.1, Illustration 4, it is easy to see that

$$\int_0^\infty |e(t)|\, dt = \infty$$

That is, condition (11.14) is not satisfied, and the Fourier transform of (11.17*a*) does not exist.

If we try to take the transform with the definition (11.13) of the Fourier transform, we find

$$\int_0^\infty 1e^{\alpha t} e^{-j\omega t}\, dt = \frac{e^{(\alpha - j\omega)t}}{\alpha - j\omega}\Big|_{t=0}^{t=\infty} \tag{11.17b}$$

This does not exist because its upper limit tends to infinity for $t \to \infty$.

D. *Modified (Unilateral) Fourier Transform*

We have demonstrated above in Illustration 3 that the Fourier transform as defined in (11.13) does *not* exist for the function $e(t) = 1e^{\alpha t}$ for $\alpha > 0$ [Eq. (11.17*a*)].

Can we modify the definition (11.13) of the Fourier transform such that the modified Fourier transform of $e(t) = 1e^{\alpha t}$ for $\alpha > 0$ does exist?   At least we can try.

A modified Fourier transform. Let us modify (11.13) by including a factor $e^{-\sigma t}$ for real σ in its integrand. We now have

Modified Fourier transform:

$$F(\sigma, \omega) = \int_0^\infty e(t)e^{-\sigma t}e^{-j\omega t}\, dt \tag{11.18}$$

The existence of the modified Fourier transform. For a given function $e(t)$, we should like to know if the improper integral on the right-hand side of (11.18) exists and converges uniformly to $F(\sigma, \omega)$.

We may apply the Weierstrass M test again. We let

$$f(\omega, t) = e(t)e^{-\sigma t}e^{-j\omega t} \qquad 0 \le t < \infty, 0 \le \omega < \infty$$

which implies

$$|f(\omega, t)| = |e(t)e^{-\sigma t}e^{-j\omega t}| = |e(t)|\, e^{-\sigma t}$$

We choose $M(t)$ in (11.8a) to be

$$M(t) = |e(t)|\, e^{-\sigma t} \qquad 0 \le t < \infty$$

Interpreting (11.9) and (11.8b) with the present notation, we may state: The modified Fourier transform

$$F(\sigma, \omega) = \int_0^\infty e(t)e^{-\sigma t}e^{-j\omega t}\, dt$$

exists, if

Condition for existence of modified Fourier transform:

$$\int_0^\infty |e(t)|\, e^{-\sigma t}\, dt < \infty \tag{11.19}$$

Illustration. We shall again try the function

$$e(t) = 1e^{\alpha t} \qquad \alpha > 0 \tag{11.20a}$$

[Eq. (11.17a)], which fails to have a Fourier transform as defined in (11.13). It is easy to verify that, for $\sigma > \alpha$,

$$\int_0^\infty |1e^{\alpha t}|\, e^{-\sigma t}\, dt = \left.\frac{e^{-(\sigma-\alpha)t}}{-(\sigma-\alpha)}\right|_{t=0}^{t=\infty} < \infty \tag{11.21}$$

That is, condition (11.19) is satisfied. This means that the modified Fourier transform of $1e^{\alpha t}$ as defined in (11.18) exists under the additional condition

$$\sigma > \alpha \tag{11.21a}$$

Using (11.18), we find this modified Fourier transform to be

$$F(\sigma, \omega) = \int_0^\infty 1e^{\alpha t}e^{-\sigma t}e^{-j\omega t}\, dt = \left.\frac{e^{-(\sigma-\alpha+j\omega)t}}{-(\sigma - \alpha + j\omega)}\right|_{t=0}^{t=\infty}$$

$$= \frac{1}{\sigma - \alpha + j\omega} \qquad \sigma > \alpha \tag{11.21b}$$

Abscissa of absolute convergence. In the above illustration, we have shown that the modified Fourier transform $F(\sigma, \omega)$ of the specific function $e(t)$ in (11.20a) exists under the condition (11.21a), i.e.,

$$\sigma > \alpha$$

We shall find that the modified Fourier transform $F(\sigma, \omega)$ as defined in (11.18) for an arbitrary function $e(t)$ exists under a certain condition

$$\sigma > \sigma_a \tag{11.22}$$

We shall call this σ_a the abscissa of absolute convergence of the function $e(t)$. Actually, σ_a is the abscissa of absolute convergence of the improper integral in the right-hand side of (11.18) associated with $e(t)$.

We have already demonstrated that the function $e(t) = 1e^{\alpha t}$ for $\alpha > 0$ has $\sigma_a = \alpha$. The abscissas of absolute convergence of some other functions are included in Table 11.1; each function $e(t)$ in this table has a modified Fourier transform $F(\sigma, \omega)$,

Table 11.1

Function $e(t)$ or $f(t)$ defined in positive-time region		Abscissa of absolute convergence, σ_a
1		0
$u(t)$		0
$u(t - a) - u(t - b)$		$-\infty$
t		0
t^2		0
t^n		0
$\sin \beta t$		0
$\cos \beta t$		0
$t \sin \beta t$		0
$e^{\alpha t}$	$\alpha > 0$	α
$e^{-\alpha t}$	$\alpha > 0$	$-\alpha$
$te^{-\alpha t}$	$\alpha > 0$	$-\alpha$
$e^{-\alpha t} \sin \beta t$	$\alpha > 0$	$-\alpha$
$e^{-\alpha t} \cos \beta t$	$\alpha > 0$	$-\alpha$
e^{t^2}		No value for σ_a

as defined in (11.18), if (11.22) is satisfied.   For $e(t) = \sin \beta t$, the modified Fourier transform $F(\sigma, \omega)$ exists if $\sigma > 0$, which implies $\sigma_a = 0$; for $e(t) = u(t) - u(t - \delta)$, $F(\sigma, \omega)$ exists for any value of σ, which implies $\sigma_a = -\infty$.   However, $e(t) = e^{t^2}$ does *not* have a modified Fourier transform in the sense of (11.18), since no finite value of σ can be found to satisfy (11.22); this implies $\sigma_a = \infty$.

11.3. Laplace transform as a generalization of the Fourier transform

A. Generalized Fourier Integral and Fourier Transform

We shall change the notation for the signal function from $e(t)$ to $f(t)$; this will enable us to use the same letter to represent a signal function $f(t)$ and its modified Fourier transform $F(\sigma, \omega)$.

Review of Fourier integral and (unilateral) Fourier transform.   For a function $f(t)$ defined in the positive-time region only, i.e.,

$$f(t) = 0 \qquad t < 0 \tag{11.23}$$

the bilateral Fourier transform (8.8b) and unilateral Fourier transform (11.13) represent the *same* expression.   If we replace the bilateral Fourier transform with the unilateral Fourier transform, Eqs. (8.8) become

Fourier integral:

$$f(t) = \frac{1}{2\pi} \int_{-\infty}^{\infty} g(\omega)e^{j\omega t} \, d\omega \qquad t \geq 0 \tag{11.24a}$$

Fourier transform:

$$g(\omega) = \int_0^\infty f(t)e^{-j\omega t}\,dt \tag{11.24b}$$

Generalized Fourier integral and Fourier transform. The modified Fourier transform (11.18) of $f(t)$ becomes

$$F(\sigma, \omega) = \int_0^\infty f(t)e^{-\sigma t}e^{-j\omega t}\,dt \tag{11.25}$$

Comparing (11.25) with (11.24b), we see that (11.25) is the original Fourier transform (11.24b) with $f_1(t) = f(t)e^{-\sigma t}$ replacing $f(t)$, and $F(\sigma, \omega)$ replacing $g(\omega)$. Replacing $f(t)$ and $g(\omega)$ with $f(t)e^{-\sigma t}$ and $F(\sigma, \omega)$ in (11.24), we have

$$f(t)e^{-\sigma t} = \frac{1}{2\pi}\int_{-\infty}^\infty F(\sigma, \omega)e^{j\omega t}\,d\omega \tag{11.26a}$$

and

$$F(\sigma, \omega) = \int_0^\infty f(t)e^{-\sigma t}e^{-j\omega t}\,dt \tag{11.26b}$$

Multiplying both sides of (11.26a) by $e^{\sigma t}$, placing $e^{\sigma t}$ on the right-hand side inside the integral sign ($e^{\sigma t}$ is not a function of ω), and rearranging (11.26b), we have

$$f(t) = \frac{1}{2\pi}\int_{-\infty}^\infty F(\sigma, \omega)e^{(\sigma+j\omega)t}\,d\omega \qquad t \geq 0 \tag{11.27a}$$

$$F(\sigma, \omega) = \int_0^\infty f(t)e^{-(\sigma+j\omega)t}\,dt \tag{11.27b}$$

We note in (11.27b) that, when ω appears in the integral on the right-hand side of (11.27), it appears together with σ in a combined term $\sigma + j\omega$. $F(\sigma, \omega)$ is therefore a function of $\sigma + j\omega$. Replacing $F(\sigma, \omega)$ with $F(\sigma + j\omega)$, and $d\omega$ with $d(\sigma + j\omega)/j$, in (11.27), and making appropriate changes in the limits of integration, we have

Generalized Fourier integral:

$$f(t) = \frac{1}{2\pi j}\int_{\sigma-j\infty}^{\sigma+j\infty} F(\sigma + j\omega)e^{(\sigma+j\omega)t}\,d(\sigma + j\omega) \qquad t \geq 0,\ \sigma > \sigma_a \tag{11.28a}$$

Generalized Fourier transform:

$$F(\sigma + j\omega) = \int_0^\infty f(t)e^{-(\sigma+j\omega)t}\,dt \qquad \sigma > \sigma_a \tag{11.28b}$$

as the *generalized Fourier integral* and *Fourier transform* of a function $f(t)$. The generalized Fourier transform (11.28b) of a given $f(t)$ exists if σ in (11.28b) satisfies (11.22), i.e., if

$$\sigma > \sigma_a \tag{11.29}$$

where σ_a is the abscissa of absolute convergence of $f(t)$.

B. *Laplace Integral and Laplace Transform*

Letting $s = \sigma + j\omega$ in (11.28), we have

Laplace integral (inverse Laplace transform):

$$f(t) = \frac{1}{2\pi j}\int_{\sigma-j\infty}^{\sigma+j\infty} F(s)e^{st}\,ds \qquad t \geq 0,\ \sigma > \sigma_a \tag{11.30a}$$

Laplace transform:

$$F(s) = \int_0^\infty f(t)e^{-st}\,dt \qquad \sigma > \sigma_a \tag{11.30b}$$

as the *Laplace integral* and *Laplace transform* of a function $f(t)$. We shall also call (11.30a) the *inverse Laplace transform* for obvious reasons.

Definition of the Laplace integral varies among authors. Equation (11.30*a*) is generalized from the Fourier integral (11.24*a*), which, in turn, is generalized from the Fourier series (7.25) in the complex form. For this reason, we shall call (11.30*a*) the "Laplace integral." Some authors call (11.30*b*) the Laplace integral as well as the Laplace transform, and call (11.30*a*) the inverse Laplace transform.

Symbolic representation. We can abbreviate (11.30) as

Inverse Laplace transform:
$$f(t) = \mathscr{L}^{-1}[F(s)] \qquad t \geq 0, \sigma > \sigma_a \qquad (11.30a')$$

Laplace transform:
$$F(s) = \mathscr{L}[f(t)] \qquad \sigma > \sigma_a \qquad (11.30b')$$

with the understanding that they represent Eqs. (11.30).

Remark 1. The Laplace transform $F(s)$ of a given $f(t)$ as defined by (11.30*b*) may or may not exist.

For example, the Laplace transform of $f(t) = e^{t^2}$ does not exist. As indicated in Table 11.1 and remarked in the discussion following (11.22), this function is identified with an abscissa of absolute convergence $\sigma_a = \infty$ and has no modified Fourier transform $F(\sigma, \omega)$ in the sense of (11.18). The Laplace transform (11.30*b*) is a form of the modified Fourier transform (11.18); therefore $f(t) = e^{t^2}$ does not have a Laplace transform.

On the other hand, all the other functions in Table 11.1 have Laplace transforms. Illustrations are provided in Art. 11.4.

Remark 2. As most of the functions encountered in electrical networks have Laplace transforms, we find a one-to-one correspondence between the function $f(t)$ and its Laplace transform $F(s)$:

$$[f(t)] \underset{\substack{\text{Given } F(s), \text{ to find } f(t):\\ \text{use (11.30}a) \text{ or Table 11.2}\\ \text{or methods in Art. 13.2}}}{\overset{\substack{\text{Given } f(t), \text{ to find } F(s):\\ \text{use (11.30}b) \text{ or Table 11.2}}}{\rightleftharpoons}} [F(s)] \qquad (11.31)$$

Knowing $f(t)$, we can obtain $F(s)$, and vice versa.

11.4. Laplace transforms of elementary functions

The Laplace transforms of some commonly encountered functions are listed in Table 11.2. We shall illustrate in this section how some of them are obtained. Table 11.2 is particularly useful if we are given a function $F(s)$ and wish to find its inverse transform $f(t)$.

A column captioned Finite Poles and Zeros of $F(s)$ is included in Table 11.2 for future reference.

A. Laplace Transform of a Unit-impulse Function

Definition. We have defined in (9.18) a unit-impulse function $\delta(t)$, a rectangular pulse starting at $t = 0$ with

Magnitude: $\qquad\qquad\qquad\qquad I \rightarrow \infty$

Duration: $\qquad\qquad\qquad\qquad t_\delta \rightarrow 0 \qquad\qquad\qquad (11.31a)$

Product: $\qquad\qquad\qquad\qquad It_\delta \rightarrow 1$

as depicted in Fig. 11.2*a*. Equation (11.31*a*) implies

$$\int_0^\infty \delta(t)\, dt = \int_0^{t_\delta} + \int_{t_\delta}^\infty = \int_0^{t_\delta} \delta(t)\, dt + 0 = \lim_{t_\delta \to 0} It_\delta = 1 \qquad (11.31b)$$

Table 11.2. Laplace Transforms of Elementary Functions

$F(s)$	Finite poles and zeros of $F(s)$	$f(t)$ for $t \geq 0$
1. 1	None	$\delta(t)$, unit-impulse function at $t = 0$
2. $\dfrac{1}{s}$	Pole: 0	1; $u(t)$, unit-step function starting at $t = 0$
3. $\dfrac{1}{s^2}$	Pole: 0 (order 2)	t
4. $\dfrac{1}{s^n}$	Pole: 0 (order n)	$\dfrac{1}{(n-1)!}\, t^{n-1}$
5. $\dfrac{1}{s-\alpha}$	Pole: α	$e^{\alpha t}$ $\alpha > 0$
6. $\dfrac{1}{s+\alpha}$	Pole: $-\alpha$	$e^{-\alpha t}$ $\alpha > 0$
7. $\dfrac{1}{(s+\alpha)^2}$	Pole: $-\alpha$ (order 2)	$te^{-\alpha t}$
8. $\dfrac{1}{(s+\alpha)^n}$	Pole: $-\alpha$ (order n)	$\dfrac{1}{(n-1)!}\, t^{n-1}e^{-\alpha t}$
9. $\dfrac{1}{s^2+\beta^2}$	Poles: $0 \pm j\beta$	$\dfrac{1}{\beta}\sin \beta t$
10. $\dfrac{1}{(s+\alpha)^2+\beta^2}$	Poles: $-\alpha \pm j\beta$	$\dfrac{1}{\beta}e^{-\alpha t}\sin \beta t$
11. $\dfrac{s}{s^2+\beta^2}$	Zero: 0 Poles: $0 \pm j\beta$	$\cos \beta t$
12. $\dfrac{s+a_0}{s^2+\beta^2}$	Zero: $-a_0$ Poles: $0 \pm j\beta$	$A\sin(\beta t + \phi)$ where $A = \dfrac{(a_0{}^2+\beta^2)^{\frac{1}{2}}}{\beta}$ $\phi = \tan^{-1}\dfrac{\beta}{a_0}$
13. $\dfrac{s+a_0}{(s+\alpha)^2+\beta^2}$	Zero: $-a_0$ Poles: $-\alpha \pm j\beta$	$Ae^{-\alpha t}\sin(\beta t + \phi)$ where $A = \dfrac{(a_0-\alpha)^2+\beta^2}{\beta}$ $\phi = \tan^{-1}\dfrac{\beta}{a_0-\alpha}$
14. $\dfrac{1}{s^2-\beta^2}$	Poles: $\pm\beta$	$\dfrac{1}{\beta}\sinh \beta t$
15. $\dfrac{s}{s^2-\beta^2}$	Zero: 0 Poles: $\pm\beta$	$\cosh \beta t$
16. $\dfrac{1}{s}e^{-as}$	Pole: 0	$u(t-a)$ $a > 0$
17. $\dfrac{1}{s}(e^{-as}-e^{-bs})$ $b > a$	Zeros: $\pm\dfrac{j2\pi n}{b-a}$ for $n = 1, 2, \ldots$	$u(t-a) - u(t-b)$ $a > 0, b > 0$

277

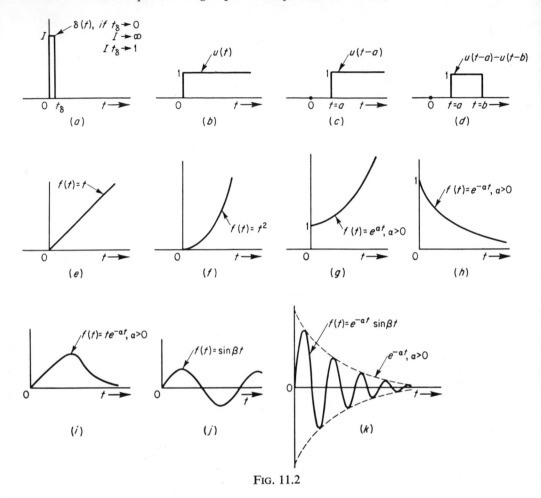

Fig. 11.2

Laplace transform of $\delta(t)$.   Using (11.30b), we have

$$\mathcal{L}[\delta(t)] = \int_0^\infty \delta(t)e^{-st}\,dt = \int_0^{t_\delta} + \int_{t_\delta}^\infty$$

$$= \lim_{t_\delta \to 0} \int_0^{t_\delta} \delta(t)e^{-st}\,dt \tag{11.32a}$$

$$\mathcal{L}[\delta(t)] = \lim_{t_\delta \to 0} e^{-s \times 0} \int_0^{t_\delta} \delta(t)\,dt \tag{11.32b}$$

$$\mathcal{L}[\delta(t)] = \lim_{t_\delta \to 0} \int_0^{t_\delta} \delta(t)\,dt = 1 \tag{11.32c}$$

The factor e^{-st} inside the integral sign in (11.32a) changes from $e^{-s \times 0} = 1$ to $\lim_{t_\delta \to 0} e^{-st} = 1$ between the limits of integration, i.e., between $t = 0$ and $t = t_\delta$.   It is obvious that this factor e^{-st} in (11.32a) behaves like a constant which equals $e^{-s \times 0} = 1$ and may be taken outside the integral sign; this results in (11.32b).   Equation (11.32b) becomes (11.32c) with the aid of (11.31b).

Our result in (11.32c) is included as item 1 in Table 11.2.

B. *Laplace Transforms of the Unit-step Function and Its Related Functions*

Laplace transform of $u(t)$. For a unit-step function as depicted in Fig. 11.2b, the Laplace transform is

$$\mathcal{L}[u(t)] = \int_0^\infty (1)e^{-st}\, dt = \frac{e^{-st}}{-s}\bigg|_{t=0}^{t=\infty} = \frac{1}{s} \tag{11.33}$$

and is included as item 2 in Table 11.2.

Laplace transform of $u(t - a)$. For a unit-step function starting at $t = a$ as depicted in Fig. 11.2c, the Laplace transform is

$$\mathcal{L}[u(t - a)] = \int_0^\infty u(t - a)e^{-st}\, dt = \int_0^a + \int_0^\infty = 0 + \int_a^\infty 1e^{-st}\, dt$$

$$= \frac{e^{-st}}{-s}\bigg|_{t=a}^{t=\infty} = \frac{1}{s}e^{-as} \qquad a > 0 \tag{11.34}$$

and is included as item 16 in Table 11.2.

Laplace transform of a nonrepeating rectangular pulse. The pulse indicated in Fig. 11.2d may be regarded as an algebraic sum of two unit-step functions $u(t - a)$ and $-u(t - b)$ and represented as $u(t - a) - u(t - b)$. Its Laplace transform is, with the aid of (11.34),

$$\mathcal{L}[u(t - a) - u(t - b)] = \frac{1}{s}(e^{-as} - e^{-bs}) \qquad a > 0, b > 0 \tag{11.35}$$

and is included as item 17 in Table 11.2.

C. *Laplace Transforms of the Powers of Time*

We are now interested in $f(t) = t^n$ as depicted in Fig. 11.2e and f.

Laplace transform of t. Using (11.30b), we have

$$\mathcal{L}[t] = \int_0^\infty te^{-st}\, dt = \frac{1}{-s}\int_0^\infty t\, de^{-st} \tag{11.36a}$$

$$\mathcal{L}[t] = -\frac{1}{s}\left(te^{-st}\bigg|_{t=0}^{t=\infty} - \int_0^\infty e^{-st}\, dt\right)^\dagger \tag{11.36b}$$

$$\mathcal{L}[t] = -\frac{1}{s}\left(0 - 0 - \frac{e^{-st}}{-s}\bigg|_{t=0}^{t=\infty}\right) = \frac{1}{s^2} \tag{11.36c}$$

which is included as item 3 in Table 11.2.

Laplace transform of t^2. For a function $f(t) = t^2$ as depicted in Fig. 11.2f, we may twice use the method of integration by parts as in the preceding case to find the Laplace transform

$$\mathcal{L}[t^2] = \int_0^\infty t^2 e^{-st}\, dt = -\frac{1}{s}\int_0^\infty t^2\, de^{-st}$$

$$= -\frac{1}{s}\left(t^2 e^{-st}\bigg|_{t=0}^{t=\infty} - \int_0^\infty e^{-st}\, dt^2\right)$$

$$= 0 - 0 + \frac{2}{s}\left[\int_0^\infty te^{-st}\, dt\right] \tag{11.37a}$$

$$\mathcal{L}[t^2] = \frac{2}{s}\frac{1}{s^2} = \frac{2}{s^3} \tag{11.37b}$$

The term inside the brackets in (11.37a) has been computed in (11.36a) and (11.36c); (11.37b) results.

† With $u = t$ and $v = e^{-st}$, (11.36a) becomes (11.36b) with the aid of the method of integration by parts, i.e., $\int u\, dv = uv - \int v\, du$.

It is now obvious that

$$\mathcal{L}[\tfrac{1}{2}t^2] = \frac{1}{s^3} \tag{11.37b}$$

which is included as item 4 for $n = 2$ in Table 11.2.

Laplace transform of t^{n-1}.   With repeated applications of the method of integration by parts, we find

$$\mathcal{L}[t^{n-1}] = \frac{(n-1)!}{s^n} \tag{11.38a}$$

or

$$\mathcal{L}\left[\frac{1}{(n-1)!}\, t^{n-1}\right] = \frac{1}{s^n} \tag{11.38b}$$

which is included as item 4 in Table 11.2.

D. Laplace Transforms of the Exponential Function and Its Related Functions

Laplace transform of $e^{\alpha t}$ for $\alpha > 0$.   For a function $f(t) = e^{\alpha t}$ depicting a runaway d-c transient in Fig. 11.2g, the Laplace transform is

$$\mathcal{L}[e^{\alpha t}] = \int_0^\infty e^{\alpha t} e^{-st}\, dt = \frac{e^{-(s-\alpha)t}}{-(s-\alpha)}\bigg|_{t=0}^{t=\infty} = \frac{1}{s-\alpha} \tag{11.39}$$

and is included as item 5 in Table 11.2.

Laplace transform of $e^{-\alpha t}$ for $\alpha > 0$.   For a function $f(t) = e^{-\alpha t}$ depicting a decaying d-c transient as in Fig. 11.2h, the Laplace transform may be obtained by replacing α with $-\alpha$ in (11.39); i.e.,

$$\mathcal{L}[e^{-\alpha t}] = \frac{1}{s+\alpha} \tag{11.40}$$

which is included as item 6 in Table 11.2.

Laplace transform of $te^{-\alpha t}$.   For a function $f(t) = te^{-\alpha t}$ as depicted in Fig. 11.2i, we have

$$\mathcal{L}[te^{-\alpha t}] = \int_0^\infty te^{-\alpha t} e^{-st}\, dt = \int_0^\infty te^{-(s+\alpha)t}\, dt$$

$$= \frac{1}{-(s+\alpha)} \int_0^\infty t\, de^{-(s+\alpha)t} \tag{11.41a}$$

$$\mathcal{L}[te^{-\alpha t}] = \frac{1}{-(s+\alpha)} \left(te^{-(s+\alpha)t}\bigg|_{t=0}^{t=\infty} - \int_0^\infty e^{-(s+\alpha)}\, dt \right) \tag{11.41b}$$

$$\mathcal{L}[te^{-\alpha t}] = \frac{1}{(s+\alpha)^2} \tag{11.41c}$$

which is included as item 7 in Table 11.2. Equation (11.41b) is obtained from (11.41a) using the method of integration by parts.

E. Transforms of Some Sinusoidal Functions

Laplace transform of $\sin \beta t$.   For a function $f(t) = \sin \beta t$ as depicted in Fig. 11.2j, we have

$$\mathcal{L}[\sin \beta t] = \int_0^\infty \sin \beta t\, e^{-st}\, dt = \int_0^\infty \frac{e^{j\beta t} - e^{-j\beta t}}{2j}\, e^{-st}\, dt$$

$$= \frac{1}{2j}\left(\frac{1}{s-j\beta} - \frac{1}{s+j\beta}\right) = \frac{\beta}{s^2+\beta^2} \tag{11.42a}$$

or

$$\mathcal{L}\left[\frac{1}{\beta} \sin \beta t\right] = \frac{1}{s^2+\beta^2} \tag{11.42b}$$

which is included as item 9 in Table 11.2.

Laplace transform of $e^{-\alpha t} \sin \beta t$. For a function $f(t) = e^{-\alpha t} \sin \beta t$ depicting a decaying sinusoid (for $\alpha > 0$) as in Fig. 11.2k, we have

$$\mathcal{L}[e^{-\alpha t} \sin \beta t] = \int_0^\infty e^{-\alpha t} \frac{e^{j\beta t} - e^{-j\beta t}}{2j} e^{-st} dt$$

$$= \frac{1}{2j} \int_0^\infty (e^{-(s+\alpha-j\beta)t} - e^{-(s+\alpha+j\beta)t}) dt$$

$$= \frac{1}{2j} \left(\frac{1}{s + \alpha - j\beta} - \frac{1}{s + \alpha + j\beta} \right) = \frac{\beta}{(s + \alpha)^2 + \beta^2} \quad (11.43)$$

Dividing both $f(t) = e^{-\alpha t} \sin \beta t$ and its Laplace transform (11.43) by β, we obtain the result in item 10, Table 11.2.

F. Remarks about the Laplace Transforms of Other Elementary Functions

The Laplace transforms of the other functions in Table 11.2 are obtained in a similar manner. However, the following remarks are sometimes useful in finding the Laplace transform of a given function $f(t)$:

1. If a circular function $\sin \beta t$ or $\cos \beta t$ appears in $f(t)$, it is often desirable to replace it with its exponential equivalent:

$$\sin \beta t = \frac{e^{j\beta t} - e^{-j\beta t}}{2j} \quad (11.44a)$$

$$\cos \beta t = \frac{e^{j\beta t} + e^{-j\beta t}}{2} \quad (11.44b)$$

2. If a hyperbolic function $\sinh \beta t$ or $\cosh \beta t$ appears in $f(t)$, it is often desirable to replace it with its exponential equivalent:

$$\sinh \beta t = \frac{e^{\beta t} - e^{-\beta t}}{2} \quad (11.45a)$$

$$\cosh \beta t = \frac{e^{\beta t} + e^{-\beta t}}{2} \quad (11.45b)$$

3. If a power of t appears in $f(t)$, for example, $f(t) = t^k g(t)$, the method of integration by parts is often helpful in finding the Laplace transform of $f(t)$.

11.5. Laplace transformations of elementary operations

A simple illustration. Suppose we are given a function $f(t)$ and its Laplace transform $F(s)$. Now we perform an *operation* on $f(t)$, for example, finding the integral of $f(t)$, and let this integral be represented as $v(t) = \int_0^t f(\tau) d\tau$. We wish to know how the Laplace transform $V(s)$ of the integral function $v(t)$ can be obtained directly from the Laplace transform $F(s)$ of the original function $f(t)$. We shall find later that

$$\begin{array}{ccc}
\text{[Given: } f(t)\text{]} \xrightarrow[\text{by (11.30b)}]{\text{Find } F(s) = \mathcal{L}[f(t)]} & \text{[Known: } F(s)\text{]} \\
\left| \begin{array}{l} \textit{Operation on } f(t): \\ \text{finding an integral} \end{array} \right. & \left| \begin{array}{l} \textit{Operation on} \\ \text{transform } F(s): \\ \text{multiplication by } 1/s \end{array} \right. \quad (11.46) \\
\left[v(t) = \int_0^t f(\tau) d\tau \right] \xrightarrow[\text{by (11.30b)}]{\text{Find } V(s) = \mathcal{L}[v(t)]} & \left[V(s) = \frac{1}{s} F(s) \right]
\end{array}$$

This means that the operation "finding an integral of a function $f(t)$" is "Laplace-transformed" into the *simpler* operation "multiplying the Laplace transform $F(s)$ by $1/s$."

Description of problem.   We shall investigate in this section (Art. 11.5) the corresponding operations performed on (1) a given function $f(t)$ and its Laplace transform $F(s)$ and (2) two given functions $f(t)$ and $g(t)$ and their Laplace transforms $F(s)$ and $G(s)$.   The results of the investigation are listed in Table 11.3.

A. Linear Operation

Again we assume that $f(t)$ and $g(t)$ are given functions and $F(s)$ and $G(s)$ are their respective Laplace transforms.

Linear combination of $f(t)$ and $g(t)$.   For the linear combination $k_1 f(t) + k_2 g(t)$, where k_1 and k_2 are two arbitrary constants, the Laplace transform is

$$\mathscr{L}[k_1 f(t) + k_2 g(t)] = k_1 F(s) + k_2 G(s) \tag{11.47}$$

This is included as item 1 in Table 11.3.

Proof.   Substitute $k_1 f(t) + k_2 g(t)$ into (11.30b):

$$\mathscr{L}[k_1 f(t) + k_2 g(t)] = \int_0^\infty [k_1 f(t) + k_2 g(t)] e^{-st}\, dt$$

$$= k_1 \int_0^\infty f(t) e^{-st}\, dt + k_2 \int_0^\infty g(t) e^{-st}\, dt$$

$$= k_1 F(s) + k_2 G(s)$$

This certainly checks with (11.47).

Multiplication by a constant.   For $f(t)$ multiplied by a constant k, the Laplace transform is

$$\mathscr{L}[k f(t)] = k F(s) \tag{11.48}$$

This is only a trivial case of (11.47) for $k_1 = k, k_2 = 0$.

Physical meaning.   Applying the theorem of superposition for linear networks, we may consider a network excitation

Superimposed excitations:

$$e_1(t) = e_A(t) + e_B(t) \tag{11.49a}$$

as consisting in two component excitations, $e_A(t)$ and $e_B(t)$, linearly superimposed. We may then find the network response $e_{2A}(t)$ subject to the component excitation $e_A(t)$, and $e_{2B}(t)$ subject to $e_B(t)$.   The network response $e_2(t)$ subject to the actual total excitation $e_1(t)$ is then a linear superposition,

Superimposed responses:

$$e_2(t) = e_{2A}(t) + e_{2B}(t) \tag{11.49b}$$

With $\mathscr{L}[e_1(t)] = E_1(s), \mathscr{L}[e_2(t)] = E_2(s), \mathscr{L}[e_A(t)] = E_A(s), \mathscr{L}[e_B(t)] = E_B(s),$ $\mathscr{L}[e_{2A}(t)] = E_{2A}(s),$ and $\mathscr{L}[e_{2B}(t)] = E_{2B}(s)$, Eq. (11.47) implies that, for superimposed excitations (11.49a) in a linear network, we have

Superimposed Laplace transforms of excitations:

$$E_1(s) = E_A(s) + E_B \tag{11.50a}$$

Superimposed Laplace transforms of responses:

$$E_2(s) = E_{2A}(s) + E_{2B}(s) \tag{11.50b}$$

This obviously illustrates the *linear property* of the Laplace transformation.

Table 11.3

Operation	$v(t)$ for $t \geq 0$	$V(s)$
Given functions and their Laplace transforms	$f(t) \qquad t \geq 0$	$F(s)$
	$g(t) \qquad t \geq 0$	$G(s)$
1. Linear operation (Art. 11.5A)	$k_1 f(t)$	$kF(s)$
	$k_1 f(t) + k_2 g(t)$	$k_1 F(s) + k_2 G(s)$
2. Differentiation (Art. 11.5B)	$f'(t) \equiv \dfrac{d}{dt}[f(t)]$	$sF(s) - f(0^+)$
	$f''(t) \equiv \dfrac{d^2}{dt^2}[f(t)]$	$s^2 F(s) - sf(0^+) - f'(0^+)$
	$f^{(n)}(t) \equiv \dfrac{d^n}{dt^n}[f(t)]$	$s^n F(s) - \displaystyle\sum_{k=1}^{n} s^{n-k} f^{(k-1)}(0^+)$
3. Integration (Art. 11.5C)	$\displaystyle\int_0^t f(t)\, dt \quad$ (definite integral)	$\dfrac{1}{s} F(s)$
	$\displaystyle\int_0^t \int_0^t f(t)\, dt\, dt \quad$ (definite integral)	$\dfrac{1}{s^2} F(s)$
	$\displaystyle\underbrace{\int \cdots \int_0^t}_{(n)} f(t)\,(dt)^n$ (definite integral)	$\dfrac{1}{s^n} F(s)$
	$f^{-1}(t) \equiv \displaystyle\int_0^t f(t)\, dt + f^{-1}(0^+)$ $\equiv \displaystyle\int f(t)\, dt$ (indefinite integral)	$\dfrac{1}{s} F(s) + \dfrac{1}{s} f^{-1}(0^+)$
	$f^{-2}(t) \equiv \displaystyle\int \int f(t)\, dt\, dt$ (indefinite integral)	$\dfrac{1}{s^2} F(s) + \dfrac{1}{s^2} f^{-1}(0^+)$ $+ \dfrac{1}{s} f^{-2}(0^+)$
	$f^{-n}(t) \equiv \displaystyle\underbrace{\int \cdots \int}_{(n)} f(t)\,(dt)^n$ (indefinite integral)	$\dfrac{1}{s^n} F(s) + \displaystyle\sum_{k=1}^{n} \dfrac{f^{-k}(0^+)}{s^{n-k+1}}$
4. Displacement along the time axis (Art. 11.5D)	$u(t-a) f(t-a)$	$e^{-as} F(s)$
5. Change of time scale (Art. 11.5E)	$f\left(\dfrac{t}{c}\right)$	$cF(cs)$
6. Multiplication by an exponential factor (Art. 11.5F)	$e^{-\alpha t} f(t) \qquad \alpha > 0$	$F(s + \alpha)$
	$e^{\alpha t} f(t) \qquad \alpha > 0$	$F(s - \alpha)$
7. Convolution of $f(t)$ and $g(t)$ (Art. 11.5G)	$\displaystyle\int_0^t f(t-\tau) g(\tau)\, d\tau$	$F(s)G(s)$

Illustration.   In item 17 in Table 11.2, we find an illustration of the linear property (11.47).   Here, $f(t) = u(t - a)$, $g(t) = u(t - b)$, $k_1 = 1$, and $k_2 = -1$; $F(s) = (1/s)e^{-as}$ and $G(s) = (1/s)e^{-bs}$ according to item 16 in Table 11.2.   According to (11.47),

$$\mathscr{L}[u(t - a) - u(t - b)] = F(s) - G(s) = \frac{1}{s}(e^{-as} - e^{-bs})$$

This is what we have in item 17 of Table 11.2.

B. *Differentiation*

Again, we assume that $f(t)$ is a given function, and $F(s)$ its Laplace transform.
Laplace transform of first derivative $f'(t)$.   For

$$f'(t) = \frac{d}{dt} f(t)$$

we find†

$$\mathscr{L}[f'(t)] = sF(s) - f(0^+) \tag{11.51}$$

where $f(0^+)$ is the initial value of $f(t)$ at $t = 0^+$.   This is included in item 2 in Table 11.3.

Proof.   Equation (11.51) may be easily verified with

$$\mathscr{L}[f'(t)] = \int_0^\infty f'(t)e^{-st} \, dt = \int_0^\infty e^{-st} \, df(t)$$

$$= f(t)e^{-st} \Big|_{t=0}^{t=\infty} - \int_0^\infty f(t) \, de^{-st}‡$$

$$= 0 - f(0^+) - (-s)\int_0^\infty f(t)e^{-st} \, dt$$

$$= -f(0^+) + sF(s)$$

which checks with (11.51) and, therefore, completes our proof.
Laplace transform of second derivative $f''(t)$.   For

$$f''(t) = \frac{d^2}{dt^2} f(t) = \frac{d}{dt}\left[\frac{d}{dt} f(t)\right] = \frac{d}{dt} f'(t)$$

we may apply (11.51) twice and find

$$\mathscr{L}[f''(t)] = s[sF(s) - f(0^+)] - f'(0^+) = s^2F(s) - sf(0^+) - f'(0^+) \tag{11.52}$$

where $f(0^+)$ and $f'(0^+)$ are the initial values of $f(t)$ and $f'(t)$ at $t = 0^+$.   This result is also included in item 2 in Table 11.3.
Laplace transform of nth derivative $f^{(n)}(t)$.   Repeated application of (11.51) leads to

$$\mathscr{L}[f^{(n)}(t)] = s^n F(s) - \sum_{k=1}^n s^{n-k} f^{(k-1)}(0^+) \tag{11.53}$$

where $f^{(k-1)}(0^+)$ for $k = 1, 2, \ldots, n$ are initial conditions of $f(t)$, $f'(t)$, $f''(t)$, $\ldots$, $f^{(n-1)}(t)$ at $t = 0^+$.   This result is also included in item 2 in Table 11.3.

---

† The Laplace transform of a function $f(t)$ as defined in (11.30b) is an improper integral of the type (11.3) with the lower limit t_a greater than, but approaching, zero.   We therefore anticipate the possibility of a *jump* at $t = 0$ for $f(t)$. $f(0^+)$ is the value of the function as the origin is approached from the right or positive side.   For convenience, we call $f(0^+)$ the *initial value* of $f(t)$ at $t = 0^+$.   In the example of the unit-step function $f(t) = u(t)$ in Fig. 11.2b we have a jump at $t = 0$, and $f(0^+) = u(0^+) = 1$.

‡ Use the method of integration by parts.   See the footnote associated with Eq. (11.36b).

Remarks. For zero initial conditions, that is, $f(0) = f'(0) = f''(0) = \cdots = f^{(n-1)}(0) = 0$, Eqs. (11.51) to (11.53) become

$$\mathcal{L}[f'(t)] = sF(s)$$
$$\mathcal{L}[f''(t)] = s^2F(s) \tag{11.54}$$
$$\mathcal{L}[f^{(n)}(t)] = s^nF(s)$$

This means that the operation of taking the derivative of a given function $f(t)$ is "Laplace-transformed" into the simpler operation of multiplying the Laplace transform $F(s)$ by s.

Illustrations. In Table 11.2 we find that $\cos \beta t$ is the derivative of $(1/\beta) \sin \beta t$, $\cosh \beta t$ is the derivative of $(1/\beta) \sinh \beta t$, $u(t)$ is the derivative of t, and $\delta(t)$ is the derivative of $u(t)$. Comparing the Laplace transforms in each case, we find that Eqs. (11.54) are true.

C. Integration

Again, we assume that $f(t)$ is a given function, and $F(s)$ its Laplace transform.
Definitions of definite and indefinite integrals. We shall call

Definite integral:†

$$\int_0^t f(t)\, dt \equiv f^{-1}(t)\Big|_{t=0^+}^{t=t} \tag{11.55a}$$

and

$$\int_0^t f(t)\, dt = f^{-1}(t) - f^{-1}(0^+) \tag{11.55a'}$$

Indefinite integral:

$$f^{-1}(t) \equiv \int f(t)\, dt = \int_{0^+}^t f(t)\, dt + f^{-1}(0^+) \tag{11.55b}$$

$$f^{-1}(t) = f^{-1}(t) - f^{-1}(0^+) + f^{-1}(0^+) \tag{11.55b'}$$

the definite and indefinite integrals of $f(t)$. It is now easy to see that (1) the definite integral includes the initial condition $f^{-1}(0^+)$ of the integral function while (2) the indefinite integral does not, as $-f^{-1}(0^+)$ and $f^{-1}(0^+)$ in (11.55b') cancel each other out.

Laplace transform of first integral $f^{-1}(t)$. For the indefinite integral $f^{-1}(t)$ as represented in (11.55b), we have, using (11.30b),

For indefinite integral:

$$\mathcal{L}[f^{-1}(t)] = \int_0^\infty \left[\int_0^t f(t)\, dt + f^{-1}(0^+) \right] d\frac{e^{-st}}{-s}$$

$$= \left[\int_0^t f(t)\, dt + f^{-1}(0^+) \right] \frac{e^{-st}}{-s}\Big|_{t=0}^{t=\infty} - \int_0^\infty \frac{e^{-st}}{-s} d\left[\int_0^t f(t)\, dt + f^{-1}(0^+) \right]^{\ddagger}$$

$$= 0 + \frac{1}{s} f^{-1}(0^+) + \frac{1}{s}\int_0^\infty e^{-st}f(t)\, dt$$

$$= \frac{1}{s}[F(s) + f^{-1}(0^+)] \tag{11.56a}$$

† To avoid confusion, we may rewrite (11.55a) as

$$\int_0^t f(\tau)\, d\tau = f^{-1}(\tau)\Big|_{\tau=0^+}^{\tau=t}$$

‡ Use the method of integration by parts [see the footnote associated with (11.36b)]. Also see the footnote associated with (11.51) for the interpretation of $f^{-1}(0^+)$.

Letting $f^{-1}(0^+) = 0$ in (11.56a), we have the Laplace transform of the definite integral (11.55a):

For definite integral:

$$\mathscr{L}\left[\int_0^t f(t)\, dt\right] = \frac{1}{s}\, F(s) \tag{11.56b}$$

The results in (11.56) are included in item 3 in Table 11.3.

Laplace transform of second integral $f^{-2}(t)$. To avoid confusion and clearly indicate which are the limits of integration, τ and γ are used as time parameters in place of t in the indefinite integral

$$f^{-2}(t) \equiv \iint f(t)\, dt\, dt \equiv \int_0^t \left[\int_0^\tau f(\gamma)\, d\gamma + f^{-1}(0^+)\right] d\tau + f^{-2}(0^+) \tag{11.57a}$$

We may find its Laplace transform by applying (11.56a) twice; i.e.,

For indefinite integral:

$$\mathscr{L}[f^{-2}(t)] = \frac{1}{s}\frac{1}{s}\,[F(s) + f^{-1}(0^+)] + \frac{1}{s}\, f^{-2}(0^+)$$

$$= \frac{1}{s^2}\, F(s) + \frac{1}{s^2}\, f^{-1}(0^+) + \frac{1}{s}\, f^{-2}(0^+) \tag{11.58a}$$

For the Laplace transform of the definite integral

$$\int_0^t \int_0^t f(t)\, dt\, dt \tag{11.57b}$$

we may let $f^{-1}(0^+) = f^{-2}(0^+) = 0$ in (11.58a):

For definite integral:

$$\mathscr{L}\left[\int_0^t \int_0^t f(t)\, dt\, dt\right] = \frac{1}{s^2}\, F(s) \tag{11.58b}$$

The results in (11.58) are included in item 3 in Table 11.3.

Laplace transform of nth integral $f^{-n}(t)$. In a similar manner, repeated application of (11.56a) leads us to

For indefinite integral:

$$\mathscr{L}[f^{-n}(t)] = \frac{1}{s^n}\, F(s) + \sum_{k=1}^{n} \frac{f^{-k}(0^+)}{s^{n-k+1}} \tag{11.59a}$$

and

For definite integral:

$$\mathscr{L}\left[\underset{(n)}{\int_0^t \cdots \int_0^t} f(t)\, (dt)^n\right] = \frac{1}{s^n}\, F(s) \tag{11.59b}$$

The results in (11.59) are included in item 3 in Table 11.3.

Remarks. Considering definite integrals and their Laplace transforms in item 3 in Table 11.3, we note that the operation of finding the definite integral of a given function $f(t)$ is "Laplace-transformed" into the simpler operation of multiplying the Laplace transform $F(s)$ by $1/s$.

Illustrations. In Table 11.2, we find that $(1/\beta) \sin \beta t$ is the integral of $\cos \beta t$, $(1/\beta) \sinh \beta t$ is the integral of $\cosh \beta t$, t is the integral of $u(t)$, and $u(t)$ is the integral of $\delta(t)$. Comparing the Laplace transforms in each case, we find that Eqs. (11.56) are true.

D. Displacement along the Time Axis

Again we assume that $f(t)$ is a given function, and $F(s)$ its Laplace transform.

A formal representation of a given function $g(t)$ used in Laplace transformation. For a given function $g(t)$ defined in the positive-time region, e.g.,

$$g(t) = \begin{cases} f(t) = t^2 & t \geq 0 & (11.60a) \\ 0 & t < 0 & (11.60b) \end{cases}$$

we can find the Laplace transform $G(s)$ according to (11.30b). The function $g(t)$ as described in (11.60a) and (11.60b) is depicted in Fig. 11.3b.

We need *both* Eqs. (11.60a) and (11.60b) to describe $g(t)$. If we use (11.60a) alone, we might mistake $g(t)$ for the function depicted in Fig. 11.3a. However, this is not

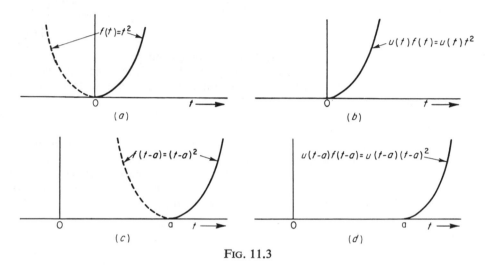

Fig. 11.3

a matter of great concern in the evaluation of the Laplace transform $G(s)$ of $g(t)$, since (11.30b) is an integral with limits $t = 0$ and $t = \infty$ and assumes (11.60b).

$g(t)$ may be more formally represented with only *one* equation:

$$g(t) = u(t) f(t) = u(t) t^2 \qquad (11.61)$$

Since $u(t) = 0$ for $t < 0$, condition (11.60b) is always implied.

Representation of a displaced function. Suppose we are to displace the function $g(t)$ (Fig. 11.3b along the time axis to the right for a time interval $a > 0$). It is obvious that we may modify (11.61) into

$$g(t - a) = u(t - a)f(t - a) = u(t - a)(t - a)^2 \qquad (11.62)$$

Since $u(t - a) = 0$ for $t < a$,

$$g(t - a) = 0 \qquad -\infty < t < a \qquad (11.62a)$$

However, if we leave out the factor $u(t - a)$ in (11.62), we shall get Fig. 11.3c instead of Fig. 11.3d. The Laplace transform, thus obtained, will be erroneous.

Laplace transform of a displaced function. For a function $f(t)$, defined for $t \geq 0$ and displaced along the time axis to the right for a time interval a, the displaced function $u(t - a)f(t - a)$ has the Laplace transform

$$\mathscr{L}[u(t - a)f(t - a)] = e^{-as}F(s) \qquad (11.63)$$

This is included as item 4 in Table 11.3.

Proof. Substitute the displaced function into (11.30b):

$$\mathscr{L}[u(t-a)f(t-a)] = \int_0^\infty [u(t-a)f(t-a)]e^{-st}\,dt = \int_0^a + \int_a^\infty$$

$$= 0 + \int_a^\infty f(t-a)e^{-st}e^{as}e^{-as}\,dt\dagger$$

$$= e^{-as}\int_a^\infty f(t-a)e^{-(t-a)s}\,dt \qquad (11.63a)$$

With $\tau = t - a$ and $d\tau = d(t-a) = dt$, and the limits $t = a$ and $t = \infty$ replaced by $\tau = a - a = 0$ and $\tau = \infty - a = \infty$, (11.63a) becomes

$$\mathscr{L}[u(t-a)f(t-a)] = e^{-as}\int_0^\infty f(\tau)e^{-\tau s}\,d\tau = e^{-as}\begin{bmatrix}\text{Eq. (11.30}b\text{) except}\\ \text{for notation}\end{bmatrix}$$

$$= e^{-as}F(s) \qquad (11.63b)$$

Equation (11.63b) is identical to (11.63); this completes our proof.

Illustration. Comparing $u(t-a)$ with $u(t)$ in Fig. 11.2, we see that $u(t-a)$ certainly represents a displaced function. Comparing their Laplace transforms in Table 11.2, we find that (11.63) is true.

E. Change of Time Scale

Again we assume that $f(t)$ is a given function, and $F(s)$ its Laplace transform.

Meaning of scale factor along the time axis. Let us consider the representation in Fig. 11.4. We may use two time scales, t in seconds or t' in microseconds. It is obvious that

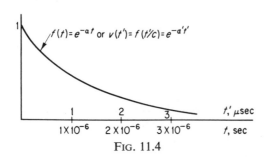

FIG. 11.4

$$t' = ct \qquad t = \frac{t'}{c} \qquad (11.64)$$

and

$$c = 10^6 \qquad (11.64a)$$

c is called a scale factor.

Description of problem. Suppose we are given a function $f(t)$, depicting a waveform, and its Laplace transform $F(s)$. The time scale t, used for $f(t)$, has unwieldy values, as indicated along the t axis in Fig. 11.4. We wish to use a new time scale t', as indicated along the t' axis in Fig. 11.4, with a scale factor

$$c = \frac{t'}{t} \qquad (11.65)$$

Describing the same waveform there is a function of t',

$$v(t') = f(t) = f\left(\frac{t'}{c}\right) \qquad (11.66)$$

which may be obtained by replacing t with t'/c in $f(t)$.

Our problem is to find the Laplace transform of $v(t')$,

$$V(s') = \mathscr{L}[v(t')]$$

directly from $F(s)$, which is either given or obtained as the Laplace transform of $f(t)$ with the aid of Eq. (11.30b) or Table 11.2.

$\dagger\ u(t-a) = 0$ for $t < a$. The first integral with limits $t = 0$ and $t = a$ therefore vanishes.

Summarizing the above, we have

Two functions depicting the same waveform:

Change of time scales:
$$t = t'/c$$

$$[f(t)] \xrightarrow{\text{Use (11.66)}} [v(t')]$$

Their Laplace transforms: (11.30) **Our problem:** Find $V(s')$ (11.30) (11.67)
from a known $F(s)$

$$[F(s)] \xrightarrow{\text{Solution: See Eq. (11.69)}} [V(s') = ?]$$

Laplace transform of a function with a changed time scale. Let $f(t)$ be a given function depicting a certain waveform, and $F(s)$ its Laplace transform. The Laplace transform of another function

$$v(t') = f(t) = f\left(\frac{t'}{c}\right) \tag{11.68a}$$

depicting the *same* waveform but with a different time scale

$$t' = ct \qquad c > 0 \tag{11.68b}$$

is found to be

$$\mathscr{L}\left[f\left(\frac{t'}{c}\right)\right] = cF(cs') \tag{11.69}$$

where $F(cs')$ is obtained by replacing s with cs' in $F(s)$. This property is included as item 5 in Table 11.3.

Proof

1. Rewrite the given condition:

$$\mathscr{L}[f(t)] = \int_0^\infty f(t)e^{-st}\, dt = F(s) \tag{11.70a}$$

2. Replace t with t'/c and dt with dt'/c in (11.70a):

$$\int_0^\infty f\left(\frac{t'}{c}\right)e^{-st'/c}\,\frac{dt'}{c} = F(s) \tag{11.70b}$$

3. Multiply both sides of (11.70b) by c, and replace s with cs' in (11.70b):

$$\int_0^\infty f\left(\frac{t'}{c}\right)e^{-s't'}\, dt' = cF(cs') \tag{11.70c}$$

4. By definition (11.30b), the left-hand side of (11.70c) is the Laplace transform of $f(t'/c)$, and

$$\mathscr{L}\left[f\left(\frac{t'}{c}\right)\right] = cF(cs') \tag{11.70d}$$

This completes our proof.

Some Remarks. We may leave out the primes on t' and s' in (11.70d) as long as all the functions (say excitations and responses) associated with the same network have the same time scale. The Laplace transforms of these functions may be linearly added in the same manner as a number of excitations (or responses) are linearly superimposed on one another.

If two functions $f(t)$ and $g(t')$ have different time scales, their Laplace transforms are $F(s)$ and $G(s')$, and the two functions of different variables s and s' cannot be added conveniently. However, we may change the time scale in $f(t)$ from t to t' and find its Laplace transform $F'(s') = cF(cs')$ with the aid of (11.69). $F'(s')$ and $G(s')$ may now be added conveniently.

Illustration. Let us use the waveform in Fig. 11.4 and assume

$$f(t) = e^{-\alpha t} = e^{-2 \times 10^6 t} \tag{11.71a}$$

Table 11.2 implies

$$F(s) = \frac{1}{s + \alpha} = \frac{1}{s + 2 \times 10^6} \tag{11.71b}$$

The time scale, t in seconds, results in unwieldy values, as indicated along the t axis in Fig. 11.4; a new time scale, t' in microseconds, is chosen. The scale factor is obviously

$$c = \frac{t'}{t} = 10^6$$

According to (11.69), we have

$$\mathscr{L}\left[f\left(\frac{t'}{c}\right)\right] = cF(cs') = c\,\frac{1}{cs' + 2 \times 10^6}$$

$$= \frac{10^6}{10^6 s' + 2 \times 10^6} = \frac{1}{s' + 2} \tag{11.72}$$

We may verify our result in (11.72) by (1) finding $v'(t) = f(t'/c) = e^{-2 \times 10^6 (t'/10^6)} = e^{-2t'}$ in Fig. 11.4 and (2) finding $\mathscr{L}[f(t'/c)] = \mathscr{L}[e^{-2t'}] = 1/(s' + 2)$, which checks with (11.72).

F. Multiplication by an Exponential Factor

Again we assume that $f(t)$ is a given function, and $F(s)$ its Laplace transform.
Laplace transform of $e^{-\alpha t}f(t)$.   For $e^{-\alpha t}f(t)$, we find

$$\mathscr{L}[e^{-\alpha t}f(t)] = F(s + \alpha) \qquad \alpha > 0 \tag{11.73a}$$

Proof.   Equation (11.73a) may be easily verified with

$$\mathscr{L}[e^{-\alpha t}f(t)] = \int_0^\infty e^{-\alpha t}f(t)e^{-st}\,dt = \int_0^\infty f(t)e^{-(s+\alpha)t}\,dt$$

$$= \int_0^\infty f(t)e^{-s't}\,dt = F(s')\dagger = F(s + \alpha)$$

Laplace transform of $e^{\alpha t}f(t)$.   Replacing α with $-\alpha$ in (11.73a), we have

$$\mathscr{L}[e^{\alpha t}f(t)] = F(s - \alpha) \qquad \alpha > 0 \tag{11.73b}$$

The results in (11.73) are included as item 6 in Table 11.3.

Illustrations.   In Table 11.2, we find that $A \sin (\beta t + \phi)$ and $Ae^{-\alpha t} \sin (\beta t + \phi)$ differ only by a factor $e^{-\alpha t}$, $(1/\beta) \sin \beta t$ and $(1/\beta)e^{-\alpha t} \sin \beta t$ also differ only by a factor $e^{-\alpha t}$, and t and $te^{-\alpha t}$ also differ by the same factor. Comparing the Laplace transforms of each pair, we find that (11.73) are true.

G. Convolution

Again we assume that $f(t)$ and $g(t)$ are given functions, and $F(s)$ and $G(s)$ are their Laplace transforms.
Convolution $f(t) * g(t)$.   We shall call

$$f(t) * g(t) \equiv \int_0^t f(t - \tau)g(\tau)\,d\tau \tag{11.74}$$

the *convolution* or *convolution integral* of $f(t)$ and $g(t)$.

† Let $s' = s + \alpha$. $F(s')$ results from the preceding integral with the aid of (11.30b).

Laplace transform of $f(t) * g(t)$.   For the convolution $f(t) * g(t)$, we find

$$\mathscr{L}[f(t) * g(t)] = F(s)G(s) \tag{11.75}$$

Proof

1. Modify (11.74) to

$$f(t) * g(t) = \int_0^t (1)f(t - \tau)g(\tau)\, d\tau + \int_t^\infty (0)f(t - \tau)g(\tau)\, d\tau$$

$$= \int_{\tau=0}^{\tau=\infty} u(t - \tau)f(t - \tau)g(\tau)\, d\tau† \tag{11.76a}$$

2. Substitute (11.76a) into (11.30b); then interchange the order of integration with respect to the variables t and τ:

$$\mathscr{L}[f(t) * g(t)] = \int_{t=0}^{t=\infty} [\text{Eq. (11.76a)}]e^{-st}\, dt$$

$$= \int_{\tau=0}^{\tau=\infty} g(\tau)\left[\int_{t=0}^{t=\infty} u(t - \tau)f(t - \tau)e^{-st}\, dt \right] d\tau \tag{11.76b}$$

$$\mathscr{L}[f(t) * g(t)] = \int_{\tau=0}^{\tau=\infty} g(\tau)\, e^{-\tau s}F(s)\, d\tau‡$$

$$= F(s)\left[\int_{\tau=0}^{\tau=\infty} g(\tau)e^{-\tau s}\, d\tau \right] \tag{11.76c}$$

3. Use the definition (11.30b) of Laplace transform again, and change (11.76c) to

$$\mathscr{L}[f(t) * g(t)] = F(s)G(s) \tag{11.76d}$$

Equations (11.75) and (11.76d) are identical; this completes our proof.   The result in (11.75) is included as item 7 in Table 11.3 and will be illustrated with network problems in Arts. 14.2 and 14.4.

11.6. Some additional properties of Laplace transforms: initial and final values of a function of time

A. Initial-value Properties

We shall assume that the Laplace transforms of both $f(t)$ and its derivative $f'(t)$ exist, and that the Laplace transform $F(s)$ of $f(t)$ is a known function.

Initial value of $f(t)$.   We shall find that

$$\lim_{t \to 0^+} f(t) = \lim_{s \to \infty} sF(s) \tag{11.77}$$

if both limits exist.

Proof. With the aid of (11.51),

$$\int_0^\infty f'(t)e^{-st}\, dt = sF(s) - f(0^+)$$

Taking limits, we have

$$\lim_{s \to \infty} \int_0^\infty f'(t)e^{-st}\, dt = \lim_{s \to \infty} sF(s) - \lim_{t \to 0^+} f(t)$$

† By definition, $u(t - \tau) = 1$ for $\tau \le t$ and $u(t - \tau) = 0$ for $\tau > t$.
‡ Use Eq. (11.63) or Table 11.3, item 4, in (11.76b).   Since $F(s)$ is not a function of τ, it may be taken outside the integral sign in (11.76c).

The limit of the integral on the left-hand side of the above equation vanishes, since the integrand $f'(t)e^{-st}$ approaches zero as $s \to \infty$; (11.77) results.

Initial value of $f'(t)$. We may extend (11.77) with the aid of (11.51) to include the initial value of the derivative $f'(t)$ if both limits exist:

$$\lim_{t \to 0^+} f'(t) = \lim_{s \to \infty} s[sF(s) - f(0^+)] \tag{11.78}$$

Remarks. Knowing $F(s)$, we may easily determine the initial values $f(0^+)$ and $f'(0^+)$ with the aid of (11.77) and (11.78).

Illustrations. For $F(s) = 1/s$ in Table 11.2, item 2, (11.77) implies an initial value $f(0^+) = \lim_{s \to \infty} sF(s) = 1$; this may be easily verified with $f(t) = \mathscr{L}^{-1}[1/s] = u(t)$, which is a unit-step function as depicted in Fig. 11.2b.

For $F(s) = 1/(s + \alpha)$ in Table 11.2, item 6, (11.77) implies an initial value $f(0^+) = \lim_{s \to \infty} sF(s) = 1$; this may easily be verified with $f(t) = \mathscr{L}^{-1}[1/(s + \alpha)] = e^{-\alpha t}$ as depicted in Fig. 11.2h.

For $F(s) = 1/(s + \alpha)$ and $f(t) = e^{-\alpha t}$ as in Table 11.2, item 6, (11.78) implies an initial value $f'(0^+) = \lim_{s \to 0} s[s/(s + \alpha) - 1] = \lim_{s \to 0} [-s\alpha/(s + \alpha)] = -\alpha$; this may be verified by finding the initial value of $f'(t) = (-\alpha)e^{-\alpha t}$ at $t = 0^+$.

B. Final-value Property

We shall, again, assume that the Laplace transforms of both $f(t)$ and its derivative $f'(t)$ exist, and that the Laplace transform $F(s)$ of $f(t)$ is a known function.

Final value of $f(t)$. We shall find that

$$\lim_{t \to \infty} f(t) = \lim_{s \to 0} sF(s) \tag{11.79}$$

if $sF(s)$ as a function of s has *no* poles on the $j\omega$ axis or in the right-hand half of the s plane.

Proof

1. Use (11.51) and take limits as $s \to 0$:

$$sF(s) - f(0^+) = \int_0^\infty f'(t)e^{-st}\, dt$$

$$\lim_{s \to 0} [sF(s) - f(0^+)] = \lim_{s \to 0} \int_{t=0}^{t=\infty} f'(t)e^{-st}\, dt \tag{11.80a}$$

2. As $s \to 0$ and then as $e^{-st} \to 1$, (11.80a) becomes

$$\lim_{s \to 0} [sF(s)] - f(0^+) = \int_{t=0}^{t=\infty} f'(t)\, dt \tag{11.80b}$$

$$\lim_{s \to 0} [sF(s)] - f(0^+) = \lim_{\tau \to \infty} \int_0^\tau f'(t)\, dt \tag{11.80c}$$

3. Because of the conditions imposed upon $sF(s)$ in (11.79), the limit of the definite integral in (11.80c) exists, and we may use (11.55a) to rewrite (11.80c) as

$$\lim_{s \to 0} [sF(s)] - f(0^+) = \lim_{\tau \to \infty} f(t) \Big|_{t=0^+}^{t=\tau} \tag{11.80d}$$

$$\lim_{s \to 0} [sF(s)] - f(0^+) = \lim_{\tau \to \infty} f(\tau) - f(0^+) \tag{11.80e}$$

4. Replace τ with t as the time parameter in (11.80e), and cancel $f(0^+)$ on both sides of the equation:

$$\lim_{t\to\infty} f(t) = \lim_{s\to 0} [sF(s)] \qquad (11.80f)$$

This checks with (11.79) and completes our proof.

Remarks. Knowing $F(s)$, we may easily determine the final value of $f(t)$ [that is, $\lim_{t\to\infty} f(t)$] with the aid of (11.79). This final value is actually the steady-state d-c value of $f(t)$.

Illustrations. For $F(s) = 1/s$ in Table 11.2, item 2, (11.79) implies a final value $\lim_{t\to\infty} f(t) = \lim_{s\to 0} [sF(s)] = 1$; this may easily be verified with $f(t) = \mathscr{L}^{-1}[1/s] = u(t)$, as depicted in Fig. 11.2b.

For $F(s) = 1/(s + \alpha)$ in Table 11.2, item 6, (11.79) implies a final value $\lim_{t\to\infty} f(t) = \lim_{s\to 0} [sF(s)] = 0$; this may easily be verified with $f(t) = \mathscr{L}^{-1}[1/(s + \alpha)] = e^{-\alpha t}$, as depicted in Fig. 11.2h.

For $F(s) = (e^{-as} - e^{-bs})/s$ with $b > a$ in Table 11.2, item 17, (11.79) implies a final value $\lim_{t\to\infty} f(t) = \lim_{s\to 0} [sF(s)] = 0$; this may easily be verified with $f(t) = \mathscr{L}^{-1}[e^{-as} - e^{-bs}/s] = u(t - a) - u(t - b)$ for $b > a$, as depicted in Fig. 11.2d.

For $F(s) = s/(s^2 + \beta^2)$ in Table 11.2, item 11, (11.79) does *not* apply, since the poles of $sF(s)$ are on the $j\omega$ axis of the s plane. For $F(s) = 1/(s^2 + \beta^2)$ in Table 11.2, item 9, (11.79) does *not* apply. Since both cases represent undamped sinusoidal waves, their steady-state d-c values (i.e., final values) are undefined, and (11.79) is naturally inapplicable.

PROBLEMS

11.1. Find the Laplace transforms of the following elementary functions, and check your results against Table 11.2:

(a) $\delta(t)$ (b) $t^{n-1}e^{-\alpha t}$ (c) $\cos \beta t$

(d) $\sinh \beta t$ (e) $A \sin (\beta t + \varphi)$ (f) $Ae^{-\alpha t} \sin (\beta t + \varphi)$

11.2. Find the Laplace transforms of the following functions:

(a) $\dfrac{1}{\sqrt{\pi t}}$ (b) $2\sqrt{\dfrac{t}{\pi}}$

(c) $\dfrac{1}{(\beta - \alpha)(\gamma - \alpha)} e^{-\alpha t} + \dfrac{1}{(\alpha - \beta)(\gamma - \beta)} e^{-\beta t} + \dfrac{1}{(\alpha - \gamma)(\beta - \gamma)} e^{-\gamma t}$

(d) $t^2 \sin \beta t$ (e) $\dfrac{1}{T^2} te^{-t/T}$

Find the Laplace transforms of the functions in Probs. 11.3 through 11.9 with the aid of Tables 11.2 and 11.3. If unable to solve a starred problem, try it again after reading Chap. 12.

11.3. The function in Fig. P 11.3.

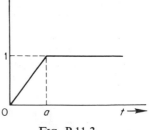

Fig. P 11.3

11.4. The function in Fig. P 11.4. HINT:

$$f(t) = mt[u(t) - u(t - \delta)]$$
$$= u(t)mt - u(t - \delta)m(t - \delta) - u(t - \delta)m\delta$$

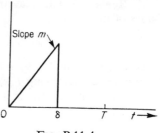

Fig. P 11.4

*11.5. The function in Prob. 11.4 extended periodically with period T for $\delta = T/2$.

11.6. The function in Fig. P 11.6.

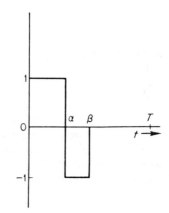

Fig. P 11.6

*11.7. The function in Prob. 11.6 extended periodically with period T.

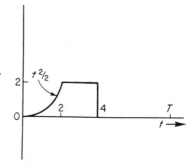

Fig. P 11.7

11.8. The function in Fig. P 11.7.

*11.9. The function in Prob. 11.7 extended periodically with period $T = 8$.

11.10. (*a*) Verify the Laplace-transform expression for the indefinite integral in (11.59*a*) for $n = 3$, 4, and 5.

(*b*) Given: $F(s) = \mathscr{L}[f(t)]$.   Find the Laplace transform of $e^{-\alpha(t-a)}f(t - a)u(t - a)$.

(*c*) Given: $f(t) = \mathscr{L}^{-1}[F(s)]$.   Find the inverse Laplace transform of

$$\frac{1}{k}\left[\frac{s}{k} F\left(\frac{s}{k}\right) - f(0^+) + F\left(\frac{s}{k}\right) + \frac{k^2}{s^2} F\left(\frac{s}{k}\right) + \frac{k^2}{s^2} f^{-1}(0^+) + \frac{k}{s} f^{-2}(0^+) \right]$$

11.11. Find the Laplace transform of

$$\int_0^t [\cos \beta(t - \tau)]\tau \, d\tau - \int_0^t (t - \tau)e^{-\alpha(t-\tau)} \cos \beta\tau \, d\tau$$

11.12. Determine the initial and final values, if they exist, of the functions $f(t)$ whose Laplace transforms $F(s) = \mathcal{L}[f(t)]$ are as follows:

(a) $F(s) = \dfrac{2}{s}$

(b) $F(s) = \dfrac{1}{s^2}$

(c) $F(s) = \dfrac{s}{s^2 + 4}$

(d) $F(s) = \dfrac{s + 2}{(s + 1)^2 + 1}$

(e) $F(s) = \dfrac{s}{s^2 - \beta^2}$

(f) $F(s) = \dfrac{1}{s}(e^{-s} - e^{-2s})$

Verify your results by finding (1) $f(t) = \mathcal{L}^{-1}[F(s)]$ with the aid of Table 11.2 and (2) the initial and final values by letting $t \to 0$ and $t \to \infty$.

12 Laplace transformation of integrodifferential equations

12.1. Finding the response of a one-loop or one-node network

A. Description of Problem

Network behavior described by a single integrodifferential equation. We are now interested in finding the response of a one-loop network, e.g., the response $i(t)$ in Fig. 12.1a, as well as the response of a one-node network, e.g., the response $v(t)$ in Fig. 12.1b. A one-node network has one independent node in addition to its "reference node" at the ground.

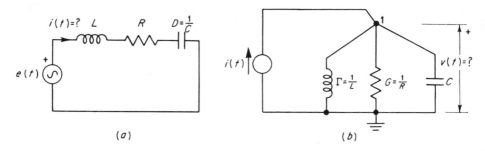

FIG. 12.1

We shall find that these two types of problems are actually the same problem with different interpretations of the notation. Both deal with a network whose behavior may be described by a single integrodifferential equation of the type

$$a\frac{d}{dt}x(t) + bx(t) + c\int x(t)\,dt = y(t) \tag{12.1}$$

Interpreting (12.1) as

$$L\frac{d}{dt}i(t) + Ri(t) + D\int i(t)\,dt = e(t) \tag{12.1a}$$

and solving it, we have obtained the response $x(t)$ or $i(t)$ of a one-loop network as depicted in Fig. 12.1a.

Interpreting (12.1) as

$$C\frac{d}{dt}v(t) + Gv(t) + \Gamma\int v(t)\,dt = i(t) \tag{12.1b}$$

and solving it, we have obtained the response $x(t)$ or $v(t)$ of a one-node network as depicted in Fig. 12.1*b*.

Method of approach.   From the above discussion, we know that our problem is only to solve an integrodifferential equation, or for brevity a differential equation, of the type (12.1).

We shall solve our differential equation using Laplace transformation. The advantage of using Laplace-transformation methods is that a problem requiring the solution of a differential equation is made into a simpler equivalent problem requiring the solution of an algebraic equation.

Remarks.   Since the problem of finding the response for a one-loop network is not any different from the problem of finding the response for a one-node network, except for notation, we shall place more emphasis on the treatment of a one-loop network (Art. 12.1B and C), with the understanding that all the techniques discussed are also applicable to a one-node network.

The problem of finding the response of a one-node network will be briefly discussed in Art. 12.1D.

B. *Finding the Steady-state and Transient Responses of a One-loop Network Having Zero-value Initial Conditions or Finding the Steady-state Sinusoidal Response of a One-loop Network*

Remarks about the problems.   We shall treat two types of problems which can be solved with the same procedure.

Problem I is to find the complete steady-state and transient responses of a one-loop network having zero-value initial conditions. This means (Fig. 12.1*a*) that at $t = 0^+$ the initial current $i(0^+) = 0$ in the circuit, and the initial charge

$$q(0^+) = i^{-1}(0^+) = 0$$

on the capacitor C.

Problem II is to find the steady-state sinusoidal response of a one-loop network subject to an excitation from a sinusoidal source. Any nonzero initial conditions will affect only the transient component of the response and will eventually die out. We may therefore ignore the initial conditions by assuming them to be *zero* and find the complete steady-state and transient response. Ignoring the transient component of this response, we obtain the steady-state sinusoidal response.

For both types of problems, we use zero-value initial values. It is obvious that both are solved in the same manner.

Remarks about the problem of finding steady-state sinusoidal response.   Finding the steady-state sinusoidal response, subject to a single sinusoidal excitation, of (1) a one-loop network or two-terminal network, (2) a multiple-loop network, and (3) a four-terminal network is perhaps one of the most common types of network problems.

For these network problems, we may use either (1) methods employing the real frequency $s = j\omega$, described as the methods of loop and nodal analysis in Arts. 2.3, 2.4, and 2.6, or (2) methods employing the complex frequency $s = \sigma + j\omega$, Laplace-transformation methods. The latter approach will be treated for the problems of one-loop networks in this section, for multiple-loop networks in Art. 12.2C, and for four-terminal networks in Art. 12.2E.

Both approaches mentioned above will give the same results for the steady-state sinusoidal response, but their *relative merits* are as follows:

1. The methods of loop and nodal analysis, as described in Chap. 2, are simpler to use, since we want only the steady-state sinusoidal response (subject to a sinusoidal excitation) and we solve for it alone.

2. The Laplace-transformation methods, which will be described in this chapter, are not the preferred methods to use for this particular problem, since we want the steady-state sinusoidal response but solve for the complete steady-state and transient responses and then ignore the transient response to obtain the steady-state sinusoidal response.   At least a part of our effort is wasted.   However, if the transient response of a linear network is desired, Laplace-transformation methods are our choice.

A Laplace-transformation method; Laplace transformation as applied to a single differential equation.   Let us use the network in Fig. 12.1*a* and assume zero-value initial conditions:

$$i(0^+) = 0 \qquad q(0^+) = i^{-1}(0^+) = 0 \tag{12.2}$$

Abbreviating *i* for *i(t)*, we have

Differential equation:

$$L\frac{di}{dt} + Ri + \frac{1}{C}\int i\, dt = e(t) \tag{12.3}$$

describing the network behavior.   We then take the Laplace transform of (12.3) by finding the Laplace transform of each of its terms:

$$\mathscr{L}\left[L\frac{di}{dt} + Ri + \frac{1}{C}\int i\, dt\right] = \mathscr{L}[e(t)]$$

or $\qquad \mathscr{L}\left[L\frac{di}{dt}\right] + \mathscr{L}[Ri] + \mathscr{L}\left[\frac{1}{C}\int i\, dt\right] = \mathscr{L}[e(t)]$

Letting

$$E(s) = \mathscr{L}[e(t)] \qquad I(s) = \mathscr{L}[i(t)] \tag{12.4}$$

and using the properties in Table 11.3 subject to the conditions (12.2), we have

$$L[sI(s)] + RI(s) + \frac{1}{C}\frac{1}{s}I(s) = E(s)$$

or

Laplace transform of differential equation:

$$Z(s)I(s) = E(s) \tag{12.5}$$

where $\qquad\qquad Z(s) = sL + R + \frac{1}{sC} \tag{12.5a}$

is the driving-point impedance function of the network in Fig. 12.1*a*.

Calling the Laplace transforms *E(s)* and *I(s)* of the excitation *e(t)* and the response *i(t)*, respectively, the *excitation function* and the *response function*, we may solve (12.5) for

Response function: $\qquad\qquad I(s) = \dfrac{E(s)}{Z(s)} \tag{12.6}$

$$I(s) = \frac{E(s)}{sL + R + \dfrac{1}{sC}} \tag{12.6a}$$

With *I(s)* computed in (12.6), we may find

Response: $\qquad\qquad i(t) = \mathscr{L}^{-1}[I(s)] \tag{12.7}$

by either following a standard procedure as discussed in Art. 13.2A or using a comprehensive table† of Laplace transforms.

† Similar to Table 11.2, but more comprehensive.   For example, see the tables in S. Goldman, "Transformation Calculus and Electrical Transients," pp. 418–423, Prentice-Hall, Inc., Englewood Cliffs, N.J., 1949.

Block-diagram analysis. Summarizing the above, we now have

Time domain:

$$\begin{bmatrix} \text{Differential} \\ \text{equation (12.3)} \end{bmatrix} \xrightarrow[\text{an involved operation}]{\textit{Solution of differential equation:}} \begin{bmatrix} \text{Response} \\ i(t) = \mathscr{L}^{-1}[I(s)] \end{bmatrix}$$

Complex-	*Laplace transformation:*	*Inverse Laplace transformation:* ↑	
frequency	Use Tables 11.2 and	Use procedure in Art. 13.2A	(12.8)
domain:	11.3	or table	

$$\begin{bmatrix} Z(s)I(s) = E(s) \end{bmatrix} \xrightarrow[\text{a simpler operation}]{\textit{Solution of algebraic equation:}} \begin{bmatrix} I(s) = \dfrac{E(s)}{Z(s)} \end{bmatrix}$$

We note here that, instead of solving a differential equation conventionally (an involved operation), the Laplace-transformation method prescribes the following procedure:

1. Apply Laplace transformation to the differential equation (12.3) describing the network, thus obtaining an algebraic equation (12.5).
2. Solve this algebraic equation for the response function $I(s)$ as indicated in (12.6).
3. Find the response $i = \mathscr{L}^{-1}[I(s)]$ as the inverse Laplace transform as in (12.7).

In other words, the Laplace-transformation method of solving a problem defined in the domain of the time t is to solve an equivalent but simpler problem in the domain of the complex frequency s, as is indicated in (12.8).

Illustration A. For zero-value initial conditions (12.2), $L = 1$, $R = 3$, $C = \frac{1}{2}$, and the excitation

$$e(t) = e^{-3t} \tag{12.9}$$

in Fig. 12.1a, find the response $i(t)$.

We first write the differential equation in the form of (12.3):

Differential equation:

$$\frac{di}{dt} + 3i + 2\int i \, dt = e^{-3t} \tag{12.10a}$$

Letting

$$\mathscr{L}[i(t)] = I(s)$$

and applying the properties in Tables 11.3 and 11.2 subject to the conditions (12.2), we have

$$\mathscr{L}\left[\frac{di}{dt}\right] = sI(s) \qquad \mathscr{L}[3i] = 3I(s)$$

$$\mathscr{L}\left[2\int i \, dt\right] = \frac{2}{s}I(s) \qquad \mathscr{L}[e^{-3t}] = \frac{1}{s+3}$$

Equation (12.10a) now becomes

$$sI(s) + 3I(s) + \frac{2}{s}I(s) = \frac{1}{s+3}$$

or

Laplace transform of differential equation:

$$\left(s + 3 + \frac{2}{s}\right)I(s) = \frac{1}{s+3} \tag{12.10b}$$

We solve the algebraic equation (12.10*b*), obtaining

Response function:

$$I(s) = \frac{s}{(s+1)(s+2)(s+3)} \tag{12.11a}$$

Following a standard procedure to be discussed in Art. 13.2A, or using a comprehensive table of Laplace transforms, we find

Response:

$$i(t) = \mathcal{L}^{-1}[I(s)] = -\tfrac{1}{2}e^{-t} + 2e^{-2t} - \tfrac{3}{2}e^{-3t} \tag{12.11b}$$

For the time being, we may consider that the response in (12.11*b*) is obtained in this manner: (1) Eq. (12.11*a*) may be represented in a partial-fraction form, $I(s) = -\tfrac{1}{2}/(s+1) + 2/(s+2) + (-\tfrac{3}{2})/(s+3)$, having three terms, and (2) these terms convert to their corresponding terms in (12.11*b*) according to item 6 in Table 11.2.

Concept of generalized Ohm's law. Examining the procedure described in (12.8), we note that instead of solving a differential equation (12.3), we solve an algebraic equation:

Response function:

$$I(s) = \frac{E(s)}{Z(s)} \tag{12.12}$$

where

Excitation function:

$$E(s) = \mathcal{L}[e(t)] \tag{12.13a}$$

and

Impedance function:

$$Z(s) = sL + R + \frac{1}{sC} \tag{12.13b}$$

Comparing (12.12) with Ohm's law, $I = E/R$, we see a close resemblance. The Laplace-transformation method has changed the problem of finding the network response into the equivalent but simpler problem of applying a generalized Ohm's law (12.12).

In Illustration A above, we first set up the differential equation (12.10*a*) and then find its Laplace transform (12.10*b*) as early steps in the problem of finding the network response. Is the setup of a differential equation really necessary for a problem of this type? The answer is "no." The concept of the generalized Ohm's law, discussed above, suggests that we need only find the excitation function (12.13*a*) and the impedance function (12.13*b*) before we proceed to find the response.

Suggested procedure in finding the response of a one-loop network having zero-value initial conditions or in finding the steady-state sinusoidal response. For the problem described in Fig. 12.1*a*, the above discussion has made it possible for us to use the following procedure without having to write the differential equation:

Step 1. Use Table 11.2 or (11.30*b*) to find

Excitation function: $E(s) = \mathcal{L}[e(t)]$ \hfill (12.14a)

Step 2. Find the network impedance function

Impedance function: $Z(s) = sL + R + \dfrac{1}{sC}$ \hfill (12.14b)

Step 3. Find

Response function: $I(s) = \dfrac{E(s)}{Z(s)}$ \hfill (12.14c)

Step 4.   Find

Response: $$i(t) = \mathscr{L}^{-1}[I(s)]$$ (12.14d)

following a standard procedure as discussed in Art. 13.2A or using a comprehensive table of Laplace transforms.

Illustration A'.   We shall now solve the problem in Illustration A and Eq. (12.9) using procedure (12.14) to bypass the setup of a differential equation.   We take the following steps:

Step 1.   From Table 11.2,

$$E(s) = \mathscr{L}[e^{-3t}] = \frac{1}{s + 3}$$ (12.15a)

Step 2.   The impedance function is

$$Z(s) = sL + R + \frac{1}{sC} = s + 3 + \frac{2}{s} = \frac{(s + 1)(s + 2)}{s}$$ (12.15b)

Step 3.   The response function is now

$$I(s) = \frac{E(s)}{Z(s)} = \frac{s}{(s + 1)(s + 2)(s + 3)}$$ (12.15c)

Step 4.   Following a standard procedure as discussed in Art. 13.2 or using a comprehensive table of Laplace transforms, we find

$$i(t) = \mathscr{L}^{-1}[I(s)] = -\tfrac{1}{2}e^{-t} + 2e^{-2t} - \tfrac{3}{2}e^{-3t}$$ (12.16)

Illustration B.   For $L = 1$, $R = 3$, $C = \tfrac{1}{2}$, and an excitation

$$e(t) = 1 \sin 2t$$ (12.17)

in Fig. 12.1a, find the steady-state response $i(t)$.   We shall use the suggested procedure (12.14) to bypass the setup of a differential equation.   We take the following steps:

Step 1.   From Table 11.2,

$$E(s) = \mathscr{L}[1 \sin 2t] = \frac{2}{s^2 + 4}$$ (12.17a)

Step 2.   The impedance function is

$$Z(s) = sL + R + \frac{1}{sC} = s + 3 + \frac{2}{s} = \frac{(s + 1)(s + 2)}{s}$$ (12.17b)

Step 3.   The response function is now

$$I(s) = \frac{E(s)}{Z(s)} = \frac{2s}{(s + 1)(s + 2)(s^2 + 4)}$$ (12.17c)

Step 4.   Following a standard procedure as discussed in Art. 13.2A, we find

$$i(t) = \mathscr{L}^{-1}[I(s)] = -\frac{2}{5}e^{-t} + \frac{1}{2}e^{-2t} + \frac{1}{\sqrt{10}} \sin(2t - 18.5°)$$ (12.17d)

For the steady-state response subject to the sinusoidal excitation (12.17), we ignore the transient terms in (12.17d) and find

Steady-state sinusoidal response:

$$i(t) = \frac{1}{\sqrt{10}} \sin(2t - 18.5°)$$ (12.17d')

For the time being, we may consider that the response in (12.17d) is obtained in this manner: (1) Eq. (12.17c) may be represented in a partial-fraction form, $I(s) = -\frac{2}{5}/(s + 1) + \frac{1}{2}/(s + 2) + (-\frac{1}{10})(s - 6)/(s^2 + 4)$, having three terms, and (2) these terms convert to their corresponding terms in (12.17*d*) according to items 6 and 12 in Table 11.2.

Comparing this illustration with Numerical Illustration 1 in Art. 2.3A, we note that they yield solutions of the same type.   The relative merits of these two methods for finding the steady-state sinusoidal response have already been discussed at the beginning of Art. 12.1B.

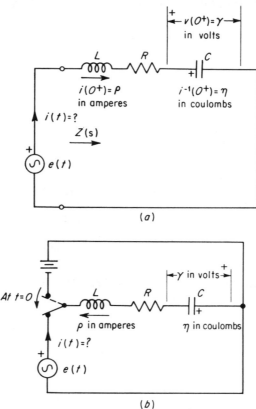

FIG. 12.2

C. Finding the Steady-state and Transient Responses of a One-loop Network with Nonzero Initial Conditions

Laplace transformation as applied to a single differential equation.   Let us use the network in Fig. 12.2*a* and assume the following initial conditions:

Initial conditions:

$$i(0^+) = \rho \qquad \text{amp} \qquad (12.18a)$$

$$i^{-1}(0^+) = \eta \qquad \text{coul} \qquad (12.18b)$$

$$v(0^+) = \gamma \qquad \text{volts} \qquad (12.18b')$$

By definition, $C = q/v$, where v is the voltage, and q is the charge across C.   At $t = 0^+$, $C = q(0^+)/v(0^+) = i^{-1}(0^+)/v(0^+) = \eta/\gamma$ in farads, which implies

$$\gamma = \frac{\eta}{C} \qquad (12.18c)$$

We are often given only ρ and η, since γ may easily be computed.

Abbreviating i for $i(t)$, we have

Differential equation:

$$L\frac{di}{dt} + Ri + \frac{1}{C}\int i\,dt = e(t) \qquad (12.19)$$

describing the network behavior. We then apply the Laplace transformation to (12.19):

$$\mathcal{L}\left[L\frac{di}{dt}\right] + \mathcal{L}[Ri] + \mathcal{L}\left[\frac{1}{C}\int i\,dt\right] = \mathcal{L}[e(t)]$$

Letting

$$E(s) = \mathcal{L}[e(t)] \qquad I(s) = \mathcal{L}[i(t)] \qquad (12.20)$$

and using the properties in Table 11.3, we now have

$$L[sI(s) - i(0^+)] + RI(s) + \frac{1}{C}\left[\frac{1}{s}I(s) + \frac{1}{s}i^{-1}(0^+)\right] = E(s)$$

or, with the notation in (12.18),

$$\left(sL + R + \frac{1}{sC}\right)I(s) = \begin{cases} E(s) + \left[Li(0^+) - \dfrac{1}{sC}i^{-1}(0^+)\right] & (12.21a) \\[2ex] E(s) + \left(L\rho - \dfrac{\eta}{sC}\right) & (12.21b) \\[2ex] E(s) + \left(L\rho - \dfrac{\gamma}{s}\right) & (12.21c) \end{cases}$$

The differential equation (12.19) has now been transformed into

Laplace transform of differential equation:

$$Z(s)I(s) = E(s) + \left(L\rho - \frac{\eta}{sC}\right) \qquad (12.22)$$

where

$$Z(s) = sL + R + \frac{1}{sC} \qquad (12.22a)$$

is the driving-point impedance function of the network in Fig. 12.2a.
We now have

Response function:

$$I(s) = \frac{E(s) + (L\rho - \eta/sC)}{Z(s)} \qquad (12.23a)$$

$$I(s) = \frac{E(s) + (L\rho - \eta/sC)}{sL + R + 1/sC} \qquad (12.23b)$$

With $I(s)$ computed in (12.23b), we may find

Response: $\qquad\qquad i(t) = \mathcal{L}^{-1}[I(s)] \qquad (12.23c)$

by either following a standard procedure as discussed in Art. 13.2A or using a comprehensive table of Laplace transforms.

It is obvious that, with $E(s)$ replaced by $E'(s) = E(s) + (L\rho - \eta/sC)$, the block-diagram analysis in (12.8) also applies here. The Laplace-transformation method of solving a problem defined in the domain of the time t is, therefore, to solve an equivalent but simpler problem in the domain of the complex frequency s, as is evident in (12.8).

Concept of equivalent excitation. Comparing the response function (12.23) subject to an excitation with initial conditions (12.18) and the response function (12.6) subject to an excitation with zero-value initial conditions (12.2), we note that we now have an equivalent excitation function

Equivalent excitation function:

$$E'(s) = E(s) + \left(L\rho - \frac{\eta}{sC}\right) \tag{12.24}$$

$$E'(s) = E(s) + \left(L\rho - \frac{\gamma}{s}\right)$$

which consists in:

1. The part contributed by the applied excitation $e(t)$,

$$E(s) = \mathscr{L}[e(t)] \tag{12.25a}$$

2. The part contributed by the initial current $i(0^+) = \rho$ in the inductance L, that is,

$$\pm L\rho \tag{12.25b}$$

where $+L\rho$ is used if ρ and $i(t)$ are in the *same* direction as in Fig. 12.2a and Eq. (12.24), and $-L\rho$ or $L(-\rho)$ is used if ρ and $i(t)$ are in opposite directions, as in Fig. 12.2b.

3. The part contributed by the initial voltage $v(0^+) = \gamma$ or the initial charge $i^{-1}(0^+) = \eta$ across the capacitance C, that is,

$$\mp \frac{\eta}{sC} \quad \text{or} \quad \mp \frac{\gamma}{s} \tag{12.25c}$$

where $-\eta/sC$ is used if η has the *proper* polarity with repect to $i(t)$ in the sense that $i(t)$ will tend to charge C to a value higher than η, as in Fig. 12.2a and Eq. (12.24), and $+\eta/sC$ is used otherwise (Fig. 12.2b).

For a given applied excitation $e(t)$ and initial conditions (12.18), we can always find an equivalent excitation function $E'(s)$ similar to the one represented in (12.24).

Some remarks. We have discussed a Laplace-transformation method in which we first set up a differential equation (12.19) and then find its Laplace transform (12.21) as early steps in finding the network response. Is the setup of a differential equation really necessary for a problem of this type? The answer is "no." The concept of the equivalent excitation function, discussed above, suggests that we need only find the equivalent excitation function (12.24) and the impedance function (12.22a) before we proceed to find the response.

Suggested procedure in finding the response of a one-loop network with nonzero initial conditions. For the problem described in Fig. 12.2a, the above discussion has made it possible for us to use the following procedure without having to write the differential equation:

Step 1. Use (12.25) to find

Equivalent excitation function:

$$E'(s) = E(s) + \left(L\rho - \frac{\eta}{sC}\right) = E(s) + \left(L\rho - \frac{\gamma}{s}\right) \tag{12.26a}$$

where $E(s) = \mathscr{L}[e(t)]$, obtained with aid of Table 11.2 or (11.30b)

ρ = initial current in L

η = initial charge across C

γ = initial voltage across C

Step 2. Find

Impedance function:
$$Z(s) = sL + R + \frac{1}{sC} \tag{12.26b}$$

Step 3. Find

Response function:
$$I(s) = \frac{E'(s)}{Z(s)} \tag{12.26c}$$

Step 4. Find

Response:
$$i(t) = \mathcal{L}^{-1}[I(s)] \tag{12.26d}$$

following a standard procedure as discussed in Art, 132.A or using a comprehensive table of Laplace transforms.

Illustration. For $L = 1$, $R = 3$, $C = \frac{1}{2}$, an excitation

$$e(t) = 1e^{-3t}$$

initial conditions

$$\rho = 1 \qquad \eta = 1 \tag{12.27}$$

and $\gamma = \eta/C = 2$ in Fig. 12.2a, find the response $i(t)$. We shall use the suggested procedure (12.26) to bypass the setup of a differential equation. We take the following steps:

Step 1. According to (12.26a),

$$E'(s) = \mathcal{L}[e(t)] + \left(L\rho - \frac{\eta}{sC}\right)$$

$$= \frac{1}{s+3} + 1 - \frac{2}{s} = \frac{s^2 + 2s - 6}{(s+3)s} \tag{12.27a}$$

Step 2. The impedance function is

$$Z(s) = sL + R + \frac{1}{sC} = s + 3 + \frac{2}{s} = \frac{(s+1)(s+2)}{s} \tag{12.27b}$$

Step 3. The response function is now

$$I(s) = \frac{E'(s)}{Z(s)} = \frac{s^2 + 2s - 6}{(s+1)(s+2)(s+3)} \tag{12.27c}$$

Step 4. Following a standard procedure as discussed in Art. 13.2A, we find the response

$$i(t) = \mathcal{L}^{-1}[I(s)] = -\tfrac{7}{2}e^{-t} + 6e^{-2t} - \tfrac{3}{2}e^{-3t} \tag{12.27d}$$

For the time being, we may consider that (12.27d) is obtained in this manner: (1) Eq. (12.27c) may be represented in a partial-fraction form, $I(s) = -\tfrac{7}{2}/(s+1) + 6/(s+2) + (-\tfrac{3}{2})/(s+3)$, having three terms, and (2) these terms convert to their corresponding terms in (12.27d) according to item 6 in Table 11.2.

D. Finding the Steady-state and Transient Responses of a One-node Network

We have remarked in Art. 12.1A that the problem of finding the response of a one-loop network as depicted in Fig. 12.1a and described by (12.1a) is not any different from the problem of finding the response of a one-node network as depicted in Fig. 12.1b and described by (12.1b), except for notation. With a change of notation, the techniques discussed above in Art. 12.1B and C are therefore applicable to a one-node network. We shall discuss the method of approach for a one-node network very briefly.

Method of approach.   Let us use the network in Fig. 12.3*a* and assume the following initial conditions:

Initial conditions:

$$\rho = \frac{1}{L} v^{-1}(0^+) = \text{initial current in inductance } L \text{ at } t = 0^+ \qquad (12.28a)$$

$$\gamma = v(0^+) = \text{initial voltage across capacitance } C \text{ at } t = 0^+ \qquad (12.28b)$$

The current in the inductance L is $i_L(t) = (1/L)\int v(t)\, dt = (1/L)v^{-1}(t)$; its initial current is therefore $\rho = i_L(0^+) = (1/L)v^{-1}(0^+)$, as indicated in (12.28*a*).

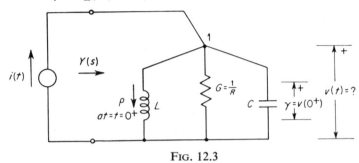

FIG. 12.3

Abbreviating v for $v(t)$, we have

Differential equation:

$$C\frac{dv}{dt} + Gv + \frac{1}{L}\int v\, dt = i(t) \qquad (12.29a)$$

Replacing the indefinite integral, as defined in Eq. (11.55*b*), with a definite integral plus the initial condition $(1/L)v^{-1}(0^+) = \rho$, we find

$$C\frac{dv}{dt} + Gv + \left(\frac{1}{L}\int_0^t v\, dt + \rho\right) = i(t) \qquad (12.29b)$$

which describes the network behavior.   We then apply Laplace transformation to (12.29*b*):

$$\mathscr{L}\left[C\frac{dv}{dt}\right] + \mathscr{L}[Gv] + \mathscr{L}\left[\frac{1}{L}\int_0^t v\, dt + \rho\right] = \mathscr{L}[i(t)]$$

Letting

$$I(s) = \mathscr{L}[i(t)] \qquad V(s) = \mathscr{L}[v(t)] \qquad (12.30)$$

and using the properties in Table 11.3, we now have

$$C[sV(s) - v(0^+)] + GV(s) + \frac{1}{L}\frac{1}{s}V(s) + \frac{\rho}{s} = I(s)$$

Or, with the notation of (12.28),

$$\left(sC + G + \frac{1}{sL}\right)V(s) = I(s) + \left[Cv(0^+) - \frac{1}{s}\rho\right] = I(s) + \left(C\gamma - \frac{\rho}{s}\right) \quad (12.31)$$

The differential equation (12.29*a*) has now been transformed into

Laplace transform of differential equation:

$$Y(s)V(s) = I'(s) \qquad (12.32)$$

where

$$Y(s) = sC + G + \frac{1}{sL} \qquad (12.32a)$$

is the driving-point admittance function of the network in Fig. 12.3a, and

$$I'(s) = I(s) + \left(C\gamma - \frac{\rho}{s}\right) \tag{12.32b}$$

is the equivalent excitation function consisting in:
   1. The part contributed by the applied excitation $i(t)$:

$$I(s) = \mathcal{L}[i(t)] \tag{12.33a}$$

   2. The part contributed by the initial voltage $v(0^+) = \gamma$ across the capacitance, i.e.,

$$\mp C\gamma \tag{12.33b}$$

where $+C\gamma$ is used if both γ and $v(t)$ have the *same* reference terminal for positive polarity as in Fig. 12.3 and (12.32b), and $-C\gamma$ is used otherwise.
   3. The part contributed by the initial current ρ in the inductance L, that is,

$$\mp \frac{\rho}{s} \tag{12.33c}$$

where $-\rho/s$ is used if the initial current ρ flows *away* from the node, as in Fig. 12.3 and (12.32b), and ρ/s is used if ρ flows into the node.
   We now have

Response function: $$V(s) = \frac{I'(s)}{Y(s)} \tag{12.34a}$$

$$V(s) = \frac{I(s) + (C\gamma - \rho/s)}{Y(s)} \tag{12.34b}$$

With $V(s)$ computed in (12.34a), we may find

Response: $$v(t) = \mathcal{L}^{-1}[V(s)] \tag{12.34c}$$

by either following a standard procedure as discussed in Art. 13.2A or using a comprehensive table of Laplace transforms.
   Suggested procedure in finding the response of a one-node network.   Changing the notation in (12.26), we have a procedure for finding the response of the one-node network depicted in Fig. 12.3 without having to write the differential equation:
   Step 1.   Use (12.33) to find

Equivalent excitation function:

$$I'(s) = I(s) + \left(C\gamma - \frac{\rho}{s}\right) \tag{12.35a}$$

where $I(s) = \mathcal{L}[i(t)]$, obtained with aid of Table 11.2 or (11.30b)
       $\gamma = $ initial voltage across C
       $\rho = $ initial current in L
   Step 2.   Find

Admittance function:

$$Y(s) = sC + G + \frac{1}{sL} \tag{12.35b}$$

   Step 3.   Find

Response function:

$$V(s) = \frac{I'(s)}{Y(s)} \tag{12.35c}$$

Step 4.   Find

Response:

$$v(t) = \mathcal{L}^{-1}[V(s)] \tag{12.35d}$$

following a standard procedure as discussed in Art. 13.2A or using a comprehensive table of Laplace transforms.

Illustration.   For $C = 1$, $G = 3$, $L = \frac{1}{2}$, an excitation

$$i(t) = 1e^{-3t}$$

and initial conditions

$$\gamma = 1 \qquad \rho = 2 \tag{12.36}$$

in Fig. 12.3, find the response $v(t)$. We shall follow the suggested procedure (12.35) to bypass the setup of a differential equation. We take the following steps:

Step 1.   According to (12.35a),

$$I'(s) = \mathcal{L}[i(t)] + \left(C\gamma - \frac{\rho}{s}\right)$$

$$= \frac{1}{s + 3} + 1 - \frac{2}{s} = \frac{s^2 + 2s - 6}{(s + 3)s} \tag{12.37a}$$

Step 2.   The admittance function is

$$Y(s) = sC + G + \frac{1}{sL} = s + 3 + \frac{2}{s} = \frac{(s + 1)(s + 2)}{s} \tag{12.37b}$$

Step 3.   The response function is now

$$V(s) = \frac{I'(s)}{Y(s)} = \frac{s^2 + 2s - 6}{(s + 1)(s + 2)(s + 3)} \tag{12.37c}$$

Step 4.   Following a standard procedure as discussed in Art. 13.2A, we find the response:

$$v(t) = \mathcal{L}^{-1}[V(s)] = -\tfrac{7}{2}e^{-t} + 6e^{-2t} - \tfrac{3}{2}e^{-3t} \tag{12.37d}$$

For the time being, we may consider that the response in (12.37d) is obtained in this manner: (1) Eq. (12.37c) may be represented in a partial-fraction form, $I(s) = -\frac{7}{2}/(s + 1) + 6/(s + 2) + (-\frac{3}{2})/(s + 3)$, having three terms, and (2) these terms convert to their corresponding terms in (12.37d) according to item 6 in Table 11.2.

12.2. Finding the response of a multiple-loop or multiple-node network

A.   *Description of Problem*

Network behavior described by a system of n differential equations.   We are interested in finding the response of an n-loop network, e.g., the response $i_1(t)$ or $i_2(t)$ of the two-loop network in Fig. 12.4a, as well as the response of an n-node network, e.g., the response $v_1(t)$ or $v_2(t)$ of the two-node network in Fig. 12.4b.

We shall find that these two types of problems are actually the same problem with different interpretations of the notation. Both deal with a network whose behavior may be described by a system of n differential equations of the type

$$\theta_{11}x_1(t) + \theta_{12}x_2(t) + \cdots + \theta_{1n}x_n(t) = y_1(t)$$

$$\theta_{21}x_1(t) + \theta_{22}x_2(t) + \cdots + \theta_{2n}x_n(t) = y_2(t)$$

$$\cdot \quad \cdot \quad \cdot \quad \cdot \quad \cdot \quad \cdot \quad \cdot \quad \cdot \quad \cdot \quad \cdot \quad \cdot \quad \cdot \tag{12.38}$$

$$\theta_{n1}x_1(t) + \theta_{n2}x_2(t) + \cdots + \theta_{nn}x_n(t) = y_n(t)$$

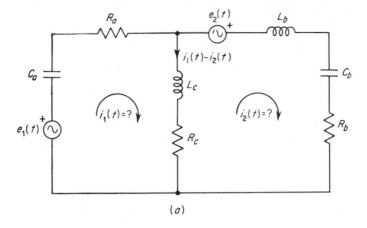

(a)

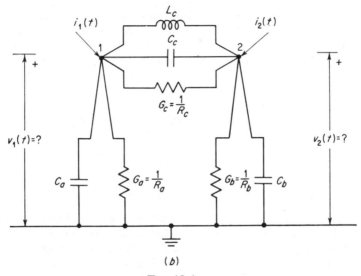

(b)

FIG. 12.4

where
$$\theta_{jk} = a_{jk}\frac{d}{dt} + b_{jk} + c_{jk}\int[\quad]\,dt \qquad (12.38a)$$

$$\theta_{jk} = a_{jk}s + b_{jk} + \frac{c_{jk}}{s}\dagger \qquad (12.38b)$$

† See the notation defined in (3.4). For a network originally at rest (i.e., having zero-value initial conditions) whose behavior is described by (1) $\sum\limits_{k=1}^{n}\theta_{jk}x_k = y_j$ (for $j = 1, \ldots, n$) in (12.38) and (2) its Laplace transform $\sum\limits_{k=1}^{n}\Theta_{jk}(s)X_k(s) = Y_j(s)$ (for $j = 1, \ldots, n$), where $X_k(s) = \mathcal{L}[x_k(t)]$ and $Y_j(s) = \mathcal{L}[y_j(t)]$, we shall find that $\theta_{jk} = a_{jk}s + b_{jk} + c_{jk}/s$ *as an operator* in (12.38b) *and* $\Theta_{jk}(s) = a_{jk}s + b_{jk} + c_{jk}/s$ *as a Laplace-transform function (i.e., an impedance or admittance) have the same form.* For example, the two-loop network in Fig. 12.4a is described by (12.42) and its Laplace transform (12.47) or (12.50); note that (1) $\theta_{11} = L_{11}s + R_{11} + 1/sC_{11}$ in (12.42a) with the notation in (3.4) and (2) $Z_{11}(s)$ in (12.50a′) have the same form.

is an operator; for example,

$$\theta_{jk} x_k(t) = a_{jk} \frac{d}{dt} x_k(t) + b_{jk} x_k(t) + c_{jk} \int x_k(t)\, dt \qquad (12.38c)$$

Interpretation for an n-loop Network. Let us interpret (12.38) for

$$x_k(t) = i_k(t) = \text{current response in loop } k \\ y_j(t) = e_j(t) = \text{voltage excitation in loop } j \qquad (12.39)$$

and

$$\theta_{jk} = \pm \left\{ L_{jk} \frac{d}{dt} + R_{jk} + \frac{1}{C_{jk}} \int [\ \ ]\, dt \right\} \qquad j \neq k \qquad (12.39a)$$

$$\theta_{jj} = L_{jj} \frac{d}{dt} + R_{jj} + \frac{1}{C_{jj}} \int [\ \ ]\, dt \qquad (12.39b)$$

where† L_{jk}, R_{jk}, and $D_{jk} = 1/C_{jk}$ are the total series inductance, resistance, and elastance in the circuit branch common to loops j and k; L_{jj}, R_{jj}, and $D_{jj} = 1/C_{jj}$ are the total series inductance, resistance, and elastance in loop j. Use the positive sign in (12.39a) if the loop currents in loops j and k are in the same direction in their common circuit branch (which consists of L_{jk}, R_{jk}, and C_{jk}); use the *negative* sign if in *opposite* directions. Equations° (12.38) therefore describe an *n-loop network;* its solution represents the response of an *n*-loop network.

Interpretation for an n-node Network. Let us interpret (12.38) for

$$x_k(t) = v_k(t) = \text{voltage response at node } k \\ y_j(t) = i_j(t) = \text{current excitation at node } j \qquad (12.40)$$

and

$$\theta_{jk} = - \left\{ C_{jk} \frac{d}{dt} + G_{jk} + \frac{1}{L_{jk}} \int [\ \ ]\, dt \right\} \qquad j \neq k \qquad (12.40a)$$

$$\theta_{jj} = C_{jj} \frac{d}{dt} + G_{jj} + \frac{1}{L_{jj}} \int [\ \ ]\, dt \qquad (12.40b)$$

where‡ C_{jk}, G_{jk}, and $\Gamma_{jk} = 1/L_{jk}$ are the total parallel capacitance, conductance, and reciprocal inductance in the circuit branch between node j and k; C_{jj}, G_{jj}, and $\Gamma_{jj} = 1/L_{jj}$ are the total parallel capacitance, conductance, and reciprocal inductance of the circuit elements having a common terminal at node j. Equation (12.38) then describes an *n-node network*. The solution of (12.38), therefore, represents the response of an *n*-node network.

Illustration 1. We may describe the behavior of the two-loop network in Fig. 12.4a [abbreviating $i_1(t)$ and $i_2(t)$ to i_1 and i_2] with

$$\left[L_c \frac{di_1}{dt} + (R_a + R_c)i_1 + \frac{1}{C_a} \int i_1\, dt \right] - \left(L_c \frac{di_2}{dt} + R_c i_2 + 0 \int i_2\, dt \right) = e_1(t)$$

$$-\left(L_c \frac{di_1}{dt} + R_c i_1 + 0 \int i_1\, dt \right) + \left[(L_b + L_c) \frac{di_2}{dt} + (R_b + R_c)i_2 + \frac{1}{C_b} \int i_2\, dt \right] = e_2(t)$$

$$(12.41)$$

---

† If this common circuit branch has two inductances $L_a = 1$ and $L_b = 2$ in series, then $L_{jk} = 1 + 2 = 3$. If this common circuit branch has two elastances $D_a = 2$ (i.e., a capacitance $C_a = 1/D_a = \frac{1}{2}$ farad) and $D_b = 3$ in series, then $D_{jk} = 2 + 3 = 5$ or $C_{jk} = 1/D_{jk} = \frac{1}{5}$ farad.

‡ If this circuit branch has two capacitances $C_a = 1$ and $C_b = 2$ in parallel, then $C_{jk} = 1 + 2 = 3$. If this circuit has two parallel inductances, say L_a and L_b, with reciprocal inductances $\Gamma_a = 2$ (that is, $L_a = 1/\Gamma_a = \frac{1}{2}$ henry) and $\Gamma_b = 3$ (that is, $L_b = 1/\Gamma_b = \frac{1}{3}$ henry), then $\Gamma_{jk} = 2 + 3 = 5$ or $L_{jk} = 1/\Gamma_{jk} = \frac{1}{5}$ henry.

or, in the form of (12.38) with the notation of (12.39),

$$\theta_{11}i_1(t) + \theta_{12}i_2(t) = e_1(t)$$
$$\theta_{21}i_1(t) + \theta_{22}i_2(t) = e_2(t) \tag{12.42}$$

where
$$\theta_{11} = L_{11}\frac{d}{dt} + R_{11} + \frac{1}{C_{11}}\int [\ \ ]\,dt \tag{12.42a}$$

$$\theta_{12} = \theta_{21} = -\left\{ L_{12}\frac{d}{dt} + R_{12} + \frac{1}{C_{12}}\int [\ \ ]\,dt \right\} \tag{12.42b}$$

$$\theta_{22} = L_{22}\frac{d}{dt} + R_{22} + \frac{1}{C_{22}}\int [\ \ ]\,dt \tag{12.42c}$$

and
$$L_{11} = L_c \qquad R_{11} = R_a + R_c \qquad \frac{1}{C_{11}} = \frac{1}{C_a} \tag{12.42a'}$$

$$L_{12} = L_{21} = L_c \qquad R_{12} = R_{21} = R_c \qquad \frac{1}{C_{12}} = \frac{1}{C_{21}} = 0 \tag{12.42b'}$$

$$L_{22} = L_b + L_c \qquad R_{22} = R_b + R_c \qquad \frac{1}{C_{22}} = \frac{1}{C_b} \tag{12.42c'}$$

It is now easy to see that Eqs. (12.38), which have the simple forms in (12.42) for this particular illustration, may be conveniently used to describe the behavior of a multiple-loop network.

Illustration 2. We may describe the behavior of the two-node network in Fig. 12.4b [abbreviating $v_1(t)$ and $v_2(t)$ to v_1 and v_2] with†

$$\left[(C_a + C_c)\frac{dv_1}{dt} + (G_a + G_c)v_1 + \frac{1}{L_c}\int v_1\,dt \right] - \left(C_c\frac{dv_2}{dt} + G_c v_2 + \frac{1}{L_c}\int v_2\,dt \right) = i_1(t)$$

$$-\left(C_c\frac{dv_1}{dt} + G_c v_1 + \frac{1}{L_c}\int v_1\,dt \right) + \left[(C_b + C_c)\frac{dv_2}{dt} + (G_b + C_c)v_2 + \frac{1}{L_c}\int v_2\,dt \right] = i_2(t) \tag{12.43}$$

or, in the form of (12.38) with the notation of (12.40),

$$\theta_{11}v_1(t) + \theta_{12}v_2(t) = i_1(t)$$
$$\theta_{21}v_1(t) + \theta_{22}v_2(t) = i_2(t) \tag{12.44}$$

where
$$\theta_{11} = C_{11}\frac{d}{dt} + G_{11} + \frac{1}{L_{11}}\int [\ \ ]\,dt \tag{12.44a}$$

$$\theta_{12} = \theta_{21} = -\left\{ C_{12}\frac{d}{dt} + G_{12} + \frac{1}{L_{12}}\int [\ \ ]\,dt \right\} \tag{12.44b}$$

$$\theta_{22} = C_{22}\frac{d}{dt} + G_{22} + \frac{1}{L_{22}}\int [\ \ ]\,dt \tag{12.44c}$$

and
$$C_{11} = C_a + C_c \qquad G_{11} = G_a + G_c \qquad \frac{1}{L_{11}} = \frac{1}{L_c} \tag{12.44a'}$$

$$C_{12} = C_{21} = C_c \qquad G_{12} = G_{21} = G_c \qquad \frac{1}{L_{12}} = \frac{1}{L_{21}} = \frac{1}{L_c} \tag{12.44b'}$$

$$C_{22} = C_b + C_c \qquad G_{22} = G_b + G_c \qquad \frac{1}{L_{22}} = \frac{1}{L_c} \tag{12.44c'}$$

† It is perhaps easier to see that the differential equation associated with node 1 is

$$C_a\frac{dv_1}{dt} + G_a v_1 + C_c\frac{d(v_1 - v_2)}{dt} + G_c(v_1 - v_2) + \frac{1}{L_c}\int (v_1 - v_2)\,dt = i_1(t)$$

which can easily be reduced to the first of Eqs. (12.43). Similar treatment for node 2 will lead to the second equation.

It is now easy to see that Eqs. (12.38), which have the simple form (12.44) for this particular illustration, may be conveniently used to describe the behavior of a multiple-node network.

Method of approach.   From the above discussion and illustrations, we see that our problem is actually to solve a system of differential equations in the form of (12.38).

We shall solve (12.38) using Laplace transformation.   We shall discover that the Laplace-transformation methods will "transform" a problem requiring the solution of a system of differential equations into a simpler equivalent problem requiring the solution of a system of algebraic equations.

Remarks.   Since the problem of finding the response of an *n*-loop network is not any different from the problem of finding the response of an *n*-node network, except for notation, we shall place more *emphasis* on the treatment of an *n*-loop network, with the understanding that all the techniques discussed are also applicable to an *n*-node network.

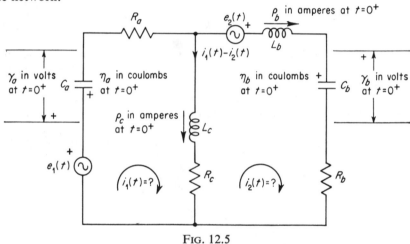

FIG. 12.5

The problem of finding the response of an *n*-node network will be briefly discussed in Art. 12.2G.

B. Illustration with a Two-loop Network

System of two differential equations describing network behavior.   We shall investigate the network in Fig. 12.4a, taking the initial conditions into consideration. For this purpose, we reproduce this network in Fig. 12.5 with conditions at $t = 0^+$ indicated.

Describing the network behavior, we have

Differential equation:
$$\text{Eqs. (12.41) or (12.42)} \tag{12.45}$$

Laplace transformation as applied to a system of two differential equations.   For the network in Fig. 12.5, we have the following initial conditions:

$$
\begin{aligned}
i_1(0^+) - i_2(0^+) &= \rho_c = \text{initial current in } L_c \\
i_2(0^+) &= \rho_b = \text{initial current in } L_b \\
i_i^{-1}(0^+) &= \eta_a = \text{initial charge on } C_a \\
i_2^{-1}(0^+) &= \eta_b = \text{initial charge on } C_b
\end{aligned}
\tag{12.46}
$$

We apply Laplace transformation to (12.45), finding

$$\mathscr{L}[\theta_{11}i_1(t)] + \mathscr{L}[\theta_{12}i_2(t)] = \mathscr{L}[e_1(t)]$$
$$\mathscr{L}[\theta_{21}i_1(t)] + \mathscr{L}[\theta_{22}i_2(t)] = \mathscr{L}[e_2(t)]$$

(12.47)

Letting

$$E_1(s) = \mathscr{L}[e_1(t)] \qquad E_2(s) = \mathscr{L}[e_2(t)]$$
$$I_1(s) = \mathscr{L}[i_1(t)] \qquad I_2(s) = \mathscr{L}[i_2(t)]$$

(12.48)

and using the properties in Table 11.3 and the notation in Eqs. (12.42a) through (12.42c'), we find

$$\mathscr{L}[\theta_{11}i_1(t)] = \mathscr{L}\left[L_{11}\frac{di_1}{dt} + R_{11}i_1 + \frac{1}{C_{11}}\int i_1\, dt \right]$$

$$= L_{11}[sI_1(s) - i_1(0^+)] + R_{11}I_1(s) + \frac{1}{C_{11}}\left[\frac{1}{s}I_1(s) + \frac{1}{s}i_1^{-1}(0^+) \right]$$

$$= \left(sL_{11} + R_{11} + \frac{1}{sC_{11}} \right)I_1(s) - L_c i_1(0^+) + \frac{1}{sC_a}i_1^{-1}(0^+)$$

and similar expressions for $\mathscr{L}[\theta_{12}i_2(t)]$, $\mathscr{L}[\theta_{21}i_1(t)]$, and $\mathscr{L}[\theta_{22}i_2(t)]$. Equations (12.47) now become

$$\left(sL_{11} + R_{11} + \frac{1}{sC_{11}} \right)I_1(s) + \left[-\left(sL_{12} + R_{12} + \frac{1}{sC_{12}} \right) \right]I_2(s)$$

$$= E_1(s) + L_c[i_1(0^+) - i_2(0^+)] - \frac{i_1^{-1}(0^+)}{sC_a}$$

$$-\left(sL_{21} + R_{21} + \frac{1}{sC_{21}} \right)I_1(s) + \left(sL_{22} + R_{22} + \frac{1}{sC_{22}} \right)I_2(s)$$

$$= E_2(s) - L_c[i_1(0^+) - i_2(0^+)] + L_b i_2(0^+) - \frac{i_2^{-1}(0^+)}{sC_b}$$

(12.49)

With the notation in (12.46), Eqs. (12.49) become

Laplace transforms of differential equations:

$$Z_{11}(s)I_1(s) + Z_{12}I_2(s) = E_1(s) + L_c\rho_c - \frac{\eta_a}{sC_a}$$

$$Z_{21}(s)I_1(s) + Z_{22}I_2(s) = E_2(s) + L_b\rho_b - L_c\rho_c - \frac{\eta_b}{sC_b}$$

(12.50)

where†

$$Z_{jj}(s) = \text{self-impedance of loop } j$$
$$= \text{sum of impedances in series in loop } j$$

(12.50a)

for example,

$$Z_{11}(s) = sL_{11} + R_{11} + \frac{1}{sC_{11}}$$

$$= sL_c + (R_a + R_c) + \frac{1}{sC_a}$$

(12.50a')

$$Z_{22}(s) = sL_{22} + R_{22} + \frac{1}{sC_{22}}$$

$$= s(L_b + L_c) + (R_b + R_c) + \frac{1}{sC_a}$$

(12.50a'')

† The *self-impedance* and *mutual impedance* are defined here for the study of the transient and steady-state responses of a multiple-loop network. They were defined earlier in Eqs. (2.17) for the study of the steady-state sinusoidal response of a multiple-loop network and illustrated in (2.30c). Compare them and note that they are of the *same* form.

for loops 1 and 2 in Fig. 12.5; and

$Z_{jk}(s)$ = mutual impedance between loop j and loop k

$\qquad$ = $\pm$sum of impedances in series in branch common to two loops$\quad$(12.50b)

A plus sign is used in (12.50b) if $i_j(t)$ and $i_k(t)$ are in the same direction through the common branch; a *negative* sign is used if they are in *opposite* directions. For example,

$$Z_{12}(s) = Z_{21}(s) = -\left(sL_{12} + R_{12} + \frac{1}{sC_{12}}\right)$$

$$= -\left(sL_c + R_c + \frac{1}{s}0\right)$$

$$= -(sL_c + R_c) \qquad (12.50b')$$

has a negative sign as $i_1(t)$ and $i_2(t)$ are in opposite directions in the common circuit branch in Fig. 12.5.

Solving (12.50), we have

Response functions:

$$I_1(s) = \frac{\begin{vmatrix} E_1'(s) & Z_{12}(s) \\ E_2'(s) & Z_{22}(s) \end{vmatrix}}{\Delta} \qquad (12.51a)$$

$$I_2(s) = \frac{\begin{vmatrix} Z_{11}(s) & E_1'(s) \\ Z_{21}(s) & E_2'(s) \end{vmatrix}}{\Delta} \qquad (12.51b)$$

where $\qquad\qquad \Delta = \begin{vmatrix} Z_{11}(s) & Z_{12}(s) \\ Z_{21}(s) & Z_{22}(s) \end{vmatrix} \qquad (12.51c)$

and $\qquad\qquad E_1'(s) = E_1(s) + L_c\rho_c - \dfrac{\eta_a}{sC_a} \qquad (12.52a)$

$$E_2'(s) = E_2(s) + L_b\rho_b - L_c\rho_c + \frac{\eta_b}{sC_b} \qquad (12.52b)$$

may be regarded as "equivalent excitation functions," which are the applied excitations $E_1(s) = \mathscr{L}[e_1(t)]$ and $E_2(s) = \mathscr{L}[e_2(t)]$ modified by the initial-condition effects. For zero-value initial conditions $\rho_b = \rho_c = \eta_a = \eta_b = 0$, we have $E_1'(s) = E_1(s)$ and $E_2'(s) = E_2(s)$.

With $I_1(s)$ and $I_2(s)$ computed in (12.51), we may find

Responses:

$$i_1(t) = \mathscr{L}^{-1}[I_1(s)] \qquad (12.53a)$$
$$i_2(t) = \mathscr{L}^{-1}[I_2(s)] \qquad (12.53b)$$

by either following a standard procedure as discussed in Art. 13.2A or using a comprehensive table of Laplace transforms.

Concept of equivalent excitations. We have remarked about (12.52) as the "equivalent excitation functions" of the network depicted in Fig. 12.5.

Let us now consider an arbitrary loop in a more complicated network (Fig. 12.6).

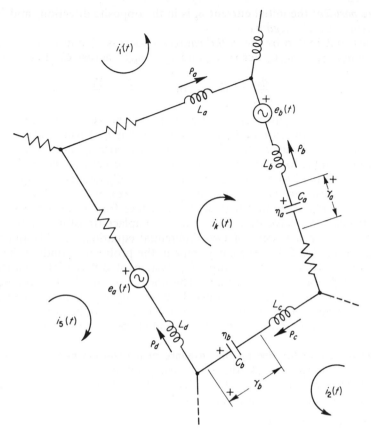

Initial conditions (at $t=0^+$):

P_a, P_b, P_c, P_d — all in amperes
η_a, η_b — all in coulombs
γ_a, γ_b — all in volts

FIG. 12.6

With reference to (12.25), we find an equivalent excitation function for this loop as

Equivalent excitation function:

$$E_k'(s) = E_k(s) + (L_a\rho_a - L_b\rho_b + L_c\rho_c + L_d\rho_d) + \left(-\frac{\eta_a}{sC_a} + \frac{\eta_b}{sC_b}\right) \quad (12.54a)$$

$$E_k'(s) = E_k(s) + (L_a\rho_a - L_b\rho_b + L_c\rho_c + L_d\rho_d) + \left(-\frac{\gamma_a}{s} + \frac{\gamma_b}{s}\right) \quad (12.54b)$$

This consists in:

1. The part contributed by the equivalent *excitation* $e_k(t) = e_a(t) - e_b(t)$ in this loop:

$$E_k(s) = \mathcal{L}[e_k(t)] \quad (12.55a)$$

2. The part contributed by the *initial currents* ρ_a in L_a, ρ_b in L_b, ρ_c in L_c, and ρ_d in L_d (Fig. 12.6):

$$L_a\rho_a - L_b\rho_b + L_c\rho_c + L_d\rho_d \quad (12.55b)$$

with positive and negative terms. The initial currents ρ_a, ρ_c, and ρ_d are in the *same* direction as the loop current $i_k(t)$, and their corresponding terms $L_a\rho_a$, $L_c\rho_c$, and $L_d\rho_d$ are *positive*; the initial current ρ_b is in the opposite direction, and its corresponding term $-L_b\rho_c$ is *negative*.

3. The part contributed by the *initial charges* η_a across C_a and η_b across C_b, or by the *initial voltages* $\gamma_a = \eta_a/C_a$ across C_a and $\gamma_b = \eta_b/C_b$ across C_b (Fig. 12.6):

$$-\frac{\eta_a}{sC_a} + \frac{\eta_b}{sC_b} \qquad \text{or} \qquad -\frac{\gamma_a}{s} + \frac{\gamma_b}{s} \qquad (12.55c)$$

also with positive and negative terms.   For an initial charge, η_a has a *proper* polarity with respect to the loop current $i_k(t)$ in the sense that $i_k(t)$ will tend to charge the capacitance C_a to a value higher than η_a, and its corresponding term $-\eta_a/sC_a$ carries a *negative* sign; for an initial charge, η_b *does not* have proper polarity, in the sense that $i_k(t)$ will tend to discharge the capacitance C_b, and its corresponding term $+\eta_b/sC_b$ carries a *positive* sign.   According to (12.18c), $\gamma_a = \eta_a/C_a$ across C_a, and $\gamma_b = \eta_b/C_b$ across C_b.   The first half of (12.55c), therefore, implies the second half.

Some remarks.   We have discussed above a Laplace-transformation method in which we first set up a system of two differential equations (12.45) and then find Laplace transforms (12.50) as the early steps in the problem of finding the response of a two-loop network.   Is the setup of a system of differential equations really necessary for a problem of this type?   The answer is "no."   The concept of the "equivalent excitation function," discussed above, suggests that we need only find the equivalent excitations $E_1'(s)$ and $E_2'(s)$ as in (12.52), and the impedance functions $Z_{11}(s)$, $Z_{12}(s)$, $Z_{21}(s)$, and $Z_{22}(s)$ as in (12.50a) and (12.50b), before we proceed to find the response.

Suggested procedure for finding the response of a two-loop network.   To find the response of a two-loop network, the above discussion has made it possible for us to proceed as follows without writing the differential equations:

Step 1.   For the given excitations $e_1(t)$ and $e_2(t)$, find

Equivalent excitation functions:

$$\begin{aligned} E_1'(s) = E_1(s) &+ L_j\rho_j \text{ terms for } \textit{initial currents} \text{ in loop 1} \\ &+ (-\eta_j/sC_j) \text{ terms for } \textit{initial charges} \text{ in loop 1} \\ E_2'(s) = E_2(s) &+ L_i\rho_i \text{ terms for } \textit{initial currents} \text{ in loop 2} \\ &+ (-\eta_j/sC_j) \text{ terms for } \textit{initial charges} \text{ in loop 2} \end{aligned} \qquad (12.56a)$$

where $E_1(s) = \mathscr{L}[e_1(t)]$ and $E_2(s) = \mathscr{L}[e_2(t)]$ are obtained with the aid of Table 11.2 or (11.30b); the $L_j\rho_j$ terms are obtained for the initial currents in *all* inductances for each loop, according to the discussion associated with (12.55b); the $-\eta_j/sC_j$ terms are obtained for the initial charges (or voltages $\gamma_j = \eta_j/C_j$) across *all* capacitances for each loop, according to the discussion associated with (12.55c).

For example, the equivalent excitation functions for the network in Fig. 12.5 are indicated in Eqs. (12.52).

Step 2.   Find

Impedance functions:

$$\begin{aligned} &Z_{11}(s) \text{ and } Z_{22}(s) \text{ as defined in } (12.50a) \\ &Z_{12}(s) \text{ and } Z_{21}(s) \text{ as defined in } (12.50b) \end{aligned} \qquad (12.56b)$$

We now have

System equations:

$$\begin{aligned} Z_{11}(s)I_1(s) + Z_{12}(s)I_2(s) &= E_1'(s) \\ Z_{21}(s)I_1(s) + Z_{22}(s)I_2(s) &= E_2'(s) \end{aligned} \qquad (12.56c)$$

which are the Laplace transforms of a system of two differential equations and are themselves a system of two algebraic equations.

Step 3.   Solving (12.56c), we have

Response functions:

$$I_1(s) = \frac{\begin{vmatrix} E_1'(s) & Z_{12}(s) \\ E_2'(s) & Z_{22}(s) \end{vmatrix}}{\Delta}$$

(12.56d)

$$I_2(s) = \frac{\begin{vmatrix} Z_{11}(s) & E_1'(s) \\ Z_{21}(s) & E_2'(s) \end{vmatrix}}{\Delta}$$

where

$$\Delta = \begin{vmatrix} Z_{11}(s) & Z_{12}(s) \\ Z_{21}(s) & Z_{22}(s) \end{vmatrix}$$

(12.56d')

Step 4.   Find

Responses:

$$i_1(t) = \mathscr{L}^{-1}[I_1(s)]$$
$$i_2(t) = \mathscr{L}^{-1}[I_2(s)]$$

(12.56e)

following a standard procedure as discussed in Art. 13.2A or using a comprehensive table of Laplace transforms.

Illustration.   We shall now follow procedure (12.56) for the network in Fig. 12.5. In order to make this illustration rather general, we shall not use numerical values for the circuit symbols.

Step 1.   For the given excitations $e_1(t)$ and $e_2(t)$, we first find $E_1(s) = \mathscr{L}[e_1(t)]$ and $E_2(s) = \mathscr{L}[e_2(t)]$ with the aid of Table 11.2.   According to (12.52), we have

Equivalent excitations:

$$E_1'(s) = E_1(s) + L_c\rho_c - \frac{\eta_a}{sC_a}$$
$$E_2'(s) = E_2(s) + L_b\rho_b - L_c\rho_c + \frac{\eta_b}{sC_a}$$

(12.57a)

Step 2.   From (12.50a'), (12.50a"), and (12.50b'),

Impedance functions:

$$Z_{11}(s) = sL_c + (R_a + R_c) + \frac{1}{sC_a}$$

$$Z_{22}(s) = s(L_b + L_c) + (R_b + R_c) + \frac{1}{sC_a}$$

(12.57b)

$$Z_{12}(s) = Z_{21}(s) = -(sL_c + R_c)$$

We already have (12.56c) as our system functions.

Step 3.   Substituting (12.57a) and (12.57b) into (12.56d), we have

Response functions:

$$I_1(s) = \frac{E_1(s)P_1(s) + E_2(s)Q_1(s) + R_1(s)}{b_4s^4 + b_3s^3 + b_2s^2 + b_1s + b_0}$$

(12.57c)

$$I_2(s) = \frac{E_1(s)P_2(s) + E_2(s)Q_2(s) + R_2(s)}{b_4s^4 + b_3s^3 + b_2s^2 + b_1s + b_0}$$

where
$$b_4 = C_a^2 L_b L_c$$
$$b_3 = C_a^2[L_b(R_a + R_c) + L_c(R_a + R_b)]$$
$$b_2 = C_a[(L_b + 2L_c) + C_a(R_a R_b + R_b R_c + R_c R_a)] \qquad (12.57c')$$
$$b_1 = C_a(R_a + R_b + 2R_c)$$
$$b_0 = 1$$

and
$$P_1(s) = C_a^2(L_b + L_c)s^3 + C_a^2(R_b + R_c)s^2 + C_a s$$
$$Q_1(s) = C_a^2 L_c s^3 + C_a^2 R_c s^2$$
$$R_1(s) = C_a^2 L_b L_c(\rho_b + \rho_c)s^3 \qquad (12.57c'')$$
$$\qquad + [C_a^2(L_b R_c \rho_b + L_c R_b \rho_c) + C_a(L_c \eta_b - L_b \eta_a - L_c \eta_a)]s^2$$
$$\qquad + [C_a L_c \rho_c + C_a(R_c \eta_b - R_b \eta_a - R_c \eta_a)]s - \eta_a$$

$$P_2(s) = C_a^2 L_c s^3 + C_a^2 R_c s^2$$
$$Q_2(s) = C_a^2 L_c s^3 + C_a^2(R_a + R_c)s^2 + C_a s$$
$$R_2(s) = C_a^2 L_b L_c \rho_b s^3 \qquad (12.57c''')$$
$$\qquad + [C_a^2(L_b R_a \rho_b + L_b R_c \rho_b - L_c R_a \rho_c) + C_a L_c(\eta_b - \eta_a)]s^2$$
$$\qquad + [C_a(L_b \rho_b - L_c \rho_c) + C_a(R_a \eta_b + R_c \eta_b - R_c \eta_a)]s + \eta_b$$

Step 4.   To find

Responses:
$$i_1(t) = \mathscr{L}^{-1}[I_1(s)]$$
$$i_2(t) = \mathscr{L}^{-1}[I_2(s)] \qquad (12.57d)$$

with $I_1(s)$ and $I_2(s)$ as computed in (12.57c), we need only follow a standard procedure as discussed in Art. 13.2A.

This illustration has several interpretations:

1. For $e_1(t) = e_2(t) = 0$, which implies $E_1(s) = E_2(s) = 0$ in (12.57c), $i_1(t)$ and $i_2(t)$ as represented in (12.57d) are the transient responses of the network in Fig. 12.5 subject to initial conditions only.

2. For $\rho_b = \rho_c = \eta_a = \eta_b = 0$, which implies $R_1(s) = R_2(s) = 0$ in (12.57c), $i_1(t)$ and $i_2(t)$ as represented in (12.57d) are the transient and steady-state responses subject to the excitations $e_1(t)$ and $e_2(t)$ with zero-value initial conditions.

3. Otherwise, $i_1(t)$ and $i_2(t)$ as represented in (12.57d) are the transient and steady-state responses subject to the nonzero excitations $e_1(t)$ and $e_2(t)$ and the nonzero initial values ρ_b, ρ_c, η_a, and η_b.

C. Finding the Steady-state and Transient Responses of a Multiple-loop Network Having Zero-value Initial Conditions or Finding the Steady-state Sinusoidal Response of a Multiple-loop Network

Remarks about the problem of finding the steady-state sinusoidal response.   The remarks at the beginning of Art. 12.1B also apply here: To find the steady-state sinusoidal response subject to sinusoidal excitation, we may (1) assume zero-value initial conditions and find the complete steady-state and transient responses and (2) obtain the steady-state sinusoidal responses by ignoring the transient components in the complete responses.

In this section, we shall discuss the method for finding the steady-state and transient responses of a multiple-loop network having zero-value initial conditions.   It is now obvious that this method can also be used to find the steady-state sinusoidal response of a multiple-loop network.

A system of n differential equations.   We have already remarked that the behavior of an n-loop network may be described by a system of n differential equations:

System of differential equations:

$$\text{Eqs. (12.38) with interpretations in Eqs. (12.39)} \qquad (12.58)$$

System equations.   In our illustration with a two-loop network, we apply Laplace transformation to the system of two differential equations (12.42) describing the network and find a system of two algebraic equations in (12.50).   For an n-loop network with zero-value initial conditions, we have a system of n algebraic equations similar to (12.50):

System equations:

$$Z_{11}(s)I_1(s) + Z_{12}(s)I_2(s) + \cdots + Z_{1n}(s)I_n(s) = E_1(s)$$
$$Z_{21}(s)I_1(s) + Z_{22}(s)I_1(s) + \cdots + Z_{2n}(s)I_n(s) = E_2(s)$$
$$\cdot\ \cdot\ \cdot\ \cdot\ \cdot\ \cdot\ \cdot\ \cdot\ \cdot\ \cdot\ \cdot\ \cdot\ \cdot\ \cdot\ \cdot \qquad (12.59)$$
$$Z_{n1}(s)I_1(s) + Z_{n2}(s)I_n(s) + \cdots + Z_{nn}(s)I_n(s) = E_n(s)$$

where $Z_{ii}(s)$ = self-impedance of loop i

$$= \text{sum of impedances in series in loop } i \qquad (12.59a)$$

$\quad Z_{ij}(s)$ = mutual impedance between loop i and loop j

$$= \pm \text{sum of impedances in series in branch common to both loops}$$

$$(12.59b)$$

A plus sign is used in (12.59b) if the currents in loops i and j are in the same direction through their common branch; and a minus sign is used if they are in opposite directions.

Comparison with loop method of analysis for the study of the steady-state sinusoidal response of a multiple-loop network.   We have studied in Art. 2.4A the loop method of analysis for the steady-state sinusoidal response of an n-loop network.   We obtained a system of n algebraic (loop) equations in (2.20).

We are now studying the transient and steady-state responses of an n-loop network having zero-value initial conditions.   We have a system of n algebraic equations in (12.59).

Comparing (2.20) with (12.59), we note the following:

1. The self-impedance $Z_{ii}(s)$ and the mutual impedance $Z_{ij}(s)$ in (12.59) are the same in form as the self-impedance Z_{ii} and the mutual impedance Z_{ij} in (2.20).

2. E_i and I_k in (2.20) are the "complex amplitudes" in the exponential representation of the excitation $e_i(t)$ and response $i_k(t)$, as illustrated in (2.7).   The complex amplitudes can be conveniently used in expressions such as (2.7) to represent steady-state sinusoidal excitations and responses.

3. $E_i(s)$ and $I_k(s)$ in (12.59) are the "Laplace transforms" of the excitation $e_i(t)$ and response $i_k(t)$, as illustrated in (12.48).   The inverse Laplace transforms of $E_i(s)$ and $I_k(s)$ are the excitation $e_i(t) = \mathscr{L}^{-1}[E_i(s)]$ and response $i_k(t) = \mathscr{L}^{-1}[I_k(s)]$.   This response $i_k(t)$ usually has both steady-state and transient components.

Suggested procedure for finding the steady-state and transient responses of a multiple-loop network having zero-value initial conditions.   We shall now extend the suggested procedure (12.56) for a two-loop network to one for an n-loop network having zero-value initial conditions.   This procedure, which like (12.56) will bypass the setup of a system of differential equations, comprises the following steps:

Step 1.   For the given excitations $e_i(t)$, $i = 1, 2, \ldots, n$, find

Excitation functions: $\qquad E_i(s) = \mathscr{L}[e_i(t)] \qquad i = 1, 2, \ldots, n \qquad (12.60a)$

with the aid of Table 11.2 or (11.30b).

Step 2.   Find

Impedance functions:

$$Z_{ii}(s) \text{ and } Z_{ij}(s) \text{ as defined in (12.59a) and (12.59b)} \qquad (12.60b)$$

We now have

System equations:

$$\text{Equations in (12.59)} \qquad (12.60c)$$

Step 3.   Solve (12.60c) to find†

Response functions:

$$I_k(s) = \frac{\Delta_{1k}}{\Delta} E_1(s) + \frac{\Delta_{2k}}{\Delta} E_2(s) + \cdots + \frac{\Delta_{nk}}{\Delta} E_n(s) \qquad k = 1, 2, \ldots, n \quad (12.60d)$$

where Δ is the system determinant and has the form

System determinant:

$$\Delta = \begin{vmatrix} Z_{11}(s) & Z_{12}(s) \cdots Z_{1n}(s) \\ Z_{21}(s) & Z_{22}(s) \cdots Z_{2n}(s) \\ \cdot \cdot \cdot \cdot \cdot \cdot \cdot \cdot \cdot \cdot \cdot \cdot \\ Z_{n1}(s) & Z_{n2}(s) \cdots Z_{nn}(s) \end{vmatrix} \qquad (12.60d')$$

and the determinants $\Delta_{1k}, \Delta_{2k}, \ldots, \Delta_{nk}$ are the cofactors of Δ.

Step 4.   Find

Responses:

$$i_k(t) = \mathscr{L}^{-1}[I_k(s)] \qquad k = 1, 2, \ldots, n \qquad (12.60e)$$

following a standard procedure as discussed in Art. 13.2A or using a comprehensive table of Laplace transforms.

Illustration.   Let us find the responses $i_1(t)$ and $i_2(t)$ for the network in Fig. 2.5a with $e_1(t) = u(t)$, $e_2(t) = 0$, $e_3(t) = e^{-t}$, $R_1 = R_2 = R_3 = R_4 = 1$, $L = 1$, and $C = \frac{1}{2}$. We shall use the procedure described above.

We may compare this illustration, step by step, with the numerical illustration associated with Eqs. (2.30) that used sinusoidal excitations and had steady-state sinusoidal responses.

Step 1.   Find

$$E_1(s) = \mathscr{L}[1] = \frac{1}{s}$$

$$E_2(s) = \mathscr{L}[0] = 0 \qquad (12.61a)$$

$$E_3(s) = \mathscr{L}[e^{-t}] = \frac{1}{s+1}$$

with the aid of Table 11.2.

Step 2.   The impedance functions, as defined in (12.59a) and (12.59b), are represented by

$$\text{Eqs. (2.30c)} \qquad (12.61b)$$

† Compare with (2.23) and (2.24).   Also see the definition of cofactor in the paragraph following (2.22).

We now have system equations similar to (12.59) with $n = 3$:

$$Z_{11}(s)I_1(s) + Z_{12}(s)I_2(s) + Z_{13}(s)I_3(s) = \frac{1}{s}$$

$$Z_{21}(s)I_1(s) + Z_{22}(s)I_2(s) + Z_{23}(s)I_3(s) = 0 \qquad (12.61c)$$

$$Z_{31}(s)I_1(s) + Z_{32}(s)I_2(s) + Z_{33}(s)I_3(s) = \frac{1}{s+1}$$

Step 3. With Δ and its cofactors evaluated in (2.30d) and subsequent equations, find, with the aid of (12.60d),

$$I_1(s) = \frac{\Delta_{11}}{\Delta}\frac{1}{s} + \frac{\Delta_{21}}{\Delta}0 + \frac{\Delta_{31}}{\Delta}\frac{1}{s+1} = \frac{4s^2 + 5s + 4}{s(5s + 4)(s + 1)} \qquad (12.61d')$$

and $\qquad I_2(s) = \frac{\Delta_{12}}{\Delta}\frac{1}{s} + \frac{\Delta_{22}}{\Delta}0 + \frac{\Delta_{32}}{\Delta}\frac{1}{s+1} = \frac{-2s}{(5s + 4)(s + 1)} \qquad (12.61d'')$

Step 4. Find the responses†

$$i_1(t) = \mathscr{L}^{-1}[I_1(s)] = 1 - \tfrac{16}{5}e^{-\frac{4}{5}t} + 3e^{-t} \qquad (12.61e')$$

and $\qquad i_2(t) = \mathscr{L}^{-1}[I_2(s)] = \tfrac{8}{5}e^{-\frac{4}{5}t} - 2e^{-t} \qquad (12.61e'')$

following a standard procedure as discussed in Art. 13.2A.

For the time being, we may consider that the responses in (12.61e') and (12.61e'') are obtained as follows: (1) Eq. (12.61d') may be represented in a partial-fraction form, $I_1(s) = 1/s + [-16/(5s + 4)] + 3/(s + 1)$, having three terms; these terms convert to their corresponding terms in (12.61e') with the aid of Table 11.2, and (2) similarly (12.61d'') may be represented as $I_2(s) = 8/(5s + 4) + [-2/(s + 1)]$, which then converts to (12.61e'').

D. *Finding the Steady-state and Transient Responses of a Multiple-loop Network Having Nonzero Initial Conditions*

Suggested procedure. This procedure for an n-loop network is an extension of the suggested procedure (12.56) for a two-loop network; it is identical to (12.60), except that the equivalent excitation functions, instead of the applied excitation functions, are used. This procedure, which like (12.56) will bypass the setup of a system of differential equations, comprises the following steps:

Step 1. For the given excitations $e_i(t)$, $i = 1, 2, \ldots, n$, find

Equivalent excitation functions:

$$E_i'(s) = E_i(s) + L_j\rho_j \text{ terms for } initial\ currents \text{ in loop } i$$
$$+ (-\eta_j/sC_j) \text{ terms for } initial\ charges \text{ in loop } i \qquad i = 1, 2, \ldots, n \quad (12.62a)$$

where $E_i(s) = \mathscr{L}[e_i(t)]$ are obtained with the aid of Table 11.2 or (11.30b); the $L_j\rho_j$ terms are obtained for the initial currents in *all* inductances for loop i according to the discussion associated with (12.55b); the $-\eta_j/sC_j$ terms are obtained for the initial charges (or voltages $\gamma_j = \eta_j/C_j$) across *all* capacitances for loop i according to the discussion associated with (12.55c).

For example, the equivalent excitation functions for the network in Fig. 12.5 are indicated in Eqs. (12.52).

Step 2. Find

Impedance functions:

$$Z_{ii}(s) \text{ and } Z_{ij}(s) \text{ as defined in (12.59a) and (12.59b)} \qquad (12.62b)$$

We now have

$$Z_{11}(s)I_1(s) + Z_{12}(s)I_2(s) + \cdots + Z_{1n}(s)I_n(s) = E_1'(s)$$
$$Z_{21}(s)I_1(s) + Z_{22}(s)I_2(s) + \cdots + Z_{2n}(s)I_n(s) = E_2'(s)$$
$$\cdot\ \cdot\ \cdot\ \cdot\ \cdot\ \cdot\ \cdot\ \cdot\ \cdot\ \cdot\ \cdot\ \cdot\ \cdot\ \cdot\ \cdot\ \cdot \qquad (12.62c)$$
$$Z_{n1}(s)I_1(s) + Z_{n2}(s)I_2(s) + \cdots + Z_{nn}(s)I_n(s) = E_n'(s)$$

Step 3.   Solve (12.62c) to find

Response functions:

$$I_k(s) = \frac{\Delta_{1k}}{\Delta} E_1'(s) + \frac{\Delta_{2k}}{\Delta} E_2'(s) + \cdots + \frac{\Delta_{nk}}{\Delta} E_n'(s) \qquad k = 1, 2, \ldots, n \quad (12.62d)$$

where Δ is the system determinant in (12.60d'), and the determinants $\Delta_{1k}, \Delta_{2k}, \ldots, \Delta_{nk}$ are the cofactors of Δ.
   Step 4.   Find

Responses:

$$i_k(t) = \mathscr{L}^{-1}[I_k(s)] \qquad k = 1, 2, \ldots, n \qquad (12.62e)$$

following a standard procedure as discussed in Art. 13.2A or using a comprehensive table of Laplace transforms.

   Illustration.   Let us use the network in Fig. 12.7 with $e_1(t) = u(t)$, $e_2(t) = 0$, $e_3(t) = e^{-t}$, $R_1 = R_2 = R_3 = R_4 = 1$, $L = 1$, $C = \frac{1}{2}$, and initial conditions $\rho = 1$ amp and $\eta = \frac{1}{2}$ coul.   We are to find the responses $i_1(t)$ and $i_2(t)$.

   This is the same illustration as in Eqs. (12.61) except that we now have initial conditions.   We shall follow procedure (12.62).

   We shall first find the equivalent excitation functions according to (12.62a):

$$E_1'(s) = \mathscr{L}[u(t)] + L\rho = \frac{1}{s} + 1 = \frac{s+1}{s}$$

$$E_2'(s) = \mathscr{L}[0] - \frac{\eta}{sC} = 0 - \frac{1}{s} = -\frac{1}{s} \qquad (12.63a)$$

$$E_3'(s) = \mathscr{L}[e^{-t}] - L\rho = \frac{1}{s+1} - 1 = \frac{-s}{s+1}$$

We then follow the other steps in (12.62) in a manner similar to that for the illustration of (12.61), obtaining

$$I_1(s) = \frac{8s^2 + 9s + 4}{s(5s + 4)(s + 1)} \qquad (12.63b')$$

and

$$I_2(s) = \frac{-4s - 2}{(5s + 4)(s + 1)} \qquad (12.63b'')$$

which implies

$$i_1(t) = 1 - \tfrac{12}{5}e^{-\frac{4}{5}t} + 3e^{-t} \quad (12.63c')$$

and

$$i_2(t) = \tfrac{8}{5}e^{-\frac{4}{5}t} - 2e^{-t} \qquad (12.63c'')$$

E. *Finding the Steady-state and Transient Responses of a Four-terminal Network*

   We shall now restrict ourselves to four-terminal networks, which usually have a single source.

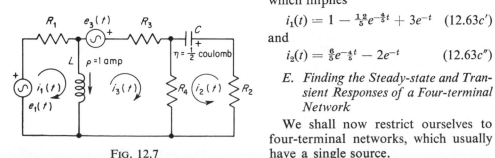

FIG. 12.7

Remarks about multiple-loop network and four-terminal network. Examining the networks in Fig. 12.8, we conclude that four-terminal networks may be considered as a special category of multiple-loop networks.   We shall consistently have loop 1 include the voltage source, and loop 2 the load impedance.

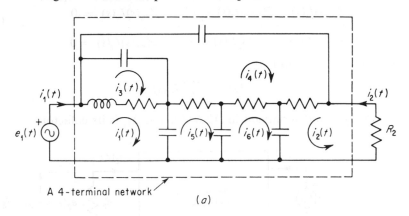

A 4-terminal network

(a)

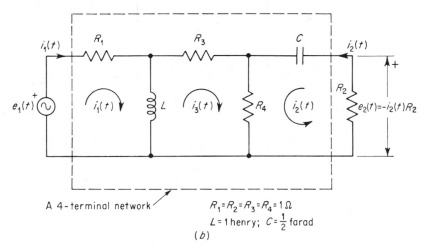

A 4-terminal network

$R_1 = R_2 = R_3 = R_4 = 1\,\Omega$
$L = 1$ henry; $C = \frac{1}{2}$ farad

(b)

FIG. 12.8

Response of a four-terminal network. Suppose the network has initial currents in its inductors, and initial charges across its capacitors; we may find the response $i_2(t)$ by following the procedure discussed in Art. 12.2D.   This type of four-terminal network problem (with initial conditions) is, however, rather uncommon.

For most of the problems of finding four-terminal network responses, zero-value initial conditions are assumed.   In that case, we may proceed as follows:

Step 1.   For the single excitation $e_1(t)$, find

Excitation function:
$$E_1(s) = \mathscr{L}[e_1(t)] \tag{12.64a}$$

with the aid of Table 11.2 or (11.30b).

Step 2.   Find

Impedance functions:

$Z_{ii}(s)$ and $Z_{ij}(s)$ as defined in (12.59a) and (12.59b)   (12.64b)

We now have

System equations:

$$Z_{11}(s)I_1(s) + Z_{12}(s)I_2(s) + \cdots + Z_{1n}(s)I_n(s) = E_1(s)$$
$$Z_{21}(s)I_1(s) + Z_{22}(s)I_2(s) + \cdots + Z_{2n}(s)I_n(s) = 0$$
$$\cdot \ \cdot \ \cdot \ \cdot \ \cdot \ \cdot \ \cdot \ \cdot \ \cdot \ \cdot \ \cdot \ \cdot \ \cdot \ \cdot \ \cdot \ \cdot \ \cdot \ \cdot$$
$$Z_{n1}(s)I_1(s) + Z_{n2}(s)I_2(s) + \cdots + Z_{nn}(s)I_n(s) = 0 \qquad (12.64c)$$

Step 3.   Solve (12.64c) to find

$$I_2(s) = \frac{\Delta_{12}}{\Delta} E_1(s) \qquad (12.64d)$$

where Δ is the system determinant in (12.60d'), and Δ_{12} is its cofactor.

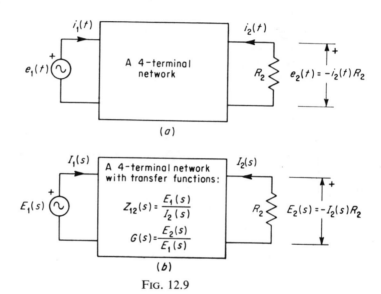

Fig. 12.9

Step 4.   Find

Response:

$$i_2(t) = \mathcal{L}^{-1}[I_2(s)] \qquad (12.64e)$$

following a standard procedure as discussed in Art. 13.2A or using a comprehensive table of Laplace transforms.

We are often interested in the output voltage as response. For example, for the arrangement in Fig. 12.9a, we have

Response:

$$e_2(t) = -i_2(t)R_2 \qquad (12.64e')$$

where $i_2(t)$ is obtained in (12.64e).

Transfer functions. A four-terminal network arrangement with voltages $e_1(t)$, $e_2(t)$ and currents $i_1(t)$, $i_2(t)$ as functions of t is depicted in Fig. 12.9a; in Fig. 12.9b, this same network arrangement is shown with the Laplace transforms of the voltages and currents,

$$E_1(s) = \mathcal{L}[e_1(t)] \qquad I_1(s) = \mathcal{L}[i_1(t)] \qquad (12.65a)$$
$$E_2(s) = \mathcal{L}[e_2(t)] \qquad I_2(s) = \mathcal{L}[i_2(t)] \qquad (12.65b)$$

But how are the quantities in (12.65a) related to those in (12.65b)? We shall now introduce two transfer functions.

We may call $Z_T(s) = E_1(s)/I_2(s)$ a *transfer impedance function*. From (12.64d), we have

$$Z_T(s) = [Z_T(s)]_{12} = \frac{E_1(s)}{I_2(s)} = \frac{\Delta}{\Delta_{12}} \tag{12.66}$$

This is the transfer impedance defined in Chap. 2. Note in Eq. (2.29) that $(Z_T)_{12} = E_1/I_2 = \Delta/\Delta_{12}$. Here, $E_1(s)$ and $I_2(s)$ are the Laplace transforms of $e_1(t)$ and $i_2(t)$, while E_1 and I_2 are the complex amplitudes of the exponential expressions (2.7) for $e_1(t)$ and $i_2(t)$. Δ/Δ_{12} is the same function of s under both definitions.

We may call $G(s) = E_2(s)/E_1(s)$ a *transfer voltage-ratio function*. From (12.64d) and Fig. 12.9, we have

$$G(s) = \frac{E_2(s)}{E_1(s)} = \frac{-I_2(s)R_2}{E_1(s)} = -R_2 \frac{\Delta_{12}}{\Delta} \tag{12.67}$$

This function was defined in Art. 3.5C. Since $G(s)$ is more commonly used than $Z_T(s)$, the term "transfer function" is often used to mean $G(s)$. Actually, both $Z_T(s)$ and $G(s)$ are transfer functions.

Response of a four-terminal network with known transfer function. Suppose the transfer impedance $Z_T(s) = [Z_T(s)]_{12}$ of a four-terminal network is known. We wish to find the response $i_2(t)$ subject to a given excitation $e_1(t)$. We may (1) find the excitation function $E_1(s) = \mathscr{L}[e_1(t)]$ with the aid of Table 11.2, (2) determine the response function $I_2(s) = E_1(s)/Z_T(s)$ with the aid of (12.66), and (3) find the response $i_2(t) = \mathscr{L}^{-1}[I_2(s)]$ following a standard procedure as discussed in Art. 13.2A or from a comprehensive table of Laplace transforms. If the response $e_2(t)$ is also desired, it may be calculated from $e_2(t) = -i_2(t)R_2$, as is evident in Fig. 12.9a.

Now suppose the transfer voltage-ratio function $G(s)$ of a four-terminal network is known, and we wish to find the response $e_2(t)$ subject to a given excitation $e_1(t)$. We may (1) find the excitation function $E_1(s) = \mathscr{L}[e_1(t)]$ with the aid of Table 11.2, (2) determine the response function $E_2(s) = E_1(s)G(s)$ according to (12.67), and (3) find the response $e_2(t) = \mathscr{L}^{-1}[E_2(s)]$ following a standard procedure as discussed in Art. 13.2A or from a comprehensive table of Laplace transforms.

Illustration 1. Let us find the transfer impedance function $Z_T(s)$ and the transfer voltage-ratio function $G(s)$, as defined, respectively, in (12.66) and (12.67), for the network arrangement in Fig. 12.8b.

Comparing Fig. 12.8b with Fig. 2.5a for $e_3(t) = 0$, we note that they are identical. The transfer impedance function for such a network arrangement has already been obtained in Eq. (2.31b). Therefore,

$$Z_T(s) = [Z_T(s)]_{12} = \frac{\Delta}{\Delta_{12}} = -\frac{5s^2 + 9s + 4}{s^2} \tag{12.68a}$$

The transfer voltage-ratio function may now be obtained by substituting Δ/Δ_{12} in (12.68a) and $R_2 = 1$ in (12.67):

$$G(s) = \frac{s^2}{5s^2 + 9s + 4} \tag{12.68b}$$

Illustration 2. The four-terminal network in Fig. 12.8b now has transfer functions as defined in Eqs. (12.68). Suppose a unit-step excitation $e_1(t) = u(t)$ is applied. Let us find the response $e_2(t)$.

We first find, with the aid of Table 11.2, the excitation function

$$E_1(s) = \mathscr{L}[e_1(t)] = \mathscr{L}[u(t)] = \frac{1}{s} \tag{12.69a}$$

Then we find the response function

$$E_2(s) = E_1(s)G(s) = \frac{1}{s} \frac{s^2}{5s^2 + 9s + 4} = \frac{s}{(s+1)(5s+4)} \qquad (12.69b)$$

Following a standard procedure in Art. 13.2A, we find

$$e_2(t) = \mathscr{L}^{-1}[E_2(s)] = -\tfrac{4}{5} e^{-\frac{4}{5}t} + e^{-t} \qquad (12.69c)$$

For the time being, we may consider that the response in (12.69c) is obtained as follows: (1) Eq. (12.69b) may be represented in a partial-fraction form, $E_2(s) = -4/(5s+4) + 1/(s+1)$, having two terms, and (2) these terms, convert to their corresponding terms in (12.69c) with the aid of Table 11.2.

Remarks about finding the response of a four-terminal network with known transmission characteristics. Suppose the transfer voltage-ratio function $G(s)$ of a four-terminal network is not available. However, we know the transmission characteristic

$$G(j\omega) = G_0(\omega)e^{-j\theta(\omega)} \qquad (12.70)$$

of this network. The transmission characteristics $G_0(\omega)$ and $\theta(\omega)$ may have been measured and plotted in graphs. In that case, we may approximate them as functions of ω. For a given excitation $e_1(t)$, we may use Fourier transforms and follow the procedure described in (8.34) to obtain the response $e_2(t)$. A typical illustration of finding the response of an idealized low-pass four-terminal network subject to a unit-step excitation is given in Art. 9.1.

F. Remarks about Finding the Steady-state Sinusoidal Response of a Four-terminal Network

Some remarks. Finding the steady-state response of a four-terminal network subject to the excitation of a single sinusoidal source is an important category of network problems. There are two approaches to this problem:

1. We may follow the procedure discussed in Art. 12.2E, finding the complete steady-state and transient responses and then ignoring the transient component of the complete response to obtain the steady-state sinusoidal response. This Laplace-transformation method is *not* the preferred method for this particular problem, since at least a part of our effort is wasted in the evaluation of the transient component.

2. The method using exponential representations, described in Chap. 2 and to be illustrated in the next paragraph, is a simpler method to use, since we want only the steady-state sinusoidal response and we solve for it alone.

Illustration. We shall use the network in Fig. 12.8b, which is known to have (2.31b) or (12.68),

$$Z_T(s) = [Z_T(s)]_{12} = \frac{5s^2 + 9s + 4}{s^2} \qquad (12.71a)$$

as its transfer impedance.

The given excitation in the exponential representation of Eqs. (2.7)† is

$$e_1(t) = E_1 e^{j\omega t} = 10e^{j\omega t} \qquad (12.71b)$$

We wish to find the response in exponential form,

$$i_2(t) = I_2 e^{j\omega t}$$

at $\omega = 1$ rad/sec.

---

† According to (2.7), the *actual* excitation and response here are $e_1(t) = \text{Im} (10e^{j\omega t}) = 10 \sin \omega t$ and $i_2(t) = \text{Im} [(10/\sqrt{82}) e^{j(\omega t - 96.4°)}] = (10/\sqrt{82}) \sin (\omega t - 96.4°)$ at the frequency $\omega = 1$ rad/sec.

By definition, $Z_T(j\omega) = E_1/I_2$. We therefore have

$$I_2 = \frac{E_1}{Z_{12}(j\omega)}\bigg|_{\omega=1} = -\frac{10(j\omega)^2}{5(j\omega)^2 + 9j\omega + 4}\bigg|_{\omega=1} = \frac{10}{\sqrt{82}}\, e^{-j96.4°}$$

and $$i_2(t) = \frac{10}{\sqrt{82}}\, e^{j(\omega t - 96.4°)} \qquad \omega = 1 \tag{12.71c}$$

G. Remarks about Finding the Steady-state and Transient Responses of a Multiple-node Network

We have remarked in Art. 12.2A that the system of differential equations in (12.38) may describe (1) the behavior of an n-loop network interpreted with the notation in (12.39) or (2) the behavior of an n-node network interpreted with the notation in (12.40). Therefore, the problem of finding the response of an n-loop network is

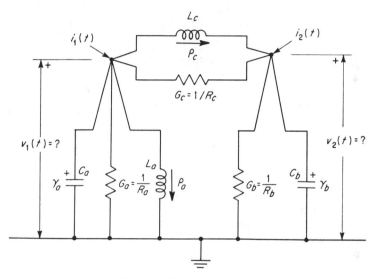

Initial currents ρ_a, ρ_c in amperes
Initial voltages γ_a, γ_b in volts

FIG. 12.10

not any different from the problem of finding the response of an n-node network, except for notation. With a change of notation, the techniques discussed in Art. 12.2B to D are applicable to a multiple-node network. We shall only briefly illustrate the method of approach for a two-node network.

Illustration. We shall use the suggested procedure (12.56) for finding the response of a two-loop network as reference and develop, through analogy and reinterpretation of notation, a procedure for finding the response of the two-node network in Fig. 12.10.

Step 1. For the given excitations $i_1(t)$ and $i_2(t)$, find

Equivalent excitation functions:

$$I_1'(s) = I_1(s) + \left(C_a\gamma_a - \frac{\rho_a}{s} - \frac{\rho_c}{s}\right)$$

$$I_1'(s) = I_2(s) + \left(C_b\gamma_b + \frac{\rho_c}{s}\right) \tag{12.72a}$$

where $I_1(s) = \mathscr{L}[i_1(t)]$ and $I_2(s) = \mathscr{L}[i_2(t)]$ are obtained with the aid of Table 11.2 or (11.30b); the term $C_a\gamma_a - \rho_a/s - \rho_c/s$ arises owing to the initial conditions of the parallel capacitive and inductive circuit elements with common terminal at node 1, according to the discussion associated with Eqs. (12.33); the term $C_b\gamma_b + \rho_c/s$, owing to those at node 2, according to the same discussion.

Step 2. By the definitions†

$$Y_{jj}(s) = \text{self-admittance at node } j$$
$$= \text{sum of admittances in parallel at node } j$$
$$Y_{jk}(s) = \text{mutual admittance between node } j \text{ and node } k$$
$$= \text{sum of admittances in parallel between two nodes} \tag{12.72b}$$

find, for the network in Fig. 12.10,

Admittance functions:

$$Y_{11}(s) = sC_a + (G_a + G_c) + \frac{1}{s}\left(\frac{1}{L_a} + \frac{1}{L_c}\right)$$

$$Y_{22}(s) = sC_b + (G_b + G_c) + \frac{1}{sL_c} \tag{12.72b'}$$

$$Y_{12}(s) = Y_{21}(s) = G_c + \frac{1}{sL_c}$$

We now have

System equations:

$$Y_{11}(s)V_1(s) - Y_{12}(s)V_2(s) = I_1'(s)$$
$$-Y_{21}(s)V_1(s) + Y_{22}(s)V_2(s) = I_2'(s) \tag{12.72c}$$

Note here that only diagonal terms on the left-hand sides of Eqs. (12.72c) are positive; all others are negative.

Step 3. Solve (12.72c) to find

Response functions:

$$V_1(s) = \frac{\begin{vmatrix} I_1'(s) & -Y_{12}(s) \\ I_2'(s) & Y_{22}(s) \end{vmatrix}}{\Delta'}$$

$$V_2(s) = \frac{\begin{vmatrix} Y_{11}(s) & I_1'(s) \\ -Y_{21}(s) & I_2'(s) \end{vmatrix}}{\Delta'} \tag{12.72d}$$

where

$$\Delta' = \begin{vmatrix} Y_{11}(s) & -Y_{12}(s) \\ -Y_{21}(s) & Y_{22}(s) \end{vmatrix} \tag{12.72d'}$$

Step 4. Find

Responses:

$$v_1(t) = \mathscr{L}^{-1}[V_1(s)]$$

$$v_2(t) = \mathscr{L}^{-1}[V_2(s)] \tag{12.72e}$$

† The *self-admittance* and *mutual admittance* are defined here for the study of the transient and steady-state responses of a multiple-node network. They were defined earlier in Eqs. (2.55) for the study of the steady-state sinusoidal response of a multiple-node network and were illustrated in (2.67b). Compare them, and note that they are of the *same* form.

following a standard procedure as discussed in Art. 13.2A or using a comprehensive table of Laplace transforms.

12.3. Use of equivalent excitation functions

We have used the term *excitation function* to describe the Laplace transform of an excitation.   For example, the excitation function of a given excitation $e(t)$ is $E(s) = \mathscr{L}[e(t)]$.

In (12.24) we defined the *equivalent excitation function* of a network loop as

$$E'(s) = E(s) + \text{terms due to initial conditions in loop} \qquad (12.73)$$

where $E(s) = \mathscr{L}[e(t)]$ is due to the applied excitation $e(t)$.   We have found that the use of equivalent excitation functions will enable us to use, with some modifications, the loop and nodal methods of steady-state analysis in Chap. 2 to find the transient and steady-state responses of a network subject to any type of excitation.

We now wish to summarize the use of equivalent excitation functions as discussed in Arts. 12.1 and 12.2 and relate it to the loop and nodal methods of analysis in Chap. 2.

A. Use of Equivalent Excitation Functions in Finding the Transient and Steady-state Responses of an n-loop Network

In Art. 12.2A, we remarked that the system of n differential equations (12.38) will describe the behavior of an n-loop network as well as an n-node network with different interpretations of the notation.   We then introduced Laplace transformation and discussed in (12.62) a suggested procedure which amounts to:

Step 1.   Find

Equivalent excitations:

$$E'_i(s) \qquad i = 1, 2, \ldots, n \qquad (12.74a)$$

for each loop i according to (12.62a).

Step 2.   Follow the procedure in Chap. 2 for the loop method of analysis to set up a system of loop equations similar to (2.20) *except* for notation.   Use $E'_i(s)$ instead of E_i, for $i = 1, 2, \ldots, n$, in (2.20), and consider all Z_{ij} and all I_k in (2.20) as functions of s.   Then solve for loop currents as in (2.24):

Response functions:

$$I_k(s) = \frac{\Delta_{1k}}{\Delta} E'_1(s) + \frac{\Delta_{2k}}{\Delta} E'_2(s) + \cdots + \frac{\Delta_{nk}}{\Delta} E'_n(s) \qquad k = 1, 2, \ldots, n \quad (12.74b)$$

Step 3.   Find

Responses:

$$i_k(t) = \mathscr{L}^{-1}[I_k(s)] \qquad k = 1, 2, \ldots, n \qquad (12.74c)$$

following a standard procedure as discussed in Art. 13.2A or using a comprehensive table of Laplace transforms.

B. Use of Equivalent Excitation Functions in Finding the Transient and Steady-state Responses of an n-node Network

Similarly, we note that the suggested procedure in (12.72) amounts to:

Step 1.   Find

Equivalent excitations:

$$I'_i(s) \qquad i = 1, 2, \ldots, n \qquad (12.75a)$$

for each node i according to (12.72a).

Step 2.   Follow the procedure in Chap. 2 for the nodal method of analysis to set up a system of nodal equations similar to (2.56) *except* for notation.   Use $I_i'(s)$ instead of I_i, for $i = 1, 2, \ldots, n$, in (2.56), and consider all Y_{ij} and all V_k or E_k in (2.56) as functions of s.   Then solve for nodal voltages as in (2.57):

Response functions:

$$V_k(s) = \frac{\Delta_{1k}'}{\Delta'} I_1(s) + \frac{\Delta_{2k}'}{\Delta'} I_2(s) + \cdots + \frac{\Delta_{nk}'}{\Delta'} I_n(s) \qquad k = 1, 2, \ldots, n \quad (12.75b)$$

Step 3.   Find

Responses:

$$v_k(t) = \mathcal{L}^{-1}[V_k(s)] \qquad k = 1, 2, \ldots, n \qquad\qquad (12.75c)$$

following a standard procedure as discussed in Art. 13.2A or using a comprehensive table of Laplace transforms.

12.4. Some excitation functions: the Laplace transforms of excitations

We shall now investigate the Laplace transforms of some selected functions and their relationships to each other.   These functions may be used as network excitations.

A. Some Nonrepeating Functions

We shall find the Laplace transforms of the nonrepeating functions in Fig. 12.11*a* to *c* and compare them with the transforms of the associated repeating functions in Fig. 12.11*a'* to *c'*.   The latter will be discussed in Art. 12.4B.

A single rectangular pulse.   For the waveform in Fig. 12.11*a*, we have

$$e_A(t) = u(t) - u(t - \delta) \qquad\qquad (12.76a)$$

Comparing Fig. 12.11*a* with Fig. 11.2*d* and using item 17 in Table 11.2, we obtain

$$E_A(s) = \mathcal{L}[e_A(t)] = \mathcal{L}[u(t) - u(t - \delta)] = \frac{1}{s}(1 - e^{-\delta s}) \qquad (12.76b)$$

A single unit-impulse function.   For the waveform in Fig. 12.11*b*, we have

$$e_B(t) = \delta(t) \qquad\qquad (12.77a)$$

a unit-impulse function as defined in Fig. 11.2*a*.   Using item 1 in Table 11.2, we obtain

$$E_B(s) = \mathcal{L}[e_B(t)] = \mathcal{L}[\delta(t)] = 1 \qquad\qquad (12.77b)$$

A single sawtooth pulse.   For the waveform in Fig. 12.11*c*, we have†

$$e_c(t) = mt[u(t) - u(t - \delta)] = u(t)mt - u(t - \delta)m(t - \delta) - u(t - \delta)m\delta \quad (12.78a)$$

Using item 4 in Table 11.3 and properties in Table 11.2, we obtain

$$E_C{}^{(s)} = \mathcal{L}[e_c(t)] = \frac{m}{s^2} - \frac{me^{-\delta s}}{s^2} - \frac{m\delta e^{-\delta s}}{s} = \frac{m}{s^2}(1 - e^{-\delta s} - \delta s e^{-\delta s}) \quad (12.78b)$$

† A function $e(t) = mt$ represents a straight line with slope m for $-\infty < t < \infty$.   The term in brackets in (12.78*a*) limits this waveform to the interval $0 \le t \le \delta$; the result is Fig. 12.11*c*.

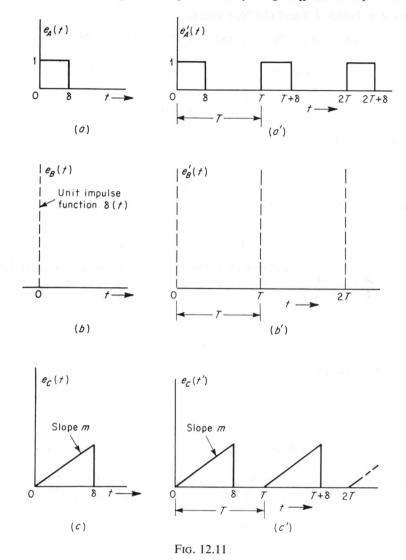

FIG. 12.11

B. Some Repeating Functions

Illustration: a repeating rectangular-pulse function. Let us first try to represent $e'_A(t)$ in Fig. 12.11a'. We note that it is equal to the sum of (1) $e_A(t)$ in Fig. 12.11a, (2) $e_A(t - T)$, which is $e_A(t)$ displaced to the right an interval T, (3) $e_A(t - 2T)$, which is $e_A(t)$ displaced to the right $2T$, (4) $e_A(t - 3T)$, (5) $e_A(t - 4T)$, etc. This means that

$$e'_A(t) = \sum_{k=0}^{\infty} e_A(t - kT) \tag{12.79a}$$

or, more formally as in (11.62),

$$e'_A(t) = \sum_{k=0}^{\infty} u(t - kT)e_A(t - kT) \tag{12.79a'}$$

Property 4 in Table 11.3 and (12.76b) lead to

$$E'_A(s) = \mathcal{L}[e'_A(t)] = E_A(s)(1 + e^{-Ts} + e^{-2Ts} + e^{-3Ts} + \cdots)$$

$$= E_A(s)\,\frac{1}{1 - e^{-Ts}}^{\dagger} \qquad s = \sigma + j\omega,\ \sigma > 0 \qquad (12.79b)$$

$$E'_A(s) = \frac{1 - e^{-\delta s}}{s}\,\frac{1}{1 - e^{-Ts}} \qquad \sigma > 0 \qquad (12.79b')$$

For the special case $T = 2\delta$, we have

$$E'_A(s) = \frac{1 - e^{-\delta s}}{s}\,\frac{1}{1 - e^{-2\delta s}} = \frac{1}{s(1 + e^{-\delta s})} \qquad \sigma > 0 \qquad (12.79c)$$

For the special case $T = 3\delta$, we have

$$E'_A(s) = \frac{1 - e^{-\delta s}}{s}\,\frac{1}{1 - e^{-3\delta s}} = \frac{1}{s(1 + e^{-\delta s} + e^{-2\delta s})} \qquad \sigma > 0 \qquad (12.79d)$$

A relation between the Laplace transforms of repeating and nonrepeating functions.
We have used the specific waveforms in Fig. 12.11a and a' for the above illustration.
It can easily be verified that, if an arbitrary nonrepeating function

$$n(t) \tag{12.80a}$$

has the Laplace transform

$$\mathcal{L}[n(t)] = N(s) \tag{12.80b}$$

then a related repeating function

$$f(t) = \sum_{k=0}^{\infty} n(t - kT) \qquad k = 0, 1, 2, \ldots \tag{12.80c}$$

has the Laplace transform

$$\mathcal{L}[f(t)] = F(s) = N(s)\,\frac{1}{1 - e^{-Ts}} \qquad s = \sigma + j\omega,\ \sigma > 0 \tag{12.80d}$$

A repeating unit-impulse function. Equation (12.77b) and the relation described by Eqs. (12.80) dictate that the Laplace transform of $e'_B(t)$ in Fig. 12.11b' is

$$E'_B(s) = \mathcal{L}[e'_B(t)] = E_b(s)\,\frac{1}{1 - e^{-Ts}} = \frac{1}{1 - e^{-Ts}} \qquad s = \sigma + j\omega,\ \sigma > 0 \quad (12.81)$$

A repeating sawtooth-pulse function. Equation (12.78b) and the relation described by Eqs. (12.80) dictate that the Laplace transform of $e'_c(t)$ in Fig. 12.11c' is

$$E'_c(s) = \mathcal{L}[e'_c(t)] = E_c(s)\,\frac{1}{1 - e^{-Ts}} = \frac{m(1 - e^{-\delta s} - \delta se^{-\delta s})}{s^2(1 - e^{-Ts})} \tag{12.82}$$

For practical circuit applications, we often use the special case $T = \delta$.

C. The Laplace Transform of a One-cycle (Nonrepeating) Sinusoidal Function as Obtained from a (Repeating) Sinusoidal Function

The relation described by (12.80) permits us to find the Laplace transform $F(s)$ of a repeating function $f(t)$ by modifying the Laplace transform $N(s)$ of a *related* nonrepeating function $n(t)$; we have $F(s) = N(s)[1/(1 - e^{-Ts})]$.

---

† For $1/(1 - x) = 1 + x + x^2 + x^3 + \cdots$, we require $|x| < 1$; for this case, $|e^{-Ts}| < 1$ or $\sigma > 0$, since $s = \sigma + j\omega$ and T is a positive quantity.

The converse should also be true. If a nonrepeating function $n(t)$ represents a complete cycle of a repeating function $f(t)$, and if $F(s) = \mathcal{L}[f(t)]$ is known, then

$$N(s) = F(s)(1 - e^{-Ts}) \tag{12.83}$$

is the Laplace transform of the nonrepeating function $n(t)$, where T is the period.

Laplace transform of a one-cycle sin βt function. From item 9 in Table 11.2, a repeating function

$$f(t) = \sin \beta t \qquad 0 \leq t < \infty \tag{12.84a}$$

has the Laplace transform

$$F(s) = \mathcal{L}[f(t)] = \frac{\beta}{s^2 + \beta^2} \tag{12.84b}$$

This repeating function is associated with an angular frequency β in radians per second, a frequency $f = \beta/2\pi$ in cycles per second, and a period $T = 1/f = 2\pi/\beta$ in seconds.

A nonrepeating function, i.e., a one-cycle sin βt function

$$n(t) = \begin{cases} \sin \beta t & 0 \leq t < T \\ 0 & T < t \end{cases} \tag{12.84c}$$

represents a complete cycle of $f(t)$ in (12.84a) and, therefore, according to (12.83), has the Laplace transform

$$N(s) = F(s)(1 - e^{-Ts}) = \frac{\beta}{s^2 + \beta^2}(1 - e^{-Ts}) = \frac{\beta}{s^2 + \beta^2}(1 - e^{-2\pi s/\beta}) \tag{12.84d}$$

Laplace transform of a one-cycle cos βt function. Similarly, from item 11 in Table 11.2, a repeating function

$$f(t) = \cos \beta t \qquad 0 \leq t < \infty \tag{12.85a}$$

has the Laplace transform

$$F(s) = \mathcal{L}[f(t)] = \frac{s}{s^2 + \beta^2} \tag{12.85b}$$

A nonrepeating function, i.e., a one-cycle cos βt function

$$n(t) = \begin{cases} \cos \beta t & 0 \leq t < T \\ 0 & T < t \end{cases} \tag{12.85c}$$

represents a complete cycle of $f(t)$ in (12.85a) and, therefore, according to (12.83), has the Laplace transform

$$N(s) = F(s)(1 - e^{-Ts}) = \frac{s}{s^2 + \beta^2}(1 - e^{-Ts}) = \frac{s}{s^2 + \beta^2}(1 - e^{-2\pi s/\beta}) \tag{12.85d}$$

PROBLEMS

Postpone the starred portions of the problems which require the evaluation of the inverse Laplace transform until Chap. 13 is read.

12.1. Given: $L = 1$ henry, $R = 4$ ohms, $C = \frac{1}{3}$ farad, $\rho = 2$ amp, and $\gamma = 3$ volts in the one-loop circuit in Fig. 12.2b.

Find the response function $I(s) = \mathcal{L}[i(t)]$ and *the response $i(t)$ for (a) $e(t) = \sin 2t$; (b) $e(t) = u(t)$; (c) $e(t) = te^{-t}$.

12.2. Given: $L_b = 1$ henry, $L_c = 2$ henrys, $R_a = R_c = 1$ ohm, $R_b = 3$ ohms, $C_a = \frac{1}{2}$ farad, $C_b = 1$ farad, $\rho_b = 1$ amp, $\rho_c = 2$ amp, $\gamma_a = 2$ volts, and $\gamma_b = 1$ volt in the two-loop circuit in Fig. 12.5.

Find the response functions $I_1(s) = \mathscr{L}[i_1(t)]$, $I_2(s) = \mathscr{L}[i_2(t)]$ and *the responses $i_1(t)$, $i_2(t)$ for

(a) $e_1(t) = u(t)$, $e_2(t) = u(t-1)$
(b) $e_1(t) = \cos 3t$, $e_2(t) = 0$

12.3. Given: $e_1(t) = 1 \cos \omega t$ volt, $e_2(t) = \sqrt{2} \sin(\omega t + 45°)$, and $e_3(t) = 2 \cos(\omega t + 30°)$ for $\omega = 1$ rad/sec in the circuit in Fig. P 2.1. Zero-value initial conditions are assumed.
(a) Obtain the response functions $I_1(s) = \mathscr{L}[i_1(t)]$ and $I_2(s) = \mathscr{L}[i_2(t)]$.
*(b) Obtain the complete responses $i_1(t)$ and $i_2(t)$.
*(c) Obtain the steady-state responses $i_1(t)$ and $i_2(t)$ by ignoring the transient components of the complete responses obtained in (b); compare them with the results of Prob. 2.1. REFERENCE: See the remarks about the problem of finding the steady-state sinusoidal response in the paragraphs preceding Eqs. (12.2).

12.4. Given: The circuit shown in Fig. P 12.4 which has already reached the steady state with the switch K in position 1 at $t = 0^-$ (that is, $t = 0 - \varepsilon$ for very small $\varepsilon > 0$).
The switch K is changed to position 2 at the instant $t = 0$. Determine the initial conditions γ_a in volts and ρ_b and ρ_c in amperes at $t = 0^+$.

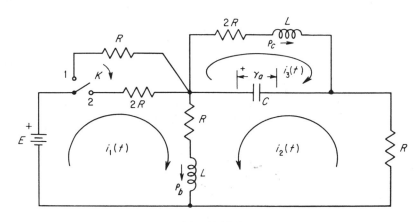

FIG. P 12.4

12.5. Given: The circuit in Fig. P 12.4 with the switch K in position 2 and the initial conditions obtained in Prob. 12.4.
(a) Write a system of differential equations describing the behavior of this circuit for $t \geq 0$.
(b) Apply the Laplace transformation to the differential equations, obtaining the system equations in the form of (12.62c).
(c) Letting $E = 1$ volt, $L = 1$ henry, $C = \frac{1}{2}$ farad, and $R = 1$ ohm, solve the system equations for the response functions $I_1(s)$ and $I_2(s)$.
*(d) Obtain the responses $i_1(t) = \mathscr{L}^{-1}[I_1(s)]$ and $i_2(t) = \mathscr{L}^{-1}[I_2(s)]$.
12.6. Given: The circuit in Fig. P 12.4 with the switch K in position 2 and the initial conditions obtained in Prob. 12.4.
Follow the procedure outlined in Eqs. (12.62) to obtain (a) the equivalent excitation functions, (b) the system functions, (c) the response functions $I_1(s)$ and $I_2(s)$, and *(d) the responses $i_1(t) = \mathscr{L}^{-1}[I_1(s)]$ and $i_2(t) = \mathscr{L}^{-1}[I_2(s)]$.
Note that the results in (b) to (d) in Probs. 12.6 and 12.5 are the same.
12.7. Given: The circuit in Fig. P 12.7 at rest, with the switch K open at $t = 0^-$.
(a) A unit-step excitation is applied at $t = 0$. Find the response functions $I_1(s)$, $I_2(s)$, and $I_3(s)$ and *the responses $i_1(t)$, $i_2(t)$, and $i_3(t)$.
*(b) The switch K is suddenly closed at $t = 1$ (or $t' = t - 1 = 0$). Find the currents ρ_a and ρ_b in the inductances and the voltages γ_c and γ_d across the capacitances at the instant $t = 1^+$ (or $t' = t - 1 = 0^+$).

(c) Using ρ_a, ρ_b, γ_c, and γ_d as the initial conditions of the circuit for $t' \geq 0$ (or $t \geq 1$), find the response functions $I_1(s') = \mathscr{L}[i_1(t')]$, $I_2(s') = \mathscr{L}[i_2(t')]$, and $I_3(s') = \mathscr{L}[i_3(t')]$ and the responses $i_1(t') = i_1(t-1)$, $i_2(t') = i_2(t-1)$, and $i_3(t') = i_3(t-1)$ for $t' \geq 0$ (or $t \geq 1$).
(d) Make a sketch of the response i_2 consisting in the portion $i_2(t)$ for $0 \leq t < 1$ obtained in *(a)* and the portion $i_2(t-1)$ for $t \geq 1$ obtained in *(c)*.

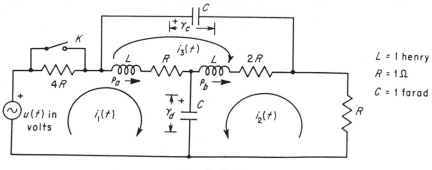

FIG. P 12.7

12.8. Given: The circuit arrangement in Fig. P 12.8.
(*a*) Find the driving-point impedance $Z_D(s) = (Z_D)_{11} = E_1(s)/I_1(s)$ and the transfer impedance $Z_T(s) = (Z_T)_{12} = E_1(s)/I_2(s)$. REMARKS: Since the circuit arrangements in Figs. P 12.8 and P 2.3 are identical except for notation, $Z_D(s)$ and $Z_T(s)$ obtained here should be the *same* as those obtained in Prob. 2.3. For reference, see the statement in the paragraph following Eq. (12.66).
(*b*) Using $Z_D(s)$ obtained in (*a*), find the response function $I_1(s)$ and ★the response $i_1(t) = \mathscr{L}^{-1}[I_1(s)]$ for a unit-step excitation $e_1(t) = u(t)$.
(*c*) Using $Z_T(s)$ obtained in (*a*), find the response function $I_2(s)$ and ★the response $i_2(t) = \mathscr{L}^{-1}[I_2(s)]$ for a unit-step excitation $e_1(t) = u(t)$.

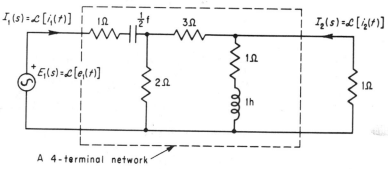

A 4-terminal network

FIG. P 12.8

12.9. Given: The four-terminal network arrangement in Fig. 12.8*b* with the reassigned circuit values $R_1 = R_2 = 1$ ohm, $R_3 = R_4 = 2$ ohms, $L = \frac{1}{2}$ henry, and $C = \frac{1}{3}$ farad.
(*a*) Obtain the transfer functions $Y_T(s) = I_2(s)/E_1(s)$ and $G(s) = E_2(s)/E_1(s)$.
(*b*) For a sinusoidal excitation $e(t) = \sin \omega t$ with $\omega = 1$ rad/sec, obtain the response functions $I_2(s)$ and $E_2(s)$ and ★the responses $i_2(t)$ and $e_2(t)$.
(*c*) For the excitation $e(t) = u(t) - u(t-1)$, that is, a rectangular pulse of unit magnitude beginning at $t = 0$ and ending at $t = 1$, obtain the response function $I_2(s)$ and ★the response $i_2(t)$.
12.10. Given: $L_a = 1$ henry, $L_c = 2$, $R_a = R_b = 1$ ohm, $R_c = 2$, $C_a = 1$ farad, $C_b = 2$, $\rho_a = 1$ amp, $\rho_c = 2$, $\gamma_a = 1$ volt, and $\gamma_b = 2$ in the two-node network in Fig. 12.10.
(*a*) For current excitations $i_1(t) = u(t)$ and $i_2(t) = u(t-1)$, find the response functions $V_1(s) = \mathscr{L}[v_1(t)]$, $V_2(s) = \mathscr{L}[v_2(t)]$ and ★the responses $v_1(t)$, $v_2(t)$.

(b) For the current excitations $i_1(t) = t$ and $i_2(t) = 0$, find the response functions $V_1(s) = \mathcal{L}[v_1(t)]$, $V_2(s) = \mathcal{L}[v_2(t)]$ and *the responses $v_1(t)$, $v_2(t)$.

12.11. Given: The four-terminal network arrangement in Fig. P 12.11, i.e., a modified version of the two-node network in Fig. 12.10 with (1) zero-value initial conditions, that is, $\rho_a = \rho_c = 0$ and $\gamma_a = \gamma_b = 0$ and (2) current source $i_2(t) = 0$. The current $i_2(t)$ in Fig. P 12.11 is not the current source $i_2(t)$ in Fig. 12.10, but is the current $i_2(t) = -v_2(t)/R_b = -e_2(t)/R_b$ flowing through the resistance R_b.

(a) Using the nodal method of analysis, obtain the transfer functions $Z_T(s) = E_2(s)/I_1(s)$ and $A(s) = I_2(s)/I_1(s)$.

(b) For the current excitation $i_1(t) = u(t)$, find the voltage response function $E_2(s) = \mathcal{L}[e_2(t)]$ and *the response $e_2(t)$.

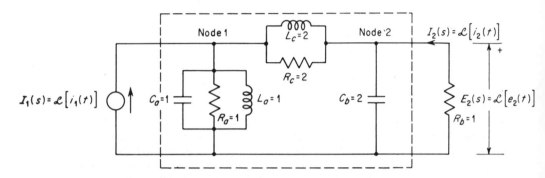

FIG. P 12.11

12.12. Given: The four-terminal network arrangement in Fig. P 12.12 with known transfer functions $G(s)$ and $Y_T(s)$.

Find the response function $E_2(s)$ and *the response $e_2(t)$ for the following excitations:
(a) $e_1(t) = e^{-2t} \sin t$
(b) $e_1(t) = e^{-t} + te^{-2t}$

(c) $e_1(t) = 1 - \cos t - \dfrac{t}{2} \sin t$

Find the response function $I_2(s)$ and *the response $i_2(t)$ for the following excitations:
(d) $e_1(t) = \sin 2\pi t \, [u(t) - u(t-1)]$
(e) $e_1(t) = \delta(t-1)$
(f) $e_1(t) = e^{-2t} - e^{-3t}$

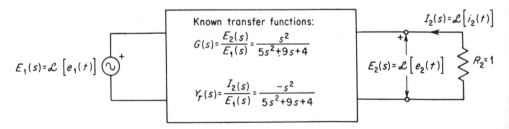

FIG. P 12.12

12.13. Given: The four-terminal network arrangement in Fig. P 12.13 with known transfer functions $A(s)$ and $Z_T(s)$.

Find the response function $I_2(s)$ and *the response $i_2(t)$ for the following excitations:
(a) $i_1(t) = u(t-1) - u(t-3)$
(b) $i_1(t) = \cosh t$
(c) $i_1(t) = e^{-t} - e^{-3t}$

Find the response function $E_2(s)$ and *the response $e_2(t)$ for the following excitations:
(d) $i_1(t) = \sin t + 2 \cos 3t$
(e) $i_1(t) = 2t[u(t - 1) - u(t - 2)]$
(f) $i_1(t) = \frac{1}{8}e^{-t} - \frac{1}{4}e^{-3t} + \frac{1}{8}e^{-5t}$

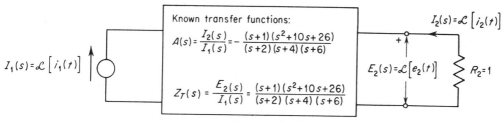

Known transfer functions:

$$A(s) = \frac{I_2(s)}{I_1(s)} = -\frac{(s+1)(s^2+10s+26)}{(s+2)(s+4)(s+6)}$$

$$Z_T(s) = \frac{E_2(s)}{I_1(s)} = \frac{(s+1)(s^2+10s+26)}{(s+2)(s+4)(s+6)}$$

$I_1(s) = \mathcal{L}[i_1(t)]$ $I_2(s) = \mathcal{L}[i_2(t)]$ $E_2(s) = \mathcal{L}[e_2(t)]$ $R_2 = 1$

Fɪɢ. P 12.13

12.14. Given: The four-terminal network arrangement in Fig. P 12.14 with known insertion voltage-ratio function e^θ. e^θ is defined in (3.43), where E_1, E_2, and E_{20} can be either (1) the complex amplitudes in exponential expressions similar to (3.7) or (2) Laplace-transform functions similar to those indicated in Fig. P 12.14.

Find the response function $E_2(s)$ and *the response $e_2(t)$ for a unit-step excitation $e_1(t) = u(t)$. SUGGESTION: Read the paragraph following Eq. (3.43) for a hint.

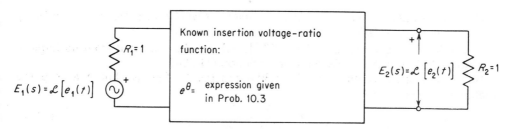

Known insertion voltage-ratio function:

$e^\theta = $ expression given in Prob. 10.3

$E_1(s) = \mathcal{L}[e_1(t)]$ $R_1 = 1$ $E_2(s) = \mathcal{L}[e_2(t)]$ $R_2 = 1$

Fɪɢ. P 12.14

12.15. Given: The four-terminal network arrangement in Fig. P 12.12 with known transfer voltage-ratio function $G(s)$.
Find the response function $E_2(s)$ and *the response $e_2(t)$ for the excitations sketched in
(a) Fig. 12.11a   (b) Fig. 12.11a'   (c) Fig. 12.11b
(d) Fig. 12.11b'   (e) Fig. 12.11c   (f) Fig. 12.11c'
with $\delta = \frac{1}{2}$ sec, $T = 1$ sec, and $m = 1$.
*12.16. Repeat Prob. 12.15 for the four-terminal network arrangement in Fig. P 12.13 with known transfer impedance $Z_T(s)$.

13 Network response and the poles of its Laplace transform

13.1. Network response as an inverse Laplace transform

In Art. 11.4 we demonstrated how to find the Laplace transform $F(s) = \mathscr{L}[f(t)]$ of a given function $f(t)$.

We now wish to investigate how to find the inverse Laplace transform $f(t) = \mathscr{L}^{-1}[F(s)]$ of a known $F(s)$. This technique has very extensive applications. For example, in all the procedures for finding the responses of networks in Chap. 12, we must find the network responses from their Laplace transforms, i.e., their response functions.

A. Remarks about Finding the Inverse Laplace Transform by Direct Evaluation of the Integral Relation

In (11.31) we suggested that $f(t) = \mathscr{L}^{-1}[F(s)]$ may be evaluated from its Laplace transform $F(s)$ with the Laplace integral relation (11.30a).

But is the direct evaluation of (11.30a) practical? Let us choose a response function from (12.61d'):

$$I_1(s) = \frac{4s^2 + 5s + 4}{s(5s + 4)(s + 1)} \tag{13.1a}$$

According to (11.30a), the response is

$$i_1(t) = \mathscr{L}^{-1}[I_1(s)] = \frac{1}{2\pi j} \int_{\sigma - j\infty}^{\sigma + j\infty} \frac{4s^2 + 5s + 4}{s(5s + 4)(s + 1)} e^{st} \, ds \qquad t \geq 0, \sigma > \sigma_a \tag{13.1b}$$

It is easy to recognize that the evaluation of (13.1b) is not too easy a task. We shall forsake this approach and look for other methods.

B. Remark about the Inversion Theorem of Laplace Transforms

We shall only describe the inversion theorem here and give a reference[†] for its proof. The inversion theorem is responsible for the simple and effective methods of finding inverse Laplace transforms to be discussed in Art. 13.2.

Description of inversion theorem. Let us assume for simplicity that

$$F(s) = \frac{P(s)}{Q(s)} = \frac{A_m s^m + A_{m-1} s^{m-1} + \cdots + A_1 s + A_0}{s^n + B_{n-1} s^{n-1} + \cdots + B_1 s + B_0} \tag{13.2}$$

$$F(s) = \frac{P(s)}{(s - p_1)(s - p_2) \cdots (s - p_n)} \overset{[\ddagger]}{} \tag{13.2a}$$

has only simple poles; that is, $p_i \neq p_j$ if $i \neq j$; we wish to find $f(t) = \mathscr{L}^{-1}[F(s)]$.

[†] S. Goldman, "Transformation Calculus and Electrical Transients," pp. 214–217, Prentice-Hall, Inc., Englewood Cliffs, N.J., 1949.

[‡] To obtain (13.2a) from (13.2), we must solve for the roots $p_1, p_2, \ldots, p_n$ of the poly-

The inversion theorem states: $f(t)$ is the sum of the residues of the function

$$F(s)e^{st} \tag{13.3}$$

with respect to all the finite poles of $F(s)$.

We shall not even attempt to define the term *residue* here. However, this theorem may be interpreted with an equivalent statement: $f(t)$ may be represented in the form

$$f(t) = \sum_{i=1}^{n} K_i e^{p_i t} = K_1 e^{p_1 t} + K_2 e^{p_2 t} + \cdots + K_n e^{p_n t} \tag{13.4}$$

where the constant K_i is the residue of $F(s)$ at $s = p_i$, and p_i is a pole of $F(s)$.

Implication of inversion theorem. Let us find the Laplace transform of Eq. (13.4):

$$F(s) = \mathscr{L}[f(t)] = \mathscr{L}[K_1 e^{p_1 t}] + \mathscr{L}[K_2 e^{p_2 t}] + \cdots + \mathscr{L}[K_n e^{p_n t}]$$

$$= \frac{K_1}{s - p_1} + \frac{K_2}{s - p_2} + \cdots + \frac{K_n}{s - p_n} \tag{13.5}$$

Comparing (13.5) with (13.2), we note that (13.5) is the partial-fraction form of (13.2). This suggests a *procedure* for finding the inverse Laplace transform of a given $F(s)$: (1) Represent $F(s)$ in a partial-fraction form similar to (13.5), (2) find the inverse transform of each term in this partial-fraction form with the aid of Table 11.2, for example, $K_i e^{p_i t} = \mathscr{L}^{-1}[K_i/(s - p_i)]$, and (3) add these inverse transforms to obtain $f(t) = \mathscr{L}^{-1}[F(s)]$ in the form of (13.4).

13.2. Methods for finding inverse Laplace transforms

The above suggested procedure will be followed in finding inverse Laplace transforms for different categories of $F(s)$.

A. Inverse Laplace Transform of a Proper Fraction $F(s)$

Proper fraction having simple poles only. We shall consider those $F(s)$ which are proper fractions in the form of (13.2) for $n \geq m + 1$ and which have simple poles only, that is, $p_i \neq p_j$ for $i \neq j$ in (13.2a).

Step 1. Represent $F(s)$ in partial-fraction form. Let us assume that $F(s)$ may be represented as

$$F(s) = \frac{P(s)}{Q(s)} = \frac{P(s)}{(s - p_1)(s - p_2) \cdots (s - p_i) \cdots (s - p_n)} \tag{13.6a}$$

$$F(s) = \frac{K_1}{s - p_1} + \frac{K_2}{s - p_2} + \cdots + \frac{K_n}{s - p_n} \tag{13.6b}$$

with unknown coefficients K_i. To determine these coefficients, we first multiply (13.6) by $(s - p_i)$:

$$\frac{(s - p_i)P(s)}{Q(s)} = \frac{K_1(s - p_i)}{s - p_1} + \frac{K_2(s - p_i)}{s - p_2} + \cdots + K_i + \cdots + \frac{K_n(s - p_i)}{s - p_n} \tag{13.7}$$

---

nomial $Q(s)$. For some standard methods of solving polynomials, see Lin's method in *J. Math. Phys.*, vol. 20, pp. 231–242, August, 1941, and vol. 22, pp. 60–77, June, 1943; Friedman's method in M. G. Salvadori and M. L. Baron, "Numerical Methods in Engineering," Prentice-Hall, Inc., Englewood Cliffs, N.J., 1952; and Graeffe's root-squaring method in R. E. Doherty and E. G. Keeler, "Mathematics of Modern Engineering," John Wiley & Sons, Inc., New York, 1936.

Letting $s \to p_i$ in (13.7) and noting that all terms except K_i on the right-hand side of (13.7) vanish, we obtain

Partial-fraction coefficients for simple poles:

$$K_i = \lim_{s \to p_i} \frac{(s - p_i)P(s)}{Q(s)} = \lim_{s \to p_i} [(s - p_i)F(s)] \qquad i = 1, 2, \ldots, n \qquad (13.8)$$

which may be used in evaluating the partial-fraction coefficients in (13.6).

Since $(s - p_i)P(s) \to 0$ and $Q(s) \to 0$ as $s \to p_i$ in (13.8),

$$K_i = \lim_{s \to p_i} \frac{(s - p_i)P(s)}{Q(s)} = \frac{0}{0}$$

is indeterminate. To evaluate K_i, we may apply Lhopital's rule, obtaining

Alternative form of (13.8):

$$K_i = \lim_{s \to p_i} \frac{d[(s - p_i)P(s)]/ds}{dQ(s)/ds} = \frac{P(p_i)}{Q'(p_i)} \qquad (13.8a)$$

as an alternative form of (13.8).

Step 2.   Find $f(t) = \mathscr{L}^{-1}[F(s)]$. With K_i evaluated using (13.8), we may find the inverse Laplace transform of (13.6) with the aid of Table 11.2:

$$f(t) = K_1 e^{p_1 t} + K_2 e^{p_2 t} + \cdots + K_n e^{p_n t} \qquad (13.9)$$

Illustration 1.   For

$$F(s) = \frac{8s^2 + 9s + 4}{s(5s + 4)(s + 1)} = \frac{(8s^2 + 9s + 4)/5}{s(s + \frac{4}{5})(s + 1)} \qquad (13.10a)$$

Eq. (13.8) implies

$$K_1 = \lim_{s \to 0} \left[(s + 0) \frac{(8s^2 + 9s + 4)/5}{s(s + \frac{4}{5})(s + 1)} \right] = 1$$

$$K_2 = \lim_{s \to -\frac{4}{5}} \left[(s + \frac{4}{5}) \frac{(8s^2 + 9s + 4)/5}{s(s + \frac{4}{5})(s + 1)} \right] = -\frac{12}{5} \qquad (13.10b)$$

$$K_3 = \lim_{s \to -1} \left[(s + 1) \frac{(8s^2 + 9s + 4)/5}{s(s + \frac{4}{5})(s + 1)} \right] = 3$$

We now have

$$F(s) = \frac{1}{s + 0} + \frac{-\frac{12}{5}}{s + \frac{4}{5}} + \frac{3}{s + 1} \qquad (13.10c)$$

which yields

$$f(t) = 1 - \tfrac{12}{5} e^{-\frac{4}{5}t} + 3e^{-t} \qquad (13.10d)$$

Illustration 2.   For

$$F(s) = \frac{s^2 + 3s + 8}{(s + 3)(s^2 + 2s + 5)} = \frac{s^2 + 3s + 8}{(s + 3)[(s + 1)^2 + 2^2]} \qquad (13.11a)$$

which may be represented in the form

$$F(s) = \frac{K_1}{s - p_1} + \frac{K_2}{s - p_2} + \frac{K_3}{s - p_3} = \frac{K_1}{s + 3} + \frac{K_2}{s + 1 - j2} + \frac{K_3}{s + 1 + j2} \qquad (13.11b)$$

application of (13.8) leads to

$$K_1 = 1 \qquad K_2 = \frac{1}{j4} = -\frac{j}{4} \qquad K_3 = -\frac{1}{j4} = \frac{j}{4} \qquad (13.11c)$$

The inverse transform of (13.11b) is therefore

$$f(t) = \mathcal{L}^{-1}[F(s)] = 1e^{-3t} + \frac{1}{j4} e^{(-1+j2)t} + -\frac{1}{j4} e^{(-1-j2)t}$$

$$= 1e^{-3t} + \frac{1}{2} e^{-t} \frac{e^{j2t} - e^{-j2t}}{2j} = 1e^{-3t} + \frac{1}{2} e^{-t} \sin 2t \qquad (13.11d)$$

Remarks. From the above illustration, we note that:
1. The condition that p_2 and p_3 be conjugates, i.e.,

$$p_2 = a_2 + jb_2 = -1 + j2 \qquad p_3 = \bar{p}_2 = a_2 - jb_2 = -1 - j2$$

implies that K_2 and K_3 are conjugates, i.e.,

$$K_2 = c_2 + jd_2 = 0 - j\tfrac{1}{4} \qquad K_3 = \bar{K}_2 = c_2 - jd_2 = 0 + j\tfrac{1}{4}$$

This means that we may represent (13.11a) as

$$F(s) = \frac{K_1}{s - p_1} + \frac{K_2}{s - p_2} + \frac{\bar{K}_2}{s - \bar{p}_2} = \frac{K_1}{s + 3} + \frac{K_2}{s + 1 - j2} + \frac{\bar{K}_2}{s + 1 + j2} \qquad (13.12)$$

and evaluate K_1 and K_2 with the aid of (13.8). $\bar{K}_2$ as the conjugate of K_2 is known without application of (13.8).
2. We may also represent (13.11a) in another partial-fraction form,

$$F(s) = \frac{s^2 + 3s + 8}{(s + 3)[(s + 1)^2 + 2^2]} = \frac{K_1}{s + 3} + \frac{K_2 s + K_3}{(s + 1)^2 + 2^2} \qquad (13.13a)$$

whose coefficients may be evaluated as follows: By letting $s = -1, 0, 1$ in (13.13a), we obtain three linear equations with K_1, K_2, K_3 as three unknowns; solving them, we find $K_1 = 1$, $K_2 = 0$, $K_3 = 1$. Equation (13.13a) now becomes

$$F(s) = \frac{1}{s + 3} + \frac{1}{(s + 1)^2 + 2^2} \qquad (13.13b)$$

By applying items 6 and 10 in Table 11.2, we now obtain

$$f(t) = \mathcal{L}^{-1}[F(s)] = 1e^{-3t} + \tfrac{1}{2}e^{-t} \sin 2t \qquad (13.13c)$$

which checks with (13.11d).
We may therefore remark: When $F(s)$ has *conjugate pairs* of poles, (1) conjugate relations such as (13.12) exist and (2) different partial-fraction forms may be used to include standard expressions in the table of Laplace transforms, e.g., items 9 to 13 in Table 11.2, for the most effective use of the table.
Proper fraction with multiple-order poles. For

$$F(s) = \frac{P(s)}{Q(s)} = \frac{P(s)}{(s - p_1)(s - p_2)(s - p_3)(s - p_4)^3} \qquad (13.14a)$$

with simple poles at p_1, p_2, and p_3 and a third-order pole at p_4, we assume a partial-fraction form

$$F(s) = \frac{P(s)}{Q(s)} = \frac{K_1}{s - p_1} + \frac{K_2}{s - p_2} + \frac{K_3}{s - p_3} + \left[\frac{K_{43}}{(s - p_4)^3} + \frac{K_{42}}{(s - p_4)^2} + \frac{K_{41}}{(s - p_4)} \right]$$

$$(13.14b)$$

Since $F(s)$ is a proper fraction, each term in (13.14b) is a proper fraction, and the sum of the terms in brackets is also a proper fraction.

As p_1, p_2, and p_3 are simple poles, Eq. (13.8) applies here.   Therefore,
Partial-fraction coefficients for simple poles:

$$K_i = \lim_{s \to p_i} \frac{(s - p_i)P(s)}{Q(s)} = \lim_{s \to p_i} [(s - p_i)F(s)] \tag{13.15}$$

for all simple poles.

We shall now try to evaluate the coefficients K_{43}, K_{42}, and K_{41} associated with the multiple-order pole p_4.   We first multiply (13.14b) by $(s - p_4)^3$:

$$(s - p_4)^3 F(s) = (s - p_4)^3 \left\{ \frac{K_1}{s - p_1} + \frac{K_2}{s - p_2} + \frac{K_3}{s - p_3} \right\}$$

$$+ K_{43} + K_{42}(s - p_4) + K_{41}(s - p_4)^2 \tag{13.16a}$$

Letting $s \to p_4$, we have

$$K_{43} = \lim_{s \to p_4} (s - p_4)^3 F(s)$$

Taking the derivative of (13.16a),

$$\frac{d}{ds} [(s - p_4)^3 F(s)] = 3(s - p_4)^2 \{ \quad \} + (s - p_4)^3 \frac{d}{ds} \{ \quad \}$$

$$+ 0 + K_{42} + 2K_{41}(s - p_4) \tag{13.16b}$$

and letting $s \to p_4$, we have

$$K_{42} = \lim_{s \to p_4} \frac{d}{ds} [(s - p_4)^3 F(s)]$$

Similarly, taking the derivative of (13.16b) and letting $s \to p_4$, we have

$$K_{41} = \frac{1}{2} \lim_{s \to p_4} \frac{d^2}{ds^2} [(s - p_4)^3 F(s)]$$

In general, for an mth-order pole at $s = p_i$, the partial-fraction form of $F(s)$ consists of the terms

Partial-fraction terms due to a multiple pole:

$$\frac{K_{im}}{(s - p_i)^m} + \frac{K_{m-1}}{(s - p_i)^{m-1}} + \cdots + \frac{K_{i1}}{s - p_i} \tag{13.17a}$$

in addition to the terms due to other poles; the coefficients in (13.17a) may be evaluated with

Partial-fraction coefficients for a pole p_i of order m:

$$K_{im} = \lim_{s \to p_i} [(s - p_i)^m F(s)]$$

$$K_{i(m-1)} = \lim_{s \to p_i} \frac{d}{ds} [(s - p_i)^m F(s)]$$

$$\cdot \ \cdot \ \cdot \ \cdot \ \cdot \ \cdot \ \cdot \ \cdot \ \cdot \ \cdot \ \cdot$$

$$K_{i(m-q)} = \frac{1}{q!} \lim_{s \to p_i} \frac{d^q}{ds^q} [(s - p_i)^m F(s)] \tag{13.17b}$$

$$\cdot \ \cdot \ \cdot \ \cdot \ \cdot \ \cdot \ \cdot \ \cdot \ \cdot \ \cdot \ \cdot$$

$$K_{i1} = \frac{1}{(m - 1)!} \lim_{s \to p_i} \frac{d^{(m-1)}}{ds^{(m-1)}} [(s - p_i)^m F(s)]$$

The inverse transform of (13.17a) may then be obtained with the aid of Table 11.2:

Inverse Laplace transform of terms due to a multiple pole:

$$\left[K_{im} \frac{1}{(m-1)!} t^{m-1} + K_{i(m-1)} \frac{1}{(m-2)!} t^{m-2} + \cdots + K_{i1} \right] e^{p_i t} \quad (13.17c)$$

Illustration 3.　For

$$F(s) = \frac{2s^5 + 4s^4 + 2s^3 + s^2 + 3s + 2}{s^3(s+1)^2(s+2)} \quad (13.18a)$$

we shall assume a partial-fraction expansion according to (13.17a):

$$F(s) = \left(\frac{K_{13}}{s^3} + \frac{K_{12}}{s^2} + \frac{K_{11}}{s} \right) + \left[\frac{K_{22}}{(s+1)^2} + \frac{K_{21}}{s+1} \right] + \frac{K_3}{s+2} \quad (13.18b)$$

For the third-order pole at $s = 0$, that is, $p_1 = 0$, (13.17b) dictates

$$K_{13} = \lim_{s \to 0} [(s-0)^3 F(s)] = 1$$

$$K_{12} = \lim_{s \to 0} \frac{d}{ds} [(s-0)^3 F(s)] = -1 \quad (13.18c)$$

$$K_{11} = \frac{1}{2} \lim_{s \to 0} \frac{d^2}{ds^2} [(s-0)^3 F(s)] = 1$$

For the second-order pole at $s = -1$, that is, $p_2 = -1$, (13.17b) dictates

$$K_{22} = \lim_{s \to -1} [(s+1)^2 F(s)] = 0$$
$$\quad (13.18d)$$
$$K_{21} = \lim_{s \to -1} \frac{d}{ds} [(s+1)^2 F(s)] = -1$$

For the simple pole at $s = -2$, that is, $p_2 = -2$, (13.15) dictates

$$K_3 = 2 \quad (13.18e)$$

The inverse transform of $F(s)$ in (13.18b), according to Table 11.2 and (13.17c), is

$$f(t) = \mathcal{L}^{-1}[F(s)] = \tfrac{1}{2}t^2 - t + 1 - e^{-t} + 2e^{-2t} \quad (13.18f)$$

B. Inverse Laplace Transform of an Improper Fraction F(s)

For $m \geq n$ in (13.2), $F(s)$ is an improper fraction. An improper fraction may be represented as a sum of a polynomial of s and a proper fraction. For example,

$$F(s) = \frac{s^4 + 5s^3 + 7s^2 + 5s + 3}{s^2 + 3s} = (s^2 + 2s + 1) + \frac{2s+3}{s^2+3s} \quad (13.19)$$

We may find the inverse transform of the proper fraction, for example, $(2s+3)/(s^2+3s)$ in (13.19), with the methods described above.

The polynomial of s in (13.19) consists in a constant term and the positive integral powers of s. The inverse transform of the constant term K may be readily obtained from Table 11.2 as an impulse function, for example, $K\delta(t)$, where $\delta(t)$ is a unit-impulse function. The inverse transforms of the positive integral powers of s are impulse functions of higher order† which are seldom encountered in practical circuit problems and, therefore, will not be treated in this text.

† See Goldman, *op. cit.*, pp. 326–330.

C. Inverse Laplace Transform of a Fraction F(s) with Infinitely Many Poles or Zeros

We are concerned here with three types of problems for an $F(s)$ with infinitely many poles or zeros:

1. $F(s)$ has a factor $1 - e^{-Ts}$ in its denominator. This means that $F(s)$ has infinitely many poles at

$$s = \frac{j2\pi K}{T} \qquad K = 0, \pm 1, \pm 2, \ldots \qquad (13.20a)$$

2. $F(s)$ has a factor $1 - e^{-Ts}$ in its numerator. This means that $F(s)$ has infinitely many zeros at

$$s = \frac{j2\pi K}{T} \qquad K = 0, \pm 1, \pm 2, \ldots \qquad (13.20b)$$

3. $F(s) = P(s)/Q(s)$, where $Q(s)$ is transcendental. In this case, $F(s)$ has infinitely many poles.

$F(s)$ with $1 - e^{-Ts}$ as a factor in its denominator. Equations (12.80) state that if $n(t)$, being a nonrepeating function, is a complete cycle of a repeating function $f(t)$, if $N(s) = \mathscr{L}[n(t)]$, and if $F(s) = \mathscr{L}[f(t)]$, then

$$F(s) = N(s)\frac{1}{1 - e^{-Ts}} \qquad (13.21)$$

This statement suggests a procedure for finding $f(t) = \mathscr{L}^{-1}[F(s)]$ if $F(s)$ is of the type (13.21):

1. Find $n(t) = \mathscr{L}^{-1}[N(s)]$, a nonrepeating function.
2. $f(t)$ has the waveform of $n(t)$ for a single cycle and repeats itself with period T. We may represent this repeating function in the form

$$f(t) = \sum_{k=0}^{\infty} n(t - kT) \qquad k = 0, 1, 2, \ldots \qquad (13.22)$$

Illustration.   Find $f(t) = \mathscr{L}^{-1}[F(s)]$ where

$$F(s) = \frac{1 - e^{-\delta s}}{s}\frac{1}{1 - e^{-Ts}} \qquad (13.23a)$$

According to the above procedure, we (1) find, with the aid of Table 11.2, the non-repeating function

$$n(t) = \mathscr{L}\left[\frac{1 - e^{-\delta s}}{s}\right] = u(t) - u(t - \delta) \qquad (13.23b)$$

which is depicted in Fig. 12.11a, and (2) extend it to a repeating function

$$f(t) = \sum_{k=1}^{\infty} n(t - kT) \qquad k = 0, 1, 2, \ldots \qquad (13.23c)$$

as in Fig. 12.11a'.

$F(s)$ with $1 - e^{-Ts}$ as a factor in its numerator. Replace $n(t)$ with $f(t)$ and $f(t)$ with $r(t)$ for changes in notation; then (12.80) suggests a procedure for finding $f(t) = \mathscr{L}^{-1}[F(s)]$ if $F(s)$ is of the type

$$F(s) = R(s)(1 - e^{-Ts}) \qquad (13.24)$$

1. Find $r(t) = \mathscr{L}^{-1}[R(s)]$, a repeating function.
2. Let $f(t)$ be a complete cycle, with a period T, of $r(t)$. $f(t)$ is a nonrepeating function.

Illustration.   Find $f(t) = \mathcal{L}^{-1}[F(s)]$, where

$$F(s) = \frac{\beta}{s^2 + \beta^2}(1 - e^{-Ts}) \qquad \beta = \frac{2\pi}{T} \tag{13.25a}$$

According to the above procedure, we (1) find, with the aid of Table 11.2, the repeating function

$$r(t) = \mathcal{L}^{-1}\left[\frac{\beta}{s^2 + \beta^2}\right] = \sin \beta t \qquad 0 \le t < \infty \tag{13.25b}$$

which is a sine function covering the entire positive-time region, and (2) let $f(t)$ be a complete cycle of $r(t)$, that is,

$$f(t) = \begin{cases} \sin \beta t & 0 \le t \le T, T = \dfrac{2\pi}{\beta} \\ 0 & T < t \end{cases} \tag{13.25c}$$

$F(s) = P(s)/Q(s)$, where $Q(s)$ is transcendental.   Here we have

$$F(s) = \frac{P(s)}{Q(s)} \tag{13.26}$$

where $Q(s)$ is a transcendental function.   We shall only remark here how the partial-fraction form of $F(s)$ is obtained, since $f(t) = \mathcal{L}^{-1}[F(s)]$ can readily be found with the aid of Table 11.2 once its partial-fraction form is known.

The procedure for finding the partial-fraction form of $F(s)$ in (13.26) is the same as described in Eqs. (13.6) and (13.7).   However, Eq. (13.6b) will now be an infinite series because $F(s)$ has infinitely many poles.

Illustration.   Find the partial-fraction form of

$$F(s) = \frac{P(s)}{Q(s)} = \frac{1}{\sin s} \tag{13.26a}$$

Since $F(s)$ in (13.26a) has poles at

$$s = 0$$
$$s = \pm n\pi \qquad n = 1, 2, \ldots \tag{13.26b}$$

we may assume the partial-fraction form

$$F(s) = \frac{K_0}{s} + \sum_{n=1}^{\infty}\left(\frac{K_n}{s - n\pi} + \frac{K_{-n}}{s + n\pi}\right)$$

$$= \frac{K_0}{s} + \frac{K_1}{s - \pi} + \frac{K_2}{s - 2\pi} + \cdots + \frac{K_{-1}}{s + \pi} + \frac{K_{-2}}{s + 2\pi} + \cdots \tag{13.26c}$$

Applying (13.8) and using Lhopital's rule to aid us in the evaluation of K_n, we find

$$K_0 = \lim_{s \to 0}\left[(s - 0)\frac{1}{\sin s}\right] = 1$$

$$K_n = \lim_{s \to n\pi}\left[(s - n\pi)\frac{1}{\sin s}\right] = \lim_{s \to n\pi}\frac{d(s - n\pi)/ds}{d(\sin s)/ds}$$

$$= \lim_{s \to n\pi}\frac{1}{\cos s}$$

$$K_n = \begin{cases} 1 & \text{for even } n \\ -1 & \text{for odd } n \end{cases}$$

$$K_{-n} = K_n = \begin{cases} 1 & \text{for even } n \\ -1 & \text{for odd } n \end{cases} \tag{13.26d}$$

The partial-fraction form of $F(s) = 1/\sin s$ is therefore

$$F(s) = \frac{1}{s} - \frac{1}{s-\pi} + \frac{1}{s-2\pi} - \frac{1}{s+3\pi} \cdots - \frac{1}{s+\pi} + \frac{1}{s+2\pi} - \frac{1}{s+3\pi} \cdots$$

$$= \frac{1}{s} - \frac{2s}{s^2 - \pi^2} + \frac{2s}{s^2 - 4\pi^2} - \frac{2s}{s^2 - 9\pi^2} \cdots$$

$$= \frac{1}{s} + \sum_{k=1}^{\infty} \left[\frac{-2s}{s^2 - (2k-1)^2\pi^2} + \frac{2s}{s^2 + (2k)^2\pi^2} \right] \qquad (13.26e)$$

D. *Remarks about the Graphical Method for Finding the Inverse Laplace Transform*

We have discussed above how to find analytically the inverse Laplace transform $f(t) = \mathscr{L}^{-1}[F(s)]$ of a given $F(s)$. However, a graphical method using the pole-and-zero plot of $F(s)$ is also available for the determination of $f(t) = \mathscr{L}^{-1}[F(s)]$. The reader may find it interesting to read about this method.†

13.3. Locations of poles of a response function and types of components in the response

A stable network is one having a stable response subject to a given excitation. This definition applies to two-terminal as well as four-terminal networks.

Suppose $f(t)$ represents a network response, and

$$F(s) = \mathscr{L}[f(t)] \qquad (13.27)$$

is the response function. We now want to know (1) if $f(t)$ is a *stable* response, what kind of response function $F(s)$ shall we have and (2) if $f(t)$ is an *unstable* response, what becomes of $F(s)$?

A. *Illustrative Examples of Stable Responses*

We shall assume $\alpha > 0$ in the following illustrative examples.

A real pole at $s = -\alpha$. For $F(s) = K/(s+\alpha)$, we obviously have

$$f(t) = \mathscr{L}^{-1}\left[\frac{K}{s+\alpha} \right] = Ke^{-\alpha t} \qquad \alpha > 0 \qquad (13.28a)$$

which is depicted in Fig. 13.1a.

A pair of purely imaginary poles at $s = \pm j\beta$. For $F(s) = K/(s^2 + \beta^2)$, we have, according to item 9 in Table 11.2,

$$f(t) = \mathscr{L}^{-1}\left[\frac{K}{s^2 + \beta^2} \right] = \frac{K}{\beta} \sin \beta t \qquad (13.28b)$$

which is depicted in Fig. 13.1b.

A pair of complex conjugate poles at $s = -\alpha \pm j\beta$. For $F(s) = K/[(s+\alpha)^2 + \beta^2]$, we have, according to item 10 in Table 11.2,

$$f(t) = \mathscr{L}^{-1}\left[\frac{K}{(s+\alpha)^2 + \beta^2} \right] = \frac{K}{\beta} e^{-\alpha t} \sin \beta t \qquad \alpha > 0 \qquad (13.28c)$$

which is depicted in Fig. 13.1c.

A multiple-order pole at $s = -\alpha$. For $F(s) = K/(s+\alpha)^2$, we have, according to item 7 in Table 11.2,

$$f(t) = \mathscr{L}^{-1}\left[\frac{K}{(s+\alpha)^2} \right] = Kte^{-\alpha t} \qquad \alpha > 0 \qquad (13.28d)$$

which is depicted in Fig. 13.1d.

† J. H. Mulligan, Jr., The Effect of Pole and Zero Locations on the Transient Response of Linear Dynamic Systems, *Proc. IRE*, vol. 37, pp. 516–532, May, 1949.

A pair of multiple-order complex conjugate poles at $s = -\alpha \pm j\beta$. For $F(s) = K/[(s+\alpha)^2+\beta^2]^2$, which has double poles at $p_1 = -\alpha + jb$ and $p_2 = -\alpha - j\beta$, we (1) follow the procedure in (13.17) to represent $F(s)$ in partial-fraction form,

$$F(s) = \left[\frac{K_{12}}{(s-p_1)^2} + \frac{K_{11}}{s-p_1}\right] + \left[\frac{K_{22}}{(s-p_2)^2} + \frac{K_{21}}{s-p_2}\right]$$

and then evaluate its coefficients and (2) find the inverse transform of each term with the aid of items 6 and 7 in Table 11.2, where α is replaced by $p_1 = -\alpha + j\beta$ and $p_2 = -\alpha + j\beta$, and then combine these terms to obtain

$$f(t) = \mathscr{L}^{-1}[F(s)] = \frac{K}{2\beta^3} e^{-\alpha t}(\sin \beta t - \beta t \cos \beta t) \qquad \alpha > 0 \qquad (13.28e)$$

which is depicted in Fig. 13.1e.

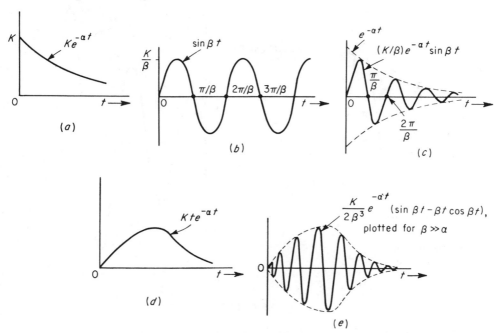

FIG. 13.1

A response function having poles of different types. Suppose a response function $F(s)$ has poles of different types. We may follow the procedure in (13.18) to represent it in partial-fraction form,

$$F(s) = F_1(s) + F_2(s) + \cdots + F_k(s) \qquad (13.29a)$$

and then find the inverse Laplace transform of each of its partial fractions, $f_i(t) = \mathscr{L}^{-1}[F_i(s)]$ for $i = 1, 2, \ldots, k$, with the aid of Table 11.2. The response is then

$$f(t) = f_1(t) + f_2(t) + \cdots + f_k(t) \qquad (13.29b)$$

where each $f_i(t)$ may be in one of the forms illustrated in (13.28) and Fig. 13.1.

A *stable* response $f(t)$ is one whose value does *not* tend to infinity as $t \to \infty$. Equations (13.28), together with Fig. 13.1, provide some illustrations of typical stable responses. A response $f(t)$ of the form of (13.29b) is stable if all its component responses $f_i(t)$ are stable.

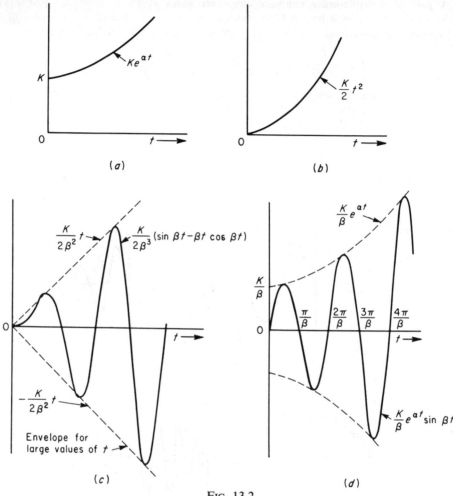

FIG. 13.2

B. Illustrative Examples of Unstable Responses

Again we shall assume $\alpha > 0$ in the following illustrative examples.

A real pole at $s = \alpha$. For $F(s) = K/(s - \alpha)$, we obviously have

$$f(t) = \mathscr{L}^{-1}\left[\frac{K}{s - \alpha}\right] = Ke^{\alpha t} \qquad \alpha > 0 \tag{13.30a}$$

which is depicted in Fig. 13.2a.

A multiple-order pole at $s = 0$. For $F(s) = K/s^3$, we have, according to item 4 in Table 11.2,

$$f(t) = \mathscr{L}^{-1}\left[\frac{K}{s^3}\right] = \frac{K}{2}t^2 \tag{13.30b}$$

which is depicted in Fig. 13.2b.

A pair of multiple-order imaginary poles at $s = \pm j\beta$. For $F(s) = K/(s^2 + \beta^2)^2$, we may let $\alpha = 0$ in (13.28e) to obtain the response

$$f(t) = \frac{K}{2\beta^3}(\sin \beta t - \beta t \cos \beta t) \tag{13.30c}$$

which is depicted in Fig. 13.2c.

Remarks about additional illustrations.   Replacing α with $-\alpha$ in Eqs. (13.28) will give us additional unstable cases.   For example, we may replace α with $-\alpha$ in the example associated with (13.28c).   This means that, for $F(s) = K/[(s - \alpha)^2 + \beta^2]$, we have

$$f(t) = \mathscr{L}^{-1}\left[\frac{K}{(s - \alpha)^2 + \beta^2}\right] = \frac{K}{\beta} e^{\alpha t} \sin \beta t \qquad \alpha > 0 \qquad (13.30d)$$

which is depicted in Fig. 13.2d.

Remarks about unstable responses.   An unstable response $f(t)$ is one whose value tends to infinity as $t \to \infty$.   Equations (13.30), together with Fig. 13.2, provide some illustrations of typical unstable responses.

A response such as (13.29b), which has a number of components, is unstable if one or more of its component responses are unstable.

C. Conditions for a Stable Response

By examining the poles of the response function $F(s)$ for stable responses in (13.28) and unstable responses in (13.30) in the above illustrations, we may conclude that a network response $f(t)$ is *stable* if

For stable response $f(t)$:

1. Its response function $F(s) = \mathscr{L}[f(t)]$ has no poles in the right-hand half of the s plane
2. Any poles of $F(s)$ on the $j\omega$ axis are simple

$$(13.31)$$

13.4. Questions of stability

We now wish to determine under what conditions a linear system (or network) will be stable.

A. System Functions

Let us use the following notation for any system under discussion:

$e(t) =$ excitation $\qquad\qquad\qquad\quad i(t) =$ response
$E(s) = \mathscr{L}[e(t)] =$ excitation function $\qquad I(s) = \mathscr{L}[i(t)] =$ response function $\qquad (13.32)$

For network applications, $e(t)$ may represent either a voltage or current excitation, and $i(t)$ a voltage or current response.

We shall define a *system function* as a function $T(s)$ which relates the excitation function $E(s)$ to the response function $I(s)$ of a linear system (Fig. 13.3a) in the following manner:

System function:

$$T(s) = \frac{I(s)}{E(s)} = \frac{\text{response function}}{\text{excitation function}} = \frac{\mathscr{L}[i(t)]}{\mathscr{L}[e(t)]} \qquad (13.33)$$

Illustration 1.   For the two-terminal network in Fig. 13.3b, if $e_1(t)$ is the excitation, and $i_1(t)$ is the response, the system function is the driving-point admittance; i.e.,

$$T(s) = \frac{\text{response function}}{\text{excitation function}} = \frac{I_1(s)}{E_1(s)} = Y_D(s) \qquad (13.34)$$

Illustration 2.   For the two-terminal network in Fig. 13.3b, if $i_1(t)$ is the excitation, i.e., a "current source" injecting current into the network, and $e_1(t)$ is the response, the system function is the driving-point impedance; i.e.,

$$T(s) = \frac{\text{response function}}{\text{excitation function}} = \frac{E_1(s)}{I_1(s)} = Z_D(s) \qquad (13.35)$$

Illustration 3. For the four-terminal network in Fig. 13.3c, if $e_1(t)$ is the excitation

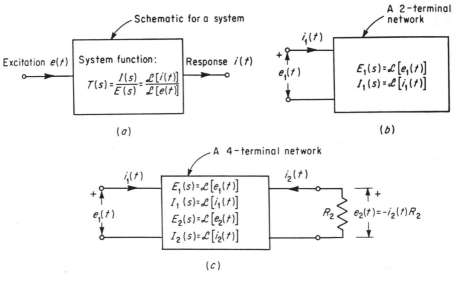

FIG. 13.3

and $i_2(t)$ is our "interested" response, the system function is related to the transfer functions $[Z_T(s)]_{12} = E_1(s)/I_2(s)$ and $[Y_T(s)]_{21} = I_2(s)/E_1(s)$,

$$T(s) = \frac{\text{response function}}{\text{excitation function}} = \frac{I_2(s)}{E_1(s)} = [Y_T(s)]_{21} = \frac{1}{[Z_T(s)]_{12}} \qquad (13.36a)$$

If $e_1(t)$ is the excitation and $e_2(t)$ is our "interested" response, the system function is the transfer voltage-ratio function $G(s) = E_2(s)/E_1(s)$; that is,

$$T(s) = \frac{\text{response function}}{\text{excitation function}} = \frac{E_2(s)}{E_1(s)} = G(s) \qquad (13.36b)$$

Illustration 4. For the four-terminal network in Fig. 13.3c, if $i_1(t)$ is the excitation and $i_2(t)$ is our "interested" response, the system function is the transfer current-ratio function $A(s) = I_2(s)/I_1(s)$; that is,

$$T(s) = \frac{\text{response function}}{\text{excitation function}} = \frac{I_2(s)}{I_1(s)} = A(s) \qquad (13.37a)$$

If $i_1(t)$ is the excitation and $e_2(t)$ is our "interested" response, the system function is related to the transfer functions $[Z_T(s)]_{21} = E_2(s)/I_1(s)$ and $[Y_T(s)]_{12} = I_1(s)/E_2(s)$ as follows:

$$T(s) = \frac{\text{response function}}{\text{excitation function}} = \frac{E_2(s)}{I_1(s)} = [Z_T(s)]_{21} = \frac{1}{[Y_T(s)]_{12}} \qquad (13.37b)$$

From the above illustrations, we are now able to obtain the system function $W(s)$ of a two-terminal or four-terminal network from its known network function.

B. Remarks about System Stability

A system (or network) is *stable* if it has a stable response $i(t)$ while subject to an arbitrary finite excitation $e(t)$.

Conditions of stability. To investigate the stability of a system subject to an arbitrary finite excitation $e(t)$, let us assume that (1) its system function $T(s)$ is a ratio of two polynomials in s,

System function:

$$T(s) = \frac{Q(s)}{P(s)} \tag{13.38a}$$

and (2) the excitation function $E(s) = \mathscr{L}[e(t)]$ is also a ratio of two polynomials in s,

Excitation function:

$$E(s) = \frac{C(s)}{D(s)} \tag{13.38b}$$

To obtain the response $i(t)$, we first obtain the response function with the aid of (13.33):

Response function:

$$I(s) = T(s)E(s) = \frac{Q(s)C(s)}{P(s)D(s)} \tag{13.38c}$$

Then we obtain the response

Response:

$$i(t) = \mathscr{L}^{-1}[I(s)] = \mathscr{L}^{-1}\left[\frac{Q(s)C(s)}{P(s)D(s)}\right] \tag{13.38d}$$

For a stable response $i(t)$, the poles of the response function $I(s)$, which are the zeros of $P(s)D(s)$ according to (13.38c), must satisfy conditions (13.31).

Since the excitation $e(t)$ is finite (i.e., stable), the poles of the excitation function $E(s)$, which are the zeros of $D(s)$ according to (13.38b), must also satisfy conditions (13.31).

From the definition of a stable system and the above two statements, we may conclude that a system (or network) is *stable* if

$$P(s) = \left[\text{denominator polynomial of system function } T(s) = \frac{Q(s)}{P(s)}\right] \tag{13.39}$$

has no zeros in the right-hand half of the s plane and only simple zeros on the $j\omega$ axis.

To detect instability in a system (or network), we now merely have to find (1) one or more zeros of $P(s)$ as defined in (13.39) in the right-hand half of the s plane or (2) one or more multiple-order zeros of $P(s)$ on the $j\omega$ axis of the s plane.

Characteristic equation and characteristic zeros. Assume the following form for $P(s)$ in (13.39):

Characteristic equation:

$$P(s) = \text{Eq. (13.39)} = a_k s^k + a_{k-1} s^{k-1} + \cdots + a_1 s + a_0 \tag{13.40a}$$

We shall call (13.40a) the *characteristic equation* of the system, and its zeros the *characteristic zeros* or *characteristic roots*:

Characteristic zeros:

$$r_1, r_2, \ldots, r_k = \text{zeros of } P(s), \text{ that is, roots of } P(s), \text{ in (13.40a)} \tag{13.40b}$$

Fundamental criterion for stability.   Using the terminology introduced in (13.40), we now restate the conditions for stability:

Fundamental criterion for stability:

> A system (or network) is *stable* if none of the zeros of its characteristic equation, as defined in (13.40), are in the right-hand half of the s plane and any characteristic zeros on the $j\omega$ axis are simple   (13.41a)

> A system (or network) is *unstable* if some of its characteristic zeros are in the right-hand half of the s plane or if there are zeros of multiple order on the $j\omega$ axis   (13.41b)

The above statement is called the *fundamental criterion for stability,* for it is the foundation of all methods or criteria for the determination of system stability.   Some of these criteria will be studied later in this text.

C. *Some Illustrations of the Determination of System Stability*

Illustration 1.   Let us consider the four-terminal network in Fig. 12.8*b* for stability. We shall first identify Fig. 12.8*b* with Fig. 13.3*c* for notation.   The transfer function $Z_T(s) = [Z_T(s)]_{12}$ has been evaluated in (12.68*a*); according to (13.36*a*), the system function of this network is

$$T(s) = \frac{1}{[Z_T(s)]_{12}} = -\frac{s^2}{5s^2 + 9s + 4} \tag{13.42a}$$

With reference to (13.40), this network has the characteristic equation

$$P(s) = 5s^2 + 9s + 4 \tag{13.42b}$$

and characteristic zeros $r_1 = -\frac{4}{5}$ and $r_2 = -1$.   Since both characteristic zeros are in the left-hand half of the s plane, this network is a *stable* one according to (13.41*a*).
    Our result checks with the well-known fact that all passive networks are stable.

Illustration 2.   Let us assume that the four-terminal network in Fig. 13.3*c* has the system function, according to (13.36*b*),

$$T(s) = G(s) = \frac{4s^2 + 5s - 6}{s^2 + s - 6} \tag{13.43a}$$

With reference to (13.40), this network has the characteristic equation

$$s^2 + s - 6 = 0 \tag{13.43b}$$

and characteristic zeros $r_1 = 2$ and $r_2 = -3$.   Since one of these characteristic roots is in the right-hand half of the s plane, this network is *unstable*.
    To illustrate that this network has an unstable response subject to an arbitrary finite excitation, let us assume the unit-step excitation

$$e_1(t) = u(t) = \begin{cases} 1 & t \geq 0 \\ 0 & t < 0 \end{cases}$$

which has the excitation function

$$E_1(s) = \mathscr{L}[e_1(t)] = \frac{1}{s}$$

The response function is then

$$E_2(s) = G(s)E_1(s) = \frac{4s^2 + 5s - 6}{s^2 + s - 6}\frac{1}{s} = \frac{1}{s} + \frac{2}{s - 2} + \frac{1}{s + 3}$$

which implies the response

$$e_2(t) = \mathcal{L}^{-1}[E_2(s)] = 1 + 2e^{2t} + 1e^{-3t} \qquad t \geq 0$$
$$= 1 + K_1 e^{r_1 t} + K_2 e^{r_2 t} \qquad t \geq 0 \qquad (13.43c)$$

Here we note that the characteristic roots r_1 and r_2 are responsible for the components $K_1 e^{r_1 t}$ and $K_2 e^{r_2 t}$ in the response. As $r_1 = 2$ is in the right-hand half of the s plane, the response $e_2(t)$, having an unstable component $2e^{2t}$, is unstable.

Remarks about some of the methods of determining system (or network) stability. We have demonstrated in the above illustrations how to determine system stability by solving for the zeros of the polynomial characteristic equation $P(s)$ [Eq. (13.40a)]. Fortunately, we had two simple polynomials in these illustrations, and their roots were readily extracted by inspection. In general, we must use various numerical methods† for the determination of the roots of the polynomial $P(s)$; these methods are often very laborious.

To find system (or network) responses to given excitations as studied in Chap. 12, it is necessary to solve numerically for the zeros of the denominator polynomial [for example, $P(s)D(s)$] of the response function [for example, $I(s) = Q(s)C(s)/P(s)D(s)$ in (13.38c)]. But we are *now* interested only in determining whether a system is stable or not, and we have no intention of finding the exact response to a given excitation. Is it then always necessary for us to solve the characteristic equation $P(s)$ numerically with laborious procedures?

The answer is "no." There are many methods and criteria for the determination of stability which do not require solution for the characteristic equation; all these methods and criteria are based on the fundamental criterion for stability (13.41). We shall study or remark about some of these methods and criteria later in this text, e.g., (1) the Routh's criterion in Art. 18.4, (2) the root-locus method in Art. 19.1B, and (3) the Nyquist criterion in Art. 19.3.

PROBLEMS

Find the inverse Laplace transforms of the functions in Probs. 13.1 through 13.14 with the aid of partial fractions, Tables 11.2 and 11.3, and the discussion associated with Eqs. (13.21) and (13.24).

13.1. $\dfrac{s + 2}{s[(s + 1)^2 + 1]}$

13.2. $\dfrac{e^{-2s}}{(s + 2)[(s + 1)^2 + 4]}$

13.3. $\dfrac{s^3 + 2s^2 + s - 1}{(s^2 + 4)(s^2 + 6s + 18)}$

13.4. $\dfrac{2s + 1}{(s + 1)^2(s - 2)}$

13.5. $\dfrac{1}{(s + \alpha)(s + \beta)(s + \gamma)}$

13.6. $\dfrac{1}{(1 + Ts)^n}$

13.7. $\dfrac{s^2 + 1}{(s + 1)^3(s - 2)(s + 3)}$

13.8. $\dfrac{1}{(s^4 - 1)(s + 3)}$

13.9. $\dfrac{s + 1 + se^{-2s}}{s^2 + 8s + 7}$

13.10. $\dfrac{s + 1}{s^2 + 3}(1 - e^{-2Ts})$, where $T = 2\pi/\sqrt{3}$ sec. Sketch the inverse Laplace transform, which is a function of the time t.

13.11. $\dfrac{1}{s}\dfrac{1}{1 - e^{-s}}$. Sketch the inverse Laplace transform.

13.12. $\dfrac{1}{s^2 + 1}\dfrac{1}{1 + e^{-Ts}}$, where $T = 2$ sec. Sketch the inverse Laplace transform. HINT: $1/(1 + e^{-Ts}) = (1 - e^{-Ts})/(1 - e^{-2Ts})$.

† See the references in the footnote associated with Eq. (13.2a) for these methods.

13.13. $\dfrac{1}{s}\dfrac{1}{e^{Ts}+1}$, where $T = 0.1$ sec.   Sketch the inverse Laplace transform.

13.14. $\dfrac{2s - 1 + e^{-2s}}{2s^2(1 - e^{-2s})}$.   Sketch the inverse Laplace transform.

Complete the unfinished portions of the problems listed below.   These portions required the evaluation of the inverse Laplace transform and were not completed in Chap. 12:

13.15. Prob. 12.1	**13.16.** Prob. 12.2	**13.17.** Prob. 12.3
13.18. Prob. 12.5	**13.19.** Prob. 12.6	**13.20.** Prob. 12.7
13.21. Prob. 12.8	**13.22.** Prob. 12.9	**13.23.** Prob. 12.10
13.24. Prob. 12.11	**13.25.** Prob. 12.12	**13.26.** Prob. 12.13
13.27. Prob. 12.14	**13.28.** Prob. 12.15	**13.29.** Prob. 12.16

Determine which of the following transfer functions of the response/excitation type are associated with unstable networks; verify your results by finding the unstable responses of the networks subject to a unit-step excitation, that is, $e_1(t) = u(t)$ or $i_1(t) = u(t)$, which implies $E_1(s) = 1/s$ or $I_1(s) = 1/s$.

13.30. $G(s) = \dfrac{E_2(s)}{E_1(s)} = -\dfrac{s - \frac{1}{3}}{s + \frac{1}{3}}$

13.31. $A(s) = \dfrac{I_2(s)}{I_1(s)} = -\dfrac{s + 1}{s^2 - 2s + 2}$

13.32. $Z_T(s) = \dfrac{E_2(s)}{I_1(s)} = \dfrac{(s + 2)(s + 4)(s + 6)}{(s - 1)(s + 3)(s - 5)}$

13.33. $G(s) = \dfrac{E_2(s)}{E_1(s)} = \dfrac{s^2 - 2s + 1}{s^2 + 2s + 1}$

13.34. $Y_T(s) = \dfrac{I_2(s)}{E_1(s)} = -\dfrac{s^2 + s + 1}{(s^2 + 1)^2}$

13.35. $G(s) = \dfrac{E_2(s)}{E_1(s)} = \dfrac{s^2}{s^2 + 9s + 20}$

Study of network responses using superposition integrals

In Part E we study network responses in the domain of the time t, whereas in two earlier parts we studied the same problem in the domains of the frequency ω and the complex frequency s.

14 Study of network responses using superposition integrals

14.1. Unit-step function and indicial function

A. *Indicial Function*

Characteristic response to a unit-step excitation. When a unit-step excitation $u(t)$ is applied to a network at rest, i.e., one with zero-value initial conditions, the response $A(t)$ of the network is called an *indicial function*.

Although the indicial function $A(t)$ has the dimension of the response, it may also be considered to have the apparent dimensions of (1) an *admittance*, if the excitation

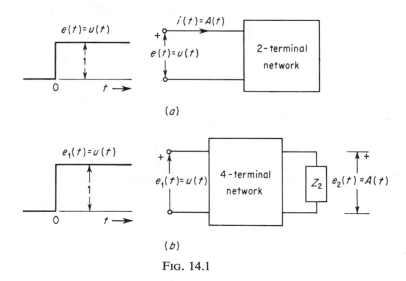

(a)

(b)

Fig. 14.1

is a unit-step voltage and the response represents a current, (2) an *impedance*, if the excitation is a unit-step current and the response represents a voltage, and (3) a *voltage ratio*, if the excitation is a unit-step voltage and the response also represents a voltage.

The indicial function of the two-terminal network in Fig. 14.1a may therefore also be called an *indicial admittance;* the indicial function of the four-terminal network in Fig. 14.1b, an *indicial voltage ratio.*

Illustrations. The current response of a simple RL network subject to a unit-step voltage excitation is well known and is, by definition, the indicial function or indicial

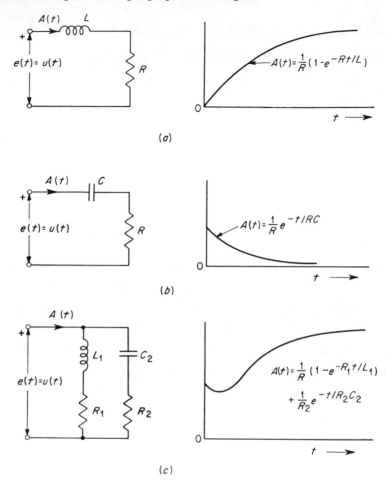

FIG. 14.2

admittance of this network.   This indicial function has the form

$$A(t) = \frac{1}{R}(1 - e^{-Rt/L}) \qquad t \geq 0 \tag{14.1a}$$

as depicted in Fig. 14.2a.

Similarly, the indicial function of a simple RC network is

$$A(t) = \frac{1}{R} e^{-t/RC} \qquad t \geq 0 \tag{14.1b}$$

as depicted in Fig. 14.2b.

For an $R_1 L_1$ and an $R_2 C_2$ branch combined into a single network, the indicial function is

$$A(t) = \frac{1}{R_1}(1 - e^{-R_1 t/L_1}) + \frac{1}{R_2} e^{-t/R_2 C_2} \qquad t \geq 0 \tag{14.1c}$$

as depicted in Fig. 14.2c.

Remarks about the methods of obtaining indicial functions.   In the above illustrations, we used some simple networks whose indicial functions $A(t)$ as the "responses subject to a unit-step excitation" are well known.

For a more complicated network, we shall find it necessary to solve (1) a differential equation or (2) a system of differential equations to determine the indicial function $A(t)$ as the "response subject to a unit-step excitation." The classical methods or the Laplace-transform methods discussed in Chap. 12 may be used in obtaining the solution of this differential equation or system of differential equations.

B. Remarks about the Indicial Function

Indicial function and characteristic response. We have called the response of a network subject to a unit-step excitation the characteristic response or indicial function of this network. Different networks will respond differently to the same unit-step excitation. Therefore, this characteristic response or indicial function characterizes a network.

A relation between an indicial function and a network function. Given the indicial function, we can find the network function, for example, $Z(s)$, as a function of the complex frequency s.

For example, for the two-terminal network arrangement in Fig. 14.1a with known indicial function $A(t)$, we find

$$\mathscr{L}[A(t)] = \mathscr{L}[i(t)] = I(s) = \frac{E(s)}{Z(s)} = \frac{1/s}{Z(s)}$$

and

$$Z(s) = \frac{1}{s\mathscr{L}[A(t)]} \qquad (14.2)$$

where $E(s) = \mathscr{L}[e(t)] = \mathscr{L}[u(t)] = 1/s$ is the excitation function. Knowing $A(t)$, we can readily compute $Z(s)$.

As a numerical illustration, let us use the indicial function in Fig. 14.2b. With the aid of Table 11.2, Eq. (14.2) becomes

$$Z(s) = \frac{1}{s\mathscr{L}[(1/R)e^{-t/RC}]} = \frac{R}{s[1/(s + 1/RC)]} = \frac{R(s + 1/RC)}{s} = R + \frac{1}{sC} \quad (14.2a)$$

which is the driving-point impedance function of the simple RC network in Fig. 14.2b.

Indicial function as a network function of time. All the network functions we have used thus far have been functions of the complex frequency s.

Let us now summarize some of the properties of the indicial function:

1. An indicial function characterizes a network.

2. Knowing an indicial function, we can find a network function, and vice versa.

3. As will be discussed in Art. 14.2, given an arbitrary excitation and the indicial function of a network, we can find the network response. Thus, the indicial function plays the role of a network function.

We may therefore consider the indicial function $A(t)$ of a network to be a *network function of time*. The network functions, for example, $Z(s)$, $Y(s)$, $Z_T(s)$, and $G(s)$, which we have studied earlier are the *network functions of the complex frequency*.

14.2. Superposition integral of step functions

A. Superposition Integral of the First Type

In Art. 9.4 and Fig. 9.10c, we considered the network response subject to a unit-step excitation to be a superposition of a large number of step functions. There is no reason why we cannot consider any given function, excitation or response, to be a superposition of a large number of step functions.

We shall (1) assume that a network excitation is the superposition of a large number of step functions, (2) find the component response of each of these step functions with the aid of the indicial function of the network, and (3) then find the response as a superposition of these component responses. The response, thus obtained, is in the form of an integral. We shall call it the superposition integral of the first type (other types will be discussed in Art. 14.4).

Superposition integral of the first type. Let us use the notation in (13.32). $e(t)$ may represent either a voltage or current excitation, and $i(t)$ a voltage or current response.

We shall assume for the time being that the excitation $e(t)$ is a continuous function of t for the time interval concerned, as depicted in Fig. 14.3a, and the network subject to this excitation $e(t)$ has an indicial function $A(t)$. We now wish to find the response $i(t)$ of this network subject to the excitation $e(t)$.

Representation of the Excitation. If we divide the time interval concerned into a large number of small time intervals $\Delta\tau$, as in Fig. 14.3a, and make $\Delta\tau$ small enough, we may represent the excitation $e(t)$ approximately as the sum of a large number of step functions. Each of these step functions is identified with a shaded area in the figure. We now have

$$e(t) \cong e(0^+)u(t) + \Delta_1 e\, u(t - \Delta\tau) + \Delta_2 e\, u(t - 2\,\Delta\tau) + \cdots + \Delta_n e\, u(t - n\,\Delta\tau)$$
(14.3a)

We have shown in Fig. 14.3a a relation for $\Delta_7 e$; this relation is also true for other $\Delta_k e$, that is,

$$\Delta_k e = \frac{\Delta_k e}{\Delta\tau}\,\Delta\tau \cong \left(\frac{\partial e}{\partial\tau}\right)_{\tau=k\Delta\tau}\Delta\tau \qquad k = 1, 2, \ldots, n \qquad (14.3b)$$

Substituting (14.3b) in (14.3a), we find

$$e(t) \cong e(0^+)u(t) + \sum_{k=1}^{n}\left[\frac{\partial e}{\partial\tau}u(t - \tau)\right]_{\tau=k\,\Delta\tau}\Delta\tau$$

Let $n \to \infty$; according to the definition of an integral as given in the footnote associated with Eq. (8.3a), the above equation becomes

$$e(t) = e(0^+)u(t) + \int_0^t \frac{\partial e(\tau)}{\partial\tau}u(t - \tau)\,d\tau \qquad (14.3c)$$

It is not necessary to use Eqs. (14.3b) and (14.3c) to derive the superposition integral. They are included here for purposes of comparison.

Representation of the Response. According to the definition of the indicial function of a network, the indicial function $A(t)$ is the response to an excitation $u(t)$. If we introduce delay in the excitation $u(t - k\,\Delta\tau)$, we shall also have delay in the response $A(t - k\,\Delta\tau)$. Now, it is easy to see that, for the excitation in (14.3a), we shall have a response

$$i(t) = e(0^+)A(t) + \Delta_1 e\, A(t - \Delta\tau) + \Delta_2 e\, A(t - 2\,\Delta\tau) + \cdots + \Delta_n e\, A(t - n\,\Delta\tau)$$
(14.4a)

Since (14.3a) may be represented in the integral form (14.3c), (14.4a) may also be represented in an integral form; this integral may be obtained by replacing $u(t)$ and $u(t - \tau)$ with $A(t)$ and $A(t - \tau)$ in (14.3c):

Superposition integral of the first type:

$$i(t) = e(0^+)A(t) + \int_0^t \frac{\partial e(\tau)}{\partial\tau}A(t - \tau)\,d\tau \qquad (14.4b)$$

Remark about the Network Problem. Equation (14.4b) may now be used to find the network response $i(t)$ with a given excitation $e(t)$ and a known indicial function $A(t)$. $e(\tau)$ is $e(t)$ with τ replacing t; both τ and t are the same time parameter.

Superposition integral of the first type for a discontinuous excitation. For the excitation with a finite number of discontinuities depicted in Fig. 14.3b, we may find

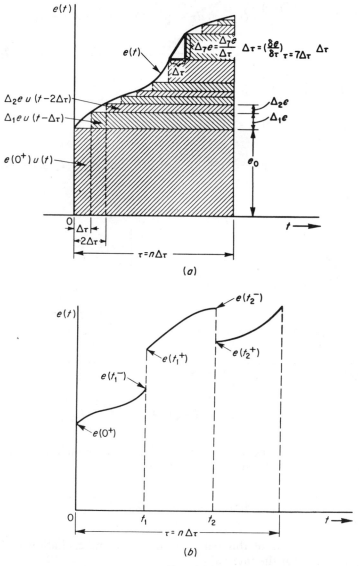

FIG. 14.3

the response for three different time intervals (1) $0 \le t < t_1$, (2) $t_1 \le t < t_2$, and (3) $t_2 \le t < \infty$. Equation (14.4b) applies to the first interval. For the second interval, we must modify (14.4) to take care of the discontinuity at $t = t_1$. For the interval $t_2 \le t < \infty$, we must take care of the discontinuities at $t = t_1$ and $t = t_2$.

We may consider that $e(t)$ in Fig. 14.3b has a discontinuity at $t = 0$; the term $e(0^+)A(t)$ in (14.4b) takes care of this discontinuity. We may similarly take care of the other discontinuities in Fig. 14.3b. The response of a network with an indicial function $A(t)$, subject to an excitation $e(t)$ as depicted in Fig. 14.3b, is therefore

$$i(t) = e(0^+)A(t) + \int_0^t \frac{\partial e(\tau)}{\partial \tau} A(t - \tau)\, d\tau \qquad 0 \leq t < t_1 \tag{14.5a}$$

$$i(t) = e(0^+)A(t) + \int_0^{t_1} \frac{\partial e(\tau)}{\partial \tau} A(t - \tau)\, d\tau + [e(t_1{}^+) - e(t_1{}^-)]A(t - t_1)$$
$$+ \int_{t_1}^t \frac{\partial e(\tau)}{\partial \tau} A(t - \tau)\, d\tau \qquad t_1 \leq t < t_2 \tag{14.5b}$$

$$i(t) = e(0^+)A(t) + \int_0^{t_1} \frac{\partial e(\tau)}{\partial \tau} A(t - \tau)\, d\tau$$
$$+ [e(t_1{}^+) - e(t_1{}^-)]A(t - t_1) + \int_{t_1}^{t_2} \frac{\partial e(\tau)}{\partial \tau} A(t - \tau)\, d\tau$$
$$+ [e(t_2{}^+) - e(t_2{}^-)]A(t - t_2) + \int_{t_2}^t \frac{\partial e(\tau)}{\partial \tau} A(t - \tau)\, d\tau \qquad t_2 \leq t < \infty \tag{14.5c}$$

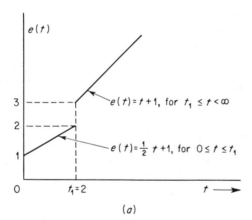
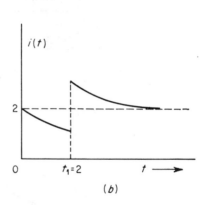

FIG. 14.4

Illustration. For a network consisting in a simple RC branch as depicted in Fig. 14.2b with $R = \frac{1}{2}$ and $C = 2$, the indicial function is

$$A(t) = \frac{1}{R} e^{-t/RC} = 2e^{-t}$$

We shall find the response of this network subject to the excitation in Fig. 14.4a. Using (14.5), we have, for the interval $0 \leq t < t_1$,

$$i(t) = 1A(t) + \int_0^t \frac{\partial}{\partial \tau}\left(\frac{1}{2}\tau + 1\right) A(t - \tau)\, d\tau$$
$$= (1)2e^{-t} + \int_0^t \left(\frac{1}{2}\right) 2e^{-(t-\tau)}\, d\tau$$
$$= 2e^{-t} + e^0 - e^{-t} = 1 + e^{-t} \qquad 0 \leq t < 2 \tag{14.6a}$$

For the interval $t_1 \leq t < \infty$,

$$i(t) = 1A(t) + \int_0^2 \frac{\partial}{\partial \tau}\left(\frac{1}{2}\tau + 1\right) A(t - \tau)\, d\tau$$

$$+ (3 - 2) A(t - 2) + \int_2^t \frac{\partial}{\partial \tau}(\tau + 1) A(t - \tau)\, d\tau$$

$$= 2 + e^{-t} + e^{-(t-2)} \qquad 2 \leq t < \infty \tag{14.6b}$$

This response is sketched in Fig. 14.4b.

B. Convolution of the Superposition Integral of the First Type

The superposition integral (14.4b) relates the excitation $e(t)$, the response $i(t)$, and the indicial function $A(t)$, which is a network function of time. In short, the superposition integral relates the functions of time.

We now want to investigate what happens if we apply Laplace transformation to the superposition integral (14.4b).

Convolution in the complex-frequency domain. Comparing the superposition integral (14.4b) with item 7 in Table 11.3, we note a convolution of $e'(t) = de(t)/dt$ and $A(t)$ in the time domain. By applying Laplace transformation to (14.4b), we obtain a convolution in the complex-frequency domain.

Let us define

$$\mathscr{L}[A(t)] = \mathbf{A}(s) \qquad \mathscr{L}[e(t)] = E(s) \qquad \mathscr{L}[i(t)] = I(s) \tag{14.7a}$$

and obtain, according to item 2 in Table 11.3,

$$\mathscr{L}\left[\frac{de(t)}{dt}\right] = sE(s) - e(0^+)$$

With the above notation, we apply Laplace transformation to the superposition integral (14.4b) with the aid of item 7 in Table 11.3. By identifying $A(t - \tau)$ with $f(t - \tau)$, $e'(\tau) = de(\tau)/d\tau$ with $g(\tau)$, and $sE(s) - e(0^+)$ with $G(s)$, we obtain

Complex convolution of superposition integral of the first type:

$$I(s) = e(0^+)\mathbf{A}(s) + \mathbf{A}(s)[sE(s) - e(0^+)] = s\mathbf{A}(s)E(s) \tag{17.7b}$$

Remarks. We now have two ways to find the network response $i(t)$ of a network with an indicial function $A(t)$ subject to an excitation $e(t)$:

1. Use the superposition integral (14.4b), which is a convolution in the domain of the time t.

2. Use (14.7b), which is a convolution in the domain of the complex frequency s, and obtain the response as $i(t) = \mathscr{L}^{-1}[I(s)]$.

We shall illustrate these two methods with the same problem.

For a network consisting in a simple RC branch as depicted in Fig. 14.2b with $R = \frac{1}{2}$ and $C = 2$, the indicial function is

$$A(t) = \frac{1}{R} e^{-t/RC} = 2e^{-t} \tag{14.8a}$$

We shall find the response $i(t)$ of this network subject to an excitation

$$e(t) = 1 \sin t \tag{14.8b}$$

Illustration 1.   We shall first solve this problem using the superposition integral of the first type in (14.4*b*):

$$i(t) = (0)2e^{-t} + \int_0^t \frac{d}{d\tau} (1 \sin \tau) \, 2e^{-(t-\tau)} \, d\tau$$

$$= 2e^{-t} \int_0^t \cos \tau \, e^\tau \, d\tau \tag{14.8c}$$

$$i(t) = \sin t + \cos t - e^{-t} \tag{14.8d}$$

Equation (14.8*d*) is obtained by identifying (14.8*c*) with the standard equation $\int e^{ax} \cos px \, dx = e^{ax}(a \cos px + p \sin px)/(a^2 + p^2)$ in a table of integrals.

Illustration 2.   We shall now solve this problem using the complex convolution in (14.7*b*):

$$A(s) = \mathscr{L}[2e^{-t}] = \frac{2}{s+1}$$

and

$$E(s) = \mathscr{L}[1 \sin t] = \frac{1}{s^2 + 1}$$

dictate that

$$I(s) = sA(s)E(s) = \frac{2s}{s+1} \frac{1}{s^2+1}$$

and, according to a standard procedure in Art. 13.2A,

$$i(t) = \mathscr{L}^{-1} \left[\frac{2s}{s+1} \frac{1}{s^2+1} \right] = \mathscr{L}^{-1} \left[\frac{1}{s^2+1} + \frac{s}{s^2+1} - \frac{1}{s+1} \right]$$

$$= \sin t + \cos t - e^{-t} \tag{14.8e}$$

which checks with (14.8*d*).

14.3. Unit-impulse function and Green's function

A. Unit-impulse Function

The unit-impulse function $\delta(t)$ was defined in (11.31*a*), and its Laplace transform evaluated in (11.32), as follows:

Definition.   A unit-impulse function $\delta(t)$ is a rectangular pulse starting at $t = 0$ with

Magnitude:	$I \to \infty$
Duration:	$t_\delta \to 0$
Product:	$It_\delta = 1$

$$\tag{14.9a}$$

as depicted in Fig. 11.2*a*.

Laplace transform of $\delta(t)$.   As in (11.32), we have

$$\mathscr{L}[\delta(t)] = 1 \tag{14.9b}$$

B. Green's Function

Characteristic response to a unit-impulse function.   When a unit-impulse excitation $\delta(t)$ is applied to a network at rest, i.e., one with zero-value initial conditions, the response $B(t)$ of the network is called a *Green's function.*   Like the indicial function, a Green's function may represent either a current response or a voltage response.

Illustrations.   The current response $i(t)$ of a simple *RL* network as depicted in Fig. 14.5*b*, subject to a unit-impulse voltage excitation, can easily be computed by

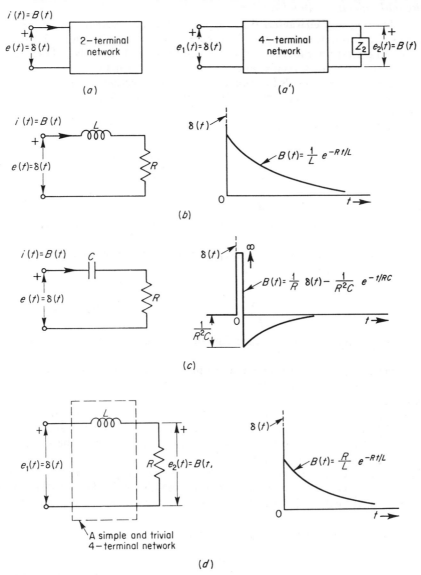

FIG. 14.5

finding, in succession, $\mathscr{L}[e(t)] = \mathscr{L}[\delta(t)] = 1$, $Z(s) = sL + R$, $I(s) = 1/(sL + R)$, and $i(t) = \mathscr{L}^{-1}[I(t)] = (1/L)e^{-Rt/L}$. This current response is, by definition, the Green's function of the network in the form

$$B(t) = \frac{1}{L} e^{-Rt/L} \qquad t \geq 0 \tag{14.10a}$$

as also depicted in Fig. 14.5b.

Similarly, the Green's function of a simple RC network is

$$B(t) = \frac{1}{R} \delta(t) - \frac{1}{R^2 C} e^{-t/RC} \qquad t \geq 0 \tag{14.10b}$$

as depicted in Fig. 14.5c, where $\delta(t)$ is a unit-impulse function as defined in (14.9a).

C. *Remarks about Green's Function*

Green's function and characteristic response. We have called the response to a unit-impulse excitation the characteristic response or Green's function. For the same (unit-impulse) excitation, different networks will respond differently. Therefore, this characteristic response or Green's function *characterizes* a network.

A relation between a Green's function and a network function. For a given Green's function, we can find the network function, for example, $Z(s)$, as a function of the complex frequency s.

For example, for the two-terminal network arrangement in Fig. 14.5a with known Green's function $B(t)$, we find

$$\mathscr{L}[B(t)] = \mathscr{L}[i(t)] = I(s) = \frac{E(s)}{Z(s)} = \frac{1}{Z(s)}$$

and

$$Z(s) = \frac{1}{\mathscr{L}[B(t)]} \tag{14.11}$$

where $E(s) = \mathscr{L}[e(t)] = \mathscr{L}[\delta(t)] = 1$ is the excitation function. Knowing $B(t)$, we can readily compute $Z(s)$.

As a numerical illustration, let us use the Green's function in Fig. 14.5b. With the aid of Table 11.2, Eq. (14.11) becomes

$$Z(s) = \frac{1}{\mathscr{L}[(1/L)e^{-Rt/L}]} = \frac{1}{(1/L)[1/(s + R/L)]}$$
$$= sL + R \tag{14.11a}$$

which is the driving-point impedance function of the simple *RL* network in Fig. 14.5b.

Green's function as a network function of time. Let us now summarize some of the properties of the Green's function:

1. A Green's function characterizes a network.

2. Knowing a Green's function, we can find a network function, and vice versa.

3. As will be discussed in Art. 14.4, given an arbitrary excitation and the Green's function of a network, we can find the network response. Thus, the Green's function plays the role of a network function.

We may therefore consider the Green's function $B(t)$ of a network to be a *network function of time*. The network functions, for example, $Z(s)$, $Y(s)$, $Z_T(s)$, and $G(s)$, which we have studied earlier are the *network functions of the complex frequency*.

14.4. Superposition integrals of impulse functions

A. *Superposition Integral of the Second Type*

Earlier, we assumed an excitation to be the sum of a large number of step functions as depicted in Fig. 14.3a; with the aid of the indicial function, we obtained the superposition integral of the first kind in (14.4b) as the network response.

We shall now assume an excitation to be the sum of a large number of impulse functions as depicted in Fig. 14.6; with the aid of the Green's function, we shall attempt to obtain another superposition integral as the network response.

Superposition integral of the second type. For a unit-impulse excitation $\delta(t)$ starting at $t = 0$, with the product of its magnitude I and time duration $t\delta$ equal to 1, the network response is $1 \times B(t)$, where $B(t)$ is the Green's function of the network.

For an impulse [e.g., the $(k + 1)$st shaded vertical strip in Fig. 14.6] in the excitation starting at $t = k\,\Delta\tau$, with the product of its magnitude $e(k\,\Delta\tau)$ and time duration $\Delta\tau$ equal to $e(k\,\Delta\tau)\,\Delta\tau$, the network response must be

$$e(k\,\Delta\tau)\,\Delta\tau\,B(t - k\,\Delta\tau) \qquad k = 0, 1, 2, \ldots, n \tag{14.12}$$

where $B(t - k\,\Delta\tau)$ is the Green's function of the network with an introduced time delay $k\,\Delta\tau$.

If we consider the excitation as a sum of a large number of impulse functions as depicted in Fig. 14.6, the principle of superposition for linear networks dictates that the response is the summation

$$i(t) = \sum_{k=0}^{n} e(k\,\Delta\tau)\,\Delta\tau\,B(t - k\,\Delta\tau)$$

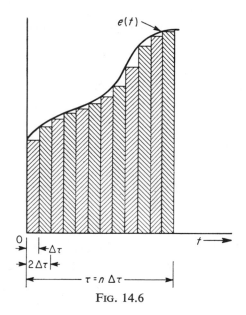

Letting $\tau = k\,\Delta\tau$ and $n \to \infty$ in the above equation, we obtain, according to the definition of an integral in the footnote associated with Eq. (8.3a),

Superposition integral of the second type:

$$i(t) = \int_0^t e(\tau)B(t - \tau)\,d\tau \qquad (14.13)$$

Remarks about the superposition integral of the second type. We find that:

1. Equation (14.13) may be used to find the network response $i(t)$ with given excitation $e(t)$ and known Green's function.

2. The Green's function of a network often contains a unit-impulse function; for example, see Fig. 14.5c. This means that the integrand $e(\tau)B(t - \tau)$ in (14.13)

Fig. 14.6

also contains a unit-impulse function, and the evaluation of this integral is not an easy task. For this reason, we shall modify (14.13) into another form which we shall call the superposition integral of the third type and treat in the next section.

B. *Superposition Integral of the Third Type*

We shall first introduce a functional relation between the indicial function and the Green's function of a network. This will enable us to represent the Green's function in terms of the indicial function and then replace the Green's function in (14.13) to obtain the superposition integral of the third type. The superposition integral of the third type has no impulse functions in its integrand.

A relation between indicial and Green's functions. Let us consider a two-terminal network with a driving-point impedance function $Z(s)$, an indicial function $A(t)$, and a Green's function $B(t)$.

We have worked out in (14.2) a relation between $A(t)$ and $Z(s)$:

$$s\mathscr{L}[A(t)] = \frac{1}{Z(s)}$$

According to item 2 in Table 11.3, the left-hand side of the above equation may be modified into

$$\mathscr{L}\left[\frac{d}{dt}A(t)\right] + A(0^+) = \frac{1}{Z(s)} \qquad (14.14a)$$

We have also worked out in (14.11) a relation between $B(t)$ and $Z(s)$:

$$\mathscr{L}[B(t)] = \frac{1}{Z(s)} \qquad (14.14b)$$

Equating (14.14*a*) with (14.14*b*) and taking the inverse Laplace transform, we find a relation between $A(t)$ and $B(t)$:

$$B(t) = \frac{d}{dt} A(t) + \mathcal{L}^{-1}[A(0^+)]$$

$$= \frac{d}{dt} A(t) + A(0^+)\,\delta(t) \qquad (14.15a)$$

If we introduce a time delay τ, the above equation becomes

$$B(t - \tau) = A(0^+)\delta(t - \tau) + \frac{\partial}{\partial t} A(t - \tau) \qquad (14.15b)$$

Superposition integral of the third type.   Substituting (14.15*b*) into (14.13), we find

$$i(t) = \int_0^t e(\tau)\left[A(0^+)\delta(t - \tau) + \frac{\partial}{\partial t} A(t - \tau)\right] d\tau$$

$$= A(0^+)\int_0^t e(\tau)\delta(t - \tau)\, d\tau + \int_0^t e(\tau) \frac{\partial}{\partial t} A(t - \tau)\, d\tau$$

The first term on the right-hand side of this equation is equal to $A(0^+)e(t)$.   This may be established in the following manner: (1) $\delta(t - \tau)$ is a unit-impulse function at $t = \tau$, and $\delta(t - \tau) = 0$ for $0 \leq \tau < t - \varepsilon$, where $\varepsilon > 0$ and $\varepsilon \to 0$.   This means $\int_0^t e(\tau)\delta(t - \tau)\, d\tau = \int_0^{t-\varepsilon} + \int_{t-\varepsilon}^t = 0 + \int_{t-\varepsilon}^t e(\tau)\delta(t - \tau)\, d\tau.$ (2) For a very small interval $t - \varepsilon \leq \tau \leq t$, $e(\tau) \cong e(t)$ is practically a constant and may be taken out of the integral sign.   This implies

$$\int_0^t e(\tau)\delta(t - \tau)\, d\tau = \int_{t-\varepsilon}^t [\quad]\, d\tau = e(t)\int_{t-\varepsilon}^t \delta(t - \tau)\, d\tau$$

(3) Letting $t' = t - \tau$ and $\int_{t-\varepsilon}^t \delta(t - \tau)\, d\tau = \int_\varepsilon^0 \delta(t')(-dt') = \int_0^\varepsilon \delta(t')\, dt' \to 1$ for $\varepsilon \to 0$ according to (11.31*b*), $\delta(t')$ being a unit-impulse function, we *now* have

$$\int_0^t e(\tau)\delta(t - \tau)\, d\tau = e(t)$$

The above expression now becomes

Superposition integral of the third type:

$$i(t) = A(0^+)e(t) + \int_0^t e(\tau) \frac{\partial}{\partial t} A(t - \tau)\, d\tau \qquad (14.16)$$

which we shall call the superposition integral of the third type.   Equation (14.16) may now be used to find the network response $i(t)$ with given excitation and known indicial function $A(t)$. $e(\tau)$ is $e(t)$ with τ replacing t; both τ and t are the same time parameter.

   Illustration.   For a network consisting in a simple *RC* branch as depicted in Fig. 14.2*b* with $R = \frac{1}{2}$ and $C = 2$, the indicial function is

$$A(t) = \frac{1}{R} e^{-t/RC} = 2e^{-t} \qquad (14.17a)$$

We shall now find the response $i(t)$ of this network subject to an excitation

$$e(t) = 1 \sin t \qquad (14.17b)$$

by applying the superposition integral of the third type in (14.16).
   We first find

$$A(0^+) = 2$$

$$\frac{\partial}{\partial t} A(t - \tau) = \frac{\partial}{\partial t} (2e^{-(t-\tau)}) = -2e^{-(t-\tau)}$$

Equation (14.16) now becomes

$$i(t) = (2)1 \sin t + \int_0^t (1 \sin \tau)(-2e^{-(t-\tau)}) \, d\tau \qquad (14.17c)$$

$$i(t) = \sin t + \cos t - e^{-t} \qquad (14.17d)$$

Equation (14.17d) is obtained by identifying the second term in (14.17c) with the standard equation $\int e^{ax} \sin px \, dx = e^{ax}(a \sin px - p \cos px)/(a^2 + p^2)$ in a table of integrals. Equation (14.17d) certainly checks with (14.8d), obtained with the aid of the superposition integral of the first type.

Remarks about the convolution in the complex-frequency domain. Comparing the superposition integral in (14.16) with item 7 in Table 11.3, we note a convolution of $A'(t) = dA(t)/dt$ and $e(t)$ in the time domain. By applying Laplace transformation to (14.16), we obtain a convolution in the complex-frequency domain.

Let us define

$$\mathcal{L}[A(t)] = \mathbf{A}(s) \qquad \mathcal{L}[e(t)] = E(s) \qquad \mathcal{L}[i(t)] = I(s) \qquad (14.18a)$$

and obtain, according to item 2 in Table 11.3,

$$\mathcal{L}\left[\frac{d}{dt} A(t)\right] = s\mathbf{A}(s) - A(0^+)$$

With the above notation, we apply Laplace transformation to the superposition integral (14.16) with the aid of item 7 in Table 11.3. By identifying $\partial A(t - \tau)/\partial t$ with $f(t - \tau)$, $e(\tau)$ with $g(\tau)$, and $s\mathbf{A}(s) - A(0^+)$ with $F(s)$, we obtain

Complex convolution of superposition integral of the third type:

$$I(s) = A(0^+)E(s) + E(s)[s\mathbf{A}(s) - A(0^+)] = s\mathbf{A}(s)E(s) \qquad (14.18b)$$

Comparing (14.7b) with (14.18b), we note that the complex convolutions of the superposition integrals of the first and the third types are the *same*. By applying Laplace transformation to (14.13) with the aid of item 7 in Table 11.3 and using the relation $\mathbf{B}(s) = s\mathbf{A}(s)$ which is obtained by equating (14.2) with (14.11), we find that the superposition integral of the second type also has the complex convolutions represented in (14.7b) and (14.18b).

C. Some Summarizing Remarks about the Superposition Integrals of the First and Third Types

Summarizing the problems of finding network responses using the superposition integrals, we have

Given problem, and solution (in time domain):

$$\begin{bmatrix} \text{Excitation } e(t) \text{ with} \\ \text{known indicial function} \\ A(t) \text{ of network} \end{bmatrix} \xrightarrow[\text{Use Eq. (14.4b) or (14.16)}]{\begin{array}{c}\text{Superposition integral of} \\ \text{1st or 3d type}\end{array}} [\text{Response } i(t)] \quad (14.19a)$$

$$\begin{array}{cc} E(s) = \mathcal{L}[e(t)] & i(t) = \mathcal{L}^{-1}[I(s)] \text{ by} \\ \text{by Table 11.2} & \text{procedure in Art. 13.2A} \end{array}$$

Equivalent problem and solution (in complex-frequency domain):

$$\begin{bmatrix} \text{Excitation function} \\ E(s) = \mathcal{L}[e(t)] \end{bmatrix} \xrightarrow[\text{Use Eq. (14.7b) or (14.18b)}]{\text{Complex convolution}} \begin{bmatrix} \text{Response} \\ \text{function } I(s) \end{bmatrix} \quad (14.19b)$$

14.5. Illustrative example: transient responses of an *RC*-coupled amplifier

A. Description of Problem

An ideal amplifier is one whose response is exactly identical to the excitation. However, no actual amplifier can accomplish this.

To study the performance of amplifiers capable of handling pulses and video signals, a unit-step excitation as indicated in Fig. 14.7a is often used as a *test signal*. This enables us to evaluate the amplifier performance in terms of:

1. *The response time*, which tells us how fast the amplifier responds to a "jump," e.g., the sudden application of a step function, in the excitation

2. *The staying power* or persistence of the response, which tells us how long the amplifier response stays up after the "jump," as the step function continues to be applied as the excitation.

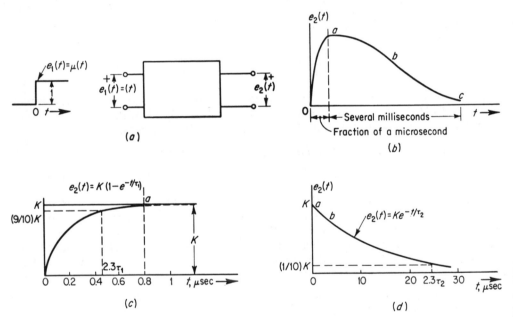

FIG. 14.7

Method of approach.   If we plot the experimental amplifier response subject to a unit-step excitation on a *distorted* time scale, we find the representation in Fig. 14.7b. If we plot with uniform time scales, we find (1) the representation in Fig. 14.7c for the rising portion of the response (time scale in microseconds) and (2) the representation in Fig. 14.7d for the rising portion (which is practically a vertical line, indicated as *oa* in the figure) as well as the decaying portion.

Knowing that two widely different time scales are involved, we shall attempt to make two separate studies, one on the *rise time* of the amplifier response, which is a measure of the "response time" (Art. 14.5C and D), and the other on the *decay time*, which is a measure of the "staying power" (Art. 14.5E and F).   Both the superposition-integral method (Art. 14.5C and E) and the Laplace-transformation method (Art. 14.5D and F) are used in making these studies.

Rise time and decay time of a network transient response. We shall define† the rise time of a network response as

$$T_1 = \text{time required for rising response to reach nine-tenths of}$$
$$\text{final maximum value} \qquad (14.20a)$$

For a simple rising response with a time constant $\tau_1 = R_1C_1$ as indicated in Fig. 14.7c, the rise time is

$$T_1 = \tau_1 \log_e 10 = 2.3\tau_1 \qquad (14.20a')$$

This may easily be verified by letting $e_2(T_1) = 9K/10$ in the expression $e_2(t) = K(1 - e^{-t/\tau_1})$ and solving for T_1.

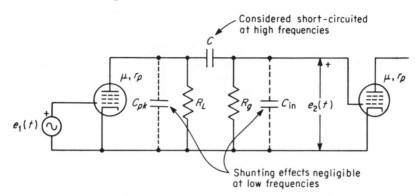

Considered short-circuited at high frequencies

Shunting effects negligible at low frequencies

FIG. 14.8

We shall define the decay time of a network response as

$$T_2 = \text{time required for decaying response to reach one-tenth of}$$
$$\text{initial maximum value} \qquad (14.20b)$$

For a simple decaying response with a time constant $\tau_2 = R_2C_2$ as indicated in Fig. 14.7d, the decay time is

$$T_2 = \tau_2 \log_e 10 = 2.3\tau_2 \qquad (14.20b')$$

This may easily be verified by letting $e_2(T_2) = K/10$ in the expression $e_2(t) = Ke^{-t/\tau_2}$ and solving for T_2.

B. Equivalent Circuits of an RC-coupled Amplifier

We shall investigate the equivalent circuits of an *RC*-coupled amplifier before we make the rise-time and decay-time studies of such an amplifier. The a-c circuit of an *RC*-coupled amplifier is given in Fig. 14.8. C_{pk} is the plate-to-cathode inter-electrode capacitance of the first tube, and C_{in} is the input capacitance of the next stage. The tubes indicated in the figure can be either triodes or pentodes. Associated with a vacuum tube, there are the parameters μ (amplification factor), g_m (transconductance), and r_p (plate resistance); an approximate relation $\mu = g_m r_p$ exists.

---

† Definitions vary among authors. The *rise time* of a network is sometimes defined as the time required for its rising response to reach 63.2 per cent, that is, $(1 - e^{-1}) \times 100$ per cent, of its final maximum value, and the *decay time* as the time required for its decaying response to reach 36.8 per cent, that is, $e^{-1} \times 100$ per cent, of its initial maximum value. With these definitions, we find $T_1 = \tau_1$ and $T_2 = \tau_2$.

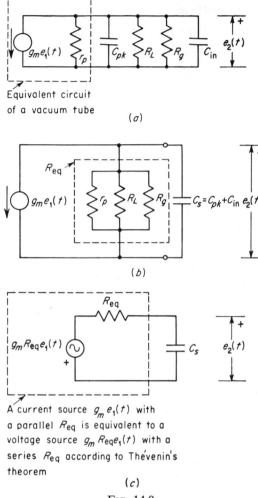

Equivalent circuit
of a vacuum tube

(*a*)

(*b*)

A current source $g_m e_1(t)$ with
a parallel R_{eq} is equivalent to a
voltage source $g_m R_{eq} e_1(t)$ with
series R_{eq} according to Thévenin's
theorem

(*c*)

FIG. 14.9

Some circuit considerations at different frequencies. At a high frequency, for instance 10 Mc/sec, the reactance X_c of the coupling capacitor C is very small. For a typical value $C = 0.01$ μf, $X_c = 1.6$ ohms. We may therefore consider C short-circuited, and leave it out in our study of the high-frequency behavior of the amplifier.

At a low frequency, for instance 10 cps, the reactances X_{pk} and X_{in} of C_{pk} and C_{in} are extremely high. For typical values $C_{pk} = C_{in} = 10$ $\mu\mu$f, $X_{pk} = X_{in} = 1.6 \times 10^9$ ohms. We may therefore consider C_{pk} and C_{in} open-circuited, and leave them out in our study of the low-frequency behavior of the amplifier.

High-frequency equivalent circuit. Using the equivalent circuit of a vacuum tube and Thévenin's theorem, we may find the high-frequency equivalent circuit of the RC-coupled amplifier in Fig. 14.9c, which is simplified from Fig. 14.9a and b, where

$$e_1(t) = \text{excitation to amplifier as shown in Fig. 14.8}$$

$$R_{eq} = \frac{1}{1/r_p + 1/R_L + 1/R_g}$$

$$C_s = C_{pk} + C_{in} \tag{14.21a}$$

Low-frequency equivalent circuit. Similarly, we find the low-frequency equivalent circuit in Fig. 14.10c, which is simplified from Fig. 14.10a and b, where

$$R'_{\text{eq}} = R_g + \frac{R_L r_p}{R_L + r_p} \tag{14.21b}$$

C. Rise-time Study of an RC-coupled Amplifier Using the Superposition Integral

Equivalent circuit for rise-time study. To study the rise-time behavior of the response is to study the rising portion *oa* of the response in Fig. 14.7b. We are therefore concerned with a very short time interval, say a fraction of a microsecond, immediately after the application of the unit-step excitation in Fig. 14.7a.

Whenever a step function is suddenly applied to a circuit containing capacitors, each capacitor will *first* offer no impedance to current passing through it and *then* offer some small but increasing impedance during a very short interval; then this impedance will increase until the capacitor behaves like an open circuit (to this step function) and stops the current. This means that, during a very short interval after the application of a unit-step function as excitation, the coupling capacitor *C* in Fig. 14.8 may be considered short-circuited and left out; the capacitances C_{pk} and C_{in}, which have considerable shunting effects, must not be neglected. This means that, if we wish to make a rise-time study, we must use the *high-frequency equivalent circuits* of the amplifier in Fig. 14.9.

Since the excitation $e_1(t)$ is a unit-step function,

$$e_1(t) = u(t) = \begin{cases} 1 & t \geq 0 \\ 0 & t < 0 \end{cases} \tag{14.22}$$

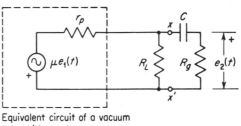

Equivalent circuit of a vacuum tube with a voltage source   *(a)*

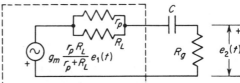

Equivalent to the portion of the network in (*a*) to the left of *xx′*
               (b)

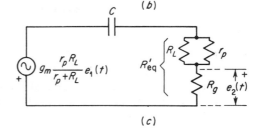

(c)

Fɪɢ. 14.10

we may replace the voltage source in Fig. 14.9c by an arrangement of a battery in series with an on-off switch, as shown in Fig. 14.11a.

Indicial function; normalized rising transient of a single-stage amplifier. For the one-stage amplifier in Fig. 14.8 subject to a unit-step excitation, the rising transient response can easily be evaluated from the equivalent circuit in Fig. 14.11a:

$$e_2(t) = -g_m R_{\text{eq}}(1 - e^{-t/\tau_1}) \qquad \tau_1 = R_{\text{eq}} C_s$$

Let us now use the normalized expression

Normalized rising response of one stage:

$$\bar{e}_2(t) = \frac{e_2(t)}{-g_m R_{\text{eq}}} = 1 - e^{-t/\tau_1} \qquad \tau_1 = R_{\text{eq}} C_s \tag{14.23}$$

The response of a network, normalized or unnormalized, subject to a unit-step excitation is, by definition (Art. 14.1A), the indicial function $A(t)$ of the network.

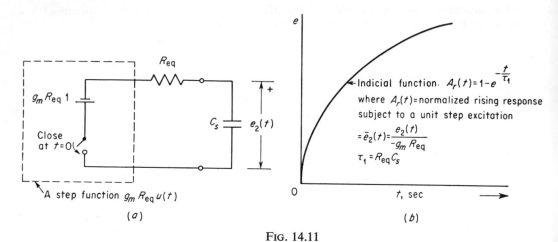

FIG. 14.11

Thus we have the indicial function, which is an indicial voltage-ratio function, for the rising portion of the response of the RC-coupled amplifier in Fig. 14.8:

Indicial function:

$$A_r(t) = 1 - e^{-t/\tau_1} \qquad \tau_1 = R_{eq}C_s \tag{14.24}$$

where R_{eq} and C_s are defined in (14.21a) and illustrated in Fig. 14.9b. This indicial function, which also represents the normalized response (14.23), has the general shape indicated in Fig. 14.11b.

Rise time for a single-stage amplifier. According to definition (14.20a), we may let $\bar{e}_2(T_1) = \frac{9}{10}$ in (14.23) or use (14.20a'):

Rise time for one stage:

$$T_1 = 2.3\tau_1 = 2.3R_{eq}C_s \qquad \text{sec} \tag{14.25}$$

where R_{eq} and C_s are defined in (14.21).

Normalized rising transient of an n-stage amplifier. Suppose that we consider an RC-coupled amplifier having n identical stages as indicated in Fig. 14.12. We shall use the following notations:

$$\bar{e}_1(t) = e_1(t) = u(t) = \text{normalized excitation to first stage}$$

$$\bar{e}_2(t) = \frac{e_2(t)}{-g_m R_{eq}} = \text{normalized response of first stage as well as normalized excitation to second stage, as in (14.23)}$$

and $\quad \bar{e}_k(t) = \dfrac{e_k(t)}{(-g_m R_{eq})^{k-1}} = \text{normalized excitation to } k\text{th stage} \qquad (14.26a)$

$$\bar{e}_{k+1}(t) = \frac{e_{k+1}(t)}{(-g_m R_{eq})^k} = \text{normalized response of } k\text{th stage} \tag{14.26b}$$

Considering the *second stage*, we have (1) normalized excitation $\bar{e}_2(t)$ in (14.23) and (2) indicial function $A_r(t)$ in (14.24). We may now use superposition integral (14.4b) or (14.16) to find the response:

$$\bar{e}_3(t) = \bar{e}_2(0^+)A_r(t) + \int_0^t \frac{\partial \bar{e}_2(\tau)}{\partial \tau} A_r(t - \tau) \, d\tau \tag{14.27}$$

With $\bar{e}_2(t)$ and $A_r(t)$ as in (14.23) and (14.24), (14.27) becomes

Normalized (rising) response of two stages:

$$\bar{e}_3(t) = \frac{e_3(t)}{(-g_m R_{eq})^2} = 1 - e^{-t/\tau_1} - \frac{1}{\tau_1}\, t e^{-t/\tau_1} \qquad \tau_1 = R_{eq}C_s \qquad (14.28)$$

Similarly, we may repeat the application (except for notation) of (14.27). For example, we find $\bar{e}_4(t)$ from the known expressions $\bar{e}_3(t)$ and $A_r(t)$, $\bar{e}_5(t)$ from the known expressions $\bar{e}_4(t)$ and $A_r(t), \ldots, \bar{e}_{n+1}(t)$ from the known expressions $\bar{e}_n(t)$ and $A_r(t)$. We find

Normalized rising response of n stages:

$$\bar{e}_{n+1}(t) = \frac{e_{n+1}(t)}{(-g_m R_{eq})^n} = 1 - \left[1 + \frac{t}{\tau_1} + \frac{1}{2!}\left(\frac{t}{\tau_1}\right)^2 + \frac{1}{3!}\left(\frac{t}{\tau_1}\right)^3 + \cdots \right.$$

$$\left. + \frac{1}{(n-1)!}\left(\frac{t}{\tau_1}\right)^{n-1} \right] e^{-t/\tau_1} \qquad (14.29)$$

where $\tau_1 = R_{eq}C_s$, and R_{eq} and C_s are defined in (14.21a) and illustrated in Fig. 14.9b.

Rise time for an *n*-stage amplifier. Letting $\bar{e}_{n+1}(T_1) = \frac{9}{10}$ in (14.29) and solving for T_1, we have the rise time of an *n*-stage amplifier. But, solving $\bar{e}_{n+1}(T_1) = \frac{9}{10}$ for T_1 is a laborious (if not impossible) task. However, T_1 can easily be determined graphically. Suppose we (1) plot (14.29) in an $\bar{e}_{n+1}(t)$ versus t graph similar to the one in Fig. 14.7c with unity as its maximum value and (2) find a point $t = T_1$ on the graph such that $\bar{e}_{n+1}(T_1) = \frac{9}{10}$. T_1, thus determined, is the rise time of the amplifier.

D. Rise-time Study of an RC-coupled Amplifier Using a Laplace-transformation Method

We may use *complex convolution* in (14.7b), the Laplace transform of the superposition integral, to find expression (14.29) for the rising transient response of n stages subject to a unit-step excitation. However, we shall use a different approach here: Let us set up the problem as well as solve it with the aid of Laplace transforms.

For the reason stated at the beginning of Art. 14.5C, we shall use the high-frequency equivalent circuit in Fig. 14.9c in the rise-time study.

Transfer function of a single stage. Taking the Laplace transforms of the quantities involved in Fig. 14.9c,

$$\mathscr{L}[e_1(t)] = E_1(s) \qquad \mathscr{L}[e_2(t)] = E_2(s) \qquad \mathscr{L}[g_m R_{eq}e_1(t)] = g_m R_{eq}E_1(s) \quad (14.30)$$

we find

$$E_2(s) = \frac{-g_m R_{eq}E_1(s)}{R_{eq} + 1/sC_s}\, \frac{1}{sC_s}$$

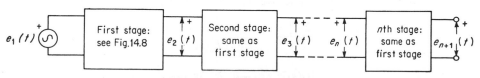

FIG. 14.12

The above equation implies a transfer function, i.e., a transfer voltage-ratio function

Transfer function:

$$G(s) = \frac{E_2(s)}{E_1(s)} = \frac{-g_m R_{\text{eq}}}{\tau_1 s + 1} \qquad \tau_1 = R_{\text{eq}} C_s \tag{14.31}$$

for a one-stage *RC*-coupled amplifier as depicted in Fig. 14.13*a*, where R_{eq} and C_s are defined in (14.21*a*) and illustrated in Fig. 14.9*b*.

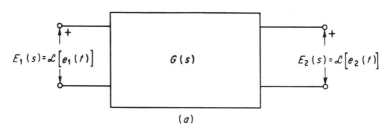

(*a*)

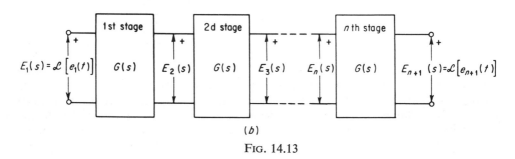

(*b*)

FIG. 14.13

Normalized rising transient of a one-stage amplifier. For a unit-step excitation $e_1(t) = u(t)$, $E_1(s) = 1/s$. Using (14.31),

$$E_2(s) = -g_m R_{\text{eq}} \frac{1}{\tau_1 s + 1} \frac{1}{s}$$

$$= -g_m R_{\text{eq}} \left(\frac{1}{s} - \frac{1}{s + 1/\tau_1} \right)$$

and finding $e_2(t) = \mathscr{L}^{-1}[E_2(s)]$ with the aid of Table 11.2, we have

Normalized rising response of one stage:

$$\bar{e}_2(t) = \frac{e_2(t)}{-g_m R_{\text{eq}}} = 1 - e^{-t/\tau_1} \qquad \tau_1 = R_{\text{eq}} C_s \tag{14.32}$$

which checks with the result in (14.23), derived with the superposition integral.

Normalized rising transient of an *n*-stage amplifier. For *n* identical stages, we use the schematic in Fig. 14.13*b*. The overall transfer function is

$$G_n(s) = \frac{E_{n+1}(s)}{E_1(s)} = \frac{E_2(s)}{E_1(s)} \frac{E_3(s)}{E_2(s)} \cdots \frac{E_{n+1}(s)}{E_n(s)}$$

$$= [G(s)]^n = (-g_m R_{\text{eq}})^n \frac{1}{(\tau_1 s + 1)^n}$$

For a unit-step excitation $e_1(t) = u(t)$, $E_1(s) = 1/s$. Using the above expression,

$$E_{n+1}(s) = (-g_m R_{eq})^n \frac{1}{(\tau_1 s + 1)^n} \frac{1}{s}$$

$$= (-g_m R_{eq})^n \left[\frac{1}{s} - \frac{1}{s + 1/\tau_1} - \frac{1/\tau_1}{(s + 1/\tau_1)^2} - \frac{(1/\tau_1)^2}{(s + 1/\tau_1)^3} - \cdots \right.$$

$$\left. - \frac{(1/\tau_1)^{n-1}}{(s + 1/\tau_1)^n} \right]$$

and finding $e_{n+1}(t) = \mathscr{L}^{-1}[E_{n+1}(s)]$ with the aid of Table 11.2, we have

Normalized rising response of n stages:

$$\bar{e}_{n+1}(t) = \frac{e_{n+1}(t)}{(-g_m R_{eq})^n}$$

$$= 1 - \left[1 + \frac{t}{\tau_1} + \frac{1}{2!}\left(\frac{t}{\tau_1}\right)^2 + \frac{1}{3!}\left(\frac{t}{\tau_1}\right)^3 + \cdots + \frac{1}{(n-1)!}\left(\frac{t}{\tau_1}\right)^{n-1} \right] e^{-t/\tau_1}$$

$$\tau_1 = R_{eq} C_s \quad (14.33)$$

which checks with the result in (14.29), derived with the superposition integral. For the computation of the rise time, see the paragraph following (14.29).

E. Decay-time Study of an RC-coupled Amplifier Using the Superposition Integral

Equivalent circuit for decay-time study. To study the decay-time behavior of the response is to study the decaying portion *abc* of the response in Fig. 14.7b or d. We are therefore concerned with a comparatively long time interval, say several milliseconds, after the application of the unit-step excitation in Fig. 14.7a.

We shall find that, during this *long* interval, the coupling capacitor *C* in Fig. 14.8 offers a considerable impedance and limits the current passing through it, until it cuts the current off entirely. On the other hand, not too much current is passing through C_{pk} and C_{in} and the shunting effects of these two capacitances are negligible. We therefore must take *C* into consideration, and may neglect C_{pk} and C_{in} entirely. This means that, if we wish to make a decay-time study, we must use the *low-frequency equivalent circuits* of the amplifier in Fig. 14.10.

Since the excitation $e_1(t)$ is a unit-step function,

$$e_1(t) = u(t) = \begin{cases} 1 & t \geq 0 \\ 0 & t < 0 \end{cases}$$

we may replace the voltage source in Fig. 14.10c by an arrangement of a battery in series with an on-off switch, as shown in Fig. 14.14a.

Indicial function; normalized decaying transient of a single-stage amplifier. For the one-stage amplifier in Fig. 14.8 subject to a unit-step excitation, the decaying transient response can be evaluated from the equivalent circuit in Fig. 14.14a:

$$e_2(t) = -g_m R_{eq} e^{-t/\tau_2} \qquad \tau_2 = R'_{eq} C$$

where R_{eq} and R'_{eq} are defined in (14.21). Let us now use the normalized expression

Normalized decaying response of one stage:

$$\bar{e}_2(t) = \frac{e_2(t)}{-g_m R_{eq}} = e^{-t/\tau_2} \qquad \tau_2 = R'_{eq} C \qquad (14.34)$$

The response of a network, normalized or unnormalized, subject to a unit-step excitation is, by definition (Art. 14.1A), the indicial function $A(t)$ of the network. Thus we have the indicial function, which is an indicial voltage-ratio function, for the decaying portion of the response of the RC-coupled amplifier in Fig. 14.8:

Indicial function:

$$A_d(t) = e^{-t/\tau_2} \qquad \tau_2 = R'_{eq}C \qquad (14.35)$$

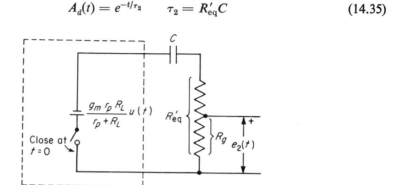

A step function $g_m r_p R_L u(t)/(r_p + R_L)$

(a)

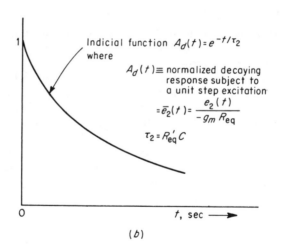

(b)

FIG. 14.14

where R'_{eq} is defined in (14.21b), and R'_{eq} and C are illustrated in Fig. 14.10c. This indicial function, which also represents the normalized response (14.34), has the general shape indicated in Fig. 14.14b.

Decay time for a single-stage amplifier. According to definition (14.20b), we may let $\bar{e}_2(T_2) = \frac{1}{10}$ in (14.34) or use (14.20b'):

Decay time for one stage:

$$T_2 = 2.3\tau_2 = 2.3R'_{eq}C \qquad \text{sec} \qquad (14.36)$$

where R'_{eq} is defined in (14.21b) and illustrated in Fig. 14.10c; C is the coupling capacitance in Fig. 14.8.

Normalized decaying transient of an *n*-stage amplifier.   Again we consider the circuit in Fig. 14.12 and use the notation in (14.26).

Considering the *second stage* in Fig. 14.12, we have (1) normalized excitation $\bar{e}_2(t)$ in (14.34) and (2) indicial function $A_d(t)$ in (14.35). We may now use super-position integral (14.4*b*) or (14.16) to find the response:

$$\bar{e}_3(t) = \bar{e}_2(0^+)A_d(t) + \int_0^t \frac{\partial \bar{e}_2(\tau)}{\partial \tau} A_d(t - \tau)\, d\tau \tag{14.37}$$

With $\bar{e}_2(t)$ and $A_d(t)$ as in (14.34) and (14.35), (14.37) becomes

Normalized decaying response of two stages:

$$\bar{e}_3(t) = \frac{e_3(t)}{(-g_m R_{eq})^2} = \left(1 - \frac{t}{\tau_2}\right)e^{-t/\tau_2} \qquad \tau_2 = R'_{eq}C \tag{14.38}$$

Similarly, we may repeat the application (except for notation) of (14.37). For example, we find $\bar{e}_4(t)$ from the known expressions $\bar{e}_3(t)$ and $A_d(t)$, $\bar{e}_5(t)$ from the known expressions $\bar{e}_4(t)$ and $A_d(t), \ldots, \bar{e}_{n+1}(t)$ from the known expressions $\bar{e}_n(t)$ and $A_d(t)$. We find

Normalized decaying response of n stages:

$$\bar{e}_{n+1}(t) = \frac{e_{n+1}(t)}{(-g_m R_{eq})^n}$$

$$= \left[1 - (n-1)\frac{t}{\tau_2} + \frac{(n-1)(n-2)}{(2!)^2}\left(\frac{t}{\tau_2}\right)^2 - \frac{(n-1)(n-2)(n-3)}{(3!)^2}\left(\frac{t}{\tau_2}\right)^3 \right.$$

$$\left. + \cdots + (-1)^{n-1}\frac{1}{(n-1)!}\left(\frac{t}{\tau_2}\right)^{n-1}\right]e^{-t/\tau_2} \tag{14.39}$$

where $\tau_2 = R'_{eq}C$, and R'_{eq} is defined in (14.21*b*) and illustrated in Fig. 14.10*c*; C is the coupling capacitance in Fig. 14.8.

Decay time for an *n*-stage amplifier.   Letting $\bar{e}_{n+1}(T_2) = \frac{1}{10}$ in (14.39) and solving for T_2, we have the decay time of an *n*-stage amplifier. But, solving $\bar{e}_{n+1}(T_2) = \frac{1}{10}$ for T_2 is a laborious (if not impossible) task. However, T_2 can easily be determined graphically. Suppose we (1) plot (14.39) in an $\bar{e}_{n+1}(t)$ versus t graph similar to the one in Fig. 14.7*d* and (2) find a point $t = T_2$ on the graph such that $\bar{e}_{n+1}(T_2) = \frac{1}{10}$. T_2, thus determined, is the decay time of the amplifier.

F. Decay-time Study of an RC-coupled Amplifier Using a Laplace-transformation Method

We may use *complex convolution* in (14.7*b*), the Laplace transform of the super-position integral, to find expression (14.39) for the decaying transient response of *n* stages subject to a unit-step excitation. However, we shall use a different approach here: Let us set up the problem as well as solve it with the aid of Laplace transforms.

For the reason stated at the beginning of Art. 14.5E, we shall use the low-frequency equivalent circuit in Fig. 14.10*c* in the decay-time study.

Transfer function of a single stage.   Taking the Laplace transforms of the quantities involved in Fig. 14.10*c*,

$$\mathscr{L}[e_1(t)] = E_1(s) \qquad \mathscr{L}[e_2(t)] = E_2(s)$$

$$\mathscr{L}\left[g_m \frac{r_p R_L}{r_p + R_L}\, e_1(t)\right] = g_m \frac{r_p R_L}{r_p + R_L}\, E_1(s) \tag{14.40}$$

we find

$$E_2(s) = \frac{[-g_m r_p R_L/(r_p + R_L)]E_1(s)}{R'_{eq} + 1/sC} R_g$$

Replacing $r_p R_L R_g/(r_p + R_L)$ in the numerator of the above equation with $R'_{eq}R_{eq}$ according to the definitions of R'_{eq} and R_{eq} in (14.21), we may readily obtain a transfer function, i.e., a transfer voltage-ratio function,

Transfer function:

$$G(s) = \frac{E_2(s)}{E_1(s)} = -g_m R_{eq} \frac{\tau_2 s}{\tau_2 s + 1} \qquad \tau_2 = R'_{eq} C \qquad (14.41)$$

for a one-stage RC-coupled amplifier as depicted in Fig. 14.13a, where R'_{eq} is defined in (14.21b) and illustrated in Fig. 14.10c, and C is the coupling capacitance in Fig. 14.8.

Normalized decaying transient of a one-stage amplifier. For a unit-step excitation $e_1(t) = u(t)$, $E_1(s) = 1/s$. Using (14.41),

$$E_2(s) = -g_m R_{eq} \frac{\tau_2 s}{\tau_2 s + 1} \frac{1}{s}$$

$$= -g_m R_{eq} \frac{1}{s + 1/\tau_2} \qquad \tau_2 = R'_{eq} C$$

and finding $e_2(t) = \mathscr{L}^{-1}[E_2(s)]$ with the aid of Table 11.2, we have

Normalized decaying response of one stage:

$$\bar{e}_2(t) = \frac{e_2(t)}{-g_m R_{eq}} = e^{-t/\tau_2} \qquad \tau_2 = R'_{eq} C \qquad (14.42)$$

which checks with the result in (14.34), derived with the superposition integral.

Normalized decaying transient of an n-stage amplifier. For n identical stages, we use the schematic in Fig. 14.13b. The overall transfer function is

$$G_n(s) = \frac{E_{n+1}(s)}{E_1(s)} = \frac{E_2(s)}{E_1(s)} \frac{E_3(s)}{E_2(s)} \cdots \frac{E_{n+1}(s)}{E_n(s)}$$

$$= [G(s)]^n = (-g_m R_{eq})^n \left(\frac{\tau_2 s}{\tau_2 s + 1}\right)^n \qquad (14.43)$$

For a unit-step excitation $e_1(t) = u(t)$, $E_1(s) = 1/s$. Using (14.43),

$$E_{n+1}(s) = (-g_m R_{eq})^n \left(\frac{\tau_2 s}{\tau_2 s + 1}\right)^n \frac{1}{s} \qquad (14.44a)$$

$$E_{n+1}(s) = (-g_m R_{eq})^n \tau_2 \left[\frac{1}{\tau_2 s + 1} - (n-1)\left(\frac{1}{\tau_2 s + 1}\right)^2 \right.$$

$$\left. + \frac{(n-1)(n-2)}{2!}\left(\frac{1}{\tau_2 s + 1}\right)^3 \cdots + (-1)^{n-1}\left(\frac{1}{\tau_2 s + 1}\right)^n\right]^\dagger \qquad (14.44b)$$

† $[\tau_2 s/(\tau_2 s + 1)]^n/s = [\tau_2/(\tau_2 s + 1)][\tau_2 s/(\tau_2 s + 1)]^{n-1} = [\tau_2/(\tau_2 s + 1)][1 - 1/(\tau_2 s + 1)]^{n-1}$ is expanded to (14.44b) according to the standard form of *binomial expansion*.

and finding $e_{n+1}(t) = \mathcal{L}^{-1}[E_{n+1}(s)]$ with the aid of Table 11.2, we have

Normalized decaying response of n stages:

$$\bar{e}_{n+1}(t) = \frac{e_{n+1}(t)}{(-g_m R_{eq})^n} = \left[1 - (n-1)\frac{t}{\tau_2} + \frac{(n-1)(n-2)}{(2!)^2}\left(\frac{t}{\tau_2}\right)^2 \right.$$

$$\left. - \frac{(n-1)(n-2)(n-3)}{(3!)^2}\left(\frac{t}{\tau_2}\right)^3 \cdots + (-1)^{n-1}\frac{1}{(n-1)!}\left(\frac{t}{\tau_2}\right)^{n-1} \right] e^{-t/\tau_2}$$

$$\tau_2 = R'_{eq} C \quad (14.45)$$

which checks with the result in (14.39), derived with the superposition integral. For the computation of the decay time, see the paragraph following (14.39).

PROBLEMS

14.1. Given: The two-terminal network in Fig. P 14.1.

(a) Find the indicial function $A(t)$ as the current response, say $i(t) = A(t)$, subject to the unit-step voltage excitation $e(t) = u(t)$.

(b) Find the Green's function $B(t)$ as the current response, say $i(t) = B(t)$, subject to the unit-impulse excitation $e(t) = \delta(t)$.

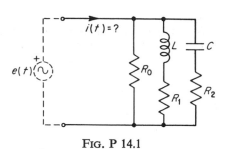

FIG. P 14.1

14.2. Given: The two-terminal network in Fig. P 14.2.

(a) Find the indicial function $A(t)$ as the voltage response, say $v(t) = A(t)$, subject to the unit-step current excitation $i(t) = u(t)$.

(b) Find the Green's function $B(t)$ as the voltage response, say $v(t) = B(t)$, subject to the unit-impulse excitation $i(t) = \delta(t)$.

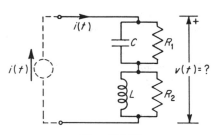

FIG. P 14.2

14.3. Given: The four-terminal network arrangement in Fig. P 12.12 with known transfer voltage-ratio function $G(s)$.

(a) Find the indicial function $A(t)$ as the voltage response, say $e_2(t) = A(t)$, subject to the unit-step voltage excitation $e_1(t) = u(t)$.

(b) Find the Green's function $B(t)$ as the voltage response, say $e_2(t) = B(t)$, subject to the unit-impulse voltage excitation $e_1(t) = \delta(t)$.

14.4. Repeat Prob. 14.3 for the four-terminal network arrangement in Fig. P 12.13 with known $A(s) = I_2(s)/I_1(s)$ for the indicial and Green functions $A(t)$ and $B(t)$ as the current responses subject to current excitations.

14.5. Given: A four-terminal network arrangement whose voltage response subject to a voltage excitation $e_1(t) = e^{-t}$ is

$$e_2(t) = \tfrac{1}{2}e^{-t} - e^{-2t} + \tfrac{1}{2}e^{-3t}$$

(a) Find the indicial function $A(t)$.

(b) Find the Green's function $B(t)$.

14.6. Given: An excitation $e(t)$ as shown in Fig. P 14.6 is applied to a network with indicial function

$$A(t) = 1 + 2e^{-t} + 3e^{-2t}$$

Find the response using a superposition integral.

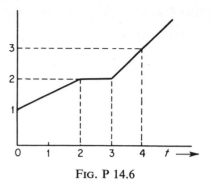

FIG. P 14.6

14.7. Given: An excitation $e(t)$ as shown in Fig. P 14.7 is applied to a network with indicial function

$$A(t) = 1 + 2e^{-t} + 3e^{-2t}$$

Find the response using a superposition integral.

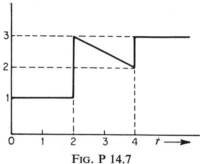

FIG. P 14.7

14.8. Given: An excitation $e(t)$ as shown in Fig. P 14.8 is applied to a network with indicial function

$$A(t) = 1 + 2e^{-t} + 3e^{-2t}$$

Find the response using a superposition integral.

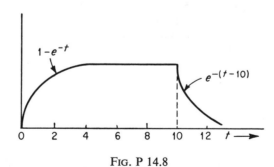

FIG. P 14.8

14.9. Given: The two-terminal network in Fig. P 14.2 with indicial function $A(t)$ and Green's function $B(t)$ obtained in Prob. 14.2 is now subject to the current excitation $i(t)$ sketched in Fig. P 14.6.

(*a*) Using $A(t)$ and a superposition integral, obtain the voltage response $e(t)$. It will be necessary to interchange the symbols i and e in the superposition integral in (14.4*b*) or (14.16) for correct notation in the present problem.

(*b*) Using $B(t)$ and a superposition integral, obtain the voltage response $e(t)$. Compare with the result of (*a*).

14.10. Repeat Prob. 14.9 for the current excitation $i(t)$ sketched in Fig. P 14.8.

14.11. Given: The four-terminal network arrangement in Fig. P 12.12 with indicial function $A(t)$ and Green's function $B(t)$ obtained in Prob. 14.3 is now subject to the voltage excitation $e_1(t)$ sketched in Fig. P 14.6.

(a) Using $A(t)$ and a superposition integral, obtain the voltage response $e_2(t)$.

(b) Using $B(t)$ and a superposition integral, obtain the voltage response $e_2(t)$. Compare with the result of (a).

14.12. Repeat Prob. 14.11 for the voltage excitation $e_1(t)$ sketched in Fig. P 14.8.

14.13. Given: A series-compensated video amplifier, which may be represented by Fig. 14.8 with a compensating inductance L added in series with R_L, with the assumptions $R_L \ll R_g$ and $R_L \ll r_p$.

(a) Perform a rise-time study, using superposition integrals for a single-stage and a two-stage amplifier. REFERENCE: See Art. 14.5C.

(b) Sketch the normalized rising responses, $\bar{e}_2(t)$ for a single-stage amplifier and $\bar{e}_3(t)$ for a two-stage amplifier.

If desired, assign appropriate circuit values, in lieu of letter symbols, in working out this problem.

part F The use of signal-flow diagrams as a tool in network analysis

In Part F we study the signal-flow method of analysis. In this method we use a "signal-flow diagram" as a graphical representation of the linear voltage-current relations of a network and reduce it to simpler forms to obtain (1) network functions and (2) network parameters, and to determine, through the network functions, (3) network responses and (4) network stability. The signal-flow method may also be used for similar problems in control systems.

Since the signal-flow method is particularly adaptable to the analysis of transistor circuits, Chaps. 15 and 17 are devoted to such a study. However, the material in Part F is so presented that the omission of Chaps. 15 and 17 will not impair reading continuity. The reader interested only in the general applications of signal-flow techniques may read Chap. 16 directly.

15 Description of transistor amplifiers for use in signal-flow analysis and stability study

15.1. Description of problem

We have reviewed, in Chap. 2, two classical methods of analysis: (1) the loop method of analysis and (2) the nodal method of analysis. They are used primarily to obtain certain functions of a given network; once a network function is obtained, we may use it to find the response of the network subject to a given excitation, as we saw in Art. 12.2E.

We shall introduce in Chap. 16 a third method of analysis employing the so-called "signal-flow diagrams." Like the loop and nodal methods, the method of signal-flow analysis is used to obtain certain functions of a given network and, indirectly, to find the response of the network subject to a given excitation. However, the method of signal-flow analysis may also be used in the study of closed-loop control systems and their stability problems.

In this chapter, we shall briefly describe some transistor amplifiers as background material for later use in the study and application of signal-flow analysis in Chaps. 16 and 17 and in the stability study of closed-loop systems in Chaps. 18 through 22. A feedback transistor amplifier is a closed-loop system and is subject to the same kind of stability problems as other closed-loop systems.

Specifically, the present chapter is written for the reasons stated in the following remarks:

Remark 1. *We shall describe some transistor amplifiers in block diagrams and introduce problems of analysis (i.e., finding certain network functions, etc.) to be solved by the signal-flow method.* After we have studied the method of signal-flow analysis in Chap. 16, the problems introduced here will be solved in Chap. 17.

Remark 2. *Illustrating with transistor feedback amplifiers, we shall show how the result of the signal-flow method may be used to determine the system (or amplifier) stability.* We shall define the so-called "return ratio $T_{p'p}$" (which is also a network function) of a transistor feedback amplifier in this chapter, solve for $T_{p'p}$ for different amplifiers with the signal-flow method in Arts. 17.3B and 17.4B, relate $T_{p'p}$ to the overall current gain $A^* = I_2/I_1$ of the transistor feedback amplifier in Arts. 17.3C and 17.4C, and use $T_{p'p}$ to study the system (i.e., amplifier) stability according to the Nyquist criterion in Chaps. 18 to 21.

The present chapter, together with Chap. 17, is, therefore, used to link the signal-flow techniques in Chap. 16 with the stability problems in Chaps. 18 to 21.

Remark 3.   *The present chapter, together with the two subsequent ones, also provides a study of transistor feedback amplifiers using the high-frequency transistor equivalent circuits.*   Broad approaches, using basic structures rather than particular circuits, are discussed and will be found useful in the design of wideband transistor amplifiers, which have extensive applications in video, switching, and many other special circuits.

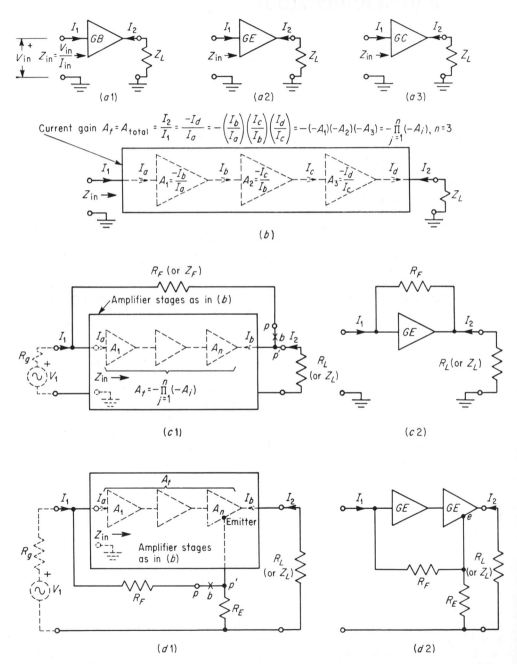

FIG. 15.1   (*a*) Basic amplifiers. (*b*) Amplifier with cascaded stages. (*c*1) Type A feedback structure; (*c*2) special case. (*d*1) Type B feedback structure; (*d*2) special case.

15.2. Basic transistor amplifiers

Block-diagram description. We shall use only block-diagram representations in the description of these amplifiers. The actual circuits and equivalent circuits will be given and discussed in Chap. 17.

A transistor is essentially a three-terminal device; the terminals are the *base*, *emitter*, and *collector*. By using the base as the "common terminal" or "common ground" for the input and the output, we form a grounded-base (*GB*) or common-base amplifier circuit. Similarly, we may have a grounded-emitter (*GE*) or a grounded-collector (*GC*) circuit. These three basic transistor amplifiers, terminated in a load impedance Z_L, are symbolically represented in Fig. 15.1a. The *GB*, *GE*, and *GC* circuits and their equivalent circuits will be given and discussed in Chap. 17.

Each of these basic amplifier circuits may be used either as a single-stage amplifier itself, as depicted in Fig. 15.1a, or as an amplifier stage in a multiple-stage amplifier, as in Fig. 15.1b. In either connection, we are interested in the current gain $A = I_2/I_1$ and input impedance $Z_{in} = V_{in}/I_1$ as two network functions.

Problems solvable with signal-flow techniques. To find the network functions $A = I_2/I_1$ and $Z_{in} = V_{in}/I_1$ for any of the arrangements in Fig. 15.1a or b, we (1) replace the individual transistor by its appropriate equivalent circuit, obtaining an "equivalent network" for the complete amplifier, and (2) use a method of analysis, to obtain the desired functions. Although the loop and nodal methods may be used to solve these problems, we shall use, in Arts. 17.1 and 17.2, the method of signal-flow analysis.

15.3. Transistor feedback amplifier: type A feedback structure

We shall investigate only two feedback structures;[†] they will be discussed here in Arts. 15.3 and 15.4 and studied in Arts. 17.3 and 17.4.

A. Description of Operation

Circuit arrangement. We shall call the circuit arrangement in Fig. 15.1c1 the "type A feedback structure." It is merely a multistage transistor amplifier as depicted in Fig. 15.1b with an output-to-input feedback loop containing resistance R_F. The voltage source V_1 in series with a very large resistance R_g is used to supply an almost constant input current $I_1 \cong V_1/R_g$. This relation $I_1 \cong V_1/R_g$ is obvious for $R_g \gg |Z_{in}|$, $R_g \gg R_F$, and $R_g \gg R_L$.

For satisfactory operation (as will be explained later) of Fig. 15.1c1 as a feedback amplifier, we shall demand:

Conditions for satisfactory operation of type A feedback structure in Fig. 15.1c1:

A *phase reversal* at low frequencies in the amplifier stages in Fig. 15.1c1   (15.1a)

A *high current gain*, that is, $|A_t| \gg 1$, provided by the amplifier stages in the figure   (15.1b)

$$|Z_{in}| \ll R_F \ll R_g \qquad (15.1c)$$

With reference to Fig. 15.1b, currents I_1 and I_2 flow *into* the network; this is the standard representation for a four-terminal network. However, the conventionally recognized load current is $I_L = -I_2$. The term *phase reversal at low frequencies* means that *the input current I_1 and the load current $-I_2$ are 180° out of phase at low*

† For additional feedback structures, see F. D. Waldhauer, Wide-band Feedback Amplifiers, *IRE Trans. on Circuit Theory*, vol. CT-4, pp. 178–190, September, 1958.

(or zero) frequencies. In other words, the expression $-A_t = -I_2/I_1$ (as $A_t = I_2/I_1$) must be a *negative* quantity, say $-K = K\underline{/180°}$, when $\omega = 0$ in this expression. Now, for the amplifier stages (inside the box) in Fig. 15.1c1, this term *phase reversal at low frequencies* means that *the input current I_a and the load current $-I_b$ are 180° out of phase at low (or zero) frequencies,* and $-A_t = -I_b/I_a$ must be negative when $\omega = 0$.

Definition of return ratio. To define the return ratio of the type A feedback structure in Fig. 15.1c1, we proceed as follows:

Defining the return ratio $T_{p'p}$ of the type A feedback structure in Fig. 15.1c1:

> *Short-circuit V_1 in Fig. 15.1c1, leaving R_g alone across the input terminals* (15.2a)

> *Break the feedback loop at b and label p and p' as indicated in the figure* (15.2b)

> *Apply a voltage V_p at p, and measure the voltage $V_{p'}$ at p', both with respect to ground; the return ratio is defined to be*

$$T_{p'p} = \frac{-V_{p'}}{V_p} \qquad (15.2c)$$

As will be established in Art. 17.3B, an approximate relation between the return ratio $T_{p'p}$ and the amplifier-stage gain A_t is $T_{p'p} \cong A_t(R_L/R_F)$. The high current-gain requirement in (15.1b) is therefore to ensure a large $|T_{p'p}| \gg 1$, necessary for satisfactory operation of the feedback amplifier. We shall discuss this near the end of this article.

Problem solvable with signal-flow techniques. To find the return ratio $T_{p'p}$ of a given transistor feedback amplifier in the form of Fig. 15.1c1 merely (1) replace the individual transistors in Fig. 15.1c1 with their appropriate equivalent circuits, obtaining an "equivalent network" for the complete amplifier, (2) modify this equivalent network according to (15.2a) and (15.2b), and (3) find a voltage-ratio function $T_{p'p} = -V_{p'}/V_p$ (that is, a "network function" as the voltage ratio of the output $-V_{p'}$ to the input V_p) by one of the methods of analysis.

Although the loop and nodal methods may be used, we shall use (in Art. 17.3B) the method of signal-flow analysis to find the return ratio $T_{p'p}$ of the type A feedback structure.

Relating the return ratio $T_{p'p}$ to the overall current gain A^*. We are usually interested in the overall current gain $A^* = I_2/I_1$ (a network function) of a transistor feedback amplifier. For a given feedback amplifier, say in the form of Fig. 15.1c1, we may find the overall current gain A^* with one of the following two approaches:

Approach 1. The overall current gain $A^* = I_2/I_1$ may be obtained directly as a network function from the "equivalent network" of the given feedback amplifier by the method of signal-flow analysis or the loop or nodal method. An illustration of this approach, for the amplifier in Fig. 15.1c2, which has the type A feedback structure in Fig. 15.1c1, will be given in Art. 17.1B and Fig. 17.7.

Approach 2. The overall current gain $A^* = I_2/I_1$ may also be obtained from the return ratio $T_{p'p}$ of the feedback amplifier through an established relation; this return ratio $T_{p'p}$, as remarked above, may have already been obtained by the method of signal-flow analysis.

Since approach 1 suggests a direct method for finding the overall current gain A^*, why should we use Approach 2 at all? This question will be answered in Art. 15.3B. For the time being, we are concerned only with the relation between $T_{p'p}$ and A^*.

For a transistor feedback amplifier with the type A feedback structure depicted in Fig. 15.1c1 satisfying the conditions in (15.1), the return ratio $T_{p'p}$ may be related to the overall current gain $A*$ as follows:

Relating $T_{p'p}$ to $A*$ for type A structure in Fig. 15.1c1:

$$A* = \frac{I_2}{I_1} \cong \frac{R_F}{R_L} \frac{T_{p'p}}{1 + T_{p'p}} \tag{15.3}$$

This relation will be derived in Art. 17.3C and Fig. 17.14.

The features of a feedback amplifier. The return ratio is a network function and, therefore, a function of s. At the real frequencies $s = j\omega$, $T_{p'p}(j\omega) = |T_{p'p}| e^{j\theta} = T_1 + jT_2$ is a complex quantity. For a large return ratio, that is, $|T_{p'p}| \gg 1$, within the operating frequency range of the amplifier, (15.3) may be approximated by

$$A* = \frac{I_2}{I_1} \cong \frac{R_F}{R_L} \frac{T_{p'p}}{T_{p'p}} \cong \frac{R_F}{R_L} \tag{15.4}$$

This means that, for $|T_{p'p}| \gg 1$, this feedback amplifier maintains a constant current gain; this constant-gain operation will not be affected by variation in circuit components due to aging, etc., fluctuations in the d-c power supply, or other disturbances. It is now obvious that feedback amplifiers are desirable for reliable operations.

Additional features of both vacuum-tube and transistor feedback amplifiers will be studied in Art. 20.4A.

B. Remarks about Stability

An amplifier is a device which amplifies an electrical signal. For example, if the input is a sinusoidal signal with frequency f_0 and magnitude $|I_1|$, we expect an output signal of the same frequency f_0 with larger magnitude $|I_2|$, where $|I_2| > |I_1|$, and $|I_2/I_1|$ is the absolute gain of the amplifier.

Sometimes, however, for no input we may find an output of a certain high frequency f_c, and for an input signal of frequency f_0 we may find in the output an undesirable signal of frequency f_c, where usually $f_c \gg f_0$, in addition to the amplified signal of frequency f_0. This amplifier apparently sustains an undesirable oscillation and behaves like an oscillator rather than an amplifier. Such an amplifier is said to be *unstable*. Unstable systems, e.g., amplifiers and control systems, will be described later in Art. 18.2A.

In designing an amplifier, we must be sure we have a stable system (i.e., amplifier). But how can we be sure? This is where the return ratio $T_{p'p}$ enters.

The return ratio $T_{p'p}(s)$ is actually a function of s whose abbreviation $T_{p'p}$ has been used in the above discussion. As will be studied in Chap. 19, a plot of $T_{p'p}(j\omega)$ versus ω in the complex plane, known as the Nyquist diagram, will tell us whether the amplifier is stable or not. If a system or amplifier design is found to be unstable, we may redesign or compensate it for stability and better performance (Chap. 21) until we succeed in obtaining a good design.

Since we must obtain the return ratio $T_{p'p}$ anyhow to test and improve stability, we often obtain the overall current gain $A* = I_2/I_1$ of the transistor feedback amplifier from its known return ratio $T_{p'p}$ through (15.3) rather than directly.

15.4. Transistor feedback amplifier: type B feedback structure

A. Description of Operation

Circuit arrangement. We shall call the circuit arrangement in Fig. 15.1d1 the "type B feedback structure." The feedback circuit in this structure consists of the two resistances R_F and R_E. The voltage source V_1 in series with a very large series resistance R_g is used to supply an almost constant input current $I_1 \cong V_1/R_g$.

For satisfactory operation (as will be explained later) of Fig. 15.1d1 as a feedback amplifier, we shall demand:

Conditions for satisfactory operation for type B feedback structure in Fig. 15.1d1:

> *No phase reversal* at low frequencies in the amplifier stages in Fig. 15.1d1 (15.5a)

> A *high current gain*, that is, $|A_t| \gg 1$, in the amplifier stages (15.5b)

$$R_g \gg |Z_{\text{in}}| \quad \text{and} \quad R_g \gg R_F + R_E \qquad (15.5c)$$

The term *no phase reversal at low frequencies* means that *the input current I_a and the load current $-I_b$ are in phase at low (or zero) frequencies and $-A_t = -I_b/I_a$ must be positive when $\omega = 0$.*

Definition of return ratio. To define the return ratio of the type B feedback structure in Fig. 15.1d1, we proceed as follows:

Defining the return ratio $T_{p'p}$ of the type B feedback structure in Fig. 15.1d1:

> *Short-circuit V_1 in Fig. 15.1d1, leaving R_g alone across the input terminals* (15.6a)

> *Break the feedback loop at b and label p and p' as indicated in the figure* (15.6b)

> *Apply a voltage V_p at p, and measure the voltage $V_{p'}$ at p', both with respect to ground; the return ratio is defined to be*

$$T_{p'p} = \frac{-V_{p'}}{V_p} \qquad (15.6c)$$

As will be established in Art. 17.4B, an approximate relation between the return ratio $T_{p'p}$ and the amplifier-stage gain A_t is $T_{p'p} \cong -A_t(R_E/R_F)$. The high current-gain requirement in (15.5b) is therefore to ensure a large $|T_{p'p}| \gg 1$, necessary for satisfactory operation of the feedback amplifier. We shall discuss this near the end of this article.

Problem solvable with signal-flow techniques. To find the return ratio $T_{p'p}$ of a given transistor feedback amplifier in the form of Fig. 15.1d1, merely (1) replace the individual transistors in Fig. 15.1d1 with their appropriate equivalent circuits, obtaining an "equivalent network" for the complete amplifier, (2) modify this equivalent network according to (15.6a) and (15.6b), and (3) find the voltage-ratio function $T_{p'p} = -V_{p'}/V_p$ (that is, a "network function" as the voltage ratio of the output $-V_{p'}$ to the input V_p) by one of the methods of analysis.

Although the loop and nodal methods may be used, we shall use (in Art. 17.4) the method of signal-flow analysis to find the return ratio $T_{p'p}$ of the type B feedback structure.

Relating the return ratio $T_{p'p}$ to the overall current gain A^*. The remarks in Art. 15.3A about relating $T_{p'p}$ to A^* for the type A feedback structure are applicable here.

For a transistor feedback amplifier of the type B feedback structure satisfying conditions (15.5), the return ratio $T_{p'p}$ may be related to the overall current gain A^* as follows:

Relating $T_{p'p}$ to A^* for type B structure in Fig. 15.1d1:

$$A^* = \frac{I_2}{I_1} \cong -\frac{R_E + R_F}{R_E} \frac{T_{p'p}}{1 + T_{p'p}} \qquad |Z_{\text{in}}| \gg R_F + R_E \qquad (15.7a)$$

$$A^* = \frac{I_2}{I_1} \cong -\frac{R_F}{R_E} \frac{T_{p'p}}{1 + T_{p'p}} \qquad R_F + R_E \gg |Z_{\text{in}}| \qquad (15.7b)$$

These relations will be derived in Art. 17.4C and Fig. 17.17.

The features of a feedback amplifier. For a large return ratio, that is, $|T_{p'p}| \gg 1$, within the operating frequency range of the amplifier, (15.7) may be approximated by

$$A^* = \frac{I_2}{I_1} \cong -\frac{R_E + R_F}{R_E} \qquad |Z_{\text{in}}| \gg R_F + R_E \qquad (15.8a)$$

$$A^* = \frac{I_2}{I_1} \cong -\frac{R_F}{R_E} \qquad R_F + R_E \gg |Z_{\text{in}}| \qquad (15.8b)$$

$$-\frac{R_E + R_F}{R_E} \leq A^* \leq -\frac{R_F}{R_E} \qquad \text{for other conditions} \qquad (15.8c)$$

For $R_F/R_E \geq 10$, the two limits $-(R_E + R_F)/R_E$ and $-R_F/R_E$ in (15.8c) are fairly close; therefore an approximate indication of the overall current gain A^* for all these conditions is obtained.

The features mentioned in the two paragraphs following (15.4) are also applicable to transistor feedback amplifiers of type B feedback structure.

However, the type B feedback structure in Fig. 15.1d1 has one feature which is not shared by the type A feedback structure: *The overall current gain $A^* = I_2/I_1$, as indicated in (15.8) for proper operation with $|T_{p'p}| \gg 1$, is independent of the load impedance Z_L (or R_L).*

B. Remarks about Stability

The remarks about stability for the type A feedback structure (Art. 15.3B) are directly applicable to the type B feedback structure.

PROBLEMS

15.1. A grounded-emitter (GE) transistor amplifier as depicted in Fig. 15.1a2 is known to have a "short-circuit current gain"

$$\beta = \frac{I_2}{I_1}\bigg|_{Z_L=0 \text{ in Fig. 15.1a2}} = \frac{\beta_0}{1 + s/\omega_\beta} \cong \frac{50}{1 + s/5 \times 10^7} \qquad s = j\omega$$

where β_0 is its short-circuit current gain at low frequencies ω, that is, $\omega \ll \omega_\beta$ or $\omega \cong 0$. By adding a feedback loop R_F, we obtain the type A feedback amplifier in Fig. 15.1c2 whose return ratio $T_{p'p}$ as defined in (15.2) is

$$T_{p'p} \cong \frac{R_L}{R_F} \beta = \frac{R_L}{R_F} \frac{50}{1 + s/5 \times 10^7} \qquad s = j\omega$$

Find the overall current gain $A^* = I_2/I_1$ of this feedback amplifier as a function of s, with $R_L = 200$ ohms and $R_F = 1,000$ ohms.

15.2. Let us assume that the feedback amplifier described in Prob. 15.1 has an operating frequency range $0 \leq \omega \leq \omega_0$, where $\omega_0 = 15 \times 10^6$ rad/sec, $\omega_0 < \omega_\beta$, and $\omega_\beta = 5 \times 10^7$ rad/sec is the "beta cutoff frequency" of the transistor as given in Prob. 15.1.

(a) Using the overall current gain A^* obtained in the preceding problem, plot $|A^*|_{s=j\omega}$ versus ω for the entire operating frequency range.   Note that the absolute overall gain $|A^*|_{s=j\omega}$ is relatively constant throughout this frequency range.

(b) For the feedback circuit in Fig. 15.1c2 with $R_L = 200$ ohms and $R_F = 1,000$ ohms, compute the absolute overall gain $|A^*|_{s=j\omega}$ at $\omega = 0$, first using transistor 1 with $\beta_0 = 50$ in the circuit and then using transistor 2 with $\beta_0 = 100$.   Note that the two absolute gains are relatively close in magnitude, while the two transistors would have respective short-circuit gains of 50 and 100 if they were used without feedback.

16 The signal-flow diagram

16.1. General description of the signal-flow diagram†

A. Simple Illustration with a GC Transistor

Let us consider a grounded-collector transistor circuit (Fig. 16.1*a*) whose equivalent circuit is given in Fig. 16.1*b*. The various parameters of transistor equivalents will be discussed in Art. 17.1; for the time being, we need only consider them constants or functions of *s*.

Voltage-current relations and signal-flow diagram. The voltage-current relations in Fig. 16.1*b* are obvious:

Voltage-current relations:

$$V_1 = (1 + \beta)z_a I_1 + z_a I_2 \tag{16.1a}$$

$$I_2 = \frac{-1}{r_e + Z_L} V_1 \tag{16.1b}$$

We may interpret the voltage-current relation (16.1*a*) as

Interpretation of the V-I relation in (16.1a):

V_1 is the result of *contributions* of (1) I_1 with $(1 + \beta)z_a$ as its *weight* of contribution and (2) I_2 with z_a as its weight (16.2*a*)

or

Another interpretation of the V-I relation in (16.1a):

V_1 is the result of *signal flow* due to (1) I_1 with $(1 + \beta)z_a$ as its *transmission* of signal flow and (2) I_2 with z_a as its transmission (16.2*b*)

which may then be graphically represented in Fig. 16.1*c*1. Here, a set of two $I_1 V_1$ and $I_2 V_1$ branches, with $(1 + \beta)z_a$ and z_a their respective weights, directed toward a vertex V_1, defines the voltage-current relation in (16.1*a*); this signal-flow representation is obtained in accordance with the following rules:

Finding the signal-flow representation of a linear voltage-current relation (see Fig. 16.1c1):

Each vertex represents a variable, say a voltage or a current (16.3*a*)

Each directed branch indicates "contribution" or "signal flow" from one variable to another in the direction of the branch (16.3*b*)

† The signal-flow diagram was originated by S. J. Mason in his paper Feedback Theory—Some Properties of Signal Flow Graphs, *Proc. IRE*, vol. 41, no. 9, pp. 1144–1159, September, 1953. An excellent exposition on the signal-flow diagram and its applications may be found in J. G. Truxal, "Automatic Feedback Control System Synthesis," chap. 2, McGraw-Hill Book Company, Inc., New York, 1955.

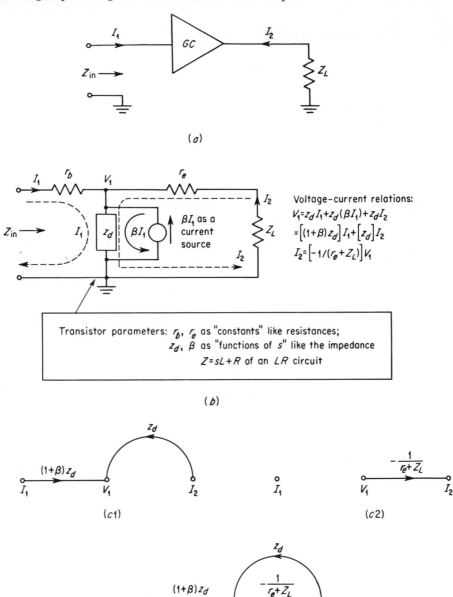

FIG. 16.1   (*a*) Grounded-collector (*GC*) transistor circuit. (*b*) Equivalent circuit and associated voltage-current relations. (*c*1) Voltage-current relation in (*b*), $V_1 = (1 + \beta)z_d I_1 + z_d I_2$,
and its signal-flow representation. (*c*2) Voltage-current relation in (*b*), $I_2 = [-1/(r_e + Z_L)]V_1$,
and its signal-flow representation. (*c*3) Signal-flow diagram of the *GC* circuit in (*a*) obtained
by combining (*c*1) and (*c*2).

> *The weight of each directed branch represents the "weight" of the contribution or the "transmission" of the signal flow*   (16.3c)
>
> *The set of "branches with weights directed toward a vertex" defines a linear voltage-current relation*   (16.3d)

Similarly, we may obtain the signal-flow representation of the voltage-current relation (16.1b) in Fig. 16.1c2.

Combining Fig. 16.1c1 and 2 into the representation in Fig. 16.1c3, we have the signal-flow diagram of the GC transistor circuit in Fig. 16.1a and b. In general, *a signal-flow diagram is a graphical representation of the linear voltage-current relations of a circuit.*

Problems solvable with the signal-flow technique. But why do we want to use the signal-flow diagram?

Again, we shall consider the simple grounded-collector (GC) transistor circuit of Fig. 16.1a and b. Altogether, we have three variables I_1, V_1, and I_2. I_1, being the excitation, is the *independent variable;* V_1 and I_2, which may be solved for with known excitation I_1 and circuit values from the voltage-current relations in (16.1), are the *dependent variables.*

In a given circuit, we may be involved in different problems and interested in solving for different dependent variables. In each particular problem, we call the interested dependent variable the "response" and solve for it.

In the example of the simple GC circuit in Fig. 16.1, there are two possible problems: (1) designating the dependent variable I_2 as the "response," and solving for this response or its related network function $A = I_2/I_1$ or (2) designating the dependent variable V_1 as the "response," and solving for this response or its related network function $Z_{in} = r_b + Z_1 = r_b + V_1/I_1$. *Let us now see what the so-called "signal-flow method" of analysis can do for each of these two problems:*

1. *To Solve for I_2* in the GC equivalent circuit in Fig. 16.1b, we (1) obtain the signal-flow diagram as indicated in Fig. 16.1c3, (2) designate I_2 as the "response" as in Fig. 16.2a1, and (3) follow a set of rules of reduction (or simplification) which will be discussed in Art. 16.2, reducing the original signal-flow diagram to a "single I_1I_2 branch with known transmission A." This transmission is the current gain $A = I_2/I_1$; the desired "response" is now readily obtainable as the product $I_2 = [A]I_1$ of the transmission A and the excitation I_1.

2. *To Solve for V_1* in the GC equivalent circuit in Fig. 16.1b, we (1) obtain the signal-flow diagram as indicated in Fig. 16.1c3, (2) designate V_1 as the "response" as in Fig. 16.2b1, and (3) follow a set of rules of reduction which will be discussed in Art. 16.2, reducing the original signal-flow diagram to a "single I_1V_1 branch with known transmission Z_1." This transmission is an impedance $Z_1 = V_1/I_1$; the desired "response" is readily obtainable as the product $V_1 = [Z_1]I_1$ of the transmission Z_1 and the excitation I_1.

Remarks about the signal-flow method of analysis. In general, we solve an analysis problem by the so-called "signal-flow method" in this fashion: (1) Construct a signal-flow diagram of the given network, (2) designate an interested dependent variable as the "response," and (3) reduce this signal-flow diagram to a "single excitation-to-response branch with known transmission T" with the rules of reduction to be discussed in Art. 16.2.

The transmission T, thus obtained, is a network function equal to the response/excitation ratio. The interested response is now readily obtained as the product of the transmission T and the excitation.

Remarks about identifying the response and the excitation. We have mentioned above that we usually designate one interested dependent variable from among

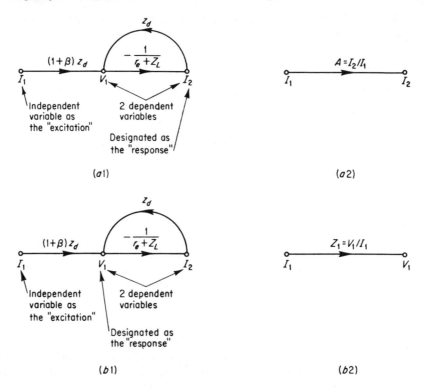

FIG. 16.2   (a1) Signal-flow diagram from Fig. 16.1c with I_2 designated as response. (a2) Result of simplification: a single $I_1 I_2$ branch with known transmission A. (b1) Signal-flow diagram in Fig. 16.1c with V_1 designated as response. (b2) Result of simplification: a single $I_1 V_1$ branch with known transmission Z_1.

a number of dependent variables to be the "response." It is not particularly necessary to change or modify the original signal-flow diagram for this purpose; all we have to do is remember which among the dependent variables is the designated "response," as exemplified in Fig. 16.3a1 and b1.

However, sometimes we may wish to identify the "response" unmistakably by adding a branch as in Fig. 16.3a2 and b2. In the example of Fig. 16.3a2, *we change I_2 in the original signal-flow diagram*, as given in Fig. 16.3a1, *to I_2' and add an $I_2' I_2$ branch with a transmission of unity.* Comparing the voltage-current relations in Fig. 16.3a1 and 2, we note that they represent the same essential equations. It is therefore justifiable and permissible to add an $I_2' I_2$ branch as described above.

Also, whenever necessary, it is a convenient practice to rearrange the signal-flow diagram such that the "response" appears farthest on the right. This will facilitate the reduction of the signal-flow diagram. For example, we rearrange the signal-flow diagram in Fig. 16.3b1 with an added $V_1' V_1$ branch into the representation in Fig. 16.3b2, where V_1 appears farthest on the right.

Although there is usually only one excitation, we may also add a branch to identify an excitation unmistakably. For example, *we change I_1 in the original signal-flow diagram*, as given in Fig. 16.3c1, *to I_1' and add an $I_1 I_1'$ branch with a transmission of unity* to identify I_1 as the excitation in Fig. 16.3c2. However, this is not particularly necessary.

B. *Representation of Linear Relations with a Signal-flow Diagram*

Signal-flow diagram of linear relations. In the preceding section, Art. 16.1A, we obtained a signal-flow diagram in Fig. 16.1c3 for the linear voltage-current relations in (16.1); i.e.,

Equations of dependent variables V_1, I_2 in terms of independent variable I_1 and dependent variables:

$$V_1 = \text{Eq. (16.1a)} \qquad I_2 = \text{Eq. (16.1b)} \tag{16.4}$$

Signal-flow diagram with I_2 designated as the "response":

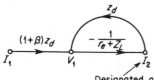

Designated as the "response"

and its associated voltage-current relations:

$$V_1 = \big[(1+\beta)z_d\big]\,I_1 + \big[z_d\big]\,I_2$$

$$I_2 = \big[-1/(r_e+Z_L)\big]\,V_1$$

(a1)

Signal-flow diagram with an added branch to identify the "response":

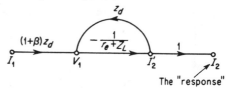

The "response"

and its associated voltage-current relations:

$$V_1 = \big[(1+\beta)z_d\big]\,I_1 + \big[z_d\big]\,I_2'$$

$$I_2' = \big[-1/(r_e+Z_L)\big]\,V_1$$

$$I_2 = \big[1\big]\,I_2' = I_2' \text{ (for the "added branch")}$$

(a2)

Signal-flow diagram:

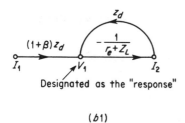

Designated as the "response"

(b1)

Signal-flow diagram with an added branch to identify the "response":

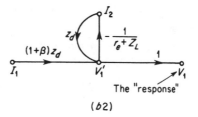

The "response"

(b2)

Signal-flow diagram:

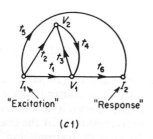

"Excitation"   "Response"

(c1)

Signal-flow diagram with added branches to identify the "excitation" as well as the "response":

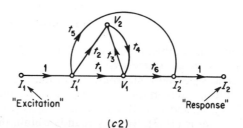

"Excitation"   "Response"

(c2)

FIG. 16.3

But is the signal-flow diagram confined to representing the linear voltage-current relations? The answer is "no." It is true that we are primarily concerned with electrical network problems here, and the signal-flow diagrams used in these problems represent linear voltage-current relations. However, *signal-flow diagrams may also be used for mechanical, hydraulic, electromechanical, and other systems, as well as for various control systems, to represent linear variable-to-variable relations.* We shall illustrate this later (Art. 16.3C) in finding the signal-flow diagrams of some closed-loop control systems.

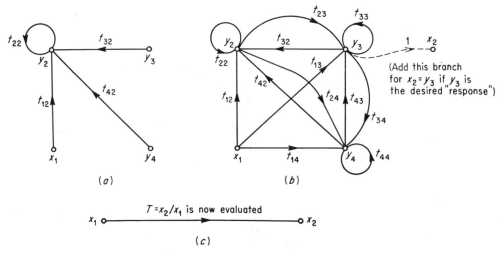

FIG. 16.4 (a) Signal-flow representation of the linear equation $y_2 = t_{12}x_1 + t_{22}y_2 + t_{32}y_3 + t_{42}y_4$; (b) signal-flow diagram for linear system in Eqs. (16.5); (c) result of simplification.

Linear Relations. Let us now consider some general linear variable-to-variable relations:

Equations of dependent variables y_2, y_3, y_4 in terms of independent variable x_1 and dependent variables y_2, y_3, y_4:

$$y_2 = t_{12}x_1 + t_{22}y_2 + t_{32}y_3 + t_{42}y_4 \tag{16.5a}$$

$$y_3 = t_{13}x_1 + t_{23}y_2 + t_{33}y_3 + t_{43}y_4 \tag{16.5b}$$

$$y_4 = t_{14}x_1 + t_{24}y_2 + t_{34}y_3 + t_{44}y_4 \tag{16.5c}$$

where independent variable x_1 represents the "excitation" of the physical system, and one of the dependent variables, say y_3, is designated as the "response x_2," i.e.,

$$x_1 = \text{excitation}$$
$$x_2 = \text{response} = y_3 \quad \text{as designated}$$

The usual problem is to solve for the response x_2 in terms of the excitation x_1 and the system parameters t_{ij}.

The signal-flow diagram. Considering y_2 on the left-hand side of (16.5a) as the result of "contribution" or "signal flow" due to (1) x_1 with t_{12} as its transmission and (2) y_2, y_3, and y_4 with t_{22}, t_{32}, and t_{42} as their respective transmissions, and following the rules in (16.3), we may readily obtain the signal-flow representation for the linear relation (16.5a) in Fig. 16.4a. The path from y_2 back to y_2 with transmission t_{22}

is called a *self-loop;* it represents the "contribution" of y_2 to itself. Since it represents a "self-contribution," we may draw a self-loop in either the clockwise or counter-clockwise direction. Similarly, we may obtain the signal-flow representations for (16.5*b*) and (16.5*c*). Combining, we obtain the signal-flow diagram in Fig. 16.4*b* for the linear relations in (16.5).

By designating y_3 as the "response x_2," we may add a y_3x_2 branch with a transmission of unity. We now have the signal-flow diagram in Fig. 16.4*b*, where x_1 represents the "excitation," and x_2 the "response."

By following a set of rules of reduction which will be discussed in Art. 16.2, we may reduce the signal-flow diagram in Fig. 16.4*b* to a "single x_1x_2 branch with known transmission T." This transmission T is a network function x_2/x_1; the desired "response" is readily obtainable as the product $x_2 = [T]x_1$ of the transmission T and the excitation x_1.

A Remark about the Signal-flow Diagram. From the above discussion, we recognize that *a signal-flow diagram is essentially the graphical representation of a set of linear relations as the "equations of the dependent variables in terms of the independent variable and the other dependent variables"* similar to those in (16.5).

C. Illustrations of Finding Signal-flow Diagrams

Some remarks about network function, network parameters, and signal-flow diagrams. We have demonstrated in Art. 16.1A and B that we may construct a signal-flow diagram for a given network and reduce it to a "single excitation-response branch with known transmission T," where T = response/excitation is a network function. In other words, the signal-flow method may be used in finding network functions.

But can the signal-flow method also be used in finding network parameters? The answer is "yes." Since a network parameter is nothing but a network function under some special condition, for example, the short-circuit or open-circuit condition, we may use the signal-flow method to find network parameters by (1) imposing the special condition on the network, thus obtaining a modified network, and (2) finding the "network function," namely, the network parameter, from this modified network.

We shall now illustrate how to obtain the network function and the network parameters for a given network with the signal-flow method.

Given a Network, to Find Its Network Function. We wish to find the network function $Y_T = I_2/E_1$ of the four-terminal network arrangement in Fig. 16.5*a*. We shall break this illustration into two parts: (1) In Illustration A1, given below, we find the signal-flow diagram for the network arrangement and (2) in Illustration A2, given in Art. 16.3A after we have learned the rules of reduction in Art. 16.2, we find the network function $Y_T = I_2/E_1$ from the signal-flow diagram.

Given a Network, to Find Its Network Parameter. We wish to find the short-circuit parameters y_{ij} of the four-terminal network in Fig. 16.5*a*. Again, we shall break this illustration into two parts: (1) In Illustration B1, given below, we find the signal-flow diagram for the four-terminal network in a modified form, i.e., intended for finding the short-circuit parameter y_{21}, and (2) in Illustration B2, given in Art. 16.3A after we have learned the rules of reduction in Art. 16.2, we find the short-circuit parameter y_{21} from the signal-flow diagram. Similar procedures will obtain for us the parameters y_{11} and y_{22}, while y_{12} is equal to y_{21} for bilateral networks and is, therefore, known.

Illustration A1. Finding the signal-flow diagram to be used for obtaining a network function. We now wish to obtain the signal-flow diagram of the network arrangement in Fig. 16.5*a*.

We may write all the voltage-current relations in Fig. 16.5a, find signal-flow representation for each relation, and combine them into the signal-flow diagram in Fig. 16.5b as we did in Fig. 16.1b and c.

Some Remarks.   But is it really necessary to write all the voltage-current relations for the circuit in Fig. 16.5a before we construct its signal-flow diagram?   We shall find that, for a ladder structure as in Fig. 16.5a, and for some other simple circuits, *we may construct signal-flow diagrams by inspecting the voltage-current relations in the circuit one by one without writing them.*   For example, we first examine the *VI* relation associated with the first *series* element Z_1, which is $I_1 = (E_1 - V_3)/Z_1$; we then construct the signal-flow representation for I_1, namely, two branches directed toward I_1 in Fig. 16.5b.   We then examine the *VI* relation associated with the first *shunt* element Z_2, which is $V_3 = (I_1 - I_3)Z_2$; we then construct the signal-flow representation for V_3, namely, two branches directed toward V_3 in Fig. 16.5b.   We then examine the subsequent *series* and *shunt* elements Z_3, Z_4, ... one by one, and complete the signal-flow diagram in Fig. 16.5b.

Illustration B1.   Finding the signal-flow diagram to be used for obtaining network parameters.   We now wish to obtain the signal-flow diagram intended for obtaining the short-circuit parameter y_{21} of the four-terminal network in Fig. 16.5a.

Since $y_{21} = (I_2/E_1)_{E_2=0}$ [according to (4.32)] is the transfer admittance I_2/E_1 of

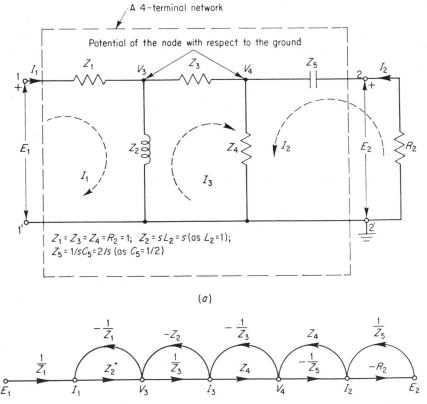

(a)

(b)

FIG. 16.5

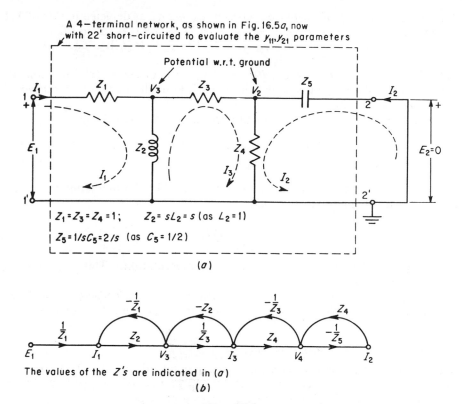

FIG. 16.6

the four-terminal network under the special condition $E_2 = 0$, that is, $22'$ short-circuited, we modify the four-terminal network by short-circuiting $22'$, as in Fig. 16.6a. We obtain the signal-flow diagram of this "modified network" in Fig. 16.6b in the manner of Illustration A1 above.

We shall use this signal-flow diagram in Illustration B2, Art. 16.3A, to obtain y_{21} for the four-terminal network.

16.2. Reduction (simplification) of signal-flow diagrams

We have remarked a number of times in Art. 16.1 that, in solving certain problems of network analysis, we reduce a signal-flow diagram associated with a network to a "single excitation-to-response branch with known transmission." We shall now establish the rules of this reducing process.

A. Three Basic Rules of Reduction

Rule A. *Two parallel paths with transmissions t_1 and t_2, as depicted in (a1) of Table 16.1, may be combined into a single path with transmission $t_1 + t_2$, as in (a2).*

This rule can be readily justified by combining the two separate contributions $[t_1]y_a$ and $[t_2]y_a$† from y_a to y_b into a single contribution $[t_1]y_a + [t_2]y_a = [t_1 + t_2]y_a$ which requires only a single path for representation. Reference is made to (16.2) for the term *contribution*.

† The bracketed expressions in the following discussions signify the transmission, either given or derived.

Rule B.   *Two series paths with transmissions t_{ab} and t_{bc}, as depicted in (b1) of Table 16.2, may be combined into a single path with transmission $t_{ab}t_{bc}$, as in (b2).*

Since $y_b = [t_{ab}]y_a$ and $y_c = [t_{bc}]y_b$, $y_c = [t_{bc}][t_{ab}]y_a = [t_{ab}t_{bc}]y_a$, and this rule is justified.

Rule C.   *A $y_a y_b y_c$ path with a self-loop at y_b, as depicted in (c1) of Table 16.1, may be replaced by a single $y_a y_c$ path, with the self-loop eliminated, with transmission* $t_{ab}t_{bc}/(1 - t_{bb})$, *as in ($c$2).*

Let us consider the linear equations implied in (c1) of Table 16.1,

$$y_b = [t_{ab}]y_a + [t_{bb}]y_b \tag{16.6a}$$
$$y_c = [t_{bc}]y_b \tag{16.6b}$$

while neglecting "contributions" to y_c by other variables.   Eliminating the variable y_b in (16.6) and solving for y_c, we obtain

$$y_c = \left[\frac{t_{ab}t_{bc}}{1 - t_{bb}}\right] y_a \tag{16.7}$$

which has (c2) of Table 16.1 as its signal-flow representation.   This justifies Rule C above.

As a special case of Rule C, *we may replace the $y_a y_b$ path together with its self-loop at y_b in (c1) of Table 16.1 by a $y_a y_b$ path without the self-loop, with transmission* $t_{ab}/(1 - t_{bb})$.

B.   *Additional Rules of Reduction: Removing a Path*

Remarks about the underlying principle.   We shall introduce four rules for removing a path from a signal-flow representation, i.e., all or part of a signal-flow diagram. All four rules are based upon the same underlying principle:

Underlying principle for removing a path:

> *Replace a path with alternative paths which will maintain the signal*
> *flow of the replaced path* (16.8)

For the interpretation of the term *signal flow*, see (16.2).

For example, if we wish to remove the $y_a y_b$ branch with transmission t_{ab} in (d1) of Table 16.1, we may replace it with these "alternative paths bypassing y_b" in (d2): (1) the $y_a y_1$ path with transmission $t_{ab}t_{b1}$—this alternative path maintains the signal flow from y_a to y_b and then to y_1, (2) the $y_a y_2$ path with transmission $t_{ab}t_{b2}$—this alternative path maintains the signal flow from y_a to y_b and then to y_2, and (3) the $y_a y_3$ path with transmission $t_{ab}t_{b3}$—this alternative path maintains the signal flow from y_a to y_b and then to y_3.

The example in the preceding paragraph is described in terms of signal flow.   In plain language, it demonstrates some mathematical "common sense": *If you wish to eliminate a variable y_b* (which corresponds to "bypassing y_b" above) *in a set of linear equations, replace it with its equivalent* [say $y_b = t_{ab}y_a$ indicating the signal flow due to y_a in (d1) of Table 16.1] *in all the linear equations containing y_b* [for example, $y_1 = t_{b1}y_b$, $y_2 = t_{b2}y_b$, and $y_3 = t_{b3}y_b$ in (d1)].   This is the elimination-of-variable technique commonly used in the solution of a system of linear equations.

We shall now state the four rules of reduction without further justification, as the underlying principle in (16.8) or the "common sense" in the above example has implied and justified them:

Rule D.   *In replacing a $y_a y_b$ path having transmission t_{ab}, as depicted in (d1) of Table 16.1, with alternative paths bypassing y_b, use $y_a y_i$ as these alternative paths with $t_{ab}t_{bi}$ as their respective transmissions, as shown in (d2), where the y_i are all the vertices*

Table 16.1

Rule	(1) Original signal-flow representation (part of signal-flow diagram)	(2) Result of applying the rule
A. Combining two parallel paths: replace with a single path having the sum $t_1 + t_2$ as its transmission	(a1)	(a2)
B. Combining two series paths: replace with a single path having the product $t_{ab}t_{bc}$ as its transmission	(b1)	(b2)
C. Eliminating a self-loop as indicated in (c1): replace with a single path with $t_{ab}t_{bc}/(1-t_{bb})$ as its transmission, as in (c2)	(c1) or	(c2)
D. Removing a path t_{ab}-- replaced with paths bypassing y_b: replace† with paths from y_a to the "vertices y_i subsequent to y_b" with $t_{ab}t_{bi}$ as its transmission	(d1) To remove y_1, y_2, y_3 -- subsequent to y_b with t_{b1}, t_{b2}, t_{b3} in heavy lines Another illustration: y_a is also "subsequent" to y_b To remove y_1, y_2, y_a -- subsequent to y_b	(d2)

Table 16.1 (continued)

Rule	(1) Original signal-flow representation (part of signal-flow diagram)	(2) Result of applying the rule

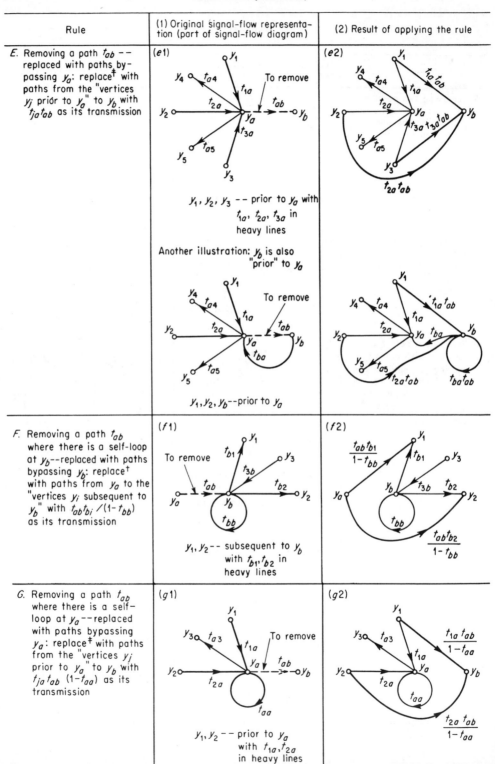

E. Removing a path t_{ab} -- replaced with paths by-passing y_a: replace† with paths from the "vertices y_j prior to y_a" to y_b with $t_{ja}t_{ab}$ as its transmission

(e1)

y_1, y_2, y_3 -- prior to y_a with t_{1a}, t_{2a}, t_{3a} in heavy lines

Another illustration: y_b is also "prior" to y_a

y_1, y_2, y_b -- prior to y_a

(e2)

F. Removing a path t_{ab} where there is a self-loop at y_b -- replaced with paths bypassing y_b: replace† with paths from y_a to the "vertices y_i subsequent to y_b" with $t_{ab}t_{bi}/(1-t_{bb})$ as its transmission

(f1)

y_1, y_2 -- subsequent to y_b with t_{b1}, t_{b2} in heavy lines

(f2)

G. Removing a path t_{ab} where there is a self-loop at y_a -- replaced with paths bypassing y_a: replace‡ with paths from the "vertices y_j prior to y_a" to y_b with $t_{ja}t_{ab}(1-t_{aa})$ as its transmission

(g1)

y_1, y_2 -- prior to y_a with t_{1a}, t_{2a} in heavy lines

(g2)

Table 16.1 (continued)

Rule	(1) Original signal-flow representation (part of signal-flow diagram)	(2) Result of applying the rule
H. Eliminating a number of self-loops as depicted in $(h1)$: replace with a single path as shown in $(h2)$	$(h1)$	$(h2)$
I. Eliminating a self-loop at a node as depicted in $(i1)$: divide all incoming transmissions or all outgoing transmissions with $1-t_{dd}$, as shown in $(i2)$	$(i1)$	$(i2)$ or

† With the exception of t_{ab}, which is being replaced, all other paths connected with y_b should remain *unchanged*. However, if y_b has only outgoing paths (say t_{b1}, t_{b2}, and t_{b3} in Table 16.1$d2$) and *no incoming paths* (say in the absence of t_{4b} and t_{5b} in Table 16.1$d2$), we may ignore and leave out from the signal-flow diagram the vertex y_b as well as all its outgoing paths (since y_b without incoming paths cannot contribute anything along its outgoing paths).

‡ With the exception of t_{ab}, which is being replaced, all other paths connected with y_a should remain *unchanged*. However, if y_a has only incoming paths (say t_{1a}, t_{2a}, and t_{3a} in Table 16.1$e2$) and *no outgoing paths* (say in the absence of t_{a4} and t_{a5} in Table 16.1$e2$), we may ignore and leave out from the signal-flow diagram the vertex y_a as well as all its incoming paths (since y_a without outgoing paths cannot contribute to any other vertices, and therefore can be ignored).

"*subsequent*" to y_b. By vertices "subsequent" to y_b are meant the vertices that have nonzero transmission from the vertex y_b.

It is of interest to note the second illustration in $(d1)$ and $(d2)$ of Table 16.1, where y_a is "subsequent" to y_b in the original signal-flow representation. The result of applying Rule D includes a $y_a y_a$ branch, i.e., a self-loop at y_a, as shown in $(d2)$.

Rule E. *In replacing a $y_a y_b$ path having transmission t_{ab}*, as depicted in $(e1)$ of Table 16.1, *with alternative paths bypassing y_a, use $y_j y_b$ as these alternative paths with $t_{ja} t_{ab}$ as their respective transmissions*, as shown in $(e2)$, *where the y_j are all the vertices* "*prior*" *to y_a.* By vertices "prior" to y_a are meant the vertices that have nonzero transmission to vertex y_a.

It is of interest to note the second illustration in $(e1)$ of Table 16.1, where y_b is "prior" to y_a in the original signal-flow representation. The result of applying Rule E includes a $y_b y_b$ branch, i.e., a self-loop at y_b, as shown in $(e2)$.

Rule F. *In replacing a $y_a y_b$ path having transmission t_{ab} where there is a self-loop of transmission t_{bb} at y_b*, as depicted in $(f1)$ of Table 16.1, *with alternative paths bypassing y_b, use $y_a y_i$ as these alternative paths with $t_{ab} t_{bi}/(1 - t_{bb})$ as their respective transmissions*, as shown in $(f2)$, *where the y_i are all the vertices* "subsequent" *to y_b.*

Rule F may be considered as a modified version of Rule D, derived with the aid of Rule C, to account for the effect of the self-loop.

Let us trace through the path from y_a to y_1 in $(f1)$ of Table 16.1: We have (1) a $y_a y_b$ path with transmission t_{ab}, (2) a self-loop or $y_b y_b$ path with transmission t_{bb}, and (3) a $y_b y_1$ path with transmission t_{b1}. To maintain this signal flow as we remove the $y_a y_b$ path, we may apply Rule C, obtaining a direct $y_a y_1$ path with transmission $t_{ab} t_{b1}/(1 - t_{bb})$ as in $(f2)$. Similarly, we may calculate the direct $y_a y_2$ path.

Rule G. *In replacing a $y_a y_b$ path having transmission t_{ab} where there is a self-loop of transmission t_{aa} at y_a, as depicted in $(g1)$ of Table 16.1, with alternative paths bypassing y_a, use $y_j y_b$ as the alternative paths with $t_{ja} t_{ab}/(1 - t_{aa})$ as their respective transmissions, as shown in $(g2)$, where the y_j are all the vertices "prior" to y_a.*

Rule G may be considered as a modified version of Rule E in much the same way that Rule F was considered as a modified version of Rule D.

C. Additional Rules and Remarks

Rule H. *A $y_a y_b y_c y_d y_e$ path with self-loops at y_b, y_c, and y_d, as depicted in $(h1)$ of Table 16.1, may be replaced with a single $y_a y_e$ path* with the self-loops eliminated *with $t_{ab} t_{bc} t_{cd} t_{de}/(1 - t_{bb})(1 - t_{cc})(1 - t_{dd})$ as its transmission, as in $(h2)$.*

Rule H is readily obtained by repeated application of Rule C.

Rule I. *A self-loop at node d, as depicted in $(i1)$ of Table 16.1, may be eliminated by dividing either (1) all incoming transmissions or (2) all outgoing transmissions by $1 - t_{dd}$, as in $(i2)$.*

Rule I includes the individual transmissions from y_a, y_b, and y_c to y_e and y_f, for example, from y_a to y_e, y_a to y_f, y_b to y_e, . . . , where these individual transmissions may be obtained with Rule C.

Remarks about additional rules of reduction. Rules A through I, introduced above, are useful tools in the reduction of signal-flow diagrams.

As we did with Rule H, we may introduce additional rules by (1) repeated applications of the same rule or (2) applications of some different rules in succession. For example, we may apply Rules E and D in succession to replace a $y_a y_b$ path with alternative paths from the vertices "prior to y_a" directly to the vertices "subsequent to y_b."

However, Rules A through I are sufficient to handle all situations in the reduction of signal-flow diagrams.

D. Some Illustrations of the Use of the Rules of Reduction

Illustration 1. Let us consider a set of linear equations,

$$y_2 = [t_1]y_1 + [t_2]y_2 + [t_5]y_3 \tag{16.9a}$$

$$y_3 = [t_3]y_2 \tag{16.9b}$$

$$y_4 = [t_4]y_2 + [t_6]y_3 \tag{16.9c}$$

and their associated signal-flow diagram in Fig. 16.7a. We shall now solve for y_4 in terms of y_1 by (1) the so-called signal-flow method, reducing the signal-flow diagram in Fig. 16.7a according to the rules of reduction, and (2) solving the linear equations in (16.9). The results of these two methods will be compared.

Solving with the Signal-flow Method. For the signal-flow diagram in Fig. 16.7a, we (1) remove the t_1 path according to Rule F in Table 16.1, as shown in Fig. 16.7b, (2) redraw for clarity in Fig. 16.7c, (3) remove the t_3 branch according to Rule D to obtain Fig. 16.7d, (4) combine the two self-loops at y_2 and the parallel $y_2 y_4$ paths according to Rule A, in Fig. 16.7d, (5) reduce the $y_3 y_2 y_4$ path to a single path according to Rule C, and then combine this path with t_6 according to Rule A to

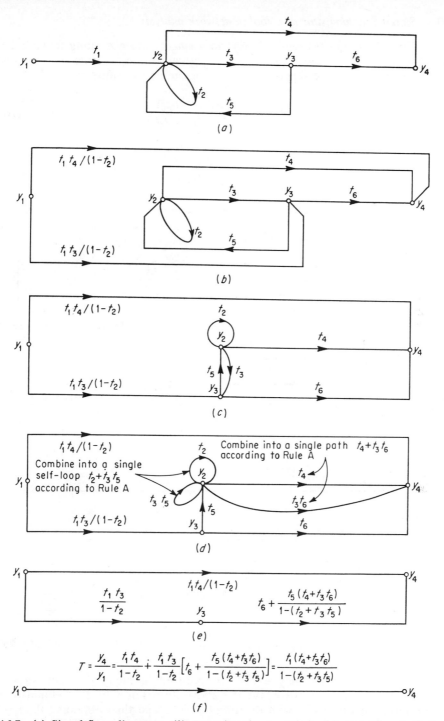

Fig. 16.7 (a) Signal-flow diagram; (b) removing the t_1 path in (a) according to Rule F in Table 16.1; (c) representation in (b) redrawn for clarity; (d) removing the t_3 branch in (c) according to Rule D, with reference to the second illustration in (d1) of Table 16.1; (e) reducing $y_3y_2y_4$ into a single path according to Rule C and then combining this path with t_6 according to Rule A; (f) reducing $y_1y_3y_4$ into a single path according to Rule B and then combining this path with the direct y_1y_4 path according to Rule A.

obtain Fig. 16.7e, and (6) reduce $y_1 y_3 y_4$ to a single path according to Rule B, and then combine this path with the direct $y_1 y_4$ path according to Rule A to obtain Fig. 16.7f. We now have the single $y_1 y_4$ path with known transmission

$$T = \frac{y_4}{y_1} = \frac{t_1(t_4 + t_3 t_6)}{1 - (t_2 + t_3 t_5)} \tag{16.10a}$$

in Fig. 16.7f, and

$$y_4 = [T]y_1 = \frac{t_1(t_4 + t_3 t_6)}{1 - (t_2 + t_3 t_5)} y_1 \tag{16.10b}$$

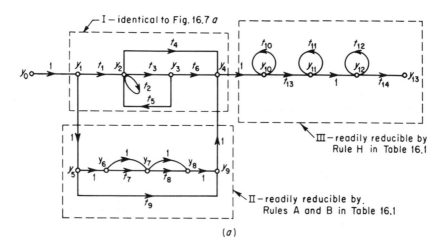

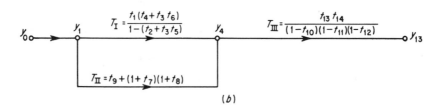

FIG. 16.8 (a) Signal-flow diagram; (b) reduction by partition; (c) final result of reduction.

A signal-flow diagram may usually be reduced in many different ways. For example, the reader may work out the above illustration by first eliminating the self-loop at y_2 in Fig. 16.7a with the aid of Rule I, and then obtaining the result in (16.10b) by perhaps an even more direct procedure.

Solving the Linear Equations. To solve for y_4 in terms of y_1 with (16.9), we (1) substitute (16.9b) into (16.9a), obtaining

$$y_2 = \frac{t_1}{1 - (t_2 + t_3 t_5)} y_1 \tag{16.11a}$$

(2) substitute (16.11a) into (16.9b), obtaining

$$y_3 = \frac{t_1 t_3}{1 - (t_2 + t_3 t_5)} y_1 \qquad (16.11b)$$

and (3) substitute (16.11a) and (16.11b) into (16.9c), obtaining

$$y_4 = \frac{t_1(t_4 + t_3 t_6)}{1 - (t_2 + t_3 t_5)} y_1 \qquad (16.11c)$$

It is apparent that the results in (16.10b) and (16.11c) check with each other.

Illustration 2. Let us try to reduce the signal-flow diagram in Fig. 16.8a. Since this diagram is rather complicated, let us partition it into three parts: I, II, and III.

Part I is identical to Fig. 16.7a, and its transmission T_I has already been obtained in Fig. 16.7 and Eq. (16.10a):

$$T_I = \frac{t_1(t_4 + t_3 t_6)}{1 - (t_2 + t_3 t_5)} \qquad (16.12a)$$

Part II may be readily reduced by Rules A and B in Table 16.1 to a single branch with known transmission

$$T_{II} = t_9 + (1 + t_7)(1 + t_8) \qquad (16.12b)$$

Part III may be readily reduced by Rule H to a single branch with known transmission

$$T_{III} = \frac{t_{13} t_{14}}{(1 - t_{10})(1 - t_{11})(1 - t_{12})} \qquad (16.12c)$$

We have now reduced the signal-flow diagram in Fig. 16.8a to the simplified version in Fig. 16.8b, which can be further reduced to Fig. 16.8c with overall transmission

$$T_{\text{overall}} = \frac{y_{13}}{y_0} = (T_I + T_{II})T_{III} = \text{expression in Fig. } 16.8c \qquad (16.12d)$$

16.3. The signal-flow method of analysis: illustrations of the solution of analysis problems with the aid of signal-flow diagrams

By the so-called "signal-flow method," we solve an analysis problem by (1) constructing a signal-flow diagram for a given network (or system) and (2) reducing this signal-flow diagram to a single branch with known transmission T. The transmission thus obtained is a "network function" or "network parameter" if a modified network is used, and is equal to the response/excitation ratio. The response may be readily obtained as the product of the transmission T and the excitation.

The signal-flow method, like the loop and nodal methods, is used to obtain *network functions* (or *system functions*), *network parameters*, or the *responses* of networks subject to given excitations.

We shall now provide some illustrations showing how the signal-flow method may be used in passive networks, active networks, and closed-loop systems.

A. *The Signal-flow Method Used in the Analysis of Passive Networks*

Illustration A2. Given a network, to find its network function. We wish to obtain the network functions $Y_T = I_2/E_1$ and $Y_D = I_1/E_1$ of the four-terminal network arrangement in Fig. 16.5a.

We have already solved the first portion of this problem in Illustration A1, Art. 16.1C, and obtained the signal-flow diagram of this network arrangement in Fig. 16.5*b*. This signal-flow diagram is now redrawn in Fig. 16.9*a* with I_2 designated as the "response" for finding $Y_T = I_2/E_1$, and in Fig. 16.10*a* with I_1 designated as the "response" for finding $Y_D = I_1/E_1$.

For Finding $Y_T = I_2/E_1$, we reduce the signal-flow diagram (Fig. 16.9*a*), by the steps described in the figure, to the single E_1I_2 branch with known transmission $Y_T = I_2/E_1$ in Fig. 16.9*g*. This transmission

Transfer admittance in Fig. 16.5a:

$$Y_T = \frac{I_2}{E_1} = \frac{-s^2}{5s^2 + 9s + 4} \qquad (16.13a)$$

is a transfer admittance of the network arrangement in Fig. 16.5*a*. The reciprocal of (16.13*a*) is, therefore, a transfer impedance of this same network:

Transfer impedance in Fig. 16.5a:

$$Z_T = \frac{E_1}{I_2} = \frac{5s^2 + 9s + 4}{-s^2} \qquad (16.13b)$$

For Finding $Y_D = I_1/E_1$, we reduce the signal-flow diagram (Fig. 16.10*a*), by steps described in the figure, to the single E_1I_1 path with known transmission $Y_D = I_1/E_1$ in Fig. 16.10*g*; this transmission

Driving-point admittance in Fig. 16.5a:

$$Y_D = \frac{I_1}{E_1} = \frac{2s^2 + 5s + 4}{5s^2 + 9s + 4} \qquad (16.14a)$$

is the driving-point admittance of the network arrangement in Fig. 16.5*a*. The reciprocal of (16.14*a*) is, therefore, the driving-point impedance of this same network:

Driving-point impedance in Fig. 16.5a:

$$Z_D = \frac{E_1}{I_1} = \frac{5s^2 + 9s + 4}{2s^2 + 5s + 4} \qquad (16.14b)$$

Remarks. For the network arrangement in Fig. 2.5*b* with $E_3 = 0$, we have obtained the transfer impedance $Z_T = E_1/I_2$ in Eq. (2.31*b*) and the driving-point impedance $Z_D = E_1/I_1$ in (2.31*a*) by the loop method of analysis.

For the network arrangement in Fig. 16.5*a*, we have obtained the transfer impedance $Z_T = E_1/I_2$ in (16.13*b*) and the driving-point impedance $Z_D = E_1/I_1$ in (16.14*b*) by the signal-flow method of analysis.

It is interesting to note that, for two identical network arrangements in these two illustrations, we have obtained two identical transfer impedances and two identical driving-point impedances by different methods of analysis.

FIG. 16.9   (*a*) Signal-flow diagram for the circuit in Fig. 16.5*a*, obtained from Fig. 16.5*b* with I_2 designated as response. (*b*) Replacing the dashed path in (*a*) with a self-loop at V_3 according to Rule D in Table 16.1 and eliminating the vertex E_2 by Rule B. (*c*) Replacing the dashed path in (*b*) with a self-loop at I_3 according to Rule F. (*d*) Replacing the dashed path in (*c*) with a self-loop at V_4 according to Rule F. (*e*) Replacing the dashed path in (*d*) with an additional self-loop at I_2' according to Rule F.(*f*) Combining the two self-loops in (*e*) as parallel paths according to Rule A. (*g*) Reducing the representation in (*f*) to a single path according to Rule H.

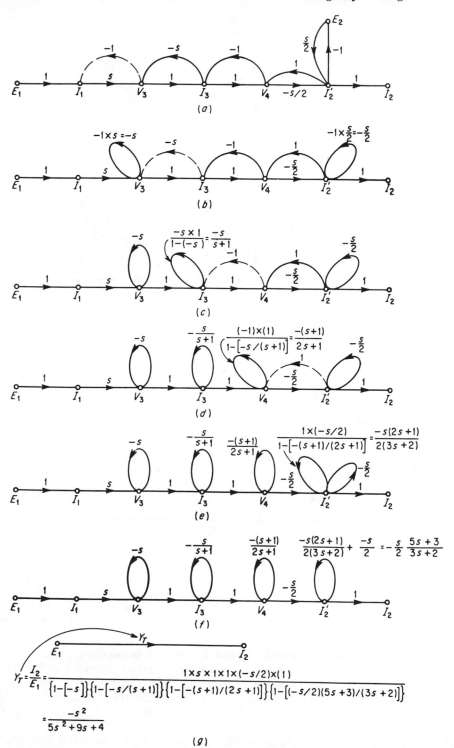

$$Y_T = \frac{I_2}{E_1} = \frac{1 \times s \times 1 \times 1 \times 1 \times (-s/2) \times (1)}{\{1-[-s]\}\{1-[-s/(s+1)]\}\{1-[-(s+1)/(2s+1)]\}\{1-[(-s/2)(5s+3)/(3s+2)]\}}$$

$$= \frac{-s^2}{5s^2 + 9s + 4}$$

(g)

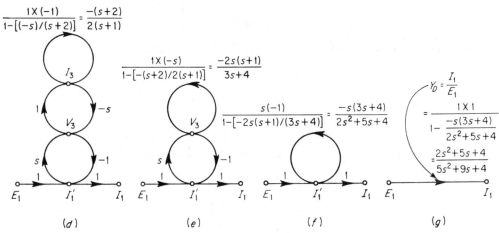

FIG. 16.10   (*a*) Signal-flow diagram for the circuit in Fig. 16.5*a*, obtained from Fig. 16.5*b* with I_1 designated as response. (*b*) Reducing (*a*) according to Rule B in Table 16.1. (*c*) Reducing (*b*) according to Rule C. (*d*) Reducing (*c*) according to Rule C. (*e*) Reducing (*d*) according to Rule C. (*f*) Reducing (*e*) according to Rule C. (*g*) Reducing (*f*) according to Rule C.

Illustration B2.   Given a network, to find its network parameters. We now wish to obtain the short-circuit parameter y_{21} of the four-terminal network in Fig. 16.5*a*.

This illustration is a continuation of Illustration B1, Art. 16.1C. Since $y_{21} = (I_2/E_1)_{E_2=0}$ according to (4.32), we need only obtain the transfer admittance I_2/E_1 of a "modified network"; this "modified network with $E_2 = 0$" is shown in Fig. 16.6*a*.

We have already obtained the signal-flow diagram of the "modified network" in Fig. 16.6*b*. This signal-flow diagram is now redrawn in Fig. 16.11*a* with I_2 designated as the "response."

We now reduce the signal-flow diagram in Fig. 16.11a, step by step as shown in the figure, to a single $E_1 I_2$ path with known transmission as indicated in Fig. 16.11d. This transmission is the sought-after y_{21}, namely,

Parameter for four-terminal network in Fig. 16.5a:

$$y_{21} = \frac{-s^2}{2s^2 + 7s + 4} \tag{16.15}$$

Remarks about Obtaining Other y_{ij} Parameters. We have demonstrated only how to obtain the y_{21} parameter with the aid of signal-flow diagrams. According to the interpretations of y_{11}, y_{12}, and y_{22} in (4.32), we may find these parameters in a similar manner. $y_{21} = y_{12}$ for all bilateral networks according to (4.33).

Remarks about the Result. For the four-terminal network in Fig. 2.7, we have obtained the y_{21} parameter in Eq. (2.36d) by the loop method of analysis.

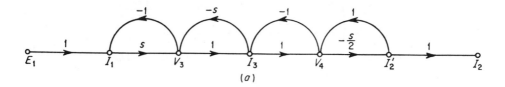

(a)

Comparing Fig. 16.11a with Fig. 16.9a, we note that they are identical except that the two paths -1 and $s/2$ between I_2' and E_2 in Fig. 16.9a are missing in Fig. 16.11a. Following the reduction in Fig. 16.9, Fig. 16.11a may therefore be reduced to "Fig. 16.9e without the $(-1)\times(s/2) = -s/2$ loop at I_2'"

(b)

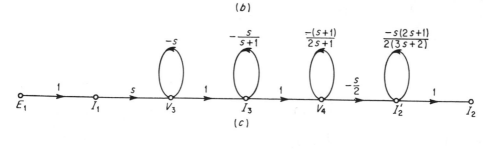

(c)

$$T = \frac{I_2}{E_1} = \frac{1 \times s \times 1 \times 1 \times (-s/2) \times 1}{\{1 - [-s]\}\{1 - [-s/(s+1)]\}\{1 - [-(s+1)/(2s+1)]\}\{1 - [-s(2s+1)/2(3s+2)]\}}$$

$$= \frac{-s^2}{2s^2 + 7s + 4}$$

(d)

FIG. 16.11 (a) Signal-flow diagram for the circuit arrangement in Fig. 16.6a, obtained from Fig. 16.6b with I_2 designated as response. (b) Figure 16.9e without the self-loop at I_2' as the simplified version of (a). (c) Representation in (b) redrawn. (d) Reducing (c) to a single path according to Rule H.

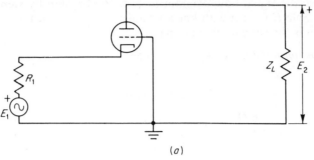

(a)

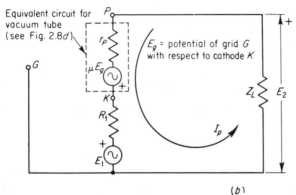

Equivalent circuit for vacuum tube (see Fig. 2.8d)

E_g = potential of grid G with respect to cathode K

Voltage–current relations:

$$E_g = -(E_1 + I_p R_1) = [-1]E_1 + [-R_1]I_p$$

$$I_p = \frac{\mu E_g - E_1}{R_1 + r_p + Z_L}$$

$$= \left[\frac{\mu}{R_1 + r_p + Z_L}\right]E_g + \left[\frac{-1}{R_1 + r_p + Z_L}\right]E_1$$

$$E_2 = [-Z_L]I_p$$

(b)

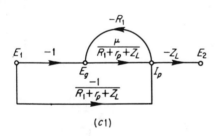

(c1)

(c2)

This self-loop replaces $-R_1$ according to Rule D of Table 16.1.

(c3)

(c4)

$$G = \frac{E_2}{E_1} = \frac{\dfrac{-(\mu+1)}{R_1+r_p+Z_L}(-Z_L)}{1 - \dfrac{-R_1\mu}{R_1+r_p+Z_L}} = \frac{(\mu+1)Z_L}{(1+\mu)R_1+r_p+Z_L}$$

FIG. 16.12

For the four-terminal network in Fig. 16.5a, we have obtained the y_{21} parameter in Eq. (16.15) by the signal-flow method of analysis.

It is interesting to note that, for two identical networks in these two illustrations, we have obtained two identical y_{21} parameters by different methods of analysis.

B. The Signal-flow Method in the Analysis of Active Networks

Illustration C. Given a vacuum-tube circuit, to find its voltage gain. For the grounded-grid vacuum-tube amplifier circuit in Fig. 16.12a, we wish to obtain the network function $G = E_2/E_1$.

We (1) replace the vacuum tube with an equivalent circuit and write the voltage-current relations in Fig. 16.12b, (2) construct the signal-flow diagram in Fig. 16.12c1, and (3) reduce it in Fig. 16.12c2 and 3, obtaining the single E_1E_2 branch with known transmission G in Fig. 16.21c4. This known transmission,

$$G = \frac{E_2}{E_1} = \frac{(\mu + 1)Z_L}{(\mu + 1)R_1 + r_p + Z_L} \tag{16.16}$$

is the sought-after voltage-gain function of the grounded-grid amplifier circuit in Fig. 16.12a. This result checks with the results obtained by other methods of analysis in standard textbooks on electronics.

Remarks about transistor circuits. We shall temporarily postpone our illustrations using transistor circuits until Chap. 17, which is devoted exclusively to the study of transistor amplifiers, with or without feedback, using the signal-flow method.

C. The Signal-flow Method in the Analysis of Closed-loop Control Systems

We shall describe closed-loop control systems more formally and study their stability problems in Chaps. 18 to 21. For the time being, we shall use only block diagrams to represent closed-loop control systems.

Some preliminary considerations. In an electrical network, we use circuit components with different impedances $Z_i(s)$ to study voltage-current relations, for example, $E_2(s) = [Z_1(s)]I_2(s)$ and $E_5(s) = [Z_3(s)]I_1(s) + [Z_4(s)]I_2(s)$. These linear voltage-current relations may be represented graphically as signal-flow representations; combining all the signal-flow representations of a network, we obtain a signal-flow diagram.

Comparable to the voltages $E_i(s)$ and currents $I_k(s)$ in an electrical network, a closed-loop control system contains the variables $R(s)$, $E_k(s)$, $B_i(s)$, $Y_j(s)$, and $C(s)$ as indicated in Table 16.2. These variables may represent voltages, currents, displacements, accelerations, etc. Comparable to the circuit components with impedances $Z_i(s)$ in an electrical network, a control system has control elements or feedback elements with transfer functions $G_i(s)$ or $H_j(s)$ as depicted in (a1) and (b1) of Table 16.2. Comparable to the voltage-current relation, for example, $E_5(s) = [Z_3(s)]I_1(s) + [Z_4(s)]I_2(s)$, a closed-loop control system has the variable-to-variable relation, for example, $E(s) = [1]Y(s) + [-1]B(s)$ for the error-sensing device in (c1) and (c2) of Table 16.2. Comparable to the signal-flow representations for the voltage-current relations of an electrical network, the closed-loop control system has the signal-flow representations for its variable-to-variable relations in Table 16.2, column 3.

We may now use block diagrams to describe a closed-loop system. This description is given so that we may apply the signal-flow method to a closed-loop control system. Closed-loop control systems will be studied later in Chaps. 18 to 21.

Table 16.2

(1) System component	(2) Variable–to–variable relations	(3) Signal–flow representation
(*a*1) A control element with a transfer function $G(s)$: $E(s)$ [or $R(s)$] → $G(s)$ → $Y(s)$ [or $C(s)$]	(*a*2) $Y(s) = [G(s)] E(s)$	(*a*3) $E(s)$ $G(s)$ $Y(s)$
(*b*1) A feedback element with a transfer function $H(s)$: $B(s)$ ← $H(s)$ ← $Y(s)$ [or $C(s)$]	(*b*2) $B(s) = [H(s)] Y(s)$	(*b*3) $Y(s)$ $H(s)$ $B(s)$
(*c*1) An error–sensing device: $Y(s)$ [or $R(s)$] + → $E(s)$, $-$ $B(s)$ [or $C(s)$]	(*c*2) $E(s) = Y(s) - B(s)$ $= [1] Y(s) + [-1] B(s)$	(*c*3) $Y(s)$ 1 $E(s)$ -1 $B(s)$
(*d*1) An error–sensing device with a feedback element: $Y(s)$ [or $R(s)$] + → $E(s)$, $-$ $B(s)$ ← $H(s)$ ← $Y^*(s)$ [or $C(s)$]	(*d*2) $E(s) = [1] Y(s) + [-1] B(s)$ $B(s) = [H(s)] Y^*(s)$ or $E(s) = [1] Y(s) + [-H(s)] Y^*(s)$	(*d*3) $Y(s)$ 1 $E(s)$ $Y^*(s)$ -1 $B(s)$ $H(s)$ or $Y(s)$ 1 $E(s)$ $Y^*(s)$ $-H(s)$

(*e*) Legend

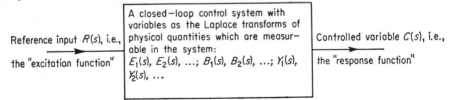

Reference input $R(s)$, i.e., the "excitation function"	A closed–loop control system with variables as the Laplace transforms of physical quantities which are measurable in the system: $E_1(s), E_2(s), \ldots; B_1(s), B_2(s), \ldots; Y_1(s), Y_2(s), \ldots$	Controlled variable $C(s)$, i.e., the "response function"

Independent variable as the
Laplace transform of a physical quantity: Reference input $R(s) = \mathcal{L}[r(t)]$

Dependent variables as the
Laplace transforms of physical quantities:
   Error functions $E_i(s) = \mathcal{L}[e_i(t)]$
   Feedback functions $B_j(s) = \mathcal{L}[b_j(t)]$
   Intermediate variables $Y_k(s) = \mathcal{L}[y_k(t)]$
   Controlled variable $C(s) = \mathcal{L}[c(t)]$

Block-diagram description of a closed-loop control system:

>   *A closed-loop control system uses the system components, listed in
>   Table 16.2, column 1, whose variable-to-variable relations and
>   signal-flow representations are respectively listed in columns 2
>   and 3*   (16.17a)
>
>   *A closed-loop control system represents an interconnection of these
>   system components as exemplified in Figs. 16.13a and 16.14a*   (16.17b)
>
>   *Subject to a reference input R(s), a closed-loop control system
>   regulates the controlled variable C(s) through other variables
>   measurable in the system, as indicated in Table 16.2e and Figs.
>   16.13a and 16.14a*   (16.17c)

We shall now illustrate the use of the signal-flow method in the analysis of closed-loop control systems.

Illustration D. Let us now consider a closed-loop control system with the simple single-loop arrangement in Fig. 16.13a.

We may readily write its three variable-to-variable relations and construct their associated signal-flow diagram in Fig. 16.13b1. However, if we use $B(s) = [H(s)]C(s)$ whenever $B(s)$ appears, we need only two variable-to-variable relations and the associated signal-flow diagram in Fig. 16.13b2.

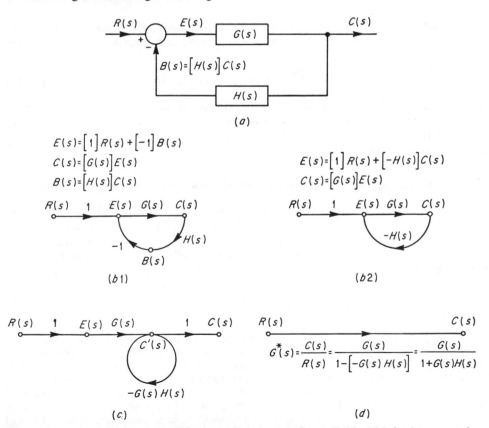

FIG. 16.13 (a) A simple closed-loop control system (refer to Table 16.2 for interpretation of symbols). (b) Signal-flow diagrams for variable-to-variable relations as listed. (c) Reducing (b) according to Rule D of Table 16.1. (d) Reducing (c) according to Rule C.

The signal-flow diagram in Fig. 16.13b1 or 2 may easily be reduced, first to Fig. 16.13c, and then to Fig. 16.13d; we obtain a single $R(s)C(s)$ branch with known transmission. This *known* transmission

$$G^*(s) = \frac{C(s)}{R(s)} = \frac{G(s)}{1 + G(s)H(s)} \qquad (16.18)$$

is the overall transfer function of the system in Fig. 16.13a.

If we are given the reference input $r(t)$ as a time function and wish to find the controlled variable $c(t)$ as a time function for the system in Fig. 16.13a, we may (1) find the reference input in Laplace-transform form, that is, $R(s) = \mathscr{L}[r(t)]$, and (2) find $C(s) = G^*(s)R(s)$ with the aid of (16.18). We then find the inverse Laplace transform of $C(s)$, i.e., $c(t) = \mathscr{L}^{-1}[C(s)]$. For the methods for finding the Laplace transform and inverse Laplace transform, see Arts. 11.4 and 13.2.

Illustration E. Let us now consider the multiple-loop control system in Fig. 16.14a.

We may write the linear variable-to-variable relations and construct the signal-flow diagram in Fig. 16.14b. Actually, this is hardly necessary. *We may observe the variable-to-variable relations in Fig. 16.14a one by one by inspection*, for example, $E_1(s) = R(s) - C(s)$, *without writing them; construct the signal-flow representation for each relation*, e.g., an RE_1 path with transmission 1 and a CE_1 path with -1 for the relation $E_1(s) = R(s) - C(s)$, *one by one, thus obtaining the complete signal-flow diagram in Fig.* 16.14b.

The signal-flow diagram may be reduced step by step, as shown in Fig. 16.14c through g, to the single $R(s)C(s)$ path with known transmission in Fig. 16.14h. This known transmission

$$G^*(s) = \frac{C(s)}{R(s)} = \textit{expression in Fig. 16.14h} \qquad (16.19)$$

is the overall transfer function of the system in Fig. 16.14a.

For a reference input $r(t)$ given as a time function in the system in Fig. 16.14a, we may find the controlled variable $c(t)$ as a time function. Reference is made to the preceding illustration for the procedure.

16.4. Obtaining the overall transmission without reducing the signal-flow diagram

In preceding sections we have discussed, illustrated, and applied the various reduction techniques for obtaining the overall transmission of a signal-flow diagram. In 1956, S. J. Mason† presented a generalized formula with which we may obtain the overall transmission of a signal-flow diagram directly without reducing the signal-flow diagram. The choice between (1) the reduction-technique method and (2) the generalized-formula method is usually a matter of personal preference.

† S. J. Mason, Feedback Theory—Further Properties of Signal Flow Graphs, *Proc. IRE*, vol. 44, no. 7, pp. 920–926, July, 1956.

FIG. 16.14 (*a*) A closed-loop control system (refer to Table 16.2 for interpretation of symbols). (*b*) Signal-flow diagram for (*a*), where abbreviations rather than functions of s are used. (*c*) Removing the $-H_1$ and $-H_2$ paths in (*b*) according to Rule D of Table 16.1. (*d*) Eliminating vertices Y_1, Y_2, E_3, Y_4, and E_4 in (*c*) according to Rule B and then eliminating the self-loop at Y_3 according to Rule C. (*e*) Removing the $-H_3$ path in (*d*) according to Rule D to obtain a self-loop at Y_5 and combining this self-loop with the $-G_5H_2$ self-loop according to Rule A. (*f*) Eliminating the self-loop at Y_5 in (*e*) according to Rule C. (*g*) Removing the -1 path in (*f*) according to Rule D and adding a $C'C$ branch to identify C as response. (*h*) Eliminating the self-loop at C' according to Rule C and restoring the original functions of s from the abbreviations.

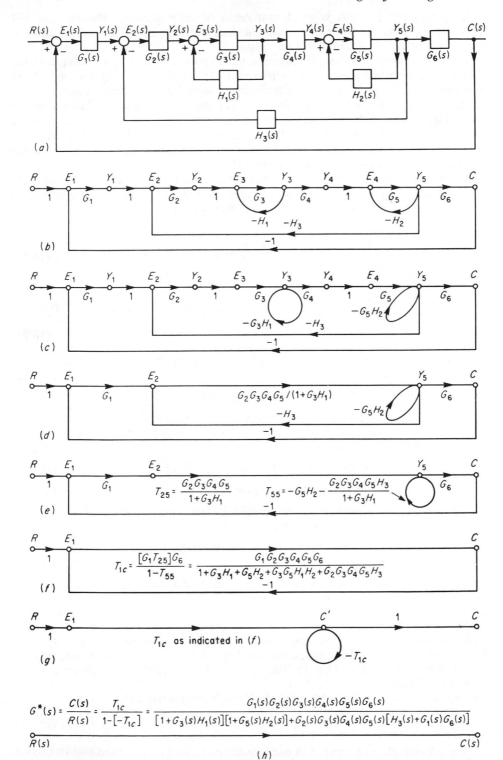

$$G^*(s) = \frac{C(s)}{R(s)} = \frac{T_{1c}}{1-[-T_{1c}]} = \frac{G_1(s)G_2(s)G_3(s)G_4(s)G_5(s)G_6(s)}{[1+G_3(s)H_1(s)][1+G_5(s)H_2(s)]+G_2(s)G_3(s)G_4(s)G_5(s)[H_3(s)+G_1(s)G_6(s)]}$$

(h)

The generalized formula is an elegant result of investigation. However, as will be illustrated later, the use of this formula does not necessarily reduce the amount of work necessary in obtaining the end result.

On the other hand, the use of reduction techniques in obtaining the overall transmission of a signal-flow diagram enables us to (1) understand fully the underlying principles as well as the various techniques of signal-flow analysis, which include the derivation of the generalized formula, (2) see the functional relations of the physical quantities as "nodes" or "variables" during each stage of reduction, and (3) employ special techniques, e.g., partitioning, approximations (which will be discussed in Chap. 17), etc., in simplifying the problem or the result. It is for these reasons that the reduction techniques are emphasized in this text.

Mason's generalized formula. We shall give Mason's generalized formula here without proof along with an illustration; the interested reader may refer to his paper.

The overall transmission of a given signal-flow diagram is

Overall transmission:

$$T = \frac{1}{\Delta} \sum_{k=1}^{M} T_k \Delta_k \tag{16.20}$$

with

$$\Delta = 1 - \sum_{i=1}^{N} P_i^{(1)} + \sum_{i=1}^{m_2} P_i^{(2)} - \sum_{i=1}^{m_3} P_i^{(3)} \cdots + (-1)^n \sum_{i=1}^{m_h} P_i^{(h)} + \cdots + (-1)^H \sum_{i=1}^{m_H} P_i^{(H)} \tag{16.21}$$

where M = number of possible forward paths between excitation and response (16.22a)

N = number of feedback loops in signal-flow diagram (16.22b)

m_h = number of possible combinations of h nontouching feedback loops (two feedback loops are "nontouching" if they do not have a common node) (16.22c)

H = largest possible number of nontouching feedback loops (16.22d)

T_k = transmission of kth forward path (16.23a)

$P_i^{(1)}$ = *loop transmission* of ith feedback loop, i.e., product of all transmissions around ith loop (16.23b)

$P_i^{(h)}$ = *product of loop transmissions* of ith combination of h nontouching feedback loops (16.23c)

Δ_k = value of Δ for that part of signal-flow diagram not touching kth forward path (16.23d)

The meanings of the above terms are given in the following illustration.

Illustration. Let us try to obtain the driving-point admittance $Y_D = I_1/E_1$ of the four-terminal network arrangement in Fig. 16.5a; the signal-flow diagram has already been obtained in Fig. 16.10a. To use Eq. (16.20), let us proceed in the following manner:

1. There is only one forward path† $E_1 I_1' I_1$; it has transmission

$$T_1 = 1 \times 1 = 1 \tag{16.24a}$$

† For an example with more than one forward path, see Fig. 16.7a and note its two forward paths $t_1 t_4$ and $t_1 t_3 t_6$.

2. The transmissions $P_i^{(1)}$ of all the individual loops are

Loop A $(I_1'V_3I_1')$: $P_1^{(1)} = t_a = t_{a1}t_{a2} = s(-1) = -s$

Loop B $(V_3I_3V_3)$: $P_2^{(1)} = t_b = 1(-s) = -s$

Loop C $(I_3V_4I_3)$: $P_3^{(1)} = t_c = 1(-1) = -1$ (16.24b)

Loop D $(V_4I_2V_4)$: $P_4^{(1)} = t_d = -\dfrac{s}{2}(1) = -\dfrac{s}{2}$

Loop E $(I_2E_2I_2)$: $P_5^{(1)} = t_e = (-1)\dfrac{s}{2} = -\dfrac{s}{2}$ $N = 5$

and their sum is

Sum: $\displaystyle\sum_{i=1}^{N} P_i^{(1)} = \text{sum of Eqs. (16.24b)} = -3s - 1$ (16.24c)

3. The products $P_i^{(2)}$ of the loop transmissions of any two nontouching loops are

Loops A, C: $P_1^{(2)} = t_a t_c = (-s)(-1) = s$

Loops A, D: $P_2^{(2)} = t_a t_d = (-s)\left(-\dfrac{s}{2}\right) = \dfrac{s^2}{2}$

Loops A, E: $P_3^{(2)} = t_a t_e = (-s)\left(-\dfrac{s}{2}\right) = \dfrac{s^2}{2}$

Loops B, D: $P_4^{(2)} = t_b t_d = (-s)\left(-\dfrac{s}{2}\right) = \dfrac{s^2}{2}$ (16.24d)

Loops B, E: $P_5^{(2)} = t_b t_e = (-s)\left(-\dfrac{s}{2}\right) = \dfrac{s^2}{2}$

Loops C, E: $P_6^{(2)} = t_c t_e = (-1)\left(-\dfrac{s}{2}\right) = \dfrac{s}{2}$ $m_2 = 6$

and their sum is

Sum: $\displaystyle\sum_{i=1}^{m_2} P_i^{(2)} = \text{sum of Eqs. (16.24d)} = \tfrac{3}{2}s + 2s^2$ (16.24e)

4. Since A, C, and E form the only set of three nontouching loops, we have

Loops A, C, E:

$$\sum_{i=1}^{m_3} P_i^{(3)} = P_1^{(3)} = t_a t_c t_e = (-s)(-1)\left(-\dfrac{s}{2}\right) = -\dfrac{s^2}{2}   \qquad m_3 = 1   \qquad (16.24f)$$

5. We do not have any set of four or more nontouching loops, so that

$$P_i^{(4)} = P_i^{(5)} = \cdots = 0   \qquad (16.24g)$$

6. According to (16.21), we have

$$\Delta = 1 - \text{Eq. } (16.24c) + \text{Eq. } (16.24e) - \text{Eq. } (16.24f) + \cdots \qquad (16.24h)$$

$$\Delta = \tfrac{1}{2}(5s^2 + 9s + 4) \qquad (16.24i)$$

7. According to (16.23d), we modify Eqs. (16.24c), (16.24e), and (16.24f) by letting $t_{a1} = t_{a2} = 0$ or $t_a = 0$ (which in effect removes the paths $I_1'V_3$ and V_3I_1' that touch the only forward path $E_1I_1'I_1$) and substitute them into (16.24h), obtaining

$$\Delta_1 = 1 - (-2s + 1) + \frac{s}{2} + s^2 - 0 = \tfrac{1}{2}(2s^2 + 5s + 4) \qquad (16.24j)$$

8. Substituting (16.24a), (16.24i), and (16.24j) into (16.20), we obtain the overall transmission

$$Y_D = \frac{I_1}{E_1} = T = \frac{2s^2 + 5s + 4}{5s^2 + 9s + 4} \qquad (16.24k)$$

This checks with our earlier result in (16.14), obtained with the reduction-technique method demonstrated in Fig. 16.10. However, considerable computation is involved in the present illustration.

Remarks. Although the signal-flow diagram of the above illustration has only a few simple, well-defined feedback loops and a single forward path (Fig. 16.10a), we hardly saved any work by using the generalized formula (16.20). For a signal-flow diagram with a large number of feedback loops (which must be carefully traced out) and a number of forward paths, the computation involved in generalized formula (16.20) could be very laborious.

16.5. Summarizing remarks about the signal-flow method

A. Some Remarks about the Signal-flow Method as a Means of Network or System Analysis

Remark 1. *The signal-flow method, employing a graphical representation of linear voltage-current or variable-to-variable relations and procedures for reduction, is an analytical method* and not a graphical method. It yields analytical results rather than the approximate, numerical solutions typical of graphical techniques.

This is true for all the illustrations given in this chapter. For example, the transfer admittance Y_T in (16.13a) for the network arrangement in Fig. 16.5a is an analytical solution.

Remark 2. *The signal-flow method may be used to obtain network functions, network parameters, system functions, and network (or system) responses subject to certain excitations, for passive and active networks as well as control systems* (including electrical, mechanical, electromechanical, and hydraulic systems, with or without closed loops).

We have illustrated the use of signal-flow methods in Art. 16.3A, B, and C for passive networks, active networks, and control systems, respectively.

Remark 3. *To analyze a network whose signal-flow diagram is very complicated, we may partition its signal-flow diagram into several simpler parts, reduce each part to a single branch with known transmission, and then combine these branches. This permits us to use the signal-flow method in the analysis of complicated networks (or systems) with relative ease.*

An illustration of partition is given in Fig. 16.8 and Eqs. (16.12).

B. Some Remarks Comparing the Signal-flow Method with the Loop and Nodal Methods

Reference is made to Chap. 2 on the loop and nodal methods of analysis.

Remark 4. *In the loop method, each equation has the form* $E_i = \sum\limits_{j=1}^{n} Z_{ij}I_j$ *and represents the voltage relation in a loop;* no equations of other forms may be used. *In the nodal method, each equation has the form* $I_j = \sum\limits_{k=1}^{n} (\pm Y_{jk}E_k)$ *and represents the current relation about a node;* no equations of other forms may be used. *In the signal-flow method, voltage-current relations (or other linear variable-to-variable relations) of different forms may be used.*

For example, note the voltage-current relations in Figs. 16.1b and 16.12b and the linear variable-to-variable relations in Fig. 16.13b in the illustrations of the signal-flow method. It is apparent that not all the equations of each set have the same form. In the voltage-current relations in Fig. 16.1b, the first equation is of the form $E_i = \sum\limits_{j=1}^{n} Z_{ij}I_j$, and the second equation of the form $I_j = \sum\limits_{k=1}^{n} (\pm Y_{jk}E_k)$. In later examples, we shall allow equations of other forms.

Remark 5. *The loop method is most suitable to the analysis of networks with only voltage sources;* we must change any "current sources" into "equivalent voltage sources" before we may apply the loop method. *The nodal method is most suitable to the analysis of networks with only current sources;* we must change any "voltage sources" into "equivalent current sources" before we may apply the nodal method. *The signal-flow method may be directly applied* with no source changes *to any network with any combination of voltage and current sources.*

Remark 6. *The signal-flow method is often better suited to active networks, in particular, transistor circuits, than the loop and nodal methods. The loop and nodal methods are often better suited to passive networks, in particular, those excited by only voltage sources or only current sources, than the signal-flow method.*

In the analysis of an active network, we always replace the active element, e.g., a vacuum tube or a transistor, with one of its two alternative equivalent circuits. This means that we have the choice of the "equivalent circuit with a voltage source" or the "equivalent circuit with a current source." In the signal-flow method, we may use either equivalent circuit; in the loop or nodal method, we are more restricted in our choice. The signal-flow method is, therefore, somewhat better suited to active networks.

For the justification of the portion of Remark 6 concerning passive networks, reference is made to Remark 5.

Remark 7. *For the analysis of ladder networks, including cascaded transistor amplifiers whose equivalent circuits have ladder forms,†† the signal-flow method is often preferred.*

For complicated networks, we must write the voltage-current relations before we can construct the signal-flow diagrams. For a ladder structure, we usually need not write the voltage-current relations first. This has been illustrated and remarked in Illustration A1 in Art. 16.1C.

Remark 8. *In problems involving practical circuits, we often wish to obtain an approximate, rather than an exact, solution. If we use the loop, nodal, or "similar" method,‡ we usually must follow through the whole procedure, obtain an exact solution,*

---

† For example, the equivalent circuit of the two cascaded transistor stages in Fig. 17.11a has the ladder structure in Fig. 17.11b.

‡ In the loop method, we solve a set of loop equations. In the nodal method, we solve a set of nodal equations. In the "similar" method, we solve a combination of loop and nodal equations, say by eliminating variables one by one.

and then approximate it by leaving out insignificant terms. If we use the signal-flow method, we often have the opportunity to make approximations in the early steps of the procedure (reducing the problem to a simpler one) *and to save much work in the solution of the problem.*

We shall give illustrations later showing how to make approximations in the early steps of the procedure of the signal-flow method.

However, we may look into one of these illustrations now. Let us find the approximate current gain $A_{GB} = I_2/I_1$ of the grounded-base (GB) transistor amplifier whose equivalent circuit is given in Fig. 17.1c, voltage-current relations in Fig. 17.2a, and signal-flow diagram in Fig. 17.2b. Practically, $r_b \ll |z_c|$ is always true. If we use the *signal-flow method*, we may immediately approximate by omitting the r_b path in the original signal-flow diagram in Fig. 17.2b for the reasons stated in the associated footnote, proceed to solve the "simpler problem" by the steps described in Fig. 17.2c and d, and obtain $A_{GB} \cong -\alpha/(1 + Z_L/z_c)$ by making one more approximation. On the other hand, if we use the *loop, nodal, or "similar" method*, we must solve the voltage-current relations in Fig. 17.2a, obtain an exact expression for I_2 in terms of I_1, and *then* approximate for $r_b \ll |z_c|$. The reader may wish to try this latter approach to judge the amount of work involved in the solution.

Remark 9. *It should be recognized that an analysis problem solvable by the loop or nodal method is also solvable by the signal-flow method, and vice versa.* An electrical engineer should be familiar with these three important methods of analysis.

For example, the results of the signal-flow method in Illustrations A2 and B2 (Art. 16.3A) and Illustration C (Art. 16.3B) check with the results of the loop and other methods of analysis.

C. Remark about Other Properties Associated with a Signal-flow Diagram

Remark 10. *We have discussed only the properties of a signal-flow diagram essential to its reduction and application in the so-called signal-flow method of analysis.* The interested reader may also wish to look into its other mathematical and topological properties.†

PROBLEMS

16.1. The loop equations describing the behavior of the three-loop network in Fig. 16.5 are

$$(1 + s)I_1 + \quad (0)I_2 + \quad (-s)I_3 = E_1$$

$$(0)I_1 + \left(2 + \frac{2}{s}\right)I_2 + \quad I_3 = 0$$

$$(-s)I_1 + \quad I_2 + (2 + s)I_3 = 0$$

where the excitation E_1 is the independent variable, and the responses I_1, I_2, and I_3 are the dependent variables.

† See Mason, *loc. cit.;* Truxal, *loc. cit.;* and other references on signal-flow diagrams. For example, the complexity of a signal-flow diagram is measured by its "order" (as defined in Truxal, p. 100). However, it is not essential to know the "order" of a signal-flow diagram in order to reduce it; therefore, we have not discussed it here. Besides, the "order" of the diagram may not reflect the complexity of the network it represents. Two engineers with different degrees of mastery of signal-flow techniques may obtain, for the same network, two signal-flow diagrams of *different* orders, say 0 and 1, as one of them has in effect reduced it mentally before he puts it down on paper. For illustration, note the order 1 diagram in Fig. 2.11 (Truxal, p. 100) and the order 0 diagram in Fig. 2.12 for the network in Fig. 2.10.

(a) Rearrange the loop equations into a set of equations for the dependent variables I_1, I_2, and I_3.

(b) Construct a signal-flow diagram with these equations for the dependent variables. Note in Art. 16.1B that the signal-flow diagram is defined as the graphical representation of the equations of the dependent variables. It is important to construct the signal-flow diagram according to this definition in order to be able to solve a variety of problems using only the simple rules of reduction in Art. 16.2. REMARKS: If we construct a signal-flow diagram as the graphical representation of another set of linear equations in this problem, say $E_1 = (1 + s)I_1 - sI_3$, $I_2 = sI_1 - (2 + s)I_3$, and $I_3 = -2(1 + 1/s)I_2$, also obtained by rearranging the above loop equations, it gives us the false indication that I_1 is the excitation, and E_1 is a response. To correct this error, we must "transform" this signal-flow diagram into the "signal-flow diagram describing the dependent-variable equations." But why do we not construct the "signal-flow diagram describing the dependent-variable equations" in the first place and save ourselves the trouble of transforming? This is exactly what we should do here.

(c) Designating I_1 as the "response," reduce the signal-flow diagram to a single $E_1 I_1$ branch, and find the transmission $Y_D = I_1/E_1$, the driving-point impedance of the network in Fig. 16.5.

(d) Designating I_2 as the "response," reduce the signal-flow diagram to a single $E_1 I_2$ branch, and find the transmission $Y_T = I_2/E_1$, the transfer admittance of the network in Fig. 16.5.

Check Y_D and Y_T obtained in (c) and (d) with (16.14a) and (16.13a), obtained from a different signal-flow diagram for the *same* network.

16.2. Given: The network depicted in Fig. P 16.2, whose excitation E_1 is the independent variable of the system of linear voltage-current relations describing the network behavior and whose responses V_3, V_4, V_5, V_6, E_2 and I_1, I_3, I_4, I_5, I_6, I_2 are the dependent variables.

(a) Express the voltage-current relations as a set of equations of the dependent variables, for example, $I_1 = (1/Z_a)E_1 + (-1/Z_a)V_3$, $V_3 = (Z_b)I_1 + (-Z_b)I_3$, $I_3 = \cdots$, etc.

(b) Construct a signal-flow diagram with the equations obtained in (a).

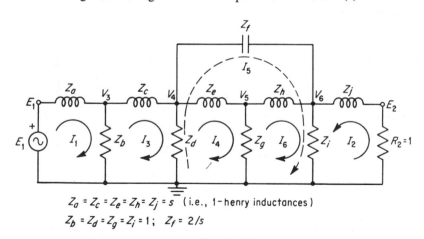

$Z_a = Z_c = Z_e = Z_h = Z_j = s$ (i.e., 1-henry inductances)
$Z_b = Z_d = Z_g = Z_i = 1$; $Z_f = 2/s$

FIG. P 16.2

(c) Construct a signal-flow diagram by inspecting the voltage-current relations in the circuit one by one without writing them. See the remarks in Illustration A1, Art. 16.1C, and compare the results of (b) and (c).

(d) Designating I_1 as the "response," reduce the signal-flow diagram to a single $E_1 I_1$ branch, and find the transmission $Y_D = I_1/E_1$, the driving-point impedance of the network.

(e) Designating E_2 as the "response," reduce the signal-flow diagram to a single $E_1 E_2$ branch, and find the transmission $G(s) = E_2/E_1$, the transfer voltage-ratio function of the network.

16.3. Repeat Prob. 16.2 for the network in Fig. P 16.3.

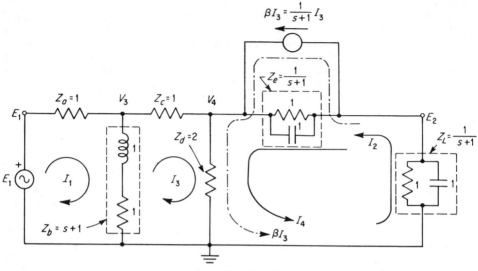

Fig. P 16.3

16.4. Given: The vacuum-tube circuit in Fig. P 16.4a and the equivalent circuit in Fig. P 16.4b.

(a) Express the voltage-current relations as a set of equations of the dependent variables I_p, V_3, E_g, V_4, and E_2.

(b) Construct a signal-flow diagram with these equations.

(c) Reduce the signal-flow diagram to a single E_1E_2 branch, and find the transmisson $G(s) = E_2/E_1$, the transfer voltage-ratio function of this circuit.

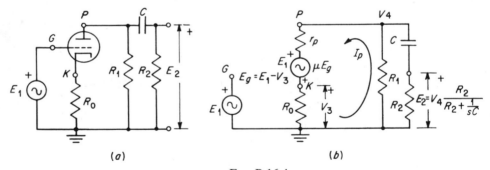

Fig. P 16.4

16.5. Given: The two-excitation network in Fig. P 16.5a whose excitations E_{1a} and E_{1b} are two independent variables of the system of linear voltage-current relations describing the network behavior and whose responses V_3, V_4, E_2 and I_1, I_3, I_4, I_2 are the dependent variables.

(a) Construct a signal-flow diagram describing the network behavior. REMARKS: Whether the reader chooses to (1) write a set of dependent-variable equations or (2) construct the signal-flow diagram directly, the signal-flow diagram must be constructed as the graphical representation of the dependent-variable equations, for the reasons given in Prob. 16.1.

(b) Using the rules in Art. 16.2, reduce the signal-flow diagram to the form given in Fig. P 16.5b, and find the transmissions G_a and G_b. It is easy to see that

$$E_2 = G_a E_{1a} + G_b E_{1b}$$

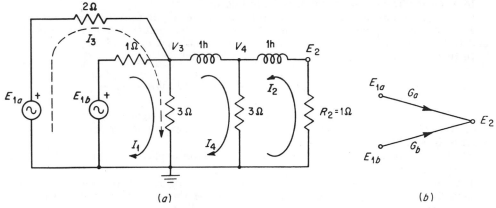

(a)   (b)

Fig. P 16.5

16.6. (a) Construct a signal-flow diagram for the network in Fig. P 16.5a with $E_{1b} = 0$, reduce it to a single $E_{1a}E_2$ branch, and obtain the transmission $G_a = E_2/E_{1a}$.

(b) Construct a signal-flow diagram for the network in Fig. 16.5a with $E_{1a} = 0$, reduce it to a single $E_{1b}E_2$ branch, and obtain the transmission $G_b = E_2/E_{1b}$.

To find E_2 in Fig. P 16.5a, we may treat the two sources E_{1a} and E_{1b} independently, as we did in (a) and (b) above, and find (by the principle of superposition)

$$E_2 = G_a E_{1a} + G_b E_{1b}$$

Compare the results of Probs. 16.5 and 16.6.

16.7. Given: The closed-loop control system in Fig. P 16.7.

(a) Construct a signal-flow diagram describing the behavior of this system.

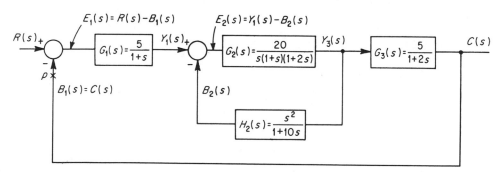

Fig. P 16.7

(b) Reduce the signal-flow diagram obtained in (a) to obtain the overall transfer function $G^*(s) = C(s)/R(s)$.

(c) Break the return path at p, and define the "open-loop transfer function" of this system as

$$T(s) = \frac{B_1(s)}{R(s)}\bigg|_{\text{return path open}}$$

Modify the signal-flow diagram obtained in (a), and reduce it to obtain $T(s)$.

16.8. Given: The signal-flow diagram in Fig. 16.7a, modified by reversing the arrowhead of path t_4.

Reduce this signal-flow diagram to a single y_1y_4 branch, and find the transmission $T = y_4/y_1$.

16.9. Given: The four-terminal network in Fig. 16.5.

Use the signal-flow method to obtain (*a*) the parameter y_{12} and (*b*) the parameter y_{22}.

The parameter y_{21} has already been obtained by the procedure described in Figs. 16.6 and 16.11.   Since $y_{12} = y_{21}$ for bilateral networks, check y_{12} with (16.15).

16.10. The transfer functions $Y_T(s) =$ Eq. (16.13*a*) and

$$G(s) = \frac{E_2(s)}{E_1(s)} = \frac{E_2}{E_1} = -R_2\frac{I_2}{E_1} = -R_2[Y_T \text{ in (16.13a)}] = \frac{s^2}{5s^2 + 9s + 4}$$

of the four-terminal network in Fig. 16.5*a* are obtained by the signal-flow method.

(*a*) If $e_1(t) = 10 \cos(\omega t + 30°)$ for $\omega = 2$ rad/sec is the excitation applied to the network, what is the steady-state response $e_2(t)$?

(*b*) If $e_1(t) = u(t)$ (unit-step function) is the excitation applied to the network, what is the response $e_2(t)$?

The signal-flow method is also used as a tool for obtaining network (or system) responses. It actually obtains only the network function; we use this network function to find the response of a network subject to a given excitation, as illustrated in this problem.

17 Analysis of transistor amplifiers by the signal-flow method

17.1. Basic transistor amplifier circuits: descriptions and analyses

We have already introduced the three basic transistor amplifier circuits with block-diagram representations and remarked about some of their applications in Chap. 15. We shall now study them as circuits and obtain their network functions by the signal-flow method. As stated in Remark 6 in Art. 16.5B, the signal-flow method is well suited to use in the analysis of transistor circuits.

A. The Grounded-base Transistor Circuit

General description. A *pnp* transistor is used in Fig. 17.1*a* and throughout this chapter for illustration. For an *npn* transistor, we must reverse the polarity of the d-c supply for proper operation, for example, by changing $-V_{cc}$ in Fig. 17.1*a* to V_{cc}. Both *pnp* and *npn* transistors have the same a-c properties and the same equivalent circuits. Our discussion in this chapter applies equally well to both types.

A transistor, as a three-terminal device (Fig. 17.1*a*), has its *base*, *emitter*, and *collector* as its three terminals. By using one of them as the "ground" or "common terminal," not necessarily grounded, for both input and output terminal pairs, we obtain a basic transistor circuit. For example, we may have a grounded-base (*GB*) circuit, a grounded-emitter (*GE*) circuit, or a grounded-collector (*GC*) circuit.

A grounded-base circuit is depicted in Fig. 17.1*a*, and its schematic in Fig. 17.1*b*. One terminal of the load impedance Z_L, which is connected to the d-c potential $-V_{cc}$ in Fig. 17.1*a*, is actually a-c grounded as in Fig. 17.1*b*. The directions of the input current I_1 and output current I_2 are so chosen in Fig. 17.1*b* that both flow *into* the network; this is standard practice for representing the currents associated with a four-terminal network. The "load current" in the conventional sense is actually $-I_2$.

Equivalent Circuit of a GB Transistor Circuit. Figure 17.1*c* depicts the high-frequency equivalent circuit† of a *GB* transistor circuit, where r_b and r_e are, respectively, the base and emitter resistances, z_c represents the impedance of the parallel combination of the collector resistance r_c and collector capacitance C_c, $\alpha I_e = \alpha I_1$

† The high-frequency equivalent circuits of *GB*, *GE*, and *GC* transistor amplifiers may be found in any textbook on transistor electronics. For example, see A. W. Lo, R. O. Endes, J. Zawels, F. W. Waldhauer, and C. C. Cheng, "Transistor Electronics," Prentice-Hall, Inc., Englewood Cliffs, N.J., 1955. For extremely high-frequency or fast-switching applications, more elaborate high-frequency equivalent circuits are used—for example, see R. B. Hurley, "Junction Transistor Electronics," chap. 12, John Wiley & Sons, Inc., New York, 1958.

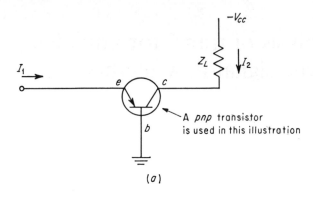

$-V_{cc}$

Z_L $\downarrow I_2$

$I_1 \rightarrow$

e c

A *pnp* transistor
is used in this illustration

b

(a)

As a 4-terminal network

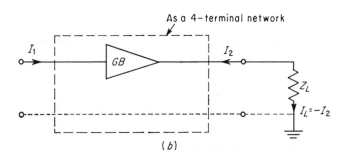

I_1 I_2

GB

Z_L

$I_L = -I_2$

(b)

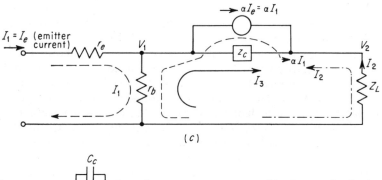

$\rightarrow \alpha I_e = \alpha I_1$

$I_1 = I_e$ (emitter current) r_e V_1

z_c V_2

$\rightarrow \alpha I_1$

I_2

I_1 r_b I_3 I_2 Z_L

(c)

C_c

$z_c = \left[\text{impedance of} \right] = \dfrac{r_c}{1+s r_c C_c}$

r_c

$\alpha = \left[\begin{array}{l} \text{alpha, i.e., short-circuit current} \\ \text{gain of } GB \text{ connection} \end{array} \right]$

$= \dfrac{-I_2}{I_1}\bigg|_{Z_L=0} = \dfrac{\alpha_0}{1+(s/\omega_a)}, \quad s=j\omega$

r_e, r_b, r_c -- emitter, base, and collector resistances, respectively

C_c -- collector capacitance

α_0 -- alpha at low frequencies

ω_a -- alpha cutoff frequency

(d)

Fig. 17.1 (a) Grounded-base (GB) transistor circuit; (b) schematic; (c) equivalent circuit.

depicts an "equivalent current source," and α, known as the *alpha* parameter, represents the "short-circuit current gain" of the *GB* circuit and is a function of the frequency ω:

$$\alpha = \frac{-I_2}{I_1}\Big|_{\substack{Z_L=0 \text{ in}\\ \text{Fig. 17.1c}}} = \frac{\alpha_0}{1 + s/\omega_\alpha} \qquad s = j\omega \qquad (17.1)$$

The parameter α_0 in (17.1) is the alpha, i.e., the "short-circuit current gain for the *GB* circuit," at low frequencies; $\omega_\alpha = 2\pi f_\alpha$ is called the alpha cutoff frequency.

Some Typical Values of Transistor Parameters. In order to get a feel for transistor equivalent circuits and to know "what terms to neglect" (as discussed in Remark 8 of Art. 16.5B) in the analysis of practical transistor amplifier circuits, we shall list some typical values of transistor parameters for later reference as well as to indicate their orders of magnitude. For example,

A set of typical transistor parameter values:

$$r_e = 20 \text{ ohms} \qquad r_b = 50 \text{ ohms} \qquad r_c = 10^6 \text{ ohms}$$

$$C_c = 50 \ \mu\mu\text{f}$$

$$\alpha_0 = 0.95 \qquad \beta_0 \cong \frac{\alpha_0}{1 - \alpha_0} = 19 \qquad\qquad (17.2a)$$

$$f_\alpha = 4 \text{ Mc} \qquad\qquad\qquad\qquad \omega_\alpha = 2\pi f_\alpha$$

$$f_\beta \cong (1 - \alpha_0)f_\alpha = 200 \text{ kc} \qquad\qquad \omega_\beta = 2\pi f_\beta$$

may represent a set of typical parameters of a commonly used transistor with medium-high current gain and medium-wide frequency range.

Another set of typical transistor parameter values:

$$r_e = 5 \text{ ohms} \qquad r_b = 100 \text{ ohms} \qquad r_c = 10^5 \text{ ohms}$$

$$C_c = 5 \ \mu\mu\text{f}$$

$$\alpha_0 = 0.98 \qquad \beta_0 \cong \frac{\alpha_0}{1 - \alpha_0} = 49 \qquad\qquad (17.2b)$$

$$f_\alpha = 750 \text{ Mc} \qquad\qquad\qquad\qquad \omega_\alpha = 2\pi f_\alpha$$

$$f_\beta = (1 - \alpha_0)f_\alpha = 15 \text{ Mc} \qquad\qquad \omega_\beta = 2\pi f_\beta$$

may represent a set of typical parameters of a high-gain, wideband transistor for fast-switching applications. Some of the parameters listed in (17.2), for example, β_0 and ω_β, have yet to be introduced.

Assumptions for Practical Transistor Circuits. For practical considerations and future reference, we shall make some assumptions which are true for typical transistor parameter values; we shall use these assumptions later to make approximations and simplify problems in the analysis of transistor circuits. Two impedances,

$z_c = $ impedance of resistance r_c and capacitance C_c in parallel

$$= \frac{r_c}{1 + sr_cC_c} \qquad s = j\omega \qquad\qquad (17.3a)$$

and $\quad z_d = $ impedance of resistance $r_c(1 - \alpha)$ and capacitance $\dfrac{C_c}{1 - \alpha}$ in parallel

$$= \frac{r_c}{1 + sr_cC_c}(1 - \alpha)$$

$$= \frac{r_c}{1 + sr_cC_c}\left(1 - \frac{\alpha_0}{1 + s/\omega_\alpha}\right) \qquad s = j\omega \qquad\qquad (17.3b)$$

$$V_1 = r_b I_1 - r_b(a I_1) - r_b I_3 = [(1-a)r_b] I_1 + [-r_b] I_3$$
$$I_3 = (V_1 - V_2)/z_c = [1/z_c]V_1 + [-1/z_c]V_2$$
$$V_2 = -Z_L I_2 = [-Z_L]I_2$$
$$I_2 = -(a I_1 + I_3) = [-a]I_1 + [-1]I_3$$

(a)

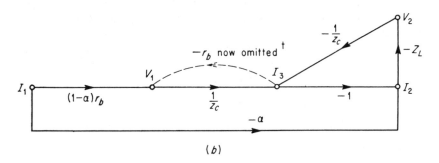

(b)

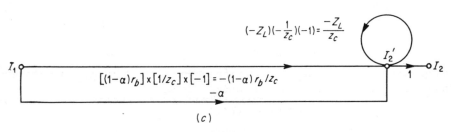

(c)

$$A_{GB} = \frac{I_2}{I_1} = \frac{-a - [(1-a)r_b/z_c]}{1 - [-Z_L/z_c]}$$

$$\cong \frac{-a}{1 + [Z_L/z_c]}, \quad r_b \ll |z_c|$$

(d)

† This r_b path may be readily replaced by a self-loop of transmission $-r_b/z_c$ at I_3 according to Rule D in Table 16.1; and, for $r_b \ll |z_c|$ in practical cases, this self-loop has a transmission $|r_b/z_c| \ll 1$ and may be omitted.

FIG. 17.2 (a) Voltage-current relations of a *GB* circuit as obtained from Fig. 17.1c. (b) Signal-flow diagram describing the voltage-current relations of (a). (c) Replacing the $I_2 V_2 I_3$ path in (b) with a self-loop at I_2 according to Rule D in Table 16.1 and adding an $I_2' I_2$ branch to identify I_2 as response. (d) Combining the two parallel $I_1 I_2'$ paths in (c) according to Rule A and then eliminating the self-loop at I_2' according to Rule C.

commonly occur in the equivalent circuits of the *GB*, *GE*, and *GC* transistor circuits, as shown in Figs. 17.1c, 17.4c, and 17.8c. Comparison of typical values of these impedances with typical values of r_e and r_b shows that

Assumptions for practical transistor circuits:

$$r_e \ll |z_d| \qquad r_b \ll |z_d| \tag{17.4a}$$

and

$$r_e \ll |z_c| \qquad r_b \ll |z_c| \tag{17.4b}$$

for frequencies f within the operating frequency range of the circuit. These frequencies f usually satisfy $f < f_\beta$ and $f \ll f_\alpha$. We shall assume that (17.4) are always true for practical transistor circuits.

Current Gain of a GB Circuit. We now wish to obtain the current gain $A_{GB} = I_2/I_1$ of the *GB* circuit depicted in Fig. 17.1 by the signal-flow method.

We (1) write the voltage-current relations of the equivalent circuit (Fig. 17.1c) in Fig. 17.2a, (2) construct the signal-flow diagram in Fig. 17.2b, (3) make approximations, e.g., by omitting the r_b path, and reduce the signal-flow diagram step by step as in Fig. 17.2b through d, and (4) obtain a "single I_1I_2 branch with known transmission." This known transmission is the sought-after current gain

$$A_{GB} = \frac{I_2}{I_1} = \frac{-\alpha - (1-\alpha)r_b/z_c}{1 + Z_L/z_c} \tag{17.5a}$$

$$A_{GB} \cong \frac{-\alpha}{1 + Z_L/z_c} \qquad r_b \ll |z_c| \tag{17.5b}$$

The approximate result in (17.5b), obtained with the assumption $r_b \ll |z_c|$ in (17.4b), is now tabulated in (a2) of Table 17.1 for later use.

Remarks about the phase relation of a *GB* circuit at low frequencies. When a transistor amplifier is used as one stage in a multiple-stage amplifier or in a feedback amplifier, we are usually interested in the phase relation between its input current I_1 and the load current $I_L = -I_2$, as indicated in Fig. 17.1b, at low (or zero) frequencies.

The phase relation between I_1 and I_L may be readily described by

$$\frac{I_L}{I_1} = \frac{-I_2}{I_1} = -[\text{Eqs. (17.5)}] = \frac{\alpha}{1 + Z_L/z_c} \tag{17.6}$$

At low frequencies, $1 + Z_L/z_c \cong 1$, since $\alpha \cong \alpha_0$ according to (17.1) and $z_c \cong r_c$ according to (17.3a) with an order of magnitude of 10^5 or 10^6 ohms according to (17.2); Z_L is usually small, say less than 10^3 ohms. Therefore, (17.6) may be approximated, at low frequencies, as

$$\frac{I_L}{I_1} \cong \alpha_0 = \alpha_0\underline{/0°} \qquad \text{at low frequencies} \tag{17.7}$$

This means that the input current I_1 and the load current I_L of a *GB* circuit are in phase at low frequencies. We often use the term *no phase reversal* to describe this phase relation; it is listed in (a4) of Table 17.1 for later use.

The input impedance of a *GB* circuit. We now wish to obtain the input impedance Z_{in} of the *GB* circuit in Fig. 17.1. According to Figs. 17.3a and 17.1c, it is obvious that

$$Z_{in} = r_e + Z_1 = r_e + \frac{V_1}{I_1} \tag{17.8}$$

This means that we need only (1) obtain $Z_1 = V_1/I_1$, where I_1 and V_1 are, respectively, a current and a voltage in the *GB* equivalent circuit in Fig. 17.1c, and (2) substitute it into (17.8) for Z_{in}.

To obtain $Z_1 = V_1/I_1$, we (1) use the signal-flow diagram of the *GB* equivalent circuit, earlier obtained in Fig. 17.2b and now redrawn for clarity in Fig. 17.3b with V_1 designated as the "response," and (2) reduce step by step as shown in Fig. 17.3c through e, until we obtain the "single I_1V_1 branch with known transmission" in Fig. 17.3e. With the assumption $r_b \ll |z_c|$ in (17.4b), and for $|Z_L| \ll |z_c|$, generally true

Table 17.1

Transistor circuit	Schematic (1)	Approximate current gain $A = \dfrac{I_2}{I_1}$ (2)	Approximate input impedance $Z_{\text{in}} = \dfrac{V_{\text{in}}}{I_1}$ (3)	Phase relation between input and output at low frequencies (4)
(a) Basic GB circuit	(a1) 	(a2) $A_{GB} \cong \dfrac{-\alpha}{1 + Z_L/z_c}$	(a3) $Z_{\text{in}} \cong r_e + (1 - \alpha)r_b$	(a4) *No phase reversal* in the sense that I_1 and I_L are in phase
(b) Basic GC circuit	(b1) 	(b2) $A_{GC} \cong \dfrac{-1/(1 - \alpha)}{1 + Z_L/z_d}$	(b3) $Z_{\text{in}} \cong r_b + (1 + \beta)(r_e + Z_L)$	(b4) *No phase reversal*

(c1)	(c2) $A_{GE} \cong \dfrac{\beta}{1 + Z_L/z_a}$	(c3) $Z_{\text{in}} \cong r_b + (1 + \beta)r_e$	(c4) *Phase reversal in the sense that I_1 and I_L are 180° out of phase*
(c) Basic *GE* circuit			
(d1)	(d2) $A_{\text{I}} \cong \dfrac{-\alpha^*/(1 - \alpha)}{1 + Z_L/z_c^*}$	(d3) $Z_{\text{in}} \cong r_b + \dfrac{1 - \alpha^*}{1 - \alpha}\,r_b^* + (r_e + r_e^*)\dfrac{1}{1 - \alpha}$	(d4) *No phase reversal*
(d) *GC-GB* circuit			
(e1)	(e2) $A_{\text{II}} \cong \dfrac{\beta\alpha^*}{1 + Z_L/z_c^*}$	(e3) $Z_{\text{in}} \cong r_b + (1 + \beta)r_e$	(e4) *Phase reversal*
(e) *GE-GB* circuit			

437

Table 17.1 (continued)

Transistor circuit	Schematic (1)	Approximate current gain $A = \dfrac{I_2}{I_1}$ (2)	Approximate input impedance $Z_{\text{in}} = \dfrac{V_{\text{in}}}{I_1}$ (3)	Phase relation between input and output at low frequencies (4)
(f) GE-GE circuit	(f1)	(f2) $A_{\text{III}} \cong \dfrac{-\beta\beta^*}{1 + Z_L/z_d^*}$	(f3) $Z_{\text{in}} \cong r_b + (1 + \beta)r_e$	(f4) *No phase reversal*
(g) GC-GE circuit	(g1)	(g2) $A_{\text{IV}} \cong \dfrac{[1/(1 - \alpha)]\beta^*}{1 + Z_L/z_d^*}$	(g3) $Z_{\text{in}} \cong r_b + (1 + \beta)r_b^* + (1 + \beta) \times [r_e + (1 + \beta^*)r_e^*]$	(g4) *Phase reversal*

Asterisks are used on all the parameters of the second-stage transistors in (d) through (f).

$$\alpha = [alpha, \text{ i.e., short-circuit current gain of a } GB \text{ circuit}] = \frac{\alpha_0}{1 + s/\omega_\alpha} = \frac{-I_2}{I_1}\bigg|_{Z_L = 0 \text{ in } (a1)} \qquad s = j\omega$$

$$\beta = [beta, \text{ i.e., short-circuit current gain of a } GE \text{ circuit}] = \frac{\beta_0}{1 + s/\omega_\beta} = \frac{-I_2}{I_1}\bigg|_{Z_L = 0 \text{ in } (c1)} \qquad s = j\omega$$

$$z_c = \left[\text{impedance of} \quad \right] = \frac{r_c(1/sC_c)}{r_c + 1/sC_c} = \frac{r_c}{1 + sr_cC_c}$$

$$z_d = \left[\text{impedance of} \quad \right] = \frac{r_c(1 - \alpha)}{1 + sr_cC_c} = (1 - \alpha)z_c$$

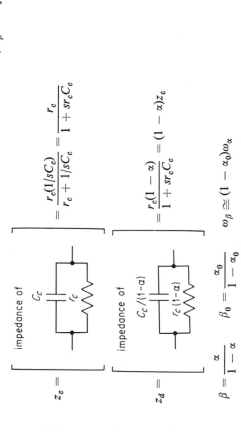

$$\beta = \frac{\alpha}{1 - \alpha} \qquad \beta_0 = \frac{\alpha_0}{1 - \alpha_0} \qquad \omega_\beta \cong (1 - \alpha_0)\omega_\alpha$$

r_e, r_b, r_c = emitter, base, and collector resistances, respectively

C_c = collector capacitance

α_0 = alpha (i.e., short-circuit GB gain) at low frequencies

ω_α = alpha cutoff frequency

β_0 = beta (i.e., short-circuit GE gain) at low frequencies

ω_β = beta cutoff frequency

439

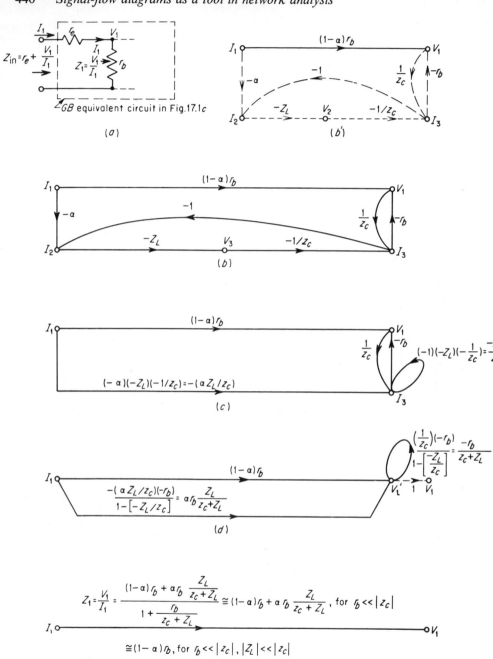

FIG. 17.3 (a) Input impedance of a GB circuit. (b) Signal-flow diagram redrawn from Fig. 17.2b for clarity, showing V_1 as the interested response. (b') Signal-flow diagram for $|Z_L| \ll |z_c|$ and $r_b \ll |z_c|$ obtained by modifying (b). (c) Removing the -1 path in (b) according to Rule D in Table 16.1, obtaining a self-loop at I_3, and then making $I_1 I_2 V_3 I_3$ a single path according to Rule B. (d) Removing the $1/z_c$ path in (c) according to Rule F, obtaining a self-loop at V_1, removing the self-loop at I_3 according to Rule C, and then adding a $V_1' V_1$ branch, as illustrated in Fig. 16.3a. (e) Combining two parallel $I_1 V_1'$ branches in (d) according to Rule A and then removing the self-loop at V_1' according to Rule C.

in practical circuits, the transmission $Z_1 = V_1/I_1$ is approximately represented in Fig. 17.3e. Substituting this $Z_1 = V_1/I_1$ into (17.8), we have

Input impedance of a GB circuit:

$$Z_{\text{in}} \cong r_e + (1 - \alpha)r_b - \alpha r_b \frac{Z_L}{z_c + Z_L} \qquad r_b \ll |z_c| \qquad (17.9a)$$

$$Z_{\text{in}} \cong r_e + (1 - \alpha)r_b \qquad r_b \ll |z_c|, |Z_L| \ll |z_c| \qquad (17.9b)$$

The result in (17.9b) is now tabulated in (a3) of Table 17.1 for later use.

Remarks about making approximations in the signal-flow diagram. In obtaining Z_{in} for a *GB* circuit, we eventually obtain the approximate result in (17.9b) if we assume $r_b \ll |z_c|$ and $|Z_L| \ll |z_c|$.

May we make these two assumptions $r_b \ll |z_c|$ and $|Z_L| \ll |z_c|$ when we start the problem, instead of solving the problem first and then making approximations, as we did above?

In general we may omit a path in a signal-flow diagram:

Rules for omitting a path in making approximations:

> When the path can be converted to a self-loop with transmission much less than 1 (17.10a)

> When the path to be omitted is parallel to another path whose transmission is much greater than the transmission of the path to be omitted (17.10b)

The justification of (17.10) is obvious.

Using these two rules for omitting a path, we may simplify the signal-flow diagram of Fig. 17.3b', redrawn from Fig. 17.3b for clarity in our discussion, as follows: (1) *Omit the $I_3 I_2$ path according to* (17.10a), as it will convert to a self-loop at I_3 with a transmission of $(-1)(-Z_L)(-1/z_c) = -Z_L/z_c$, where $|-Z_L/z_c| \ll 1$ under our assumption $|Z_L| \ll |z_c|$. (2) With the $I_3 I_2$ path omitted, *we may omit the $V_1 I_3$ path according to* (17.10a), as it will convert to a self-loop at V_1 with a transmission of $(1/z_c)(-r_b) = -r_b/z_c$, where $|-r_b/z_c| \ll 1$ under our assumption $r_b \ll |z_c|$. (3) With the $I_3 I_2$ and $V_1 I_3$ paths omitted, *we may omit the $I_1 I_2 V_2 I_3 V_1$ path according to* (17.10b), as this path, with transmission $(-\alpha)(-Z_L)(-1/z_c)(-r_b) = (\alpha r_b)(Z_L/z_c)$, is in parallel with a path with much greater transmission $(1 - \alpha)r_b$ under our assumptions $|Z_L| \ll |z_c|$ and $r_b \ll |z_c|$. (4) As a result of the preceding steps, *we now have the "approximated" signal-flow diagram depicted in solid lines in Fig. 17.3b', consisting of a "single $I_1 V_1$ path with known transmission $Z_1 = V_1/I_1 = (1 - \alpha)r_b$."* No further reduction of this signal-flow diagram is necessary. Substituting $Z_1 = V_1/I_1 = (1 - \alpha)r_b$ into (17.8), we have

Input impedance of a GB circuit:

$$Z_{\text{in}} \cong r_e + (1 - \alpha)r_b \qquad r_b \ll |z_c|, |Z_L| \ll |z_c| \qquad (17.9c)$$

which checks with the earlier result in (17.9b).

B. The Grounded-emitter Transistor Circuit

General description. A grounded-emitter circuit is shown in Fig. 17.4a, and its schematic in Fig. 17.4b.

Figure 17.4c depicts a high-frequency equivalent circuit, with parameters defined in Table 17.1. z_d represents the impedance of a frequency-varying capacitance $C_c/(1 - \alpha)$ and a frequency-varying resistance $r_c(1 - \alpha)$ in parallel, where α is a

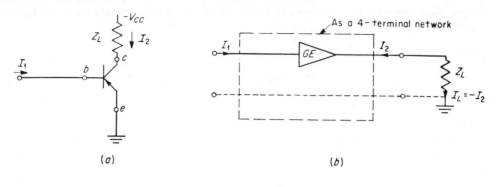

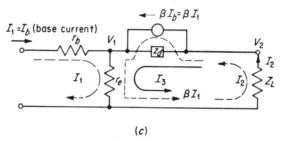

FIG. 17.4 (a) Grounded-emitter (GE) transistor circuit; (b) schematic; (c) equivalent circuit (refer to Table 17.1 for symbols).

frequency-varying parameter as indicated in (17.1). $\beta I_b = \beta I_1$ depicts an "equivalent current source"; β, known as the *beta* parameter, represents the "short-circuit current gain" of the *GE* circuit and is a function of the frequency ω:

$$\beta = \frac{I_2}{I_1}\bigg|_{\substack{Z_L=0 \text{ in} \\ \text{Fig. 17.4}c}} = \frac{\beta_0}{1 + s/\omega_\beta} \qquad s = j\omega \qquad (17.11)$$

The parameter β_0 in (17.11) is the beta (i.e., the "short-circuit current gain for the *GB* circuit") at low frequencies; $\omega_\beta = 2\pi f_\beta$ is called the beta cutoff frequency. See (17.2) for typical values of the transistor parameters defined here.

The following relations among transistor parameters may readily be found in standard textbooks on transistor electronics:

$$\beta = \frac{\alpha}{1-\alpha} \qquad \beta_0 = \frac{\alpha_0}{1-\alpha_0} \qquad \omega_\beta \cong (1-\alpha_0)\omega_\alpha \qquad (17.12)$$

Current gain of a *GE* circuit. For the *GE* circuit and equivalent circuit in Fig. 17.4, we (1) construct the signal-flow diagram in Fig. 17.5a, (2) make an approximation by omitting the r_e path in Fig. 17.5a, (3) reduce step by step as indicated in Fig. 17.5b and c, and (4) obtain a "single $I_1 I_2$ branch with known transmission." This known transmission is the sought-after current gain

$$A_{GE} = \frac{I_2}{I_1} \left\{ \begin{array}{ll} = \dfrac{\beta(1 - r_e/\alpha z_d)}{1 + Z_L/z_d} & (17.13a) \\[3ex] \cong \dfrac{\beta}{1 + Z_L/z_d} & r_e \ll |z_d| \qquad (17.13b) \end{array} \right.$$

The approximate result in (17.13b), obtained with the assumption $r_e \ll |z_d|$ in (17.4a), is now listed in (c2) of Table 17.1 for later use.

Remarks about the phase relation at low frequencies of a *GE* circuit. Reference is made to the discussion concerning the phase relation of a *GB* circuit [Eqs. (17.6) and (17.7)]. A similar approach will be followed here.

Again we are interested in the phase relation between the input current I_1 and the load current $I_L = -I_2$ (Fig. 17.4b) at low (or zero) frequencies. Assuming $|Z_L| \ll |z_d|$ at low frequencies for practical circuits, we find the following expressions, similar to (17.6) and (17.7), for the *GB* circuit:

$$\frac{I_L}{I_1} = \frac{-I_2}{I_1} \begin{cases} = -[\text{Eq. (17.13)}] \cong -\dfrac{\beta}{1 + Z_L/z_d} \cong -\beta & (17.14a) \\[2mm] \cong -\beta_0 = \beta_0 \underline{/180°} & \text{at low frequencies} \quad (17.14b) \end{cases}$$

This means that I_1 and I_L of a *GE* circuit are 180° out of phase at low frequencies.

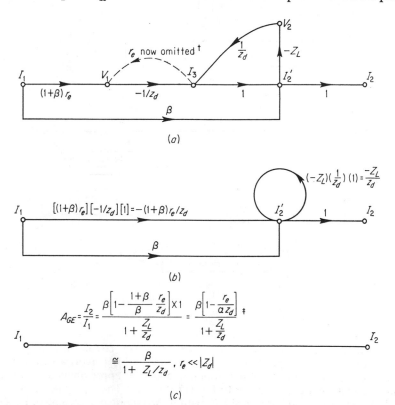

(a)

(b)

(c)

† This r_e path may be readily replaced by a self-loop of transmission $-r_e/z_d$ at I_3 according to Rule D in Table 16.1; and, for $r_e \ll |z_d|$ in practical cases, this self-loop has practically *zero* transmission and may be omitted.

‡ For $\beta = \alpha/(1 - \alpha)$, as indicated in Table 17.1, $\alpha = \beta/(1 + \beta)$ or $(1 + \beta)/\beta = 1/\alpha$ may be readily obtained.

FIG. 17.5 (a) Signal-flow diagram for a *GE* circuit, describing the voltage-current relations in Fig. 17.4c, with an $I_2'I_2$ branch to identify I_2 as the response. (b) Replacing the $I_2'V_2I_3$ path in (a) with a self-loop at I_2' according to Rule D of Table 16.1 and then making $I_1V_1I_3I_2'$ a single path according to Rule B. (c) Combining the two parallel I_1I_2' paths according to Rule A and then eliminating the self-loop at I_2' according to Rule C.

This "phase-reversal" relation in a *GE* circuit is now listed in (*c*4) of Table 17.1 for later use.

The input impedance of a *GE* circuit.   According to Figs. 17.6*a* and 17.4*c*, the input impedance Z_{in} of a *GE* circuit is

$$Z_{in} = r_e + Z_1 = r_e + \frac{V_1}{I_1} \tag{17.15}$$

To obtain $Z_1 = V_1/I_1$ in (17.15), we may use the *GE* signal-flow diagram, obtained earlier in Fig. 17.5*a* and now redrawn for clarity in Fig. 17.6*b*.

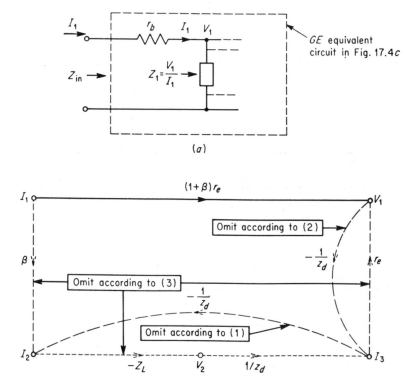

(a)

(b)

Fig. 17.6   (*a*) Input impedance $Z_{in} = r_b + V_1/I_1$ of a *GE* circuit, for $|Z_L| \ll |z_d|$ and $r_e \ll |z_d|$. (*b*) Signal-flow diagram for $|Z_L| \ll |z_d|$ and $r_e \ll |z_d|$, redrawn from Fig. 17.5*a* for clarity, showing V_1 as the interested response, and then approximated as follows: (1) The $I_3 I_2$ path is first omitted according to Eq. (17.10*a*). (2) The $V_1 I_3$ path is then omitted according to Eq. (17.10*a*). (3) The $I_1 I_2 V_2 I_3 V_1$ path is then omitted according to Eq. (17.10*b*). We now have an "approximated" signal-flow diagram, depicted by the solid lines in the figure.

We may either (1) reduce this signal-flow diagram, obtaining the exact $Z_1 = V_1/I_1$, and make approximations with the assumptions $r_e \ll |z_d|$ according to (17.4*a*) and $|Z_L| \ll |z_d|$ for practical circuits or (2) first make approximations with the aid of (17.10) and then reduce the "approximated" signal-flow diagram (if necessary). We shall use the second approach.   If we omit the dotted and broken-line branches (Fig. 17.6*b*), the "approximated" signal-flow diagram has only a "single $I_1 V_1$ branch with known transmission $Z_1 = V_1/I_1 = (1 + \beta)r_e$." No reduction is necessary. Substituting this transmission Z_1 into (17.15), we now have

Input impedance of a GE circuit:

$$Z_{\text{in}} \cong r_b + (1 + \beta)r_e \qquad r_e \ll |z_d|, \; |Z_L| \ll |z_d| \qquad (17.16)$$

The reader may try the other approach and check the result with (17.16). Reference is made to the discussions preceding (17.9b) and (17.9c), where the results of both approaches were obtained for the *GB* circuit.

A *GE* circuit with a feedback loop. Now, suppose we add a feedback loop to a *GE* circuit, as indicated in Fig. 17.7a.

For a feedback amplifier of this type, i.e., the type A feedback structure earlier described in Art. 15.3 and Fig. 15.1c, we shall, in Art. 17.3, study the return ratio $T_{p'p}$ as a network function for the determination of stability, and then find the current gain A_{GE}^* from the return ratio $T_{p'p}$. This indirect method of obtaining the current gain $A_{GE}^* = I_2/I_1$ from the return ratio $T_{p'p}$ has been described as approach 2 in Art. 15.3A.

We shall now use the direct approach to obtain the current gain A_{GE}^* of the circuit (Approach 1 in Art. 15.3A). To do this, we replace the *GE* block in Fig. 17.7a with its equivalent circuit in Fig. 17.4c, obtaining an "equivalent network" for the *GE* circuit with feedback loop. From this equivalent network, we construct the signal-flow diagram in Fig. 17.7b with the assumption that the input a-c voltage is much less than V_2.

But if the signal-flow diagram of a *GE* circuit without feedback is already available, e.g., in Fig. 17.5a or in the dashed block in Fig. 17.7b, we need only *modify* it for the feedback loop and changes in notation. We then obtain, through modification, the signal-flow diagram for a "*GE* circuit with feedback loop" in Fig. 17.7b.

Reducing the signal-flow diagram in Fig. 17.7b, step by step as indicated in Fig. 17.7c and d, we finally obtain "a single I_1I_2 branch with known transmission." Assuming $r_e \ll |z_d|$ and $|Z_L| \ll |z_d|$ for practical circuits, we approximate this known transmission and represent the approximate current gain for a *GE* circuit with a feedback loop in Fig. 17.7a as follows:

$$A_{GE}^* = \frac{I_2}{I_1} \cong \begin{cases} \dfrac{\beta}{1 + \dfrac{Z_L}{z_d} + \dfrac{Z_L}{Z_F}\left(1 + \dfrac{Z_L}{z_d} + \beta\right)} & r_e \ll |z_d| & (17.16a) \\[4ex] \dfrac{\beta}{1 + (Z_L/Z_F)(1 + \beta)} & |Z_L| \ll |z_d|, \; r_e \ll |z_d| & (17.16b) \\[3ex] \dfrac{\beta}{1 + (R_L/R_F)(1 + \beta)} & \begin{array}{l} \text{resistive } Z_L = R_L, \; Z_F = R_F \\ \text{as additional conditions} \end{array} & (17.16c) \end{cases}$$

Remarks about the Operation of the GE Circuit with Feedback Loop. For the circuit in Fig. 17.7a to operate satisfactorily as a feedback amplifier, we must use a very high gain transistor, say $\beta_0 \gg 1$, in the *GE* circuit. In the operating frequency range of this feedback amplifier, and for $\beta_0 \gg 1$, we have $|\beta| \gg 1$ according to (17.11), and

$$A_{GE}^* = \frac{I_2}{I_1} = \text{Eq. (17.16c)} \cong \frac{R_F}{R_L} \qquad |\beta| \gg 1, \; |Z_L| \ll |z_d|, \; r_e \ll |z_d| \qquad (17.17)$$

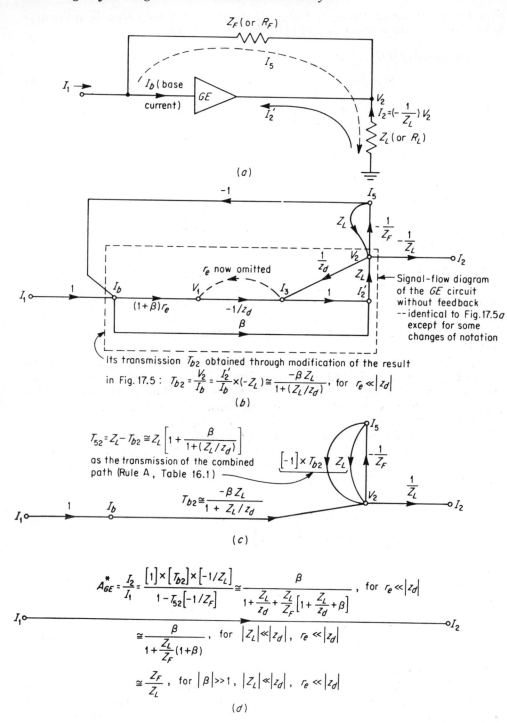

FIG. 17.7

This checks with (15.4). It means that, for $|\beta| \gg 1$, the feedback amplifier in Fig. 17.7*a* maintains a constant gain and possesses other features of a feedback amplifier (Arts. 15.3A and 20.4A). But $\beta_0 \gg 1$ or $|\beta| \gg 1$ means a very high gain transistor. An alternative means of obtaining a good feedback amplifier with a type A structure is to use multiple stages as in Fig. 15.1*c*1, where a higher gain in $|A_i| \gg 1$ may be easily realized with more stages, rather than in a single *GE* stage. However, the more stages we use, the more serious the stability problem; this is particularly true if we wish to design a feedback amplifier with a *very wide* frequency band.

C. The Grounded-collector Transistor Circuit

A grounded-collector (*GC*) circuit is shown in Fig. 17.8*a*; its schematic, in Fig. 17.8*b*; its high-frequency equivalent circuit, in Fig. 17.8*c*; and its signal-flow diagram, in Fig. 17.8*d*.

With treatments similar to those for the *GB* and *GE* circuits in preceding sections (Art. 17.1A and B), we may readily obtain the current gain, phase relation, and input impedance; these are listed in (*b*2), (*b*4), and (*b*3) of Table 17.1 for later use.

17.2. Multistage transistor amplifier: description and analysis

A. Circuit Arrangement

We shall consider the multistage transistor amplifier depicted in Fig. 17.9*a*, where each stage belongs to one of three possible categories:

Description of the "stages" in the multistage transistor amplifier in Fig. 17.9a:

> The *"standard" single-transistor GB, GE, or GC stages*—the current gains and input impedances of these "standard" stages are tabulated in (*a*), (*b*), and (*c*) of Table 17.1 (17.18*a*)

> The *other single-transistor stages* which are modified forms of the "standard" *GB, GE,* or *GC* stages—for example, this stage may be a "*GE* connection with a local feedback loop" as depicted in Fig. 17.10*a* or† a "*GE* connection with resistance R_e in the emitter circuit" as depicted in Fig. 17.10*a* (17.18*b*)

> *Composite stages of two or more transistors* that are not two or more "standard" single-transistor stages in cascade‡—for example, this stage may be a "*GE* connection followed by a *GB* connection with feedback loop" as depicted in Fig. 17.10*c* (17.18*c*)

B. Analysis of Multistage Transistor Amplifier: First Approach

We now wish to discuss the means of obtaining the current gain and input impedance of a multistage amplifier as depicted in Fig. 17.9*a* and described in (17.18). There are two approaches to the solution of this problem.

---

† Such a resistance R_e provides "negative feedback" for stabilization of this amplifier stage in much the same way that the load resistance of a cathode-follower vacuum-tube amplifier provides "negative feedback." For this modified *GE* circuit with R_e, the current-gain and input-impedance equations in (*c*2) and (*c*3) of Table 17.1 should be rederived or modified. For example, R_e is in essence in series with the emitter resistance; the input impedance may be obtained by replacing r_e in (*c*3) of Table 17.1 with $r_e + R_e$: $Z_{\text{in}} \cong r_b + (1 + \beta)(r_e + R_e)$.

‡ For example, see the "composite transistors" in fig. 3 in Lo et al., *op. cit.*, p. 181.

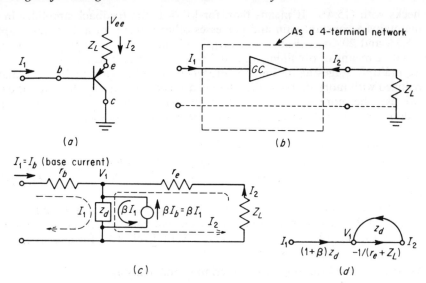

(a)

(b)

(c)

(d)

Fig. 17.8   (a) Grounded-collector (GC) transistor circuit;   (b) schematic;   (c) equivalent circuit (refer to Table 17.1 for symbols);   (d) signal-flow diagram as already obtained in Fig. 16.1c3.

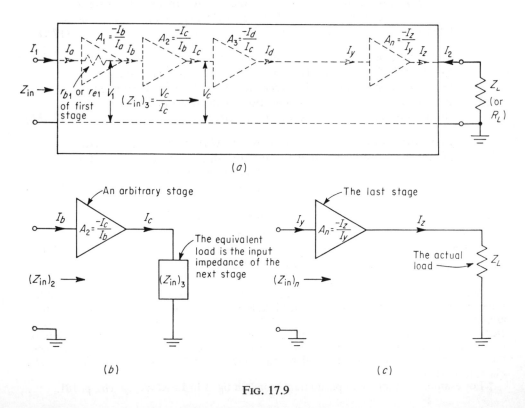

(a)

(b)

(c)

Fig. 17.9

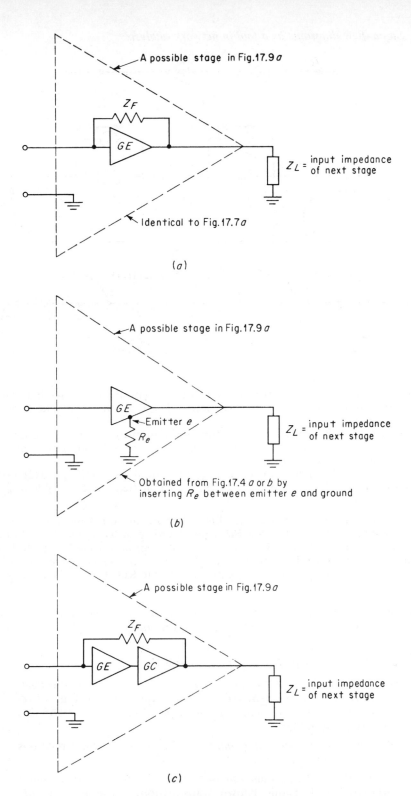

FIG. 17.10

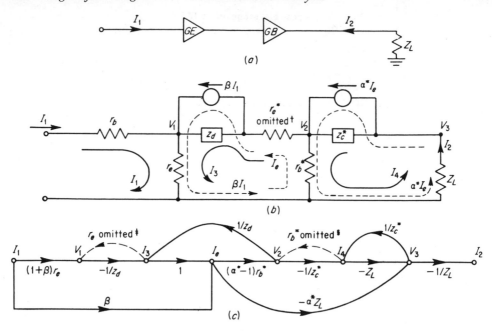

† r_e is in series with z_d, where the current source βI_1 has infinite internal impedance and is considered open-circuited. In practical cases, $r_e^* \ll |z_d|$ and we may leave out r_e^* for approximate result.

‡ We may replace this r_e path with a self-loop of transmission $-r_e/z_d$ at I_3 according to Rule D in Table 16.1. For $r_e \ll |z_d|$ in practical cases, this self-loop has an almost zero transmission and may be omitted.

§ We may replace this r_b path with (1) an $I_4 I_3$ path of transmission r_b^*/z_d and (2) a self-loop of transmission $-r_b^*/z_c^*$. Both of these paths may be omitted for $r_b^* \ll |z_d|$ and $r_b^* \ll |z_c^*|$.

FIG. 17.11 (a) Two-stage amplifier. (b) Equivalent circuit. (c) Signal-flow diagram. (d) Replacing the $V_2 I_3$ path in (c) with a $V_2 I_e$ path according to Rule D of Table 16.1 and replacing the $V_3 I_4$ path with a $V_3 V_3$ path (i.e., a self-loop) also according to Rule D. (e) Combining the two parallel $I_1 I_e$ paths according to Rule A and replacing the $V_2 I_e$ path with a $V_2 V_2$ path (i.e., a self-loop) and a $V_2 V_3$ path according to Rule D. (f) Combining the two

Description of approach I. *In this approach, we use the signal-flow method to treat the "whole network" together, finding its network functions. The procedure is as follows:*

Analyzing multistage amplifier in Fig. 17.9a: approach I:

> *Replace each transistor in the amplifier with its appropriate equivalent circuit, e.g., the GB, GE, or GC equivalent in Fig. 17.1c, 17.4c, or 17.8c, thus obtaining an "equivalent network" for this multistage amplifier*   (17.19a)

> *Construct a signal-flow diagram from the voltage-current relations of this "equivalent network"*   (17.19b)

> *Reduce this signal-flow diagram to a "single $I_1 I_2$ branch with a known transmission A_t"; this known transmission is the current gain $A_t = I_2/I_1$ of the multistage amplifier*   (17.19c)

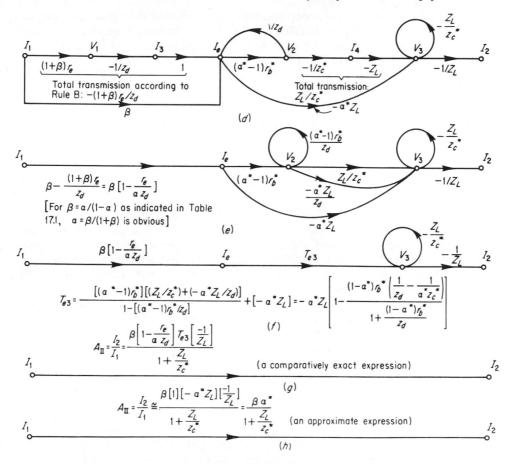

$$T_{e3} = \frac{[(a^{*}-1)r_b^*][(Z_L/z_c^*)+(-a^*Z_L/z_d)]}{1-[(a^*-1)r_b^*/z_d]} + [-a^*Z_L] = -a^*Z_L\left[1-\frac{(1-a^*)r_b^*\left(\frac{1}{z_d}-\frac{1}{a^*z_c}\right)}{1+\frac{(1-a^*)r_b^*}{z_d}}\right]$$

(f)

$$A_{II} = \frac{I_2}{I_1} = \frac{\beta\left[1-\frac{r_e}{a\,z_d}\right]T_{e3}\left[\frac{-1}{Z_L}\right]}{1+\frac{Z_L}{z_c^*}}$$

(a comparatively exact expression)

(g)

$$A_{II} = \frac{I_2}{I_1} \cong \frac{\beta[1][-a^*Z_L]\left[\frac{-1}{Z_L}\right]}{1+\frac{Z_L}{z_c^*}} = \frac{\beta\,a^*}{1+\frac{Z_L}{z_c^*}}$$

(an approximate expression)

(h)

parallel V_2V_3 paths according to Rule A, eliminating the self-loop at V_2 according to Rule C, thus obtaining an I_eV_3 path, and combining the I_eV_3 path thus obtained with the existing path $-\alpha^*Z_L$ according to Rule A. (g) Removing the self-loop at V_3 in (f) according to Rule C. (h) Assuming practical conditions $r_e \ll |z_d|$, $r_b^* \ll |z_d|$, and $r_b^* \ll |z_c^*|$, which imply $T_{e3} \cong -\alpha^*Z_L$, and simplifying (g).

> Reduce the signal-flow diagram constructed in (17.19b) to a "single I_1V_1 branch with known transmission Z_1"; the *input impedance* of this multistage amplifier (Fig. 17.9a) is now $Z_{in} = r_{b1} + V_1/I_1 = r_{b1} + Z_1$ if the first stage is a *GE* or *GC* circuit, or $Z_{in} = r_{e1} + V_1/I_1 = r_{e1} + Z_1$ if it is a *GB* circuit   (17.19d)

I_1, I_2, and V_1 are currents and voltage as indicated in Fig. 17.9a. r_{b1} (or r_{e1}) is the base resistance (or emitter resistance) of the transistor in the first stage.

Illustration A. Analysis of a two-stage transistor amplifier by approach I. We shall now analyze the two-stage *GE-GB* transistor amplifier in Fig. 17.11a.

Following (17.19), we replace the *GE* stage and the *GB* stage with their respective equivalent circuits from Figs. 17.4c and 17.1c. We use symbols without asterisks for the parameters of the first stage, and symbols with asterisks for those of the second stage. We now have an "equivalent network (circuit)" in Fig. 17.11b; we construct its signal-flow diagram in Fig. 17.11c.

Current Gain. By making approximations and reducing the signal-flow diagram in Fig. 17.11c, step by step as described in Fig. 17.11d through h, we obtain a "single I_1I_2 branch with known transmission A_{II}." This transmission is the current gain of the two-stage amplifier in Fig. 17.11a:

Comparatively exact expression:

$$A_{\mathrm{II}} = \frac{I_2}{I_1} = \text{expression in Fig. 17.11g} \qquad (17.20a)$$

Approximate expression:

$$A_{\mathrm{II}} \cong \frac{\beta\alpha^*}{1 + Z_L/z_c^*} \qquad \text{under practical circuit conditions} \qquad (17.20b)$$

The result in (17.20b) is listed in (e2) of Table 17.1 for later use.

Phase Relation at Low Frequencies. Since a *GE* circuit has a "phase reversal," i.e., a phase shift of 180°, and a *GB* circuit has "no phase reversal," i.e., a phase shift of 0°, at low frequencies, as indicated in (c4) and (a4) of Table 17.1, a two-stage *GE-GB* circuit must have a "phase reversal," i.e., a phase shift of $180° + 0° = 180°$, at low frequencies. This is listed in (e4) of Table 17.1 for later use.

Input Impedance. By making approximations† reducing the signal-flow diagram in Fig. 17.11c to a "single I_1V_1 branch with known transmission $Z_1 = V_1/I_1 \cong (1 + \beta)r_e$," and following (17.19d), we obtain the input impedance of the two-stage amplifier in Fig. 17.11a in an approximate form:

$$Z_{\mathrm{in}} \cong r_b + (1 + \beta)r_e \qquad (17.21)$$

under practical circuit conditions: $r_e \ll |z_d|, r_b^* \ll |z_d|, r_b^* \ll |z_c^*|$. The result (17.21) is listed in (e3) of Table 17.1 for later use.

Remarks about additional illustrations. Following the same procedure, we may analyze the two-stage amplifiers in (d1) through (g1) of Table 17.1, obtaining their current gains, phase relations, and input impedances as listed in Table 17.1.

Similarly, we may analyze three-stage, four-stage, and other multistage amplifiers.

C. Analysis of Multistage Transistor Amplifier: Second Approach

Again we consider a multistage amplifier as depicted in Fig. 17.9a.

Description of approach II. *In this approach, we use the signal-flow method or tabulated results of the signal-flow method to study one amplifier stage, as defined in (17.18), at a time; the results are put together to obtain the network functions of the multistage amplifier.* We proceed as follows:

Analyzing multistage amplifier in Fig. 17.9a: approach II:

> *Using the actual load Z_L as depicted in Fig. 17.9c, find the current gain A_n and the input impedance $(Z_{\mathrm{in}})_n$ of the last (i.e., the nth) stage from the tabulated results in Table 17.1 or by the signal-flow method* (17.22a)

> *Using the input impedance $(Z_{\mathrm{in}})_n$ of the nth stage as the load, as exemplified in Fig. 17.9b for $n = 3$, find the current gain A_{n-1} and the input impedance $(Z_{\mathrm{in}})_{n-1}$ of the $(n-1)$st stage from the tabulated results in Table 17.1 or by the signal-flow method* (17.22b)

† If we approximated as we did in Fig. 17.6b, the signal-flow diagram in Fig. 17.11c would have only a single I_1V_1 branch with a transmission $(1 + \beta)r_e$.

Repeat (17.22b) for each preceding stage, one by one, until the current gain A_i and the input impedance $(Z_{in})_i$ are obtained for all stages   (17.22c)

The overall current gain of the multistage transistor amplifier, as depicted in Fig. 17.9a, is

$$A_t = \frac{I_2}{I_1} = \frac{-I_z}{I_a} = -\frac{I_b}{I_a}\frac{I_c}{I_b} \cdots \frac{I_z}{I_y}$$

$$= -(-A_1)(-A_2)\cdots(-A_n) = -\prod_{i=1}^{n}(-A_i)$$

and its input impedance is that of the first stage, i.e.,

$$Z_{in} = (Z_{in})_1 \qquad (17.22d)$$

Illustration B.   Analysis of a two-stage transistor amplifier with approach II.   We shall now analyze the two-stage *GE-GB* transistor amplifier in Fig. 17.11a using approach II, and then check the results against those obtained using approach I in Illustration A (Art. 17.2B).

We shall use symbols without asterisks for the parameters of the first (*GE*) stage, and symbols with asterisks for those of the second (*GB*) stage.

Current Gain.   According to (17.22a), we first find from Table 17.1a:

For second (GB) stage:

$$A_{GB}^* \cong \frac{-\alpha^*}{1 + Z_L/z_c^*} \qquad (17.23a)$$

$$Z_{in}^* \cong r_e^* + (1 - \alpha^*)r_b^* \qquad (17.23b)$$

Following (17.22b), we use Z_{in}^* as the load to the first stage in (c2) and (c3) of Table 17.1:

For first (GE) stage:

$$A_{GE} \cong \frac{\beta}{1 + Z_{in}^*/z_d}$$

$$\cong \beta \qquad\qquad r_e^* \ll |z_d|, r_b^* \ll |z_d| \qquad (17.24a)$$

$$Z_{in} \cong r_b + (1 + \beta)r_e \qquad (17.24b)$$

The approximate expression $A_{GE} \cong \beta$ in (17.24a) is obtained in this manner: r_e^*, r_b^*, r_d^*, and r_c^* are the parameters of the second transistor, while r_e, r_b, r_d, and r_c are for the first transistor. Corresponding parameters should have magnitudes of the same order; therefore, $r_e^* \ll |z_d|$ and $r_b^* \ll |z_d|$ are implied for practical circuits according to (17.4). For $r_e^* \ll |z_d|, r_b^* \ll |z_d|$, and $|\alpha^*| < 1$, we find $|Z_{in}^*| \ll |z_d|$; (17.24a) results.

According to (17.22d), we have

Current gain and input impedance of two-stage amplifier in Fig. 17.11a:

$$A_{II} = \frac{I_2}{I_1} \cong -(-\beta)\left(-\frac{\alpha^*}{1 + Z_L/z_c^*}\right) \cong \frac{\beta\alpha^*}{1 + Z_L/z_c^*} \qquad (17.25a)$$

$$Z_{in} \cong r_b + (1 + \beta)r_b \qquad (17.25b)$$

for practical circuit conditions.

Comparing (17.25a) and (17.25b) with the earlier results in (17.20b) and (17.21), we see that they do check.

Remarks. For the analysis of a multistage transistor amplifier in the form of Fig. 17.9a, it is perhaps more convenient, as demonstrated above, to use approach II as described in (17.22). In approach II, caution must be exercised when using results from tables or other analyses in which approximations have been made.

17.3. Type A feedback structure: description and analysis

We have already discussed some of the general aspects of the type A feedback structure and the various problems involved in the analysis of this feedback arrangement in Art. 15.3 and Fig. 15.1c1. We shall now find solutions to these problems.

A. General Description

Circuit arrangement. To the multistage transistor amplifier depicted in Fig. 17.9a described in (17.18), and satisfying the "phase-reversal" condition in (15.1a), we now add an output-to-input feedback loop containing resistance R_F, obtaining the feedback amplifier in Fig. 17.12a. This represents the type A feedback structure. It is customary to use, in transistor circuits, a voltage generator V_1 in series with a large resistance R_g to supply an almost-constant input current $I_1 \simeq V_1/R_g$.

Description of problem. We have already defined the return ratio $T_{p'p}$ for this feedback structure in (15.2). As remarked in Art. 15.3B, we may plot the Nyquist diagram $T_{p'p}(j\omega)$ with this return ratio and determine the stability of the feedback amplifier. Therefore, our *immediate problem* is to obtain the return ratio $T_{p'p}$ of this feedback structure; this will be done in Art. 17.3B.

We also remarked in Art. 15.3A that the overall current gain $A^* = I_2/I_1$ of the type A feedback structure in Fig. 15.1c1 or 17.12a may be obtained from its return ratio $T_{p'p}$ through the relation established in (15.3). Our *next problem* is, therefore, to derive this relation; this will be done in Art. 17.3C.

B. Obtaining the Return Ratio $T_{p'p}$ for the Type A Feedback Structure

We shall now find the return ratio $T_{p'p}$ for the type A feedback structure in Fig. 17.12a or 15.1c1 according to its definition in (15.2). For clarity, we shall redraw the circuit arrangement, intended for measuring the return ratio $T_{p'p}$, in Fig. 17.12b. According to (15.2c), our problem is merely to find a voltage-ratio function $T_{p'p} = -V_{p'}/V_p$, that is, a "network function" as the voltage ratio of the output $-V_{p'}$ to the input V_p, for the circuit arrangement in Fig. 17.12b.

Finding the exact expression for $T_{p'p}$. We may (1) replace each individual transistor by its appropriate equivalent circuit, thus obtaining an "equivalent network" for the circuit arrangement in Fig. 17.12b, (2) construct the signal-flow diagram, and (3) reduce this signal-flow diagram to a "single $V_p V_{p'}$ branch with known transmission $G = V_{p'}/V_p$." The return ratio is equal to the negative of this known transmission; i.e.,

Finding the exact $T_{p'p}$:

$$T_{p'p} = \frac{-V_{p'}}{V_p} = -\frac{V_{p'}}{V_p} = -\; known \text{ transmission } G \text{ of signal-flow diagram} \quad (17.26)$$

The term "exact expression for $T_{p'p}$" is used here only in a comparative sense and is meant as the "most complete expression for $T_{p'p}$" which is obtainable with the assumed equivalent circuits of the transistors and which has not been approximated for practical circuit conditions.

For most practical circuits, we usually approximate the exact $T_{p'p}$ obtained in (17.26) by using assumptions such as those in (17.4) for practical considerations.

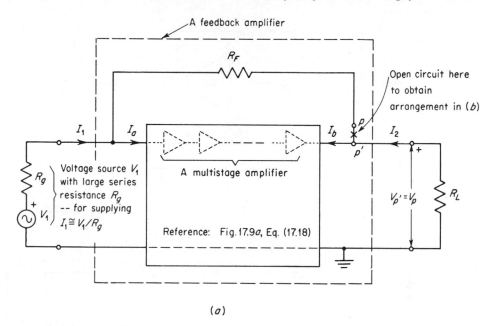

(*a*)

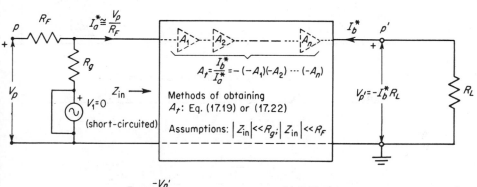

$$T_{p'p} = \frac{-V_{p'}}{V_p} \qquad\text{(definition)}$$

$$\cong \frac{-(-I_b^* R_L)}{I_a^* R_F} \cong A_f \frac{R_L}{R_F} \qquad\text{(approximate relation)}$$

(*b*)

FIG. 17.12

But the multistage amplifier inside the box in Fig. 17.12*b* may be a complicated circuit; to obtain the "equivalent network" of Fig. 17.12*b*, to construct its signal-flow diagram, and then to reduce this diagram, as required by the above procedure, may very well be an involved process.

Let us now try to find an approximate $T_{p'p}$ directly by a simpler means.

Finding an approximate expression for $T_{p'p}$.   We shall assume

$$|Z_{\text{in}}| \ll R_F \ll R_g \tag{17.27}$$

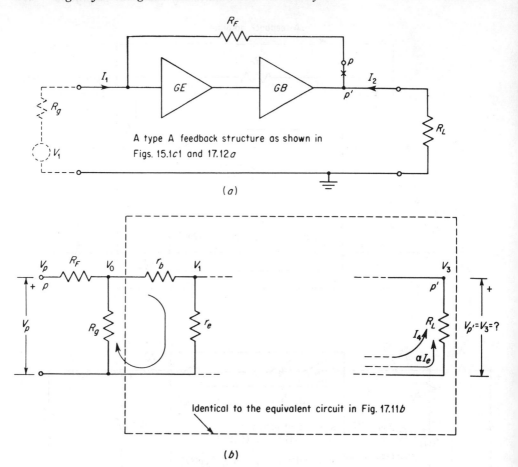

(a)

(b)

$$T_{p'p} = \frac{-V_{p'}}{V_p} \cong \frac{R_L}{R_F} \cdot \frac{\beta a^*}{1 + \dfrac{R_L}{z_c^*}} = \frac{R_L}{R_F} \cdot \frac{a}{1-a} \cdot \frac{a^*}{1 + \dfrac{R_L}{z_c^*}} = \frac{R_L}{R_F} \cdot \frac{\dfrac{a_0}{1 + s/\omega_a}}{1 - \dfrac{a_0}{1 + s/\omega_a}} \cdot \frac{\dfrac{a_0^*}{1 + s/\omega_a^*}}{1 + \left\{ R_L / \left[r_c^* / (1 + s r_c^* C_c^*) \right] \right\}}$$

$$\cong \frac{K}{(T_1 s + 1)(T_2 s + 1)(T_3 s + 1)} \quad \dagger \text{ for } K = \frac{R_L}{R_F} \beta_0 a_0^*$$

$$\text{where } \beta_0 = \frac{a_0}{1-a_0}; \quad T_1 = \frac{1}{(1-a_0)\omega_a} \cong \frac{1}{\omega_\beta}; \quad T_2 = \frac{1}{\omega_a^*}; \quad T_3 = R_L C_c^*; \quad \text{and } R_L \ll r_c^*$$

(c)

† Approximations are made with the assumptions in Eqs. (17.4) for practical circuits.

FIG. 17.13

If this assumption is not true for a particular circuit, the approach associated with (17.26) should be used.

We may now consider $I_a^* \cong V_p/R_F$ as a current source to a multistage transistor amplifier similar to the one depicted in Fig. 17.9a and described in (17.18); the current gain $A_i = I_b^*/I_a^*$ may be obtained by the approach in (17.19) or (17.22).

Since $V_p \cong I_a^* R_F$, $V_{p'} = -I_b^* R_L$, and $A_t = I_b^*/I_a^*$ in Fig. 17.12b, and $T_{p'p} = -V_{p'}/V_p$ according to its definition in (15.2), we readily obtain

Finding the approximate $T_{p'p}$:

$$T_{p'p} = \frac{-V_{p'}}{V_p} \cong \frac{-(-I_b^* R_L)}{I_a^* R_F} \cong A_t \frac{R_L}{R_F} \qquad (17.28)$$

where $\quad A_t = \dfrac{I_b^*}{I_a^*} =$ current gain of multistage amplifier in Fig. 17.12b   (17.28a)
$\qquad\qquad$ obtainable with (17.19) or (17.22)

Illustration 1. Finding the return ratio $T_{p'p}$ of the type A feedback amplifier in Fig. 17.13a. Since a *GE* stage has a "phase reversal" at low frequencies as indicated in (c4) of Table 17.1, and a *GB* stage has "no reversal" as indicated in (a4) of Table 17.1, the two-stage *GE-GB* amplifier without the feedback loop R_F in Fig. 17.13a has a "*phase reversal*" at low frequencies. We may, therefore, add an output-to-input feedback loop R_F to this two-stage amplifier, as shown in Fig. 17.13a, obtaining a feedback amplifier with a type A feedback structure.

To find $T_{p'p}$ for this feedback amplifier, we need only follow (17.28). Since we have already obtained the current gain A_t of this two-stage *GE-GB* amplifier in Eq. (17.20b) with the signal-flow method described in Fig. 17.11b through h, let us substitute (17.20b) into (17.28), obtaining

$$T_{p'p} = \frac{-V_{p'}}{V_p} \cong \frac{R_L}{R_F} \times \text{Eq. (17.20b)} = \frac{R_L}{R_F} \frac{\beta\alpha^*}{1 + R_L/z_c^*} \qquad (17.29)$$

where the parameter β without asterisk refers to the first *GE* transistor, and the parameters α^* and z_c^* with asterisk refer to the second *GB* transistor.

$T_{p'p}$ is a network function and is usually expressed as a function of s. We shall now represent (17.29) as a function s. To do this, we follow the legend in Table 17.1, replace the transistor parameters in (17.29) with their equivalent quantities as "constants" or "functions of s" as indicated in Fig. 17.13c, and approximate with the assumptions in (17.4) and $R_L \ll r_c^*$ for practical circuits:

Return ratio of the type A feedback amplifier in Fig. 17.13a:

$$T_{p'p} \cong \frac{K}{(T_1 s + 1)(T_2 s + 1)(T_3 s + 1)} \qquad (17.30)$$

where $\qquad K = \dfrac{R_L}{R_F} \beta_0 \alpha_0^*$

$$T_1 \cong \frac{1}{\omega_\beta} \qquad T_2 \cong \frac{1}{\omega_\beta^*} \qquad T_3 = R_L C_c^* \qquad (17.30a)$$

K is usually referred to as the "open-circuit gain constant," T_1, T_2, and T_3 as the "time constants."

C. Relating the Return Ratio $T_{p'p}$ to the Overall Current Gain A^* for the Type A Feedback Structure

We shall now relate the return ratio $T_{p'p}$, as defined in (15.2) and obtainable with (17.26) or (17.28), to the overall current $A^* = I_2/I_1$ of the type A feedback amplifier in Fig. 17.12a as follows:

1. We first rearrange the circuit in Fig. 17.12a to the representation in Fig. 17.14a. Keeping $V_{p'} = V_p$ as an imposed condition in Fig. 17.14a is equivalent to "keeping

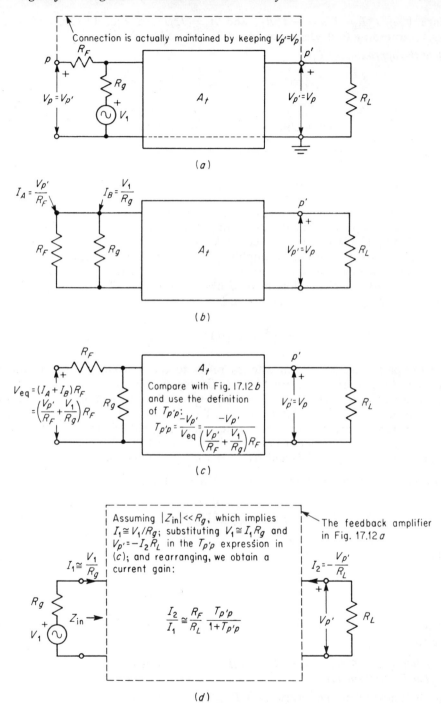

FIG. 17.14   (*a*) Rearrangement of the circuit in Fig. 17.12*a*. (*b*) A voltage source V_1 in series with R_g and another equivalent voltage source $V_{p'}$ (or V_p) in series with R_F converted into equivalent current sources. (*c*) $I_A + I_B$ considered as a single current source and converted with R_F into an equivalent voltage source V_{eq} with R_F. (*d*) Obtaining the current-gain expression for the circuit arrangement in Fig. 17.12*a*.

p and p' connected" in this circuit. In other words, the circuit arrangement in Fig. 17.14a with $V_{p'} = V_p$ is identical to the circuit in Fig. 17.12a with p and p' connected together; therefore, it also represents the feedback amplifier under operating conditions.

2. Considering that we have a voltage source V_1 in series with R_g *and* another equivalent voltage source $V_{p'}$ (or V_p) in series with R_F, we convert them into equivalent current sources I_B and I_A in Fig. 17.14b. Reference is made to Art. 2.5A and Fig. 2.11 for the means of finding equivalent sources.

3. We combine I_A and I_B into a single current source $I_A + I_B$.

4. We then convert the current source $I_A + I_B$ with R_F to an equivalent voltage source V_{eq} in series with R_F, as depicted in Fig. 17.14c.

5. Comparing Fig. 17.14c with Fig. 17.12b, we find them to be identical. However, Fig. 17.12b is merely a circuit arrangement used for the definition of $T_{p'p}$ while Fig. 17.14c is the "equivalent" of the feedback amplifier in Fig. 17.12a under the operating condition, that is, $V_{p'} = V_p$. This means that the definition of $T_{p'p}$ also applies to the arrangement in Fig. 17.14c as $T_{p'p} = -$output voltage/input voltage; i.e.,

$$T_{p'p} = \frac{-V_{p'}}{V_{eq}} = \frac{-V_{p'}}{(V_{p'}/R_F + V_1/R_g)R_F} \tag{17.31}$$

6. Assuming $|Z_{in}| \ll R_g$, which is almost always true in any transistor circuit and which implies $V_1 \cong I_1 R_g$ in Fig. 17.14d, we may substitute $V_1 \cong I_1 R_g$ and $V_{p'} = -I_2 R_L$ into (17.31), rearrange it, and obtain the current gain:

For type A feedback structure in Fig. 17.12a:

$$A^* = \frac{I_2}{I_1} \cong \frac{R_F}{R_L} \frac{T_{p'p}}{1 + T_{p'p}} \tag{17.32}$$

We have now related the return ratio $T_{p'p}$ to the current gain $A^* = I_2/I_1$ for the type A feedback structure in Fig. 17.12a.

Illustration 2. Finding the current gain A^* of the type A feedback amplifier in Fig. 17.13a from its known return ratio $T_{p'p}$. We need only substitute $T_{p'p}$ from (17.30) into (17.32), finding

Current gain of the type A feedback amplifier in Fig. 17.13a:

$$A^* = \frac{I_2}{I_2} \cong \frac{R_F}{R_L} \frac{K}{(T_1 s + 1)(T_2 s + 1)(T_3 s + 1) + K} \tag{17.33}$$

where K, T_1, T_2, and T_3 are defined in (17.30a).

17.4. Type B feedback structure: description and analysis

We have already discussed some of the general aspects of the type B feedback structure and the various problems involved in the analysis of this feedback arrangement in Art. 15.4 and Fig. 15.1d1. We shall now find solutions for these problems.

A. General Description

Circuit arrangement. To the multistage transistor amplifier depicted in Fig. 17.9a, described in (17.18), having a GE stage with a resistor R_E between emitter and ground as its last stage, and satisfying the "no-phase-reversal" condition in (15.5a), we now add the feedback loop R_F, obtaining the feedback amplifier in Fig. 17.15a. This represents the type B feedback structure.

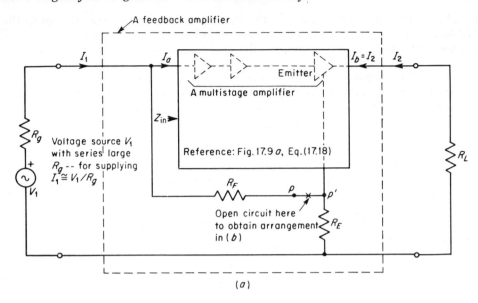

(a)

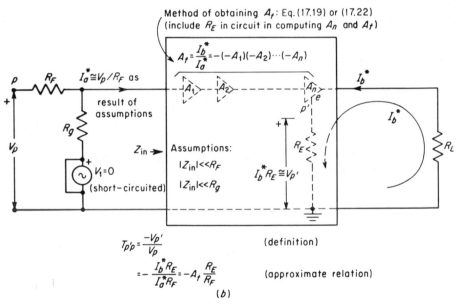

(b)

FIG. 17.15

It is customary to use, in transistor circuits, a voltage source V_1 in series with a large resistance R_g to supply an almost-constant input current $I_1 \simeq V_1/R_g$.

Description of problem. We have already defined the return ratio $T_{p'p}$ for this feedback structure in (15.6). As remarked in Art. 15.3B, we may plot the Nyquist diagram $T_{p'p}(j\omega)$ with this return ratio and determine the stability of the feedback amplifier. Therefore, our *immediate problem* is to obtain the return ratio $T_{p'p}$ of this feedback structure; this will be done in Art. 17.4B.

We also remarked in Art. 15.4A that the overall current gain $A^* = I_2/I_1$ of the type B feedback structure in Fig. 15.1d1 or 17.15a may be obtained from its return ratio $T_{p'p}$ through the relations indicated in (15.7). Our *next problem* is, therefore, to derive these relations; this will be done in Art. 17.4C.

B. Obtaining the Return Ratio $T_{p'p}$ for the Type B Feedback Structure

We shall now find the return ratio $T_{p'p}$ for the type B feedback structure in Fig. 17.15a or 15.1d1 according to its definition in (15.6). For clarity, we shall redraw the circuit arrangement, intended for measuring $T_{p'p}$, in Fig. 17.15b. According to (15.6c), our problem is merely to find a voltage-ratio function $T_{p'p} = -V_{p'}/V_p$, that is, a "network function" as the ratio of the voltage $-V_{p'}$ to the input voltage V_p, of the circuit arrangement in Fig. 17.15b.

Finding the exact expression for $T_{p'p}$. We may (1) replace each individual transistor by its appropriate equivalent circuit, thus obtaining an "equivalent network" for the circuit arrangement in Fig. 17.15b, (2) construct the signal-flow diagram, and (3) reduce this signal-flow diagram to a "single $V_p V_{p'}$ branch with known transmission $G = V_{p'}/V_p$." The return ratio is equal to the negative of this known transmission; i.e.,

Finding the exact $T_{p'p}$:

$$T_{p'p} = \frac{-V_{p'}}{V_p} = -\frac{V_{p'}}{V_p} = -\ known\ \text{transmission } G \text{ of signal-flow diagram}\quad (17.34)$$

The term "exact expression for $T_{p'p}$" is used here only in a comparative sense and is meant as the "most complete expression for $T_{p'p}$" which is obtainable with the assumed equivalent circuits of the transistors and which has not been approximated for practical circuit conditions.

For most practical circuits, we usually approximate the exact $T_{p'p}$ obtained in (17.34) by using assumptions such as those in (17.4) for practical considerations.

But the multistage amplifier inside the box in Fig. 17.15b may be a complicated circuit; to obtain the "equivalent network" of Fig. 17.15b, to construct its signal-flow diagram, and then to reduce this diagram, as required by the above procedure, may very well be an involved process.

Let us now try to find an approximate $T_{p'p}$ directly by a simpler means.

Finding an approximate expression for $T_{p'p}$. We shall assume

$$|Z_{in}| \ll R_F \ll R_g \quad (17.35)$$

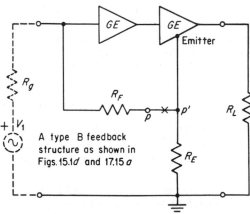

Fig. 17.16

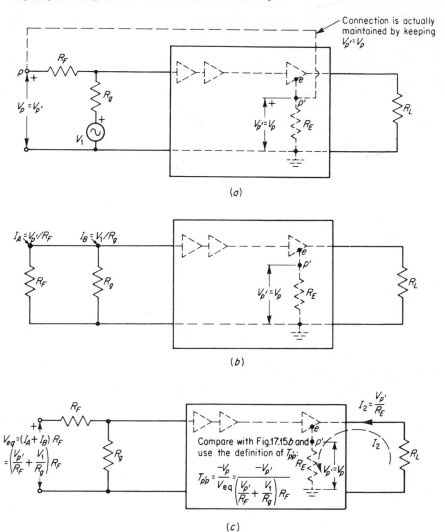

FIG. 17.17   (*a*) Rearrangement of the circuit in Fig. 17.15*a*. (*b*) A voltage source V_1 in series with R_g and another equivalent voltage source $V_{p'}$ (or V_p) in series with R_F converted into equivalent current sources. (*c*) $I_A + I_B$ considered as a single current source and converted with R_F into an equivalent voltage source V_{eq} with R_F. (*d*) Obtaining the current-gain expression for the circuit arrangement in Fig. 17.14*a*.

If this assumption is not true for a particular circuit, the approach associated with (17.34) should be used.

We may now consider $I_a^* \cong V_p/R_F$ in Fig. 17.15*b* as a current source to a multistage transistor amplifier similar to the one depicted in Fig. 17.9*a* and described in (17.18); the current gain $A_t = I_b^*/I_a^*$ may be obtained by the approach in (17.19) or (17.22).

Since $V_p \cong I_a^* R_F$, $V_{p'} \cong I_b^* R_E$, and $A_t = I_b^*/I_a^*$ in Fig. 17.15*b*, and $T_{p'p} = -V_{p'}/V_p$ according to its definition in (15.6), we readily obtain

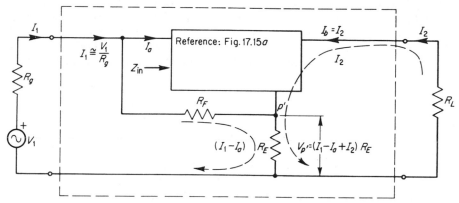

1. Assuming $|Z_{in}|$ large as compared with $R_F + R_E$, that is, $R_g \gg |Z_{in}| \gg R_F + R_E$, which implies $I_1 - I_a \cong I_1$; substituting $V_{p'} = (I_1 - I_a + I_2)R_E \cong (I_1 + I_2)R_E$ and $V_1 \cong I_1 R_g$ into the $T_{p'p}$ expression in (c); and rearranging, we obtain the *current gain*

$$\frac{I_2}{I_1} \cong -\frac{R_E + R_F}{R_E}\frac{T_{p'p} + R_E/(R_E + R_F)}{1 + T_{p'p}} \cong -\frac{R_E + R_F}{R_E}\frac{T_{p'p}}{1 + T_{p'p}} \quad \text{for } |Z_{in}| \gg R_F + R_E$$

2. Assuming small $|Z_{in}|$, say $R_g \gg R_F + R_E \gg |Z_{in}|$, which implies $I_1 \cong I_a$; substituting $V_{p'} = (I_1 - I_a + I_2)R_E \cong I_2 R_E$ and $V_1 \cong I_1 R_g$ into the $T_{p'p}$ expression in (c); and rearranging, we obtain the *current gain*

$$\frac{I_2}{I_1} \cong -\frac{R_F}{R_E}\frac{T_{p'p}}{1 + T_{p'p}} \quad \text{for } R_F + R_E \gg Z_{in}$$

$$(d)$$

FIG. 17.17 (*continued*)

Finding the approximate $T_{p'p}$:

$$T_{p'p} = \frac{-V_{p'}}{V_p} \cong \frac{-I_b^* R_E}{I_a^* R_F} = -A_t \frac{R_E}{R_F} \tag{17.36}$$

where $A_t = \dfrac{I_b^*}{I_a^*} =$ current gain of multistage amplifier in Fig. 17.15*b* (17.36*a*)
obtainable with (17.19) or (17.22)

Remarks. Since a single *GE* stage has a "phase reversal" at low frequencies as indicated in (*c*4) of Table 17.1, a two-stage *GE-GE* amplifier without the feedback loop R_F in Fig. 17.16 has *no phase reversal* at low frequencies. We may, therefore, add a feedback loop R_F to this two-stage amplifier, as shown in Fig. 17.16, obtaining a type B feedback structure.

We may follow the procedure suggested in (17.34) or (17.36) to obtain the return ratio $T_{p'p}$ of this type B feedback amplifier in the same way that we obtained $T_{p'p}$ for the type A feedback amplifier in Fig. 17.13*a* in Illustration 1, Art. 17.3B. The reader may find it interesting to work out this illustration.

C. Relating the Return Ratio $T_{p'p}$ *to the Overall Current Gain* A^* *for the Type B Feedback Structure*

We shall now relate the return ratio $T_{p'p}$, as defined in (15.6) and obtainable with (17.34) or (17.36), to the overall current gain $A^* = I_2/I_1$ of the type B feedback amplifier in Fig. 17.15*a* as follows:

1. We first rearrange the circuit in Fig. 17.15a to the representation in Fig. 17.17a. Keeping $V_{p'} = V_p$ as an imposed condition in Fig. 17.17a is equivalent to "keeping p and p' connected" in this circuit. In other words, the circuit arrangement in Fig. 17.17a with $V_{p'} = V_p$ is identical to the circuit arrangement in Fig. 17.15a with p and p' connected together; therefore, it also represents the feedback amplifier under operating conditions.

2. Considering that we have a voltage source V_1 in series with R_g *and* another equivalent voltage source $V_{p'}$ (or V_p) in series with R_F, we convert them into equivalent sources I_B and I_A in Fig. 17.17b. Reference is made to Art. 2.5A and Fig. 2.11 for the means for finding equivalent sources.

3. We combine I_A and I_B into a single current source $I_A + I_B$.

4. We then convert the current source $I_A + I_B$ with R_F into an equivalent voltage source V_{eq} in series with R_F, as depicted in Fig. 17.17c.

5. Comparing Fig. 17.17c with Fig. 17.15b, we find them to be identical. However, Fig. 17.15b is merely a circuit arrangement used for the definition of $T_{p'p}$, while Fig. 17.17c is the "equivalent" of the feedback amplifier in Fig. 17.15a under the operating condition, that is, $V_{p'} = V_p$. This means that the definition of $T_{p'p}$ also applies to the arrangement in Fig. 17.17c as $T_{p'p} = -$(voltage across R_E)/input voltage; i.e.,

$$T_{p'p} = \frac{-V_{p'}}{V_{eq}} = \frac{-V_{p'}}{(V_{p'}/R_F + V_1/R_g)R_F} \tag{17.37}$$

6. It is almost always true that R_g in Fig. 17.15a or 17.17d is a very large resistance used in series with the signal-generator voltage V_1 to provide an almost-constant current source $I_1 \simeq V_1/R_g$ in transistor circuits. We may, therefore, assume $R_g \gg |Z_{in}|$ and $R_g \gg R_F + R_E$.

Under the additional assumption $|Z_{in}| \gg R_F + R_E$, which implies $I_1 - I_a \simeq I_1$ in Fig. 17.17d, we substitute $V_{p'} = (I_1 - I_a + I_2)R_E \simeq (I_1 + I_2)R_E$ and $V_1 \simeq I_1R_g$ into (17.37) and rearrange it to obtain the current gain:

For type B structure in Fig. 17.15a for $|Z_{in}| \gg R_F + R_E$:

$$A^* = \frac{I_2}{I_1} \simeq -\frac{R_E + R_F}{R_E}\frac{T_{p'p} + R_E/(R_E + R_F)}{1 + T_{p'p}} \tag{17.38a}$$

$$A^* = \frac{I_2}{I_1} \simeq -\frac{R_E + R_F}{R_E}\frac{T_{p'p}}{1 + T_{p'p}} \tag{17.38b}$$

Equation (17.38b) is an approximation for (17.38a), since in general $R_E/(R_E + R_F)$ is a rather small fraction, and $|T_{p'p}|$ is quite large as compared with $R_E/(R_E + R_F)$.

However, under another assumption $R_F + R_E \gg |Z_{in}|$, which implies $I_1 \simeq I_a$ in Fig. 17.17d, we substitute $V_{p'} = (I_1 - I_a + I_2)R_E \simeq I_2R_E$ and $V_1 \simeq I_1R_g$ into (17.37) and rearrange it to obtain the current gain:

For type B structure in Fig. 17.15a for $R_F + R_E \gg |Z_{in}|$:

$$A^* = \frac{I_2}{I_1} \simeq -\frac{R_F}{R_E}\frac{T_{p'p}}{1 + T_{p'p}} \tag{17.39}$$

We have now related the return ratio $T_{p'p}$ to the current gain $A^* = I_2/I_1$ under certain assumptions for the type B feedback structure in Fig. 17.15a.

The relations in (17.38b) and (17.39) have been discussed below Eqs. (15.8a) and (15.8b).

PROBLEMS

17.1. Find the approximate current gain of the *GC-GB* circuit in (*d1*) of Table 17.1, and check the result against (*d2*).   Reference is made to Fig. 17.11 for a similar problem.

17.2. Find the approximate current gain of the *GE-GE* circuit in (*f1*) of Table 17.1, and check the result against (*f2*).

17.3. Find the approximate current gain of the *GC-GE* circuit in (*g1*) of Table 17.1, and check the result against (*g2*).

17.4. Given: The transistor feedback amplifier in Fig. 17.13a whose return ratio $T_{p'p} = f(s)$ is obtained in Fig. 17.13c.

Assuming that both transistors in this circuit have the circuit values in (17.2b) ($R_L = 500$ ohms and $R_F = 2,500$ ohms in Fig. 17.13a), plot the $T_{p'p}$ diagram for the entire frequency range.   SUGGESTION: We may choose different values of ω, say $\omega = -1,000, \ldots, -5,$ $-1, 0, 1, 5, 10, 50, 100, 500, \ldots,$ compute the corresponding values of $T_{p'p} = f(j\omega) = U(\omega) + jV(\omega)$, mark a point for each pair $U(\omega_k)$, $V(\omega_k)$ at $\omega = \omega_k$ in a complex plane which we designate the $T_{p'p}$ plane, obtain a continuous curve corresponding to the entire frequency range $-\infty < \omega < \infty$, and call this curve the $T_{p'p}$ diagram.

This $T_{p'p}$ diagram, the Nyquist diagram for the transistor feedback amplifier, tells us the stability property of the amplifier.   We shall study the Nyquist criterion for stability later in Chap. 19.

17.5. Find the approximate return ratio $T_{p'p}$ for the transistor feedback amplifier in Fig. P 17.5.   Reference is made to Fig. 17.13 for a similar problem.

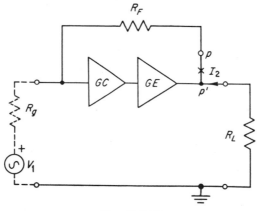

FIG. P 17.5

17.6. Given: The transistor feedback amplifier in Fig. P 17.5 and the return ratio $T_{p'p}$ as obtained in Prob. 17.5.

Assuming that both transistors in this circuit have the circuit values in (17.2b) ($R_L = 100$ ohms and $R_F = 5 \times 10^3$ ohms), plot the $T_{p'p}$ diagram (i.e., the Nyquist diagram) for the entire frequency range.   SUGGESTION: For the method of constructing this $T_{p'p}$ diagram, see Prob. 17.4.

17.7. Given: The transistor feedback amplifier in Fig. P 17.5 and the return ratio $T_{p'p}$ obtained in Prob. 17.5, where both transistors in this circuit have the circuit values in (17.2b).

(*a*) Letting $R_F = \lambda R_L$, obtain the overall current gain $A^* = I_2/I_1$ as a function of R_L, λ, and $s = j\omega$.

(*b*) Letting $R_L = 100$ ohms, plot $|A^*|$ versus ω for $\lambda = 10, 20, 30, 40,$ and 50.   Note that each curve representing the current gain indicates a relatively flat characteristic for a broad bandwidth, and, for low frequencies, $|A^*| \cong \lambda = R_F/R_L$.

ENGLAND

part G Stability problems in closed-loop control systems

In Part G we study means for determining the stability of a closed-loop system (which may be a vacuum-tube or transistor feedback amplifier) or a servomechanism and discuss some of the underlying principles of compensation for improving stability and accuracy.

In discussing Routh's criterion for stability, we emphasize special provisions for use when the normal procedure fails. The Nyquist criterion for stability is studied by an approach which makes it possible for us to investigate the behavior of the Nyquist diagram at infinity. Although the "clockwise orientation" of the Nyquist diagram at infinity is almost universally accepted, investigation shows that "counterclockwise orientation" is also possible.

18 Conditions for stability

18.1. Open-loop and closed-loop control systems

A. Some Simple Illustrations

Open-loop control system. A simple open-loop control system is illustrated in Fig. 18.1b and schematically represented in Fig. 18.1a. We define the transfer function as

$$G = \frac{C}{R} = \frac{magnitude \text{ of control variable}}{magnitude \text{ of reference input}} \tag{18.1}$$

Note that both R and C are d-c quantities in this illustration.

Closed-loop control system. A simple and rather trivial closed-loop system representing a position-control servomechanism is illustrated in Fig. 18.2b. We have two markers: r and c. Our *objective* is to control the positioning of c with r. If we move r to the right a distance R, we expect c to move to the right a distance C, where $C = R$.

To understand the *operation* of the closed-loop arrangement in Fig. 18.2b, we follow these steps:

1. The system is first at rest. The potentiometer tap p is centered, and no voltage is applied to the motor.

2. We now suddenly move the reference marker r to the right a distance R, identified as the *reference input*.

3. The movable idler moves down a distance E, identified as the *actuating error*, and moves the potentiometer tap p down a distance E.

4. The potentiometer tap p is not centered; there is a potential across p and g. This potential drives the motor and moves the marker c to the right a distance C, identified as the *controlled variable*, until $C = R$.

5. When $C = R$, the actuating error $E = R - C = 0$, and the potentiometer tap p is again centered, the arrangement in Fig. 18.2b is at rest in a new position.

The above is a description of an oversimplified version of the operation of a closed-loop control system. A symbolic representation is given in Fig. 18.2a with the following notation:

$$R = \text{reference input} \qquad\qquad C = \text{controlled variable}$$

$$E = R - C = \text{actuating error} \qquad G = \frac{C}{E} = \text{transfer function} \tag{18.2}$$

We note that in a closed-loop control system the output quantity, i.e., the *controlled variable C*, is monitored and compared with a desired quantity, i.e., the *reference input R*. If any difference exists, this difference, i.e., the *actuating error E*, is used to actuate the system and cause the output to equal the desired value.

469

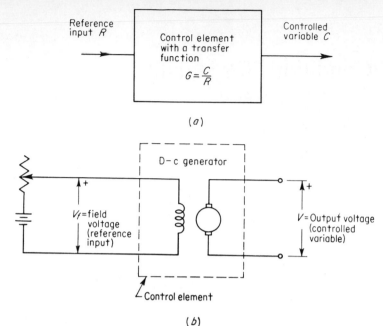

Reference
input R

Control element
with a transfer
function

$$G = \frac{C}{R}$$

Controlled
variable C

(a)

D-c generator

V_f=field
voltage
(reference
input)

+

+

V= Output voltage
(controlled
variable)

Control element

(b)

FIG. 18.1

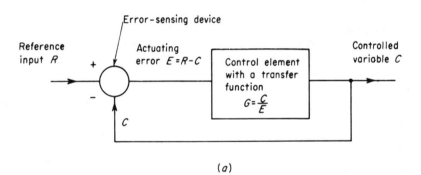

Error-sensing device

Reference
input R

+

Actuating
error $E = R - C$

Control element
with a transfer
function

$$G = \frac{C}{E}$$

Controlled
variable C

−

C

(a)

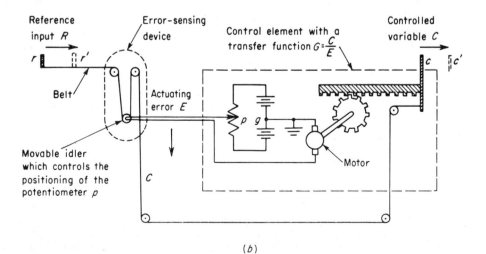

Reference
input R

Error-sensing
device

Control element with a
transfer function $G = \frac{C}{E}$

Controlled
variable C

r

r'

Belt

Actuating
error E

p g

Motor

c

c'

Movable idler
which controls the
positioning of the
potentiometer p

C

(b)

FIG. 18.2

B. Use of the Laplace-transform Expressions

We assume d-c quantities $R = V_f$ and $C = V$ in the simple illustration associated with (18.1) and Fig. 18.1. In this case, the transfer function (18.1) is the ratio of these two *magnitudes*.

Illustration with a four-terminal network. Let us use the four-terminal network depicted in Fig. 18.3a. Now we are considering time functions $e_1(t)$ and $e_2(t)$ rather than d-c quantities as in Fig. 18.1. What happens to the transfer function?

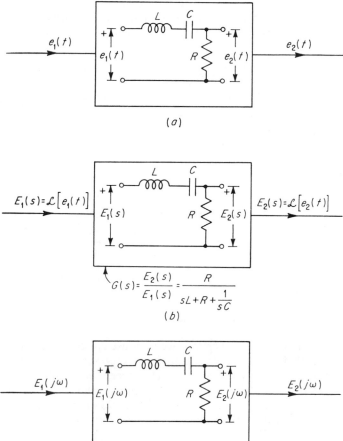

FIG. 18.3

Since both $e_1(t)$ and $e_2(t)$ will have frequency components with *complex amplitudes* rather than plain "magnitudes" as in (18.1), we expect a transfer function to (1) be a function of frequency and (2) represent a ratio of complex amplitudes of the controlled variable or network response to the reference variable or network excitation.

We now take the Laplace transforms of the quantities in Fig. 18.3a and represent them in Fig. 18.3*b*.   We then have the transfer function

$$G(s) = \frac{E_2(s)}{E_1(s)} = \frac{R}{sL + R + 1/sC} \tag{18.3a}$$

as defined earlier.   For physical interpretation, we let $s = j\omega$ and find

$$G(j\omega) = \frac{E_2(j\omega)}{E_1(j\omega)} = \frac{R}{j\omega L + R + 1/j\omega C} \tag{18.3b}$$

as depicted in Fig. 18.3*c*.   This expression certainly satisfies the two requirements of a transfer function as stated above: Equation (18.3*b*) is (1) a function of frequency and (2) a ratio of the complex amplitude $E_2(j\omega) = |E_2(j\omega)|e^{j\phi_2(\omega)}$ of the controlled variable $e_2(t)$ to the complex amplitude $E_1(j\omega) = |E_1(j\omega)|e^{j\phi_1(\omega)}$ of the reference input $e_1(t)$.

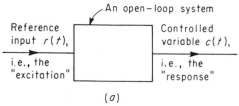

(*a*)

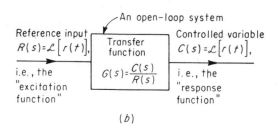

(*b*)

Fig. 18.4

Open-loop control system.   In general, we may use either a time-function representation as in Fig. 18.4*a* or a Laplace-transform representation as in Fig. 18.4*b* to represent an open-loop control system.   However, the Laplace-transform representation is always preferred for the simple functional relation $G(s) = C(s)/R(s)$.

Transfer function.   We shall call $G(s)$ in Fig. 18.4*b* a transfer function.   An illustration of a typical transfer function of a simple four-terminal network is provided in Fig. 18.3*b*.

We have discussed a number of transfer functions for four-terminal networks. In closed-loop control systems, we are interested in the transfer functions of four-terminal networks, other electrical components (e.g., motors, generators, amplidynes, tachometers, and potentiometers as will be discussed in Art. 20.1B), and nonelectrical components.

C. Closed-loop Control Systems

Schematic representations.   Corresponding to Fig. 18.2*a*, but in Laplace-transform representation, a typical schematic of a closed-loop control system is shown in Fig. 18.5*b*.   In this instance, the controlled variable $C(s)$ is directly compared with the reference input $R(s)$; the actuating error $E(s) = R(s) - C(s)$ is used to monitor the control element.   This system may be considered as one with a direct feedback loop; Fig. 18.5*a* depicts its time-function representation.

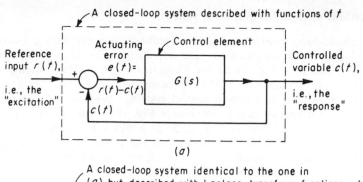

A closed-loop system described with functions of t

Reference input $r(t)$, i.e., the "excitation"

Actuating error $e(t) = r(t)-c(t)$

Control element $G(s)$

Controlled variable $c(t)$, i.e., the "response"

$c(t)$

(a)

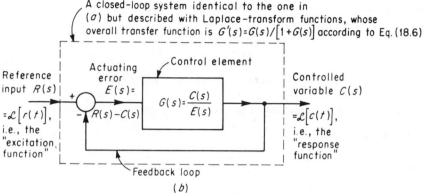

A closed-loop system identical to the one in (a) but described with Laplace-transform functions, whose overall transfer function is $G'(s) = G(s)/[1+G(s)]$ according to Eq. (18.6)

Reference input $R(s)$ $= \mathcal{L}[r(t)]$, i.e., the "excitation function"

Actuating error $E(s) = R(s)-C(s)$

Control element $G(s) = \dfrac{C(s)}{E(s)}$

Controlled variable $C(s)$ $= \mathcal{L}[c(t)]$, i.e., the "response function"

Feedback loop

(b)

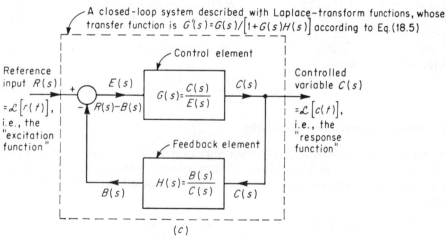

A closed-loop system described with Laplace-transform functions, whose transfer function is $G'(s) = G(s)/[1+G(s)H(s)]$ according to Eq. (18.5)

Reference input $R(s)$ $= \mathcal{L}[r(t)]$, i.e., the "excitation function"

$E(s) = R(s)-B(s)$

Control element $G(s) = \dfrac{C(s)}{E(s)}$

$C(s)$

Controlled variable $C(s)$ $= \mathcal{L}[c(t)]$, i.e., the "response function"

Feedback element $H(s) = \dfrac{B(s)}{C(s)}$

$B(s)$ $C(s)$

(c)

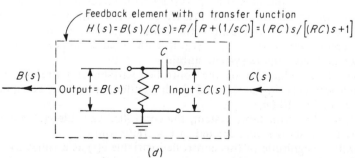

Feedback element with a transfer function
$H(s) = B(s)/C(s) = R/[R+(1/sC)] = (RC)s/[(RC)s+1]$

C

$B(s)$

Output $= B(s)$ $\quad R \quad$ Input $= C(s)$

$C(s)$

(d)

Fig. 18.5

473

In a number of closed-loop control systems, a feedback element with a transfer function $H(s)$ is included in the feedback loop, as depicted in Fig. 18.5c. A typical feedback element is included in Fig. 18.5d for illustration. A feedback element is used to improve system performance, as will be discussed in Art. 21.2A.

Overall transfer function of a closed-loop control system. We may consider that the system in Fig. 18.5b is a special case of the one in Fig. 18.5c with $H(s) = 1$.

Considering the closed-loop system in Fig. 18.5c as a black box marked by the dashed boundary in the figure, we now wish to find the overall transfer function $G'(s)$ as a ratio of the controlled variable $C(s)$ to the reference input $R(s)$. From the block diagram in Fig. 18.5c, we have the following functional relations:

$$B(s) = H(s)C(s)$$

$$E(s) = R(s) - H(s)C(s) \qquad (18.4)$$

$$C(s) = G(s)E(s) = G(s)[R(s) - H(s)C(s)]$$

This last equation may be rearranged to give

Overall transfer function:

$$G'(s) = \frac{C(s)}{R(s)} = \frac{G(s)}{1 + G(s)H(s)} \qquad (18.5)$$

which represents the relationship between the controlled variable $C(s)$ and the reference input $R(s)$ of the closed-loop control system in Fig. 18.5c, this relationship being expressed in terms of the transfer functions of the control and feedback elements of the system.

Treating the system in Fig. 18.5b as a special case of the above with $H(s) = 1$, we find its transfer function:

$$G'(s) = \frac{C(s)}{R(s)} = \frac{G(s)}{1 + G(s)} \qquad (18.6)$$

18.2. Intuitive interpretation of stability

We have discussed the questions of stability in Art. 13.4. This discussion applies equally to networks and closed-loop control systems. We shall now attempt to give an intuitive interpretation of stability, slanted toward the closed-loop control system.

A. Remarks about the Stability of a Closed-loop System

Let us look into the simple closed-loop system with direct feedback loop in Fig. 18.5a and b; the controlled variable is *directly* compared with the reference input, and their difference is used to monitor the control element of the system. We idealize the reference input $r(t) = \mathscr{L}^{-1}[R(s)]$ with a step function. With these assumptions, we shall investigate system stability.

Stable system. In a stable system, the controlled variable $c(t)$ attempts to follow the step-function reference input $r(t)$ and finally settles down to a constant value. This is illustrated in Fig. 18.6a.

Unstable system. In an unstable system, the controlled variable $c(t)$ is a runaway transient or unstable response, as depicted in Fig. 18.6b and c.

Theoretically, the magnitude of this controlled variable $c(t)$ as a runaway transient will tend to infinity for $t \to \infty$. However, this requires infinite energy in the system, and no physical system can supply an infinite amount of energy. For this reason,

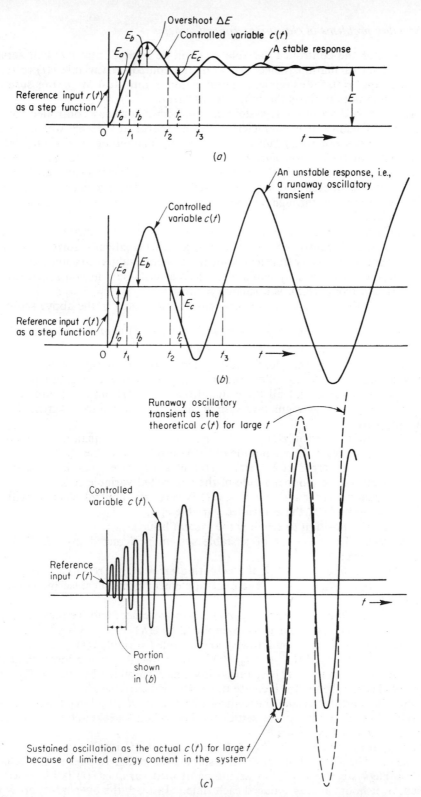

FIG. 18.6

the magnitude of the controlled variable $c(t)$ will be limited, and $c(t)$ will actually be in a sustained oscillation. Since we want the controlled variable $c(t)$ to follow the reference input $r(t)$, for example, a step function in our illustration, this sustained oscillation is as undesirable as the runaway transient.

We have described an unstable system as one with a runaway controlled variable or response. In reality, it is characterized by a controlled variable which *tends* to run away (but does not really run away to infinite magnitude) and then becomes associated with an undesirable sustained oscillation. In the mathematics we have been using, we usually find only the presence or absence of a runaway transient, with no evidence of the undesirable sustained oscillation. The presence of a runaway transient, as discovered through mathematics, actually implies the existence of a sustained oscillation.

Remarks. From the above discussion, we may state: An unstable closed-loop system is one whose controlled variable $c(t)$, as mathematically solved for in the system equation, is a runaway transient while the system is subject to a finite excitation. For example, the closed-loop system in Fig. 18.5b is unstable if its controlled variable $c(t) = \mathcal{L}^{-1}[C(s)]$, from (18.5), is a runaway transient.

From now on, the term *system stability* will be interpreted in the above sense.

B. Simple Illustrations Showing Stable and Unstable System Behaviors Subject to a Step-function Reference Input

Again we are studying the closed-loop system depicted in Fig. 18.5a; we desire the controlled variable $c(t)$ to follow the reference input $r(t)$, a step function. For simplicity, let us assume that all three quantities, $r(t)$, $c(t)$, and $e(t)$, are electrical voltages, e.g., in a voltage-regulating system, and that the control element has the following properties:

1. If the actuating error $e(t) = r(t) - c(t)$ is a positive quantity, the control element will help increase the magnitude of the controlled variable $c(t)$.

2. If the actuating error $e(t) = r(t) - c(t)$ is a negative quantity, the control element will help reduce the magnitude of the controlled variable $c(t)$.

3. If the actuating error $e(t) = r(t) - c(t)$ is zero, the control element will help maintain the magnitude of the controlled variable $c(t)$.

Now we are in a position to see how the system behaves.

Stable system. The behavior of a stable system is depicted in Fig. 18.6a and described as follows:

1. *For the Time Interval $t < t_1$*, the actuating error $e(t) = r(t) - c(t)$ is positive. For example, $e(t_a) = E_a = (+)$. The control element helps increase the controlled variable $c(t)$.

2. *For the Time Interval $t_1 < t < t_2$*, $c(t)$ is overincreased, and we must reduce it. Now $e(t) = r(t) - c(t)$ is negative, as exemplified by $e(t_b) = E_b = (-)$. The control element then helps reduce or pull down the controlled variable $c(t)$.

3. *For the Time Interval $t_2 < t < t_3$*, $c(t)$ is overreduced, and we must build it up again. Now $e(t) = r(t) - c(t)$ is again positive, as exemplified by $e(t_c) = E_c = (+)$. The control element then helps increase the controlled variable $c(t)$.

By increasing and decreasing the controlled variable $c(t)$ and reducing the overshoots each time, a stable system settles the controlled variable $c(t)$ at a constant value, as depicted in Fig. 18.6a.

Unstable system. On the other hand, the behavior of an unstable system is depicted in Fig. 18.6b. The above description of a stable system also applies to the behavior of an unstable system, except that as the controlled variable $c(t)$ is increased and decreased, overshoots are *not* reduced each time. Instead, the overshoots grow with each cycle, leading to a runaway transient.

18.3. Determination of the stability of a closed-loop system using the characteristic zeros; fundamental criterion for stability

A. Characteristic Zeros of a Closed-loop System

Review of system stability.   We discussed system stability in Art. 13.4 and defined the system function in (13.33) as

System function:

$$T(s) = \frac{\text{response function } I(s)}{\text{excitation function } E(s)} = \frac{Q(s)}{P(s)} \tag{18.7}$$

which has the form of a ratio of two polynomials $Q(s)$ and $P(s)$.   We call $P(s)$ the characteristic equation of the system, and its zeros $r_1, r_2, \ldots, r_k$ the characteristic zeros.

The locations of the characteristic zeros in the s plane dictate the stability of the system or network according to the fundamental criterion for stability in (13.41).

A closed-loop system as a black box.   Let us now examine the schematic representations of closed-loop systems in Fig. 18.5.   Figure 18.5a shows one representation, with the reference input $r(t)$ and controlled variable $c(t)$ as functions of time, while Fig. 18.5b or c shows another, with the reference input $R(s) = \mathscr{L}[r(t)]$ and controlled variable $C(s) = \mathscr{L}[c(t)]$ as Laplace-transform functions or functions of the complex frequency.

Comparing the closed-loop system schematic in Fig. 18.5b or c with the general system schematic in Fig. 13.3a, we note that they are identical except for terminology. This means that the system function of the closed-loop system in Fig. 18.5b or c is also the overall transfer function of the system; i.e.,

System function:

$$T(s) = \frac{\text{controlled variable } C(s)}{\text{reference input } R(s)} = G'(s) \tag{18.8}$$

where

$$G'(s) = \frac{C(s)}{R(s)} = \frac{G(s)}{1 + G(s)H(s)} \tag{18.9}$$

for the arrangement in Fig. 18.5c, and

$$G'(s) = \frac{C(s)}{R(s)} = \frac{G(s)}{1 + G(s)} \tag{18.10}$$

for the special case $H(s) = 1$ in Fig. 18.5b.

Characteristic function and characteristic equation of a closed-loop system.   Let us consider the system in Fig. 18.5c and (18.9).   We shall call

Characteristic function:

$$W(s) = 1 + G(s)H(s) \tag{18.11a}$$

its characteristic function, which has the form $W(s) = P(s)/F(s)$, the ratio of two polynomials, and we shall call

Characteristic equation:

$$P(s) = \text{numerator polynomial of } W(s) \text{ in } (18.11a)$$
$$= a_k s^k + a_{k-1} s^{k-1} + \cdots + a_1 s + a_0 \tag{18.11b}$$

its characteristic equation, and

Characteristic zeros:

$$r_1, r_2, \ldots, r_k = \text{zeros of characteristic function } W(s) \text{ or characteristic}$$
$$\text{equation } P(s) \qquad (18.11c)$$

its characteristic zeros.   According to our earlier discussion, the locations of these characteristic zeros in the s plane dictate the stability of the system.

B. Fundamental Criterion for Stability

We shall now slightly modify the fundamental criterion for stability in (13.41) so that we may use it conveniently in the stability study of closed-loop systems:

Fundamental criterion for stability:

> A closed-loop system, as depicted in Fig. 18.5c, is *stable* if none of the zeros of its characteristic function $W(s) = P(s)/F(s) = 1 + G(s)H(s)$ or its characteristic equation $P(s)$ are in the right-hand half of the s plane and if all characteristic zeros on the $j\omega$ axis are simple   (18.12a)

> A closed-loop system is *unstable if* some of its characteristic zeros are in the right-hand half of the s plane or if it has multiple-order characteristic zeros on the $j\omega$ axis   (18.12b)

Illustration 1.   Let us assume that the closed-loop system in Fig. 18.5c is a speed-regulator system with the following characteristic function:

$$W(s) = 1 + G(s)H(s) = 1 + \frac{10}{(1 + 0.5s)(1 + 0.1s)} = \frac{(1 + 10) + 0.6s + 0.05s^2}{(1 + 0.5s)(1 + 0.1s)}$$

According to (18.11b), this system has the characteristic equation

$$P(s) = 0.05s^2 + 0.6s + 11$$

and characteristic zeros $r_1, r_2 = -6 \pm j\sqrt{184}$.   Since both characteristic zeros are in the left-hand half of the s plane, this system is stable.

Illustration 2.   Let us hypothetically assume that a closed-loop system has a characteristic equation

$$P(s) = s^2 + s - 6$$

which implies the following characteristic zeros: $r_1 = 2$, $r_2 = -3$. Since one of these characteristic zeros is in the right-hand half of the s plane, this system is unstable.

18.4. Routh's criterion for stability[†]

A. A Test for the Existence of Characteristic Zeros with Positive Real Parts

Routh's criterion provides a method for determining the number of characteristic zeros with positive real parts, i.e., the number of characteristic zeros located in the

---

[†] E. T. Routh, "Dynamics of a System of Rigid Bodies," 3d ed., The Macmillan Company, New York, 1877.

right-hand half of the s plane, by manipulating the coefficients of the characteristic equation.

According to the fundamental criterion for stability in (13.41) or (18.12), the application of Routh's criterion determines system stability subject to the assumption that

An assumption for practical problems:

> The system has no multiple-order characteristic zeros on the $j\omega$ axis
> except at $s = 0$ (18.13)

The above assumption is almost always true for practical problems. Multiple-order characteristic zeros at $s = 0$ can easily be detected by inspection. For example, the characteristic equation $P(s) = s^6 + 2s^5 + 8s^4 + 4s^3 + 3s^2$ is recognized to have a double characteristic zero at $s = 0$.

Inasmuch as the Routh's criterion for stability is a satisfactory means for determining system stability for practical problems, we shall not repeat assumption (18.13) in our subsequent discussion.

Routh's criterion is based upon the fact that the roots and coefficients of an algebraic equation are related; the manipulation of the coefficients enables us to detect how many of the roots have positive real parts. Let us consider an algebraic equation

$$P(s) = a_k s^k + a_{k-1} s^{k-1} + \cdots + a_1 s + a_0 \tag{18.14}$$

which may be interpreted as the characteristic equation of a closed-loop system. We shall (1) manipulate the coefficients of (18.14) into an array of numbers which we shall call the Routh's array and (2) determine the number of changes of algebraic sign in the first column of this array; this number indicates how many roots have positive real parts.

The construction of a Routh's array. For a given characteristic equation (18.14), we generally first make sure that the first coefficient a_k is a positive quantity. If a_k is a negative quantity, we may divide (18.14) through by a_k or multiply it by -1 to obtain an algebraic equation with a positive first coefficient. We then proceed as follows:

Step 1. Use the first, third, fifth, . . . coefficients of (18.14) to form the first row, and the second, fourth, sixth, . . . coefficients to form the second row of the array:

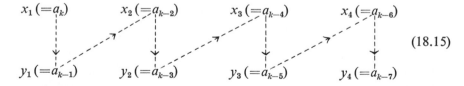

$$\tag{18.15}$$

For example, suppose we have $k = 7$ in (18.14). The first two rows have the form

$$
\begin{array}{cccc}
a_7 & a_5 & a_3 & a_1 \\
a_6 & a_4 & a_2 & a_0
\end{array}
\tag{18.16a}
$$

Another example, for $k = 8$, has

$$
\begin{array}{ccccc}
a_8 & a_6 & a_4 & a_2 & a_0 \\
a_7 & a_5 & a_3 & a_1 &
\end{array}
\tag{18.16b}
$$

as its first two rows.

Step 2.   Construct the complete Routh's array.   Let us consider an array of five columns, for $k = 9$, to illustrate the method of computation.

$$
\begin{array}{lllll}
x_1 & x_2 & x_3 & x_4 & x_5 \\
y_1 & y_2 & y_3 & y_4 & y_5 \\
z_1 & z_2 & z_3 & z_4 \\
w_1 & w_2 & w_3 & w_4 \\
u_1 & u_2 & u_3 \\
v_1 & v_2 & v_3 \\
p_1 & p_2 \\
q_1 & q_2 \\
r_1 \\
t_1
\end{array}
\left.\begin{array}{l}
\\
\end{array}\right\} \text{Known coefficients from the characteristic equation according to (18.15)}
$$

Right brace for the remaining rows: *Compute* with the aid of (18.18)   (18.17)

The first two rows of the array come from the characteristic equation; we compute the remaining portion of the array with the aid of the following expressions:

$$
z_i = \frac{-\begin{vmatrix} x_1 & x_{i+1} \\ y_1 & y_{i+1} \end{vmatrix}}{y_1} = \frac{-(x_1 y_{i+1} - x_{i+1} y_1)}{y_1} \qquad i = 1, 2, 3, 4 \qquad (18.18a)
$$

NOTE: x, y are the next two rows above z.   Use $y_5 = 0$ in computation if there is no number at this position as in (18.16b).

$$
w_i = \frac{-\begin{vmatrix} y_1 & y_{i+1} \\ z_1 & z_{i+1} \end{vmatrix}}{z_1} = \frac{-(y_1 z_{i+1} - y_{i+1} z_1)}{z_1} \qquad i = 1, 2, 3, 4 \qquad (18.18b)
$$

NOTE: y, z are the next two rows above w.   Use $z_5 = 0$ in computation, as there is no number at this position.

$$
u_i = \frac{-\begin{vmatrix} z_1 & z_{i+1} \\ w_1 & w_{i+1} \end{vmatrix}}{w_1} \qquad i = 1, 2, 3 \qquad (18.18c)
$$

$$
v_i = \frac{-\begin{vmatrix} w_1 & w_{i+1} \\ u_1 & u_{i+1} \end{vmatrix}}{u_1} \qquad i = 1, 2, 3 \qquad (18.18d)
$$

$$
p_i = \frac{-\begin{vmatrix} u_1 & u_{i+1} \\ v_1 & v_{i+1} \end{vmatrix}}{v_1} \qquad i = 1, 2 \qquad (18.18e)
$$

$$
q_i = \frac{-\begin{vmatrix} v_1 & v_{i+1} \\ p_1 & p_{i+1} \end{vmatrix}}{p_1} \qquad i = 1, 2 \qquad (18.18f)
$$

$$r_1 = \frac{- \begin{vmatrix} p_1 & p_2 \\ q_1 & q_2 \end{vmatrix}}{q_1} \tag{18.18g}$$

$$t_1 = \frac{- \begin{vmatrix} q_1 & q_2 \\ r_1 & 0 \end{vmatrix}}{r_1} \tag{18.18h}$$

Illustration 1. For

$$P(s) = 2s^4 + 2s^3 + 8s^2 + 3s + 2 \tag{18.19a}$$

we find the Routh's array with the aid of (18.17):

s^4	2	8	2
s^3	2	3	
s^2	5	2	
s^1	$\frac{11}{5}$		
s^0	2		

$(18.19b)$

A reference column with powers of s is included in the array. Each term in this reference column represents the highest power of s in the *polynomial* of even or odd powers of s associated with a given row; the coefficients of the *associated polynomials* are the numbers in this row. For example, the first row has an associated polynomial of *even* powers of s in the form $2s^4 + 8s^2 + 2$; the second row, of *odd* powers in the form $2s^3 + 3s$; the given polynomial (18.19a) is the sum of these two associated polynomials. The associated polynomials of the three derived rows are $5s^2 + 2$, $\frac{11}{5}s$, and 2.

Routh's criterion. A Routh's array of numbers (18.17) may be constructed for a system associated with a characteristic equation of the form (18.14). The number of changes in algebraic sign in the first-column terms in this array indicates how many characteristic zeros (roots) have positive real parts. The system is stable if all the first-column terms of this array have the same algebraic sign.

Remark about Illustration 1. An inspection of the first-column terms in (18.19b) reveals that all terms are positive, and the system is stable.

Some rules for simplification in the construction of a Routh's array. We shall often find that the numbers involved in the array (18.17) are either too large or too small for convenient manipulation. However, we may follow some rules to convert these numbers to values of proper magnitude for easy manipulation:

1. When we are given a characteristic equation $P(s)$ with *unwieldy* coefficients, we may change the scale factor of its variable by introducing $\bar{s} = s/k$, where k is an appropriate positive quantity; we divide the equation through by a constant to obtain a new characteristic equation $\bar{P}(\bar{s})$ with coefficients of medium magnitude. $P(s)$ and $\bar{P}(\bar{s})$ have the same stability property, as their corresponding roots differ only by a positive constant factor k. For the purpose of determining system stability, we may construct the Routh's array for $\bar{P}(\bar{s})$ instead of that for $P(s)$. For example, suppose

$$P(s) = s^5 + 15s^4 + 270s^3 + 1{,}300s^2 + 65{,}000s + 1{,}500{,}000 \tag{18.20a}$$

We may introduce $\bar{s} = s/10$ in (18.20a); we obtain [by substituting $s = 10\bar{s}$ into (18.20a)] $P(s) = 10^5 \bar{P}(\bar{s})$, where

$$\bar{P}(\bar{s}) = \bar{s}^5 + 1.5\bar{s}^4 + 2.7\bar{s}^3 + 1.3\bar{s}^2 + 6.5\bar{s} + 15 \tag{18.20b}$$

2. During the construction of a Routh's array, we may divide every number in any row by an arbitrary *positive* quantity, as long as we use this modified row in the construction of all new rows of the array. It is often convenient to choose the *absolute value of the first number* of a newly obtained row to be this positive quantity, thus making the first number of the modified row $+1$ or -1.

The array obtained with the above-described modification and the one obtained without it are actually *different* arrays. However, they provide the *same* indication of system stability; for the purpose of determining system stability, we are not particular about which array we use.

Illustration 2.   Let us consider the characteristic equation

$$P(s) = s^5 + 2s^4 + 12s^3 + 32s^2 + 16s + 64 \qquad (18.21a)$$

We first construct the Routh's array with the aid of the rule of simplification as described above:

				Rule of simplification:	
s^5	1	12	16		
s^4	$\cancel{2}$	$\cancel{32}$	$\cancel{64}$	Dividing by $|2| = 2$	
	1	16	32		
s^3	$\cancel{-4}$	$\cancel{-16}$		Dividing by $|-4| = 4$	
	-1	-4			
s^2	$\cancel{12}$	$\cancel{32}$		Dividing by $|12| = 12$	$(18.21b)$
	1	$\frac{8}{3}$			
s^1	$\cancel{-\frac{4}{3}}$			Dividing by $|-\frac{4}{3}| = \frac{4}{3}$	
	-1				
s^0	$\cancel{\frac{8}{3}}$			Dividing by $|\frac{8}{3}| = \frac{8}{3}$	
	1				

An inspection of the first-column terms reveals four changes of algebraic signs, i.e., from 1 to -1, -1 to 1, 1 to -1, and -1 to 1.   This means there are four characteristic zeros in $(18.21a)$ having positive real parts, and the system is unstable.

B. Special Cases in which the Normal Procedure in the Construction of a Routh's Array Fails

Suppose we are to construct a Routh's array for a given characteristic equation $P(s)$.   We first tabulate the coefficients of $P(s)$ to form the first two rows of the array as in (18.17).   When $y_1 = 0$, all numbers in the next z row approach infinity according to (18.18a).   This is true when any first-column number is equal to zero, for example, $z_1 = 0$ or $v_1 = 0$.   We can actually have two different situations when a first-column number is zero: (1) a complete row of zeros or (2) a row with only the first term equal to zero.

A special case in which a row of zeros appears in the normal procedure.   Suppose the mth row of a Routh's array would be a "row of zeros" if we followed the normal procedure.   Instead of using this row of zeros as our mth row, we follow these steps: (1) write the associated polynomial of the $(m - 1)$st row and (2) take the derivative of this associated polynomial, using its coefficients to form the mth row of the array.

Illustration 3.   We shall now attempt to find the Routh's array for

$$P(s) = s^6 + 6s^4 + 11s^2 + 6 \qquad (18.22a)$$

The second row, i.e., the mth row for $m = 2$, according to the normal procedure, would be a row of zeros.   By our present discussion, we (1) find the associated polynomial of the first row, i.e., the $(m - 1)$st row for $m = 2$, which is $(18.22a)$ itself, and (2) find its derivative $P'(s) = 6s^5 + 24s^3 + 22$ and use the coefficients of $P'(s)$ to form the second row of the Routh's array, which now has the form

$$
\begin{array}{c|cccc}
s^6 & 1 & 6 & 11 & 6 & \text{Coefficients of } P(s)\\
s^5 & \cancel{6} & \cancel{24} & \cancel{22} & & \text{Coefficients of } P'(s)\\
    & 1 & 4 & \tfrac{11}{3} & \\
s^4 & \cancel{2} & \cancel{\tfrac{22}{3}} & \cancel{6} & \\
    & 1 & \tfrac{11}{3} & 3 & \\
s^3 & \cancel{\tfrac{1}{3}} & \cancel{\tfrac{9}{3}} & & \\
    & 1 & 2 & & \\
s^2 & \cancel{\tfrac{5}{8}} & \cancel{3} & & \\
    & 1 & \tfrac{9}{5} & & \\
s^1 & \cancel{\tfrac{1}{5}} & & & \\
    & 1 & & & \\
s^0 & \cancel{\tfrac{9}{5}} & & & \\
    & 1 & & &
\end{array}
\qquad (18.22b)
$$

The rule of simplification, as illustrated in (18.21b), is applied here.

Since all the first-column terms of (18.22b) are positive, the system having (18.22a) as its characteristic equation is stable.

Illustration 4.   By inspection, we know that the system with

$$P(s) = s^5 + 3s^4 - 3s^3 - 9s^2 - 4s - 12 \qquad (18.23a)$$

as its characteristic equation is unstable. All the coefficients of the characteristic equation of a stable system must have the same algebraic sign; this condition is not satisfied by (18.23a).

Now let us verify this with the Routh's criterion. By following the normal procedure for constructing a Routh's array, we find

$$
\begin{array}{c|ccc}
s^5 & 1 & -3 & -4\\
s^4 & \cancel{3} & \cancel{-9} & \cancel{-12}\\
    & 1 & -3 & -4\\
s^3 & 0 & 0 & 0
\end{array}
\qquad (18.23b)
$$

We have encountered a row of zeros in the third row, that is, for $m = 3$. In such a case, we (1) find the associated polynomial of the second row, i.e., the $(m - 1)$st row for $m = 3$, which is $A(s) = 1s^4 - 3s^2 - 4$, and (2) find its derivative $A'(s) = 4s^3 - 6s$ and use the coefficients of $A'(s)$ to form the third row, i.e., the mth row for $m = 3$, of the Routh's array, which now has the form

$$
\begin{array}{c|ccc}
s^5 & 1 & -3 & -4 & \\
s^4 & \cancel{3} & \cancel{-9} & \cancel{-12} & \\
    & 1 & -3 & -4 & \text{Coefficients of } A(s)\\
s^3 & \cancel{4} & \cancel{-6} & & \text{Coefficients of } A'(s)\\
    & 1 & -\tfrac{3}{2} & & \\
s^2 & \cancel{-\tfrac{3}{2}} & \cancel{-4} & & \\
    & -1 & -\tfrac{8}{3} & & \\
s^1 & \cancel{-\tfrac{25}{6}} & & & \\
    & -1 & & & \\
s^0 & \cancel{-\tfrac{8}{3}} & & & \\
    & -1 & & &
\end{array}
\qquad (18.23c)
$$

An inspection of the first-column terms reveals one change of algebraic sign, i.e., from 1 to -1. This means there is one characteristic zero of (18.23a) having a positive real part, and the system is unstable.

For further verification we may solve (18.23*a*), finding $\pm j$, ± 2, and -3 as characteristic zeros. The characteristic zero $+2 = +2 + j0$ has a positive real part.

Another special case in which the first term of a row is zero in the normal procedure. By inspection, we know that the system with

$$P(s) = s^4 - 2s^2 - 3s - 2 \tag{18.24a}$$

as its characteristic equation is unstable, as some of the coefficients in (18.24*a*) are negative.

Now let us verify this with the Routh's criterion and find out how many characteristic roots have positive real parts. By following the normal procedure for constructing a Routh's array, we find that the second row of

$$\begin{array}{c|ccc} s^4 & 1 & -2 & -2 \\ s^3 & 0 & -3 \end{array} \tag{18.24b}$$

has a first-term zero. According to (18.18*a*), the terms in the next row approach infinity as $y_1 = 0$, and we fail in our attempt to construct the complete array. There are two remedies for this special case:

1. We may replace s with $1/\bar{s}$ in the given characteristic equation $P(s)$ and obtain an auxiliary characteristic equation $\bar{P}(\bar{s})$. The Routh's arrays of $P(s)$ and $\bar{P}(\bar{s})$ must give the *same* indication of stability. Therefore, we may construct a Routh's array for $\bar{P}(\bar{s})$ to determine the system stability for $P(s)$.

$P(s)$ and $\bar{P}(\bar{s})$ have the same stability indication for the following reasons: If $P(s)$ has $r_1 = c$ as a root, $\bar{P}(\bar{s})$ has $\bar{r}_1 = \bar{c}$ as a root, where $\bar{c} = 1/c$. If $P(s)$ has $r_1, r_2 = a \pm jb$ as a pair of conjugate roots, $\bar{P}(\bar{s})$ has $r_1, r_2 = \bar{a} \mp jb$ as a pair of conjugate roots, where $\bar{a} = a/(a^2 + b^2)$ and $\bar{b} = b/(a^2 + b^2)$. It is obvious that if c is positive (negative), $\bar{c}$ is positive (negative); if a is positive (negative), $\bar{a}$ is positive (negative). Therefore, $P(s)$ and $\bar{P}(\bar{s})$ must have the same number of roots with positive real parts.

2. We may multiply the given characteristic equation $P(s)$ by a factor $s + k$, where k is a positive quantity and $-k$ is not a root of $P(s)$. An auxiliary characteristic equation $\bar{P}(s) = P(s)(s + k)$ is obtained. The Routh's arrays of $P(s)$ and $\bar{P}(s)$ must give the *same* indication of stability. Therefore, we may construct a Routh's array for $\bar{P}(s)$ to determine the system stability for $P(s)$.

$P(s)$ and $\bar{P}(s)$ have the same stability indication since $s = -k$, as an additional root in $\bar{P}(s)$, is *not* one with a positive real part. $P(s)$ and $\bar{P}(s)$, therefore, must have the same number of roots with positive real parts.

Illustration 5.   We shall use remedy 1 above to determine the number of characteristic roots of (18.24*a*) having positive real parts. Substituting $s = 1/\bar{s}$ into (18.24*a*), we obtain an auxiliary characteristic equation

$$\bar{P}(\bar{s}) = 2\bar{s}^4 + 3\bar{s}^3 + 2\bar{s}^2 - 1 \tag{18.25a}$$

which has the following Routh's array:

$$\begin{array}{c|ccc} \bar{s}^4 & \begin{matrix}\not{2}\\1\end{matrix} & \begin{matrix}\not{2}\\1\end{matrix} & \begin{matrix}-\not{1}\\-\frac{1}{2}\end{matrix} \\ \bar{s}^3 & \begin{matrix}\not{3}\\1\end{matrix} & \begin{matrix}\not{0}\\0\end{matrix} & \\ \bar{s}^2 & 1 & -\frac{1}{2} & \\ \bar{s}^1 & \begin{matrix}\frac{1}{2}\\1\end{matrix} & & \\ \bar{s}^0 & \begin{matrix}-\frac{1}{2}\\-1\end{matrix} & & \end{array} \tag{18.25b}$$

An inspection of the first-column terms reveals one change of algebraic sign, from 1 to -1. This means that (18.24a) has one characteristic zero with a positive real part, and the system is unstable.

For further verification, we may solve (18.24a), finding $-1, +2$, and $(-1 \pm j\sqrt{3})/2$ as the characteristic zeros. The characteristic zero $+2 = +2 + j0$ has a positive real part.

Illustration 6. Let us use remedy 2 above to determine the number of characteristic zeros of (18.24a) having positive real parts. Substituting $s = -3$ into (18.24a), we note that $P(s) = P(-3) \neq 0$, and -3 is therefore not a root of $P(s) = 0$.

Letting $\bar{P}(s) = (s + 3)P(s)$, we obtain an auxiliary characteristic equation

$$\bar{P}(s) = s^5 + 3s^4 - 2s^3 - 9s^2 - 11s - 6 \qquad (18.26a)$$

which has the following Routh's array:

$$
\begin{array}{c|ccc}
s^5 & 1 & -2 & -11 \\
s^4 & \cancel{3} \;\; \cancel{-9} \;\; \cancel{-6} & & \\
    & 1 & -3 & -2 \\
s^3 & 1 & -9 & \\
s^2 & \cancel{6} \;\; \cancel{-2} & & \\
    & 1 & -\frac{1}{3} & \\
s^1 & -\cancel{\frac{28}{3}} & & \\
    & -1 & & \\
s^0 & -\cancel{\frac{1}{3}} & & \\
    & -1 & &
\end{array}
\qquad (18.26b)
$$

An inspection of the first-column term reveals one change of algebraic sign. This is consistent with our earlier result showing that there is only one characteristic zero of (18.24a) having a positive real part; the system is unstable.

PROBLEMS

18.1. Given: A differential equation which may have been obtained from a system of differential equations by eliminating all dependent variables except $x(t)$:

$$\left(a_k \frac{d^k}{dt^k} + a_{k-1}\frac{d^{k-1}}{dt^{k-1}} + \cdots + a_0\right)x = \left(b_n \frac{d^n}{dt^n} + b_{n-1}\frac{d^{n-1}}{dt^{n-1}} + \cdots + b_0\right)y \qquad (a)$$

where $y = y(t)$ represents the excitation to a system, and $x = x(t)$ represents the "interested" response.

(a) Find the Laplace transform of Eq. (a).

(b) Rearranging the result of part a to the form of Eq. (18.7), obtain the system function $T(s) = Q(s)/P(s)$ and the characteristic equation $P(s)$.

(c) In the classical method of solution of differential equations, we always first obtain a characteristic equation; the characteristic equation for the differential equation is

$$P(s) = a_k s^k + a_{k-1}s^{k-1} + \cdots + a_0 \qquad (b)$$

Compare (1) the characteristic equation obtained with the aid of Laplace transformation in part b and intended for the determination of system stability and (2) the characteristic equation (b) obtained by the classical method of solution of differential equations. Note that they are the *same* equation.

Using the Routh's criterion for stability, determine which of the characteristic equations in Probs. 18.2 through 18.12 have characteristic zeros in the right-hand half of the s plane and are, therefore, associated with unstable systems.

18.2. $P(s) = s^5 + 5s^4 + 23s^3 + 53s^2 + 106s + 120$
18.3. $P(s) = s^6 + 10s^5 + 5 \times 10^2 s^4 + 5 \times 10^3 s^3 + 10^4 s^2 + 5 \times 10^5 s + 4 \times 10^6$
18.4. $P(s) = 2s^5 + 3s^4 + 8s + 12$
18.5. $P(s) = s^8 + 7s^6 + 16s^4 + 28s^2 + 48$
18.6. $P(s) = s^5 + 4s^4 + 14s^3 + 42s^2 + 39s + 29$
18.7. $P(s) = s^6 + 5s^5 + 18s^4 + 56s^3 + 81s^2 + 68s + 29$
18.8. $P(s) = s^3 + s^2 - 3s + 1$
18.9. $P(s) = s^7 + 9s^5 + 23s^3 + 15s$
18.10. $P(s) = s^3 + 0.7s^2 + 0.02s + 0.015$
18.11. $P(s) = s^4 + 2s^2 + 3s + 1$
18.12. $P(s) = 81s^4 - 9 \times 10^4 s^2 + 15 \times 10^6 s - 2 \times 10^8$

18.13. Given: The closed-loop control system in Fig. 18.5c with characteristic function

$$W(s) = 1 + G(s)H(s) = 1 + \frac{K}{s(1 + 0.05s)(1 + 0.5s)}$$

where the system gain K is yet to be chosen for stable operation of the system.
   (a) Using the definition in (18.11b), find the characteristic equation $P(s)$, expressing some of its coefficients in terms of K.
   (b) Construct the Routh's array, also in terms of K.
   (c) Determine the values of K for stable operation of the system.
18.14. Repeat Prob. 18.13 for

$$W(s) = 1 + G(s)H(s) = 1 + \frac{K(s + 1)}{s(s + 2)(s^2 + s + 1)}$$

19 Nyquist criterion for stability[†]

19.1. Some practical considerations in the design of a closed-loop system

In general, the Routh's criterion for stability as described in the preceding chapter tells us if the system is unstable, but gives us no indication as to changes in design which would ensure system stability and improve system performance.

A. Some Remarks about the Nyquist Criterion for Stability

The Nyquist criterion for stability, like the Routh's criterion, is based upon the fundamental criterion for stability in (18.12) and applicable subject to assumption (18.13). The Nyquist diagram, which is a graph plotted in a complex plane, usually tells us whether there are zeros of the characteristic function $W(s) = 1 + G(s)H(s)$, as defined in (18.11a), in the right-hand half of the s plane. The Nyquist diagram as a graphical representation shows us the direction we must take to improve system design.

Some background material for the Nyquist criterion is provided in Art. 19.2; the Nyquist criterion itself is studied in Art. 19.3 and applied in the remaining portion of this chapter.

B. Some Remarks about the Root-locus Method

The root-locus method of closed-loop control-system design is based upon a relation between the characteristic zeros of the system and the poles and zeros of its open-loop transfer function. When a system parameter is changed, the characteristic zeros of the system also change. The loci of the characteristic zeros in the s plane subject to changes in the system parameter are studied, and a proper system parameter is chosen to ensure system stability in accordance with the fundamental criterion for stability.

We do not attempt to treat the root-locus method here; the interested reader is referred to the text by Evans.[‡] However, a description of this method in simple terms will be included here to serve as another illustration of the application of the fundamental criterion for stability to the study and design of a closed-loop control system.

Notation for a simple illustration. Let us consider the system with a direct-feedback loop as shown in Fig. 18.5b. This is a special case of Fig. 18.5c for $H(s) = 1$. Equation (18.11a), representing the characteristic function, now has the form

$$W(s) = 1 + G(s) \tag{19.1a}$$

where the transfer function $G(s)$ of the control element may be represented in terms

[†] H. Nyquist, Regeneration Theory, *Bell System Tech. J.*, vol. 11, pp. 126–147, 1932.

[‡] W. R. Evans, "Control-system Dynamics," McGraw-Hill Book Company, Inc., New York, 1954.

of its poles and zeros,

$$G(s) = \frac{K(s - r_1)(s - r_2) \cdots (s - r_m)}{(s - p_1)(s - p_2) \cdots (s - p_n)} \qquad (19.1b)$$

and K is the gain of the control element.

Description of the root locus.   The zeros of the characteristic function $W(s)$ are the characteristic zeros of the system according to their definitions in (18.11). If a zero of $W(s)$ is in the right-hand half of the s plane, the system is unstable. Therefore, we are interested in finding the locations of the zeros of $W(s)$.

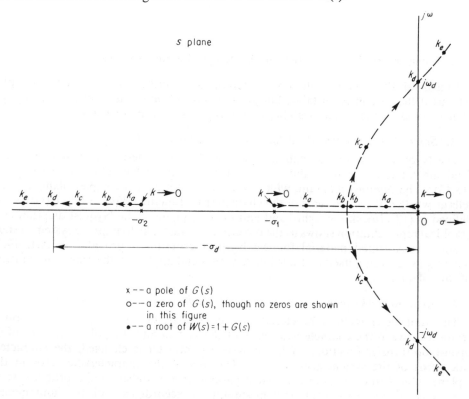

x -- a pole of $G(s)$
o -- a zero of $G(s)$, though no zeros are shown
    in this figure
● -- a root of $W(s) = 1 + G(s)$

FIG. 19.1

Let us assume in our illustration that the poles $p_1, p_2, \ldots, p_n$ and the zeros $r_1, r_2, \ldots, r_m$ of the transfer function $G(s)$ are known to us, while the gain K is to be determined.

But how are we to find the roots (i.e., zeros) of $W(s) = 1 + G(s)$, where K is an unknown quantity in $G(s)$?   It is suggested that the root loci be constructed for different values of K.   For example, the root loci for

$$W(s) = 1 + G(s) = 1 + \frac{K}{s(s + \sigma_1)(s + \sigma_2)} \qquad \sigma_2 > \sigma_1 > 0 \qquad (19.2)$$

are depicted by dashed lines in Fig. 19.1.   For very small K, say $K \to 0$, the characteristic zeros of $W(s)$ almost coincide with the poles of $G(s)$.   For each value of K, there are three characteristic zeros, as indicated in the figure.   When $K = K_a$, the characteristic zeros are $s = -\sigma_d$ and $s = \pm j\omega_d$ and a sustained oscillation occurs.

When the gain K is greater than K_d, for example, $K = K_e$, the system becomes unstable. With the root loci available, an appropriate gain K for the control element may be chosen.

Remarks about rules for the construction of root loci. The root-locus method owes its success as a design method to the ease with which the root loci can be constructed. There are many rules for the construction of the root loci; we shall not discuss them here. However, it is to be remarked that most of these rules are based upon a *phase relation*, to be discussed, and its special asymptotic cases.

Let

$$s_j = \text{characteristic zero of system}$$

$$= \text{zero of characteristic function according to (18.11)} \qquad (19.3a)$$

Using the notation in (19.1), we have

$$W(s_j) = 1 + G(s_j) = 0 \qquad (19.3b)$$

which implies

$$G(s_j) = -1 = 1\,\underline{/180° + k360°} \qquad k = \text{integer} \qquad (19.4a)$$

or

$$\frac{K(s_j - r_1)(s_j - r_2) \cdots (s_j - r_m)}{(s_j - p_1)(s_j - p_2) \cdots (s_j - p_n)} = 1\,\underline{/180° + k360°} \qquad (19.4b)$$

Considering $s_j - p_i = B_i\,\underline{/\beta_i}$ as a vector from the pole p_i to a point s_j, and $s_j - r_i = A_i\,\underline{/\alpha_i}$ as a vector from the zero r_i to a point s_j [as we did in Eq. (10.1) and Fig. 10.2, except that s_j here is not confined to the $j\omega$ axis of the s plane], we obtain from (19.4b) a *phase relation*

$$\sum_{i=1}^{m} \alpha_i - \sum_{i=1}^{n} \beta_i = 180° + k360° \qquad k = \text{integer} \qquad (19.5)$$

where
$$\alpha_i = \text{phase angle of vector from pole } p_i \text{ of } G(s) \text{ to point } s_j \text{ in } s \text{ plane} \quad (19.5a)$$
$$\beta_i = \text{phase angle of vector from zero } r_i \text{ of } G(s) \text{ to point } s_j \text{ in } s \text{ plane} \quad (19.5b)$$

To construct the root loci, i.e., the loci of the characteristic zeros or roots s_j of the system, is to find the loci of points s_j satisfying Eqs. (19.5).

19.2. An intuitive discussion of mapping

The Nyquist criterion for stability is often treated in a classical manner.† Here we attempt to (1) give an intuitive concept of conformal mapping and (2) discuss the Nyquist criterion in an intuitive manner. It is hoped that this intuitive approach will give the reader an understanding of the problem.

Throughout Arts. 19.2 and 19.3, we shall use $W(s)$ to represent the characteristic function as defined in (18.11a),

Characteristic function:

$$W(s) = 1 + G(s)H(s) \qquad (19.6a)$$

and assume that it may be represented in the following form:

$$W(s) = K\frac{(s - r_1)(s - r_2) \cdots (s - r_m)}{(s - p_1)(s - p_2) \cdots (s - p_n)} \qquad (19.6b)$$

where $r_1, r_2, \ldots, r_m$ are characteristic zeros of the system.

† See H. W. Bode, "Network Analysis and Feedback Amplifier Design," chap. 8, D. Van Nostrand Company, Inc., Princeton, N.J., 1945.

A. Correspondences between the s Plane and the W Plane

Illustration 1.   Let us arbitrarily choose a simple function,

$$W(s) = \frac{s+2}{s+1} \tag{19.7}$$

which may be expressed in the form

$$W(\sigma + j\omega) = \frac{\sigma + 2 + j\omega}{\sigma + 1 + j\omega} \frac{\sigma + 1 - j\omega}{\sigma + 1 - j\omega}$$

$$= \frac{(\sigma + 2)(\sigma + 1) + \omega^2}{(\sigma + 1)^2 + \omega^2} + j\frac{-\omega}{(\sigma + 1)^2 + \omega^2}$$

$$= U(\sigma, \omega) + jV(\sigma, \omega) \tag{19.8}$$

If we choose, as a reference point in the s plane (Fig. 19.2),

$$s_0 = -2 + j2 \tag{19.9a}$$

we find a corresponding reference point in the W plane with the aid of (19.8):

$$W_0 = W(s_0) = \frac{4 - j2}{5} \tag{19.9b}$$

W_0 is the *map* of s_0.   Similarly, if we trace various points (for example, $s_1 = 0 + j2$, $s_2 = -1 + j3$, $s_3 = -3 + j3$, $s_4 = -4 + j2, \ldots$) along a given closed curve C in the s plane, we may find their maps [for example, $W_1 = (6 - j2)/5$, $W_2 = (3 - j)/3$, $W_3 = (11 - j3)/13$, $W_4 = (10 - j2)/13, \ldots$] with the aid of (19.8) and construct a closed curve Σ in the W plane, where Σ is the map of C.

One-to-one correspondences as observed in illustration 1.   By examining the graphs in Fig. 19.2 and considering special cases, we observe the following correspondences:

s plane	*W plane*	
A *point* s_0 or s_1	A *point* W_0 or W_1	(19.10a)
An *open curve*, say $s_1 s_2 s_3 s_4$	An *open curve*, say $W_1 W_2 W_3 W_4$	(19.10b)
A *closed curve* C	A *closed curve* Σ	(19.10c)
A closed curve C *oriented* with respect to a reference point s_0	A closed curve Σ *similarly oriented* with respect to a reference point W_0	(19.10d)

To interpret the terms *oriented* and *similarly oriented* used above, consider the following:

1. By imagining oneself moving with a representative point s_R along C, one notes that s_0 is either on one's left or right.

2. As s_R moves along C, its map W_R moves along Σ.   By imagining oneself moving with W_R along Σ, one finds that W_0 (i.e., the map of s_0) is either on one's left or right.

3. If the reference points s_0 and W_0 are both on the *same* side of the traveler as he moves along C and Σ in the directions of s_R and W_R, then C and Σ are *similarly oriented* with respect to s_0 and W_0, respectively.

In the example of Fig. 19.2, s_R moves along C in the counterclockwise direction, with s_0 on its left.

Illustration 2.   Let us consider another function,

$$W(s) = s^2 \tag{19.11}$$

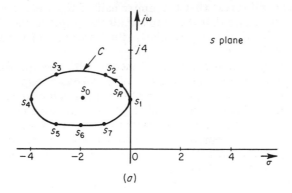

(a)

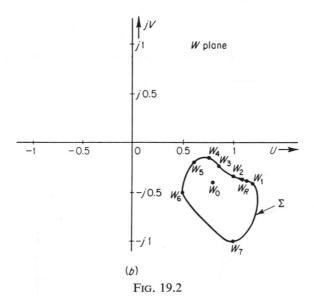

(b)

FIG. 19.2

which may be expressed in the form

$$W(\sigma + j\omega) = (\sigma + j\omega)^2 = \sigma^2 - \omega^2 + j2\sigma\omega$$
$$= U(\sigma, \omega) + jV(\sigma, \omega) \qquad (19.11a)$$

We may choose a closed curve C and a reference point s_0 in the s plane, as indicated in Fig. 19.3, and find their maps Σ and W_0 in the same manner as in Illustration 1. We find that relations (19.10) are satisfied between C, s_0 and Σ, W_0.

Let us now choose another closed curve C' and another reference point s_0' in the s plane, also indicated in Fig. 19.3, and find their maps Σ' and W_0' in the same manner as in Illustration 1. Relations (19.10) are also satisfied between C', s_0' and Σ', W_0'.

The concept of Riemann surface. In Illustration 2, it seems that we have two-to-one (instead of one-to-one) correspondence, as evidenced by s_4 and s_4' having the same map $W_4 (= W_4')$. This is because we have a multiple-valued function. We may rewrite (19.11) as $s = \pm W^{\frac{1}{2}}$, which is equivalent to two single-valued functions $s = W^{\frac{1}{2}}$ and $s = -W^{\frac{1}{2}}$. For a given value of W, we find two values of s. A study of Eq. (19.11) will reveal that the upper half of the s plane has the entire W plane as its map in the sense that the maps of all the points in the upper half of the s plane cover the entire W plane.   Similarly, the lower half of the s plane also has the entire W plane as its map.

In order to visualize a multiple-valued function with the simplicity of a single-valued function, we introduce the concept of a *Riemann surface*.   In the above illustration, let us consider that (1) the map of the upper half of the s plane is printed on a transparent sheet, which we shall call sheet 1 of a Riemann surface, and (2) the map of the lower half of the s plane is printed on another transparent sheet called sheet 2; the W plane is a Riemann surface which is a superposition of these two sheets.   When a continuous curve crosses the positive σ axis of the s plane, its map crosses from one sheet of the Riemann surface to another.

A Riemann surface is therefore an idealized representation of a plane using a number of superimposed sheets, so that a multiple-valued function may be studied in the same manner as a single-valued function.

B. The Zeros of $W(s)$ and Their Maps in the W plane

Illustration 3.   A zero and its map.   Again we shall use the function in (19.7),

$$W(s) = \frac{s+2}{s+1} = \frac{s-r_1}{s-p_1} \tag{19.12}$$

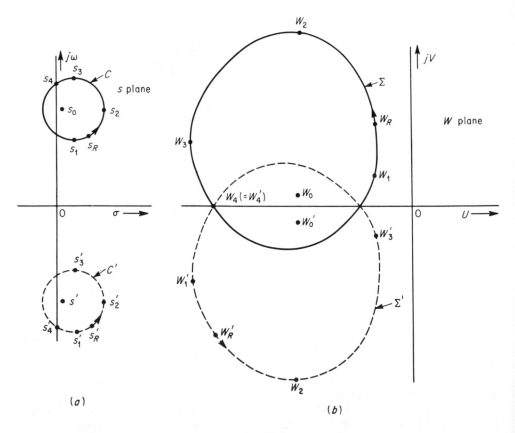

(a)

(b)

FIG. 19.3

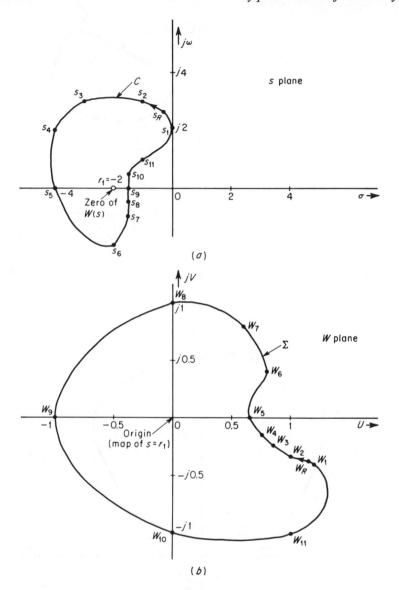

FIG. 19.4

which has $r_1 = -2$ as a zero.   We now have the following correspondence:

s plane	W plane
$s = r_1$ [zero of $W(s)$]	$W = 0$ (origin of W plane) (19.12a)

Suppose we trace the various points, for example, $s_1 = j2$, $s_2 = -1 + j3$, $s_3 = -3 + j3$, $s_4 = -4 + j2$, $s_5 = -4$, $s_6 = -2 - j2$, $s_7 = -(3 + j2)/2$, $s_8 = -(3 + j)/2$, $s_9 = -3/2$, $s_{10} = -(3 - j)/2$, $s_{11} = -1 + j$, along an arbitrarily chosen closed curve C around r_1 in the s plane, as depicted in Fig. 19.4. We may find the maps of these points with the aid of (19.12) or (19.8) and construct a closed curve Σ in the W plane, where Σ is the map of C.

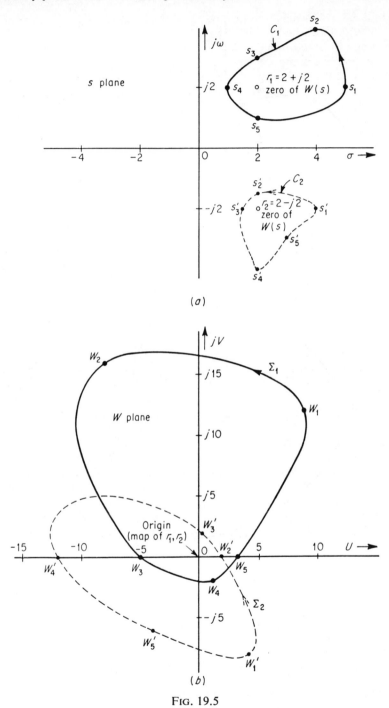

(a)

(b)

FIG. 19.5

Correspondences observed in Illustration 3.   It is easy to see that the correspondences listed in (19.10) are satisfied.

With changes in notation, (19.10d) may be rewritten in this manner: The map of a closed curve C encircling a single zero r_1 of $W(s)$ in the s plane in the counterclockwise direction is a closed curve Σ encircling the origin of the W plane in the counterclockwise direction.   Figure 19.4 depicts (1) the representative point s_R on the curve C encircling r_1 in the counterclockwise direction and (2) its map W_R on the curve Σ encircling the origin of the W plane in the counterclockwise direction.

Illustration 4.   Two zeros and their maps.   Let us use the function

$$W(s) = s^2 - 4s + 8 = (s - r_1)(s - r_2) = [s - (2 + j2)][s - (2 - j2)] \quad (19.13)$$

which has $r_1, r_2 = 2 \pm j2$ as zeros.   We now have the following correspondences:

s plane	*W* plane	
$s = r_1$ [zero of $W(s)$]	$W = 0$ (origin of W plane)	
$s = r_2$ [zero of $W(s)$]	$W = 0$ (origin of W plane)	(19.13a)

Suppose we arbitrarily draw two closed curves C_1 and C_2, respectively, around r_1 and r_2, as depicted in Fig. 19.5.   We first trace the various points, for example, $s_1 = 5 + j2$, $s_2 = 4 + j4$, $s_3 = 2 + j3$, $s_4 = 1 + j2$, $s_5 = 2 + j$, along the closed curve C_1 around r_1 in the s plane, then find their maps with the aid of (19.13), and finally join them to form a closed curve Σ_1 in the W plane. Σ_1 is the map of C_1. Similarly, we may trace the various points, for example, $s_1' = 4 - j2$, $s_2' = 2 - j\frac{3}{2}$, $s_3' = \frac{3}{2} - j2$, $s_4' = 2 - j4$, $s_5' = 3 - j3$, along the closed curve C_2 around r_2 in the s plane and construct Σ_2 in the W plane, where Σ_2 is the map of C_2.

In this illustration and Fig. 19.5 we note that the correspondences listed in (19.10) are satisfied by C_1 and Σ_1, with $s = r_1$ and $W = 0$ as their respective reference points, and by C_2 and Σ_2, with $s = r_2$ and $W = 0$ as their respective reference points. With changes in notation, (19.10d) may be rewritten in this manner: The maps of two closed curves C_1 and C_2 encircling two zeros r_1 and r_2 of $W(s)$ in the counterclockwise direction in the s plane are two closed curves Σ_1 and Σ_2 encircling the origin of the W plane in the counterclockwise direction.

Illustration 5.   A modified version of Illustration 4.   Figure 19.6a follows from Illustration 4 and Fig. 19.5a.   Here we have two portions of C_1 and C_2 arbitrarily close; as a consequence, two portions of Σ_1 and Σ_2 are arbitrarily close.

When we let a coincide with e, and b coincide with d, and leave out the ab and ed portions of C_1 and C_2, Fig. 19.6a reduces to Fig. 19.6b.   Here we note the following: The map of a closed curve C encircling *two* zeros r_1 and r_2 of $W(s)$ in the counterclockwise direction in the s plane is a closed curve Σ encircling the origin of the W plane *twice* in the counterclockwise direction.

This property may be generalized for an arbitrary number of zeros.   Also, if we choose C to encircle zeros in the clockwise direction, its map Σ is found to encircle the origin of W plane in the clockwise direction.   Summarizing our present discussion, we have the following criterion:

Criterion A.   Concerning the encirclement of the zeros of $W(s)$.   The map of a closed curve C encircling Z zeros and no poles of $W(s)$ in the counterclockwise direction in the s plane is a closed curve encircling the origin of the W plane Z times in the counterclockwise direction.

C. The Poles in the s plane and Their Maps in the W Plane

Illustration 6.   A pole and its map.   Again we shall use the function in (19.7),

$$W(s) = \frac{s + 2}{s + 1} = \frac{s - r_1}{s - p_1} \quad (19.14)$$

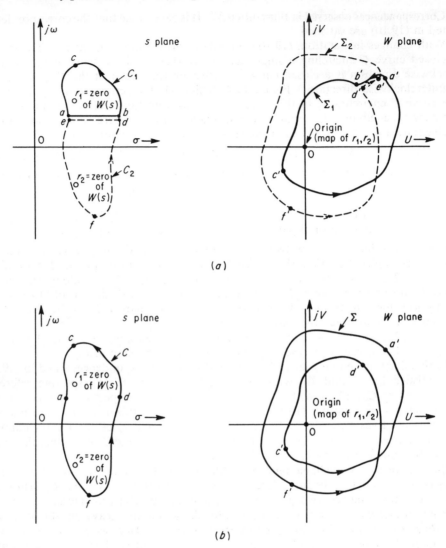

FIG. 19.6 [The graphs in this figure are not plotted for any given function $W(s)$, but are arbitrarily sketched for the illustration of some specific properties.]

which has a pole at $p_1 = -1$. We now have the following correspondence:

s plane	*W plane*
$s = p_1$ [pole of $W(s)$]	$W = \infty$ (points at infinity of W plane, with W_∞ as representative symbol) (19.14a)

Suppose we trace the various points, for example, $s_1 = j2$, $s_2 = -1 + j2$, $s_3 = -2 + j$, $s_4 = -\frac{3}{2}$, $s_5 = -1 - j$, $s_6 = -j$, $s_7 = 1 + j$, along an arbitrarily chosen curve C around p_1 in the s plane, as depicted in Fig. 19.7. We may find the maps of these points with the aid of (19.14) and construct a closed curve Σ in the W plane, where Σ is the map of C.

It is easy to see that the correspondences listed in (19.10) are satisfied here. Let us imagine ourselves moving with the representative points s_R and W_R along C and Σ in Fig. 19.7. We *observe* that (1) $s = p_1$ is on our *left* as we move along C and (2) W_∞ is *also* on our *left* as we move along Σ; we therefore *conclude* that C and Σ are *similarly oriented* with respect to p_1 and W_∞.

But we also note in Fig. 19.7 that as the representative point s_R moves along C in the counterclockwise direction, its map W_R *must* move along Σ in the clockwise direction in order that C and Σ be *similarly oriented* with respect to p_1 and W_∞.

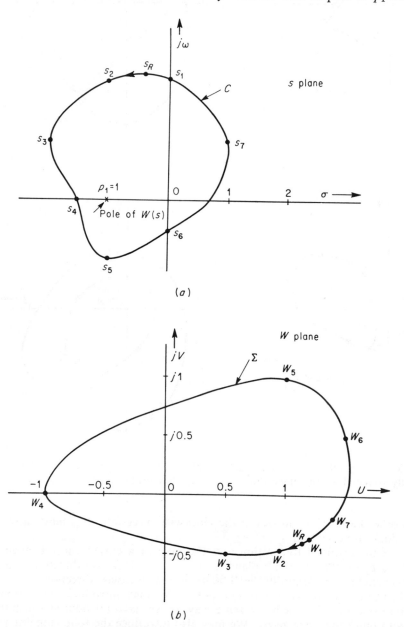

(a)

(b)

FIG. 19.7

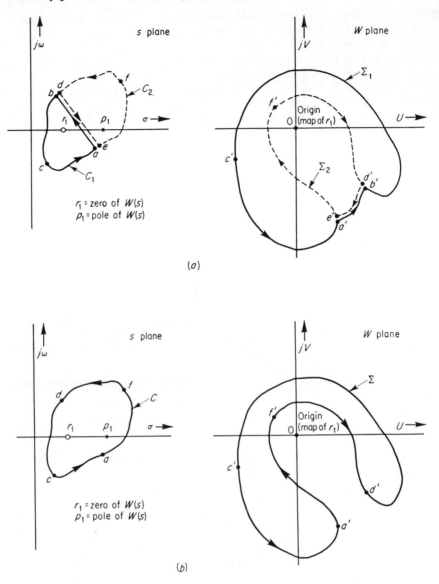

FIG. 19.8   [The graphs in this figure are not plotted for any given function $W(s)$, but are arbitrarily sketched for the illustration of some specific properties.]

On the other hand, if s_R moves in the clockwise direction, W_R *must* move in the counterclockwise direction.

We state the result of Illustration 6:   The map of a closed curve C encircling a single pole p_1 of $W(s)$ in the s plane in the counterclockwise direction is a closed curve Σ encircling the origin of the W plane in the clockwise direction.

In Illustration 6, we have only one pole.   We may introduce illustrations with more than one pole in much the same way as we have introduced Illustrations 4 and 5 with more than one zero.   We may also introduce the following criterion for the poles of $W(s)$, corresponding to Criterion A for the zeros.

Criterion B.   Concerning the encirclement of the poles of $W(s)$.   The map of a closed curve C encircling P poles and no zeros of $W(s)$ in the counterclockwise direction in the s plane is a closed curve Σ encircling the origin of the W plane P times in the clockwise direction.

D. A Criterion Concerning the Encirclement of the Poles and Zeros of $W(s)$

Illustration 7.   One pole and one zero.   We use two closed curves C_1 and C_2 to encircle a zero r_1 and a pole p_1 of $W(s)$, as indicated in Fig. 19.8.   The map of curve C_1 encircling r_1 in the counterclockwise direction is a closed curve Σ_1 encircling the

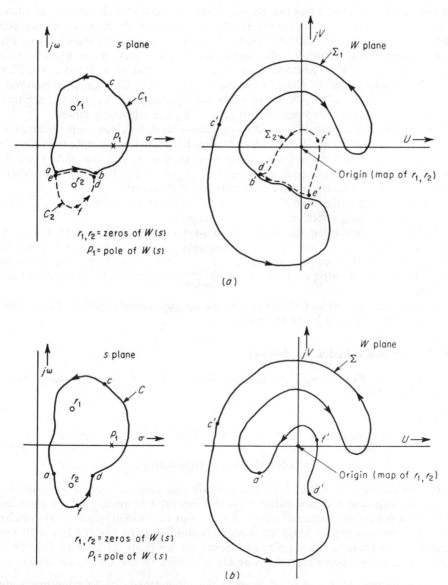

FIG. 19.9 [The graphs in this figure are not plotted for any given function $W(s)$, but are arbitrarily sketched for the illustration of some specific properties.]

origin of the W plane in the counterclockwise direction as prescribed by Criterion A in Art. 19.2B.   The map of curve C_2 encircling p_1 in the counterclockwise direction is a closed curve Σ_2 encircling the origin of the W plane in the clockwise direction as prescribed by Criterion B in Art. 19.2C.   Now we draw two portions of C_1 and C_2 arbitrarily close; as a consequence, two portions of Σ_1 and Σ_2 are arbitrarily close.

When we let a coincide with e, and b coincide with d, and leave out the ab and de portions of C_1 and C_2, Fig. 19.8a reduces to Fig. 19.8b.   Here we note the following: The map Σ of a closed curve C encircling one zero r_1 and one pole p_1 of $W(s)$ in the counterclockwise direction does not encircle (or encircles $Z - P = 1 - 1 = 0$ times) the origin of the W plane.

Illustration 8.   One pole and two zeros.   Here we use a closed curve C_1 to encircle a pole p_1 and a zero r_1 in the counterclockwise direction; its map is a closed curve Σ_1 not encircling the origin of the W plane (Fig. 19.9a), as was illustrated in Fig. 19.8b and discussed in Illustration 7.   We use another closed curve C_2 to encircle a zero r_2 in Fig. 19.9a in the counterclockwise direction; its map is a closed curve Σ_2 encircling the origin of the W plane in the counterclockwise direction as prescribed by Criterion A in Art. 19.2B.   Now we draw two portions of C_1 and C_2 arbitrarily close; as a consequence, two portions of Σ_1 and Σ_2 are arbitrarily close.

When we let a coincide with e, and b coincide with d, and leave out the ab and de portions of C_1 and C_2, Fig. 19.9a reduces to Fig. 19.9b.   Here we note the following: The map Σ of a closed curve C encircling two zeros r_1, r_2 and one pole p_1 of $W(s)$ in the counterclockwise direction encircles the origin of the W plane once (that is, $Z - P = 2 - 1 = 1$ time) in the counterclockwise direction.

Similarly, we may illustrate Z zeros $r_1, r_2, \ldots, r_Z$ and P poles $p_1, p_2, \ldots, p_P$ to arrive at the following criterion:

Criterion C.   Concerning the encirclement of the poles and zeros of $W(s)$.   The map of a closed curve C encircling Z zeros (say $r_1, r_2, \ldots, r_Z$) and P poles (say $p_1, p_2, \ldots, p_P$) of $W(s)$ in the counterclockwise direction in the s plane is a closed curve Σ encircling the origin of the W plane $Z - P$ times in the counterclockwise† direction.

This criterion, as well as Criteria A and B, applies equally well if the directions of encirclement of C and Σ are reversed.

19.3.   The Nyquist criterion for stability

A.   *A Criterion Concerning the Poles and Zeros of $W(s)$ in the Right-hand Half of the s plane*

We shall let

$$Z = \text{number of zeros of } W(s) \text{ in right-hand half of } s \text{ plane}$$

(19.15)

$$P = \text{number of poles of } W(s) \text{ in right-hand half of } s \text{ plane}$$

For the special case in which $W(s)$ has no poles or zeros along the $j\omega$ axis of the s plane, we may use a closed curve C as the idealized boundary of the right-hand half of the s plane, as indicated in Fig. 19.10a.   For the case in which $W(s)$ does have poles and zeros on the $j\omega$ axis, we need only modify C in Fig. 19.10a with small indentations to exclude these poles and zeros, as we shall do later in Fig. 19.16a. Assuming that the representative point on C moves in the clockwise direction as

† An encirclement of $Z - P = -3$ times in the counterclockwise direction means three times in the clockwise direction; an encirclement of -2 times in the clockwise direction means two times in the counterclockwise direction.

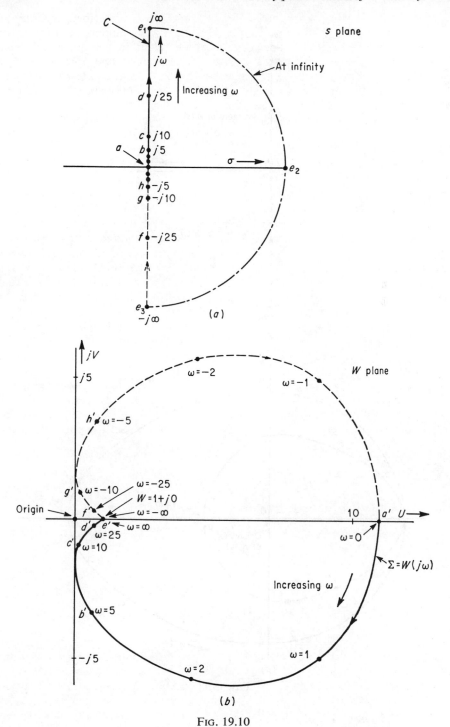

FIG. 19.10

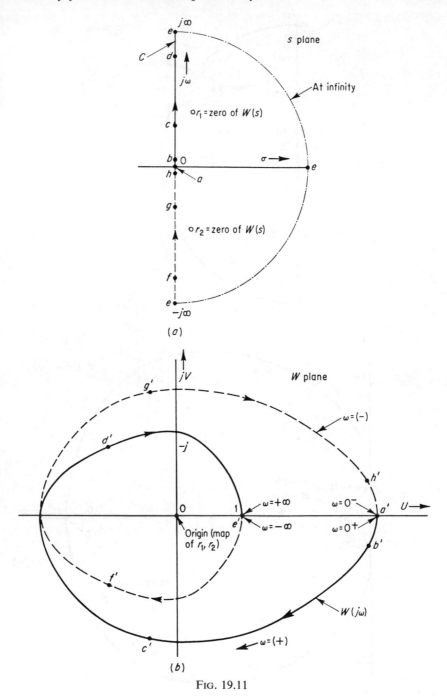

FIG. 19.11

indicated by the arrows along C in Fig. 19.10a, we may plot its map Σ in the W plane. According to Criterion C, the number of encirclements of Σ around the origin of the W plane in the clockwise direction is $Z - P$, where Z and P are defined in (19.15). Summarizing, we have:

Criterion D. If we use the idealized boundary, for example, *abcdefgha* as depicted in Fig. 19.10a, as a closed curve C encircling the right-hand half of the s plane in the clockwise direction, the map of C as prescribed by a given function $W(s)$ is a closed curve Σ encircling the origin of the W plane $Z - P$ times in the clockwise direction, where Z and P are defined in (19.15).

Illustration 1. $Z = 0$ **and** $P = 0$. Let us consider a characteristic function as defined in (18.11a) and (19.6a):

$$W(s) = 1 + G(s)H(s) = 1 + \frac{10}{(1 + 0.5s)(1 + 0.1s)} \tag{19.16}$$

We first choose C to be the idealized boundary for the right-hand half of the s plane and assume that the representative point on C moves in the clockwise direction, as indicated by the arrow in Fig. 19.10a. We now trace the various points, for example, $s = j0$, $s = j1$, $s = j2$, $s = j5$, $s = j10$, $s = j25$, $s = j\infty$, $s = \infty + j0$, $s = -j\infty$, $s = -j25$, $s = -j10$, $s = -j5$, $s = -j2$, $s = -j1$, $s = -j0$, along C and find their maps with the aid of (19.16), constructing a closed curve Σ in Fig. 19.10b. For instance, the map of $s = j5$ is $W(j5) = 1 + 10/(1 + 0.5 \times j5)(1 + 0.1 \times j5) = 0.725 - j3.31$; $s = j5$ and its map are the points b and b' in Fig. 19.10. Σ is the map of C. We note that Σ does *not* encircle the origin of the W plane.

This is a rather trivial example. We may easily solve for the poles and zeros of $W(s)$ in (19.16) and find that none of them are in the right-hand half of the s plane. This means $P = 0$ and $Z = 0$. According to Criterion D, Σ encircles the origin of the W plane $P - Z = 0$ times. It checks with the observed result.

The $W(j\omega)$ **diagram.** We note in the above illustration that all points at infinity in the s plane have the same map $W = 1 + j0$. For example, by substituting $s = +j\infty$, $s = \infty + j0$, and $s = -j\infty$ into (19.16), we obtain $W(+j\infty) = W(\infty + j0) = W(-j\infty) = 1$.

This will also be true for other illustrations. For most practical problems, we shall expect that the gain $|G(s)| \to 0$ for $s = j\omega$ as the frequency $\omega \to \infty$; consequently $|G(s)H(s)| \to 0$ for $s \to \infty$, where $G(s)$ and $H(s)$ are transfer functions as depicted in Fig. 18.5c. We shall then find $W(s) = 1 + G(s)H(s) \to 1$ for $s \to \infty$.

As is evident in Fig. 19.10b, Σ, as the map of C, is plotted with $W(j\omega)$, where ω changes (1) from $\omega = 0^+$ to $\omega = \infty$ and (2) from $\omega = -\infty$ to $\omega = 0^-$. We may very well label Σ the "$W(j\omega)$ diagram."

Some remarks about the construction of the $W(j\omega)$ **diagram.** Since $W(s) = 1 + G(s)H(s)$ is a rational function of s and representable as a ratio of two polynomials of s with real coefficients, $W(j\omega)$ and $W(-j\omega)$ are conjugate functions in the form $U \pm jV$. This is why the two portions of $W(j\omega)$ for $\omega = (+)$ and $\omega = (-)$ are symmetrical with respect to the U axis, as illustrated in Fig. 19.11b. In the construction of a $W(j\omega)$ diagram, we therefore need only (1) plot $W(j\omega)$ with a set of positive values of ω for its positive-frequency portion, as depicted by the solid curve in Fig. 19.11b, and (2) construct the negative-frequency portion of the $W(j\omega)$ diagram through *symmetry* with respect to the U axis, as depicted by the dashed curve in Fig. 19.11b.

We may now restate Criterion D in the following form:

Criterion E. Concerning the poles and zeros of $W(s)$ **in the right-hand half of the** s **plane.** The $W(j\omega)$ diagram constructed by assuming increasing values of ω from $\omega = 0^+$ to ∞ and then from $\omega = -\infty$ to $\omega = 0^-$ is a closed curve (1) encircling the origin of the W plane $Z - P$ times in the clockwise direction if $Z > P$, where Z and P are, respectively, the numbers of zeros and poles of $W(s)$ in the right-hand half of the s plane, (2) encircling the origin $P - Z$ times in the counterclockwise direction if $P > Z$, and (3) not encircling the origin if $P = Z$.

Illustration 2. Figure 19.11 depicts a typical $W(j\omega)$ diagram for a characteristic function $W(s)$ which has two zeros but no poles in the right-hand half of the s plane; that is, $Z = 2$ and $P = 0$.

B. A Suggested Method for Determining System Stability

Description of problem. As implied in Art. 19.1A, a system is unstable if any of the zeros of its characteristic function

$$W(s) = 1 + G(s)H(s) \tag{19.17}$$

are in the right-hand half of the s plane.   We now wish to determine system stability using this property.

Procedure. With the notation in (19.15), the discussion in Art. 19.3A suggests this procedure:

> Find $Z - P$ by applying Criterion E in Art. 19.3A or the Nyquist criterion, which is a modified form of Criterion E to be given in Art. 19.3C $\tag{19.18a}$

> Find P by inspection or by applying Routh's criterion to the denominator of $W(s)$ or $G(s)H(s)$ $\tag{19.18b}$

> $Z = (Z - P) + P$, where $Z - P$ and P are determined in the two preceding steps. If $Z = 0$, the system is stable; if $Z \neq 0$, the system is unstable $\tag{19.18c}$

Some remarks about this suggested method. Let us now look into this question: Are all the steps in (19.18) really necessary for most practical problems?   We shall find that the following siuations exist:

1. In most practical problems, there are no poles of $W(s)$ in the right-hand half of the s plane, that is, $P = 0$.   In other words, $G(s)$ and $H(s)$ as transfer functions depicted in Fig. 18.5c have no poles in the right-hand half of the s plane.   The procedure in (19.18) therefore reduces to the mere application of the Nyquist criterion. This is why a number of textbooks prescribe system stability to be determined merely by application of the Nyquist criterion.

2. If there is doubt whether $P = 0$ or $P \neq 0$, we may find P by inspection or by applying Routh's criterion.   The characteristic function is usually represented with $G(s)H(s)$ in a factored form, for example,

$$W(s) = 1 + G(s)H(s)$$
$$= 1 + \frac{K(1 + \tau_1 s)(1 + \tau_2 s) \cdots}{s^n(1 + T_1 s)(-1 + T_2 s)(1 + 2\eta T_3 s + T_3{}^2 s^2)} \tag{19.19a}$$

where K, τ_1, τ_2, T_1, T_2, T_3, T_4, and η are positive quantities, and n is an integer, *or* in a more complicated form which is readily reducible to

$$W(s) = 1 + G(s)H(s) = 1 + K\frac{\text{polynomial of } s}{\text{another polynomial of } s} \tag{19.19b}$$

Since the poles of $G(s)H(s)$ are also the poles of $W(s)$, P also represents the number of the poles of $G(s)H(s)$ in the right-hand half of the s plane.   If $W(s)$ is of the form (19.19a), P may be determined by inspection.   For the specific example in (19.19a), we have a pole at $s = 1/T_2$ which is in the right-hand half of the s plane, and $P = 1$. If $W(s)$ is of the form (19.19b), P may be determined with the aid of Routh's criterion.

C. The Nyquist Diagram and Its Interpretation for System Stability

A translation of coordinates.   Procedure (19.18), in conjunction with Criterion E, tells us how to determine system stability.   According to this procedure, we must plot a $W(j\omega)$ diagram, where

$$W(s) = 1 + G(s)H(s) \tag{19.20a}$$

is the characteristic function of the system under investigation.   For example, we have plotted $W(j\omega) = U(\omega) + jV(\omega)$ in the W plane in Figs. 19.10 and 19.11 and tried to determine the number of encirclements of the origin of the W plane for each case as an indication of stability.

From (19.20a), we have

$$G(j\omega)H(j\omega) = W(j\omega) - 1 = [U(\omega) - 1] + jV(\omega) \tag{19.20b}$$

This means that we may translate the coordinate axes, obtaining $W = 1 + j0$ as the origin of a new GH plane.   An illustration is shown in Fig. 19.12.   Criterion E then must be appropriately modified; its modified version is the so-called "Nyquist criterion."   With a $G(j\omega)H(j\omega)$ diagram plotted as illustrated in Fig. 19.12b, we try to determine the number of encirclements of the critical point -1 in the GH plane, which corresponds to the origin of the W plane, as an indication of stability discussed in (19.18).   The $G(j\omega)H(j\omega)$ diagram is the so-called "Nyquist diagram."

Open-loop transfer function.   Opening the feedback loop of the closed-loop system in Fig. 19.13a as shown in Fig. 19.13b, we may define

Open-loop transfer function:

$$G(s)H(s) = \frac{B(s)}{R(s)} = \frac{\text{open-loop feedback}}{\text{reference input}} \tag{19.21}$$

as the open-loop transfer function.   The Nyquist diagram in the form of $G(j\omega)H(j\omega)$ is actually a graphical plot of the open-loop transfer function at the real frequencies $s = j\omega$.

The advantages of using the GH-plane representation.   The principal advantage of using the GH-plane representation instead of the W-plane representation lies in the fact that the former is directly associated with the readily measurable *physical* quantity $G(j\omega)H(j\omega)$.

There are also other advantages in using the GH-plane representation.   For example, we may conveniently use polar representations of $G(j\omega)$ and $H(j\omega)$ to obtain $G(j\omega)H(j\omega)$ in the GH plane.   For $G(j\omega_1) = G_1 e^{j\phi_1}$ and $H(j\omega_1) = H_1 e^{j\psi_1}$ at a particular frequency ω_1, we may conveniently plot $G(j\omega_1)H(j\omega_1)$ in polar coordinates with magnitude $G_1 H_1$ and phase $\phi_1 + \psi_1$.

We often have $G(s)H(s)$ in the form as indicated in (19.19a) or (19.19b), where the system gain K is to be adjusted for stable system operation.   For example, suppose

$$G(s)H(s) = K \frac{s^3 + 8s + 8}{6s^3 + 16s^2 + 56s + 32} \tag{19.22}$$

and we wish to determine a value of K such that the system will be stable.   We may plot the $G(j\omega)H(j\omega)$ diagram in Fig. 19.14a with an arbitrary K, say $K = 15$; we find that this diagram encircles the critical point -1, and the system is unstable. Since we are using GH-plane representation, the system gain K is our scale factor, as is obvious in (19.22).   Scaling K down to a smaller value, say $K = 10$, we obtain the $G(j\omega)H(j\omega)$ diagram in Fig. 19.14*b* which does not encircle the critical point -1; the system is then a stable one.

Combining Criterion E and (19.18) for the GH plane, we obtain the Nyquist criterion as follows:

Nyquist criterion.   *Let P be the number of poles of the open-loop transfer function G(s)H(s) of a closed-loop system in the right-hand half of the s plane.   Let the Nyquist diagram G(jω)H(jω) of this system, which is traced in the direction of increasing ω, encircle the critical point −1 in the GH plane N times in the clockwise direction.   The*

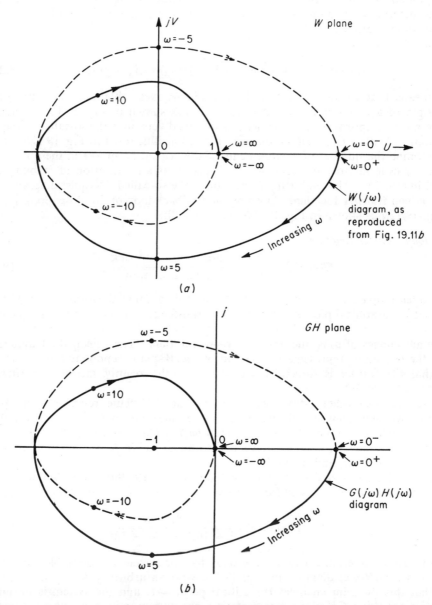

(a)

(b)

FIG. 19.12

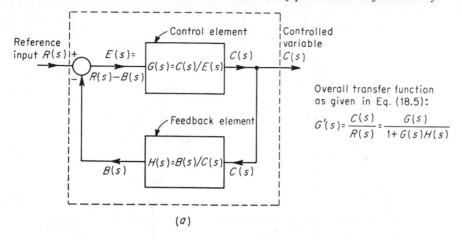

(a)

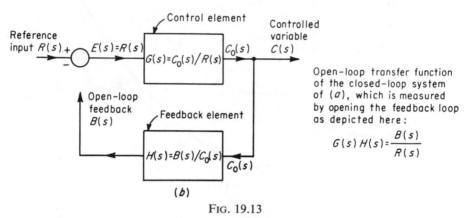

(b)

FIG. 19.13

system is stable under the conditions (1) $N = 0$ *and* $P = 0$ *or* (2) $N < 0$ *and* $P + N = 0$, *and unstable under all other conditions, namely,* (3) $N > 0$, (4) $N = 0$ *and* $P \neq 0$, *or* (5) $N < 0$ *and* $N + P > 0$.

To determine P, follow (19.18b). If the Nyquist diagram is found to encircle the critical point **—1** in the counterclockwise direction, use a *negative N*, where $N = $ —(number of counterclockwise encirclements).

Since, in different closed-loop systems, different symbols are used for the "open-loop transfer functions" or "return ratios," the Nyquist criterion given above may have to be modified slightly [by allowing appropriate symbols to replace $G(s)H(s)$ or GH] for different applications: (1) In a closed-loop control system in general, $G(s)H(s)$ is used for the "open-loop transfer function," and the above criterion is used without modification. (2) In a vacuum-tube feedback amplifier, $G(s)H(s)$, $G(s)\beta$, $-A\beta$, $-K\beta$, T, or $-\mu\beta$ is used for the "return ratio."† (3) In a transistor

† Some authors use $A\beta$, $K\beta$, and $\mu\beta$ for the "loop transmission," and $-A\beta$, $-K\beta$, and $T = -\mu\beta$ for the "return ratio." See, for example, J. D. Ryder, "Engineering Electronics," chap. 7, McGraw-Hill Book Company, Inc., New York, 1957; L. B. Arguimbau, "Vacuum Tube Circuits," chap. 8, John Wiley & Sons, Inc., New York, 1948; Bode, *op. cit.*, pp. 153–155. Some other authors call $A\beta$ and $\mu\beta$ the "return ratio." See, for example, P. E. Pfeiffer, "Linear Systems Analysis," p. 475, McGraw-Hill Book Company, Inc., New York, 1961. Reference is made to Prob. 19.13, which shows the reader how to use the Nyquist criterion under these various conditions.

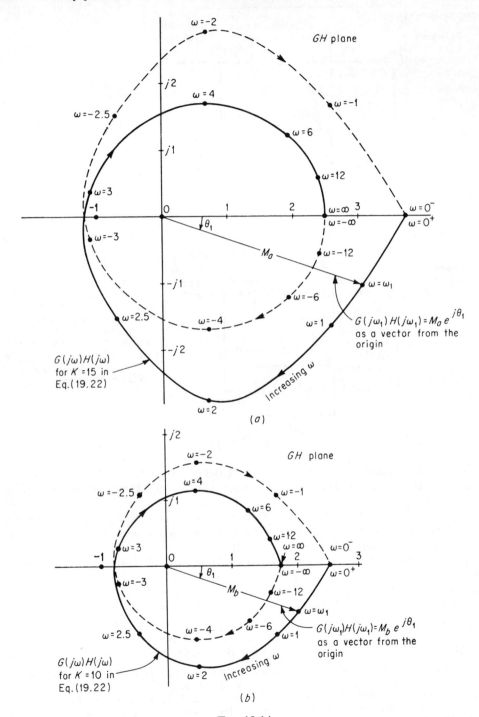

FIG. 19.14

feedback amplifier, $T_{p'p}$ or $T(s)$ is used for the "return ratio," as defined in (15.2c) and (15.6c).

The Nyquist criterion is based upon the fundamental criterion of stability and prescribes a method for determining the number Z of characteristic zeros of the system in the right-hand half of the s plane. If $Z \neq 0$, the system is unstable. The characteristic zeros of the system are the zeros of its characteristic function $W(s) = 1 + G(s)H(s)$ as depicted in Eq. (18.11a) or (19.6a). By comparing with (19.18), we note that the Nyquist criterion determines the value of $Z = N + P$ and interprets the system stability accordingly.

Remark 1. Concerning the construction of the negative-frequency portion of the Nyquist diagram $G(j\omega)H(j\omega)$. Since the Nyquist diagram $G(j\omega)H(j\omega)$ is nothing but the $W(j\omega)$ diagram discussed in Art. 19.3A and B with a new origin for its coordinate system (Fig. 19.12), the method of constructing the $W(j\omega)$ diagram can be applied. For a given open-loop transfer function $G(s)H(s)$, we may *plot $G(j\omega)H(j\omega)$ for the positive frequencies, say from $\omega = 0^+$ to $\omega = \infty$, and then construct the negative-frequency portion of $G(j\omega)H(j\omega)$ through symmetry with respect to the real horizontal axis.* For example, we may plot the positive-frequency portion of the $G(j\omega)H(j\omega)$ diagram for the function $G(s)H(s)$ in (19.22) with $K = 15$ by (1) assuming various values of ω, for example, $\omega = 0^+$, $\omega = 1$, $\omega = 2, \ldots$, and (2) computing the values of $G(j\omega)H(j\omega)$ using (19.22) with $s = j\omega$, for example, $G(j0)H(j0) = 3.75$, $G(j1)H(j1) = 2.59 - j1.65$, $G(j2)H(j2) = 0.75 - j2.75, \ldots$. The positive-frequency portion of the Nyquist diagram plotted with the computed values is depicted as the solid curve in Fig. 19.14a. The negative-frequency portion (dashed curve) is constructed through symmetry with respect to the real horizontal axis.

Remark 2. Concerning the construction of the Nyquist diagram $G(j\omega)H(j\omega)$ at or near infinity in the GH plane. We have shown examples in which the Nyquist diagram $G(j\omega)H(j\omega)$ is entirely contained in the finite region of the GH plane as depicted in Fig. 19.14. Two exceptions arise (1) when $G(s)H(s)$ has poles on the $j\omega$ axis and (2) when $G(s)H(s)$ has poles in the right-hand half of the s plane, arbitrarily close to the $j\omega$ axis.

Case 1. Poles of $G(s)H(s)$ on the $j\omega$ axis. Let us assume that $p_1 = j\omega_1$ for $\omega_1 \geq 0$ is a pole of $G(s)H(s)$. We expect that $G(j\omega)H(j\omega) \to \infty$ in the infinite region of the GH plane as $\omega \to \omega_1$. To construct the Nyquist diagram for the frequency range including ω_1, we may (1) plot $G(j\omega)H(j\omega)$ for the various values of ω except between $\omega_1^- = \omega_1 - \epsilon$ and $\omega_1^+ = \omega_1 + \epsilon$, where ϵ is an arbitrarily chosen small positive quantity, and (2) join the two points $G(j\omega_1^-)H(j\omega_1^-)$ and $G(j\omega_1^+)H(j\omega_1^+)$ in the GH plane with a curve representing a portion of the circumference of an arbitrarily large circle, such that the representative point G_R moves *clockwise* in the direction of increasing ω, that is, from ω_1^- to ω_1^+.

For example,

$$G(s)H(s) = \frac{25}{s(1 + s)(1 + 0.25s)} \tag{19.23}$$

has a pole at $s = j0$. We may plot its $G(j\omega)H(j\omega)$ diagram for $\omega = 0^+$ to $\omega = \infty$ ($b'c'd'e'$ in Fig. 19.15b) and for $\omega = -\infty$ to $\omega = 0^-$ ($e'f'g'h'$). We now wish to connect b' (for $\omega = 0^+$) and h' (for $\omega = 0^-$). According to the suggested procedure, the Nyquist diagram for (19.23) is completed as in Fig. 19.15b.

The suggested procedure is based upon the "similarly oriented" relationship discussed in the statement following (19.10). The map of the idealized boundary C of the right-hand half of the s plane as depicted in Fig. 19.15a, where a small indentation with radius approaching zero is used to exclude a pole $p_1 = 0$ of $G(s)H(s)$ in (19.23), is, in the GH plane, the closed curve Σ in Fig. 19.15b. The map of the

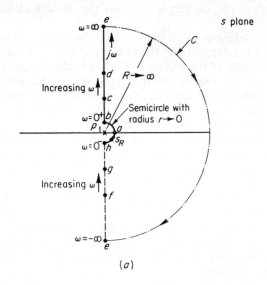

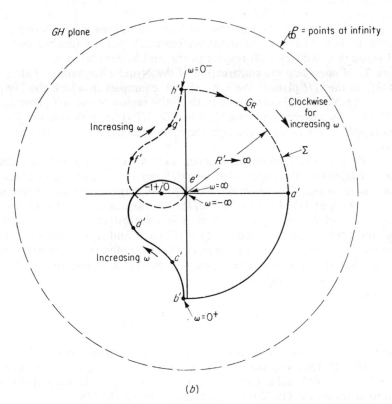

(b)

FIG. 19.15

pole $p_1 = 0$ of $G(s)H(s)$ is $\text{\reflectbox{P}\hspace{-0.9em}\raisebox{0.3ex}{\scriptsize o}}$, where $\text{\reflectbox{P}\hspace{-0.9em}\raisebox{0.3ex}{\scriptsize o}}$ is a symbol introduced here to represent the

points at infinity of the *GH* plane. Since Σ is the map of C, and $\text{\reflectbox{P}\hspace{-0.9em}\raisebox{0.3ex}{\scriptsize o}}$ is the map of

p_1, C and Σ must be *similarly oriented* with respect to p_1 and $\text{\reflectbox{P}\hspace{-0.9em}\raisebox{0.3ex}{\scriptsize o}}$. This is true for the representative point G_R moving *clockwise*, as prescribed by the procedure, along the $h'a'b'$ portion of the Σ curve in the direction of increasing ω from 0^- to 0^+, for the

following reason: p_1 is on the *left* of s_R, and $\text{\reflectbox{P}\hspace{-0.9em}\raisebox{0.3ex}{\scriptsize o}}$ is on the *left* of G_R, in Fig. 19.15, where s_R and G_R are the corresponding representative points on C and Σ moving in the directions of increasing ω. Therefore, C and Σ are *similarly oriented* with

respect to p_1 and $\text{\reflectbox{P}\hspace{-0.9em}\raisebox{0.3ex}{\scriptsize o}}$.

As another illustration, let us consider

$$G(s)H(s) = \frac{s+1}{s^2+1} \tag{19.24}$$

which has a pair of poles p_1, $p_2 = \pm j1$ on the $j\omega$ axis. According to the suggested procedure, we first plot $G(j\omega)H(j\omega)$ for $\omega = 0$ to $\omega = 1^-$ and for $\omega = 1^+$ to $\omega = \infty$ as depicted by solid curves in Fig. 19.16b; we then connect them with a curve representing a portion of the circumference of an arbitrarily large circle such that the representative point G_R moves *clockwise* in the direction of increasing ω, that is, from ω_1^- to ω_1^+, where $\omega_1 = 1$, thus completing the positive-frequency portion of the Nyquist diagram. According to Remark 1, we construct the negative-frequency portion of the Nyquist diagram through symmetry with respect to the real horizontal axis from the positive-frequency portion already plotted; this negative-frequency portion is represented by dashed curves in Fig. 19.16b. As in the preceding illustration, the procedure may be justified with the aid of the s-plane representation in Fig. 19.16a.

Case 2. Poles of $G(s)H(s)$ in the Right-hand Half of the s Plane and Arbitrarily Close to the $j\omega$ Axis. Although this case occurs only occasionally, it may be considered as the limiting case with poles of $G(s)H(s)$ in the right-hand half of the s plane, which are close to, if not arbitrarily close to, the $j\omega$ axis.

Let us assume that $p_1 = \delta_1 + j\omega_1$, for $\delta_1 \to 0$ and $\omega_1 \geq 0$, is a pole of $G(s)H(s)$. We expect that $G(j\omega)H(j\omega) \to \infty$ as $\omega \to \omega_1$ along the $j\omega$ axis. To construct the Nyquist diagram for the frequency range including ω_1, we (1) plot $G(j\omega)H(j\omega)$ for the various values of ω, except between $\omega_1^- = \omega_1 - \epsilon$ and $\omega_1^+ = \omega_1 + \epsilon$, where ϵ is an arbitrarily chosen small positive quantity, and (2) join the two points $G(j\omega_1^-)H(j\omega_1^-)$ and $G(j\omega_1^+)H(j\omega_1^+)$ in the *GH* plane with a curve representing a portion of the circumference of an arbitrarily large circle such that the representative point G_R moves *counterclockwise* in the direction of increasing ω, that is, from ω_1^- to ω_1^+.

For illustration, let us consider

$$G(s)H(s) = \frac{s+1}{s^2 - \eta s + 1} \qquad \eta = 10^{-15} \tag{19.25}$$

which has a pair of poles p_1, p_2 in the right-hand half of the s plane very close to $\pm j\omega_1$ for $\omega_1 = 1$. According to the suggested procedure, we first plot $G(j\omega)H(j\omega)$ for $\omega = 0$ to $\omega = 1^-$ and for $\omega = 1^+$ to $\omega = \infty$ as depicted by solid curves in Fig. 19.17b; we then connect them with a curve representing a portion of the circumference of an arbitrarily large circle such that the representative point G_R moves *counterclockwise* in the direction of increasing ω, that is, from ω_1^- to ω_1^+, where $\omega_1 = 1$, thus completing the positive-frequency portion of the Nyquist diagram. According to Remark 1, we construct the negative-frequency portion of the Nyquist diagram

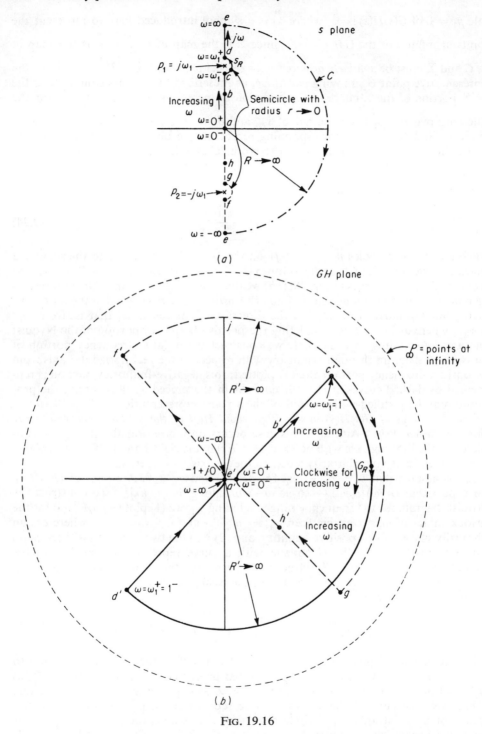

(a)

(b)

FIG. 19.16

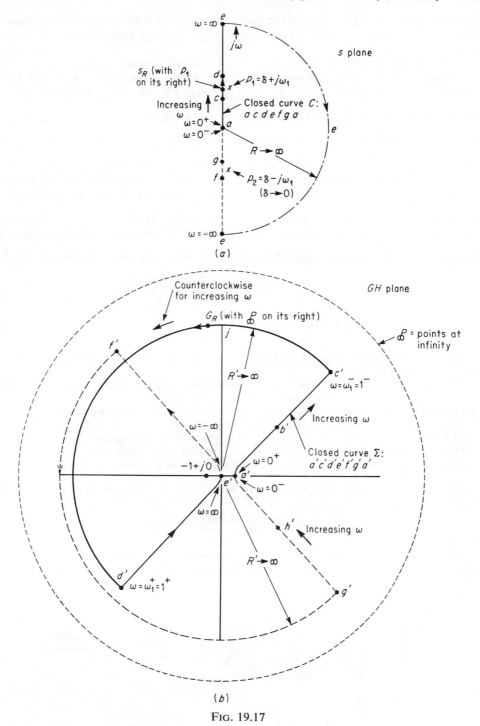

(a)

(b)

FIG. 19.17

through symmetry with respect to the real horizontal axis from the positive-frequency portion already plotted; this negative-frequency portion is represented by a dashed curve in Fig. 19.17*b*.

The suggested procedure here is also based upon the *similarly oriented* relationship discussed in the statement following (19.10). The map of the idealized boundary C of the right-hand half of the s plane as depicted in Fig. 19.17*a* is, in the GH plane, the closed curve Σ in Fig. 19.17*b*. The map of the pole p_1 of $G(s)H(s)$ is $\wp$. Since Σ is the map of C, and $\wp$ is the map of p_1, C and Σ must be similarly oriented with respect to p_1 and $\wp$; this is true for the representative point G_R moving *counterclockwise*, as prescribed by the procedure, along the $c'd'$ portion of the Σ curve in the direction of increasing ω from $\omega = 1^-$ to $\omega = 1^+$ for the following reason: p_1 is on the *right* of s_R, and $\wp$ is on the *right* of G_R, in Fig. 19.17, where s_R and G_R are the corresponding representative points on C and Σ moving in the directions of increasing ω. Therefore, C and Σ are *similarly oriented* with respect to p_1 and $\wp$.

PROBLEMS

Let

$$W(s) = \frac{(s - r_1)(s - r_2)}{s - p_1} = \frac{(s - 2 - j2)(s - 2 + j2)}{s - 5} \tag{a}$$

be used as the mapping function, and choose appropriate closed curves C, C_1, and C_2 in Probs. 19.1 through 19.6.

19.1. Repeat Illustration 3 in Art. 19.2B, and observe similar correspondences. Actual computation of the points on Σ, the map of C, is required.

19.2. Repeat Illustration 4 in Art. 19.2B, and observe similar correspondences.

19.3. Repeat Illustration 5 in Art. 19.2B, and generalize it to establish Criterion A.

19.4. Repeat Illustration 6 in Art. 19.2C, and generalize it to establish Criterion B.

19.5. Repeat Illustration 7 in Art. 19.2D, and observe similar correspondences.

19.6. Repeat Illustration 8 in Art. 19.2D, and generalize it to establish Criterion C.

19.7. Given: The closed-loop control system in Fig. P 19.7 with open-loop transfer function

$$G_1(s)H(s) = \frac{K(s + 1)}{s(s + 2)(s^2 + s + 1)} \tag{b}$$

where K is the system gain.

(*a*) Construct the Nyquist diagram $G_1(j\omega)H(j\omega)$ for $K = 5$ and determine the system stability. Label the point on this G_1H diagram associated with $\omega = \omega_1 = 0.1$ rad/sec as "A,"

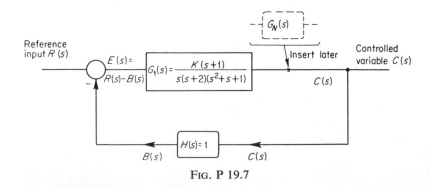

FIG. P 19.7

and measure the distance M_a from the origin O to the point A. The magnitude M_a represents the open-loop gain of the system at the low frequency $\omega = \omega_1 = 0.1$ rad/sec.

(b) Using the definition in (18.11), obtain the characteristic equation $P(s)$ for $K = 5$, and determine the system stability with the aid of the Routh's criterion.

Answer: (a, b) Unstable.

19.8. (a) Repeat Prob. 19.7a for $K = 1$. To construct this Nyquist diagram, we need only scale down the one already obtained in Prob. 19.7a from $K = 5$ to $K = 1$. To avoid confusion, let us mark the point "B" (instead of "A") on this $G_1 H$ diagram associated with $\omega = \omega_1 = 0.1$ rad/sec.

(b) Repeat Prob. 19.7b for $K = 1$.

Answer: (a, b) Stable.

19.9. From the results of Probs. 19.7 and 19.8, observe the following:

(a) The Routh's criterion tells us whether or not the system is stable. However, it usually does not tell us whether we should scale K up or down, nor does it indicate the magnitude of the change of scale needed for stable operation.

(b) The Nyquist criterion does indicate to us the necessary scale-up or scale-down, as well as the magnitude of the change in scale of K necessary to achieve stable operation. Compare the Nyquist diagrams obtained in Probs. 19.7a and 19.8a for this observation.

(c) For some simple systems, we may allow K to be an unknown quantity in the construction of the Routh's array, and then determine the values of K for stable operation. But for complicated systems this procedure is often cumbersome.

(d) Granting that the Routh's criterion enables us to improve the "stability" of a system with a change of scale for the system gain K, this change in K is often accompanied by a loss in the "accuracy" of the system operation. To maintain or improve "accuracy," i.e., to minimize error, we must maintain high gain at the low frequencies, as will be seen in Chap. 21. Note that the low-frequency gain M_b obtained in Prob. 19.8a is only a small fraction of the low-frequency gain M_a obtained in Prob. 19.7a. This means that we have reduced the system gain K to improve "stability" at the expense of "accuracy," and consequently it is an example of poor design.

(e) From the Nyquist diagram $G_1(j\omega)H(j\omega)$ obtained in Prob. 19.7a, we note that "stability" can be improved if we can bring the high-frequency portion of the diagram to the other side of the critical point -1; the "accuracy" can be maintained if we can keep the low-frequency portion of the diagram from being scaled down too much. This can be readily accomplished by using an appropriate compensating network $G_N(s)$ as indicated in Fig. P 19.7. The methods of compensation for stability and accuracy, to be discussed in Chap. 21, are the direct consequences of our insight into the heart of the problem; the Nyquist diagram has gained us this insight.

From the above observations, would you conclude that *the Nyquist criterion, together with the Nyquist diagram, shows us the direction we must take to improve stability and accuracy in the design of closed-loop control systems?*

19.10. Construct the Nyquist diagram and determine system stability for the open-loop transfer function

$$G(s)H(s) = \frac{15s}{(1 + 0.05s)(1 + 0.25s)(1 + s)}$$

19.11. Given: A closed-loop control system with the open-loop transfer function

$$G(s)H(s) = \frac{10P(s)}{(1 - \eta_1 s + s^2)(4 + s^2)Q(s)} \qquad \eta_1 = 10^{-7}$$

where $Q(s)$ has no roots on the $j\omega$ axis or in the right-hand half of the s plane, *and* the finite portion of its Nyquist diagram in Fig. P 19.11.

(a) Complete the Nyquist diagram.

(b) Assuming that the critical point -1 is located at the point "A" in the figure, determine the system stability.

(c) Repeat (b) for the point "B."

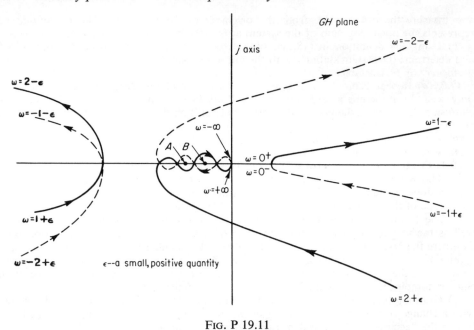

FIG. P 19.11

19.12. Construct the Nyquist diagram and determine the system stability for the open-loop transfer function

$$G(s)H(s) = \frac{10}{s(s^2 + 1)(s^2 - \eta s + 4)} \qquad \eta = 10^{-6}$$

19.13. We shall find that (1) the overall transfer function has $1 + T(s)$ in its denominator and (2) the Nyquist criterion in Art. 19.3C uses $T = -1$ in the T plane as its critical point, where $T(s)$ is the open-loop transfer function or return ratio defined in this text. For example, in closed-loop control systems the open-loop transfer function is $T(s) = G(s)H(s)$, and the overall transfer function is $G'(s) = G(s)/[1 + G(s)H(s)] = G(s)/[1 + T(s)]$ according to (18.5). And, for example, in transistor feedback amplifiers the return ratio is defined in (15.2) and (15.6) to be $T(s) = T_{p'p} = -V_{p'}/V_p$, and the overall current gain is $I_2/I_1 = KT_{p'p}/(1 + T_{p'p}) = KT_{p'p}/[1 + T(s)]$ according to (15.3) and (15.7).

In some papers and texts, the open-loop transfer function or return ratio (or loop gain) $T^*(s)$ is defined differently, and

$$\text{Overall transfer function} = K\frac{T^*(s)}{1 - T^*(s)} \qquad (c)$$

has $1 - T^*(s)$ in its denominator.

(a) If we plot $T^*(j\omega)$, call it the Nyquist diagram, and try to use the Nyquist criterion in Art. 19.3C, where should the new critical point be located in the T^* plane?

(b) Assuming that a return ratio $T^*(s)$ has no poles in the right-hand half of the s plane, and $T^*(j\omega)$ is depicted in Fig. P 19.13, determine the system stability.

(c) Can we define $T(s) = -T^*(s)$, plot $T(j\omega)$ or $-T^*(j\omega)$, and then use the Nyquist criterion in Art. 19.3C directly? *Answer:* Yes.

Remarks about the Use of the Nyquist Criterion under Various Conditions. For closed-loop control systems, the *open-loop transfer function* defined as $G(s)H(s)$, or $G(s)$ if $H(s) = 1$, is almost universally used, and the Nyquist criterion in Art. 19.3C is directly applicable.

For vacuum-tube feedback amplifiers, the majority of textbooks use $\mu\beta$ or $A\beta$ and call it the *loop gain* or *loop transmission* (some authors also call $\mu\beta$ or $A\beta$ the *return ratio*, while others define $-\mu\beta$ or $-A\beta$ as the *return ratio*). The overall gain is usually given in the form

$\mu' = \mu/(1 - \mu\beta)$ or $A' = A/(1 - A\beta)$, which compares with Eq. (*c*) above for $T^*(s) = \mu\beta$ or $T^*(s) = A\beta$. To determine stability, we need only (1) plot $T(j\omega) = -T^*(j\omega) = -\mu\beta$ or $T(j\omega) = -A\beta$ and use the Nyquist criterion in Art. 19.3C directly, as suggested in part *c* of this problem, or (2) plot $T^*(j\omega) = \mu\beta$ or $T^*(j\omega) = A\beta$ and use the Nyquist criterion in Art. 19.3C with a new critical point in the T^* plane, as suggested in part *a* of this problem.

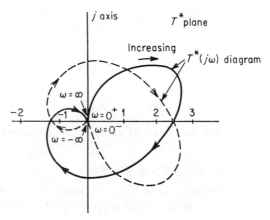

FIG. P 19.13

For transistor feedback amplifiers, some authors use $T_{p'p} = -V_{p'}/V_p$ as the definition of the return ratio as in (15.2) and (15.6), while others use $T^*_{p'p} = V_{p'}/V_p$ and $T_{p'p} = -T^*_{p'p}$. For $T^*_{p'p} = V_{p'}/V_p$ as the *return ratio*, we may either (1) plot $T_{p'p} = -T^*_{p'p}$ and use the Nyquist criterion directly, as suggested in part *c* of this problem, or (2) plot $T^*_{p'p}$ and use the Nyquist criterion in Art. 19.3C with a new critical point in the T^* plane, as suggested in part *a*.

20 Description of some simple closed-loop control systems

20.1. Description of transfer functions of components commonly used in closed-loop control systems

A. Transfer Functions of Some RC Networks

The *RC* networks under discussion here are used as compensating networks in improving the performance of a closed-loop control system, as will be seen in Chap. 21.

We shall use Laplace-transform notation as exemplified in Fig. 18.3b; $e_1(t)$ and $e_2(t)$ are the input (i.e., excitation) and output (i.e., response) of each four-terminal network, $E_1(s)$ and $E_2(s)$ their respective Laplace transforms, and $G(s) = E_2(s)/E_1(s)$ the transfer function of the network.

A phase-lead network. Let us consider the network in Fig. 20.1a. It is easy to see that

$$G(s) = \frac{E_2(s)}{E_1(s)} = \frac{R_2}{R_1(1/sC_1)/(R_1 + 1/sC_1) + R_2}$$

$$= \frac{R_2(1 + R_1C_1s)}{R_1 + R_2 + R_2R_1C_1s} \tag{20.1a}$$

$$G(s) = \frac{\alpha(1 + T_1s)}{1 + \alpha T_1s} \tag{20.1b}$$

where
$$T_1 = R_1C_1 \qquad \alpha = \frac{R_2}{R_1 + R_2} \tag{20.1b'}$$

For the real frequencies $s = j\omega$,

$$G(j\omega) = \frac{E_2(j\omega)}{E_1(j\omega)} = \left|\frac{E_2(j\omega)}{E_1(j\omega)}\right| e^{j\phi(\omega)}$$

$$= G_0(\omega)e^{j\phi(\omega)} = G_0(\omega)\underline{/\phi(\omega)} \tag{20.2}$$

is an output-input relation of the network, where

$$G_0(\omega) = \text{ratio of magnitude of output to magnitude of input} \tag{20.2a}$$

$$\phi(\omega) = \text{phase angle by which output } \textit{leads} \text{ input} \tag{20.2b}$$

If we replace $s = j\omega$ in (20.1b) and plot $G(j\omega)$ for different values of ω from 0^+ to ∞, we obtain the semicircular locus in Fig. 20.1a''. By connecting the origin and an arbitrary point associated with a frequency ω_a on this semicircle with a vector, we may measure the quantities $G_0(\omega)$ and $\phi(\omega)$ as defined in (20.2a) and (20.2b) at

518

frequency ω_a. It is easy to see that $\phi(\omega)$ is *positive* for all frequencies from $\omega = 0^+$ to $\omega = \infty$. This indicates that the network in Fig. 20.1a will introduce a *phase lead* in its output relative to its input.

Another phase-lead network. Letting $R_1 = \infty$, $R_2 = R$, and $C_1 = C$ in Fig. 20.1a, we obtain the special case in Fig. 20.1b. We now have

$$G(s) = \frac{Ts}{1 + Ts} \tag{20.3}$$

where

$$T = RC \tag{20.3a}$$

and a *phase lead* is introduced in the output relative to the input, as depicted in Fig. 20.1b''.

A phase-lead network with double RC sections. If we consider Fig. 20.1b as a single RC section, then we have double RC sections in Fig. 20.1c. We may follow some standard procedure, e.g., the loop or signal-flow method of analysis, to obtain the transfer function

$$G(s) = \frac{E_2(s)}{E_1(s)} = \frac{T_1 T_2 s^2}{T_1 T_2 s^2 + (T_1 + T_2 + T_{12})s + 1} \tag{20.4}$$

where

$$T_1 = R_1 C_1 \qquad T_2 = R_2 C_2 \qquad T_{12} = R_1 C_2 \tag{20.4a}$$

$G(j\omega)$ is plotted in Fig. 20.1c'' to show the output-input relation. We again note that the network in Fig. 20.1c will introduce a *phase lead* in its output relative to its input.

A phase-lag network. Let us now consider the network in Fig. 20.1d. It is easy to see that

$$G(s) = \frac{E_2(s)}{E_1(s)} = \frac{R_2 + 1/sC_2}{R_1 + R_2 + 1/sC_2}$$

$$= \frac{1 + R_2 C_2 s}{1 + (R_1 + R_2)C_2 s} \tag{20.5a}$$

$$G(s) = \frac{1 + T_2 s}{1 + (1/\beta)T_2 s} \tag{20.5b}$$

where

$$T_2 = R_2 C_2 \qquad \beta = \frac{R_2}{R_1 + R_2} \tag{20.5b'}$$

$G(j\omega)$ is plotted in Fig. 20.1d'' to show the output-input relation. We note that $\phi(\omega)$ is negative from $\omega = 0^+$ to $\omega = \infty$; the network in Fig. 20.1d introduces a *phase lag* in its output relative to its input.

Another phase-lag network. Letting $R_2 = 0$, $R_1 = R$, and $C_2 = C$ in Fig. 20.1d, we obtain the special case in Fig. 20.1e. We now have

$$G(s) = \frac{1}{1 + Ts} \tag{20.6}$$

where

$$T = RC \tag{20.6a}$$

and a *phase lag* is introduced in the output relative to the input, as depicted in Fig. 20.1e''.

A phase-lag network with double RC sections. If we consider Fig. 20.1e as a single RC section, then we have double RC sections in Fig. 20.1f. We may follow some standard procedure to obtain the transfer function

$$G(s) = \frac{E_2(s)}{E_1(s)} = \frac{1}{T_1 T_2 s^2 + (T_1 + T_2 + T_{12})s + 1} \tag{20.7}$$

where

$$T_1 = R_1 C_1 \qquad T_2 = R_2 C_2 \qquad T_{12} = R_1 C_2 \tag{20.7a}$$

Network	Transfer function $G(s)=\dfrac{E_2(s)}{E_1(s)}$	Output-input relation $G(j\omega)=\dfrac{E_2(j\omega)}{E_1(j\omega)}=\left|\dfrac{E_2(j\omega)}{E_1(j\omega)}\right|e^{j\phi(\omega)}=G_0(\omega)e^{j\phi(\omega)}$
A phase-lead network (a)	$G(s)=\dfrac{\alpha(1+T_1 s)}{1+\alpha T_1 s}$ $\quad \alpha=\dfrac{R_2}{R_1+R_2}$ where $\quad T_1=R_1 C_1,\ R_2=R$ (a')	(a'')
A phase-lead network (b)	$G(s)=\dfrac{Ts}{1+Ts}$ $\qquad T=RC$ where NOTE: This is a special case of the above for $R_1=\infty,\ R_2=R,\ C_1=0$ (b')	(b'')
A phase-lead network (c)	$G(s)=\dfrac{T_1 T_2 s^2}{T_1 T_2 s^2+(T_1+T_2+T_{12})s+1}$ $T_1=R_1 C_1 \quad T_2=R_2 C_2 \quad T_{12}=R_1 C_2$ where NOTE: This represents a double section of the above (c')	(c'')

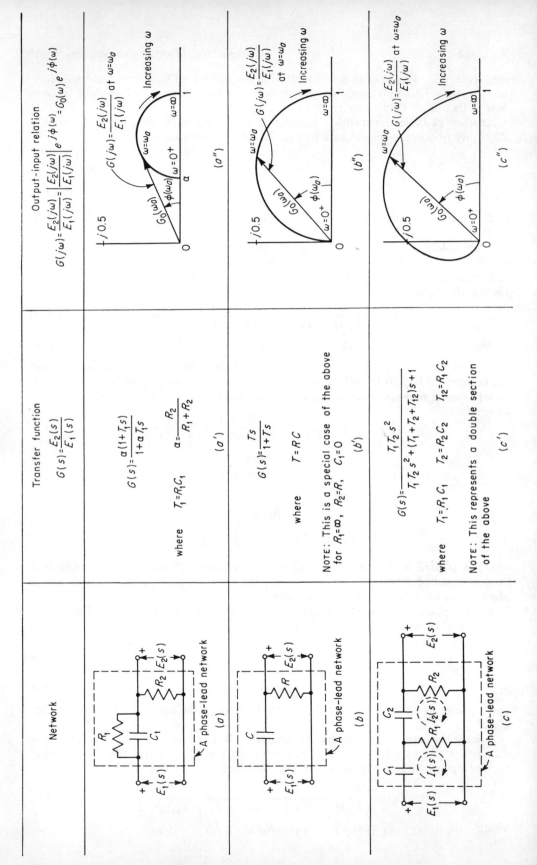

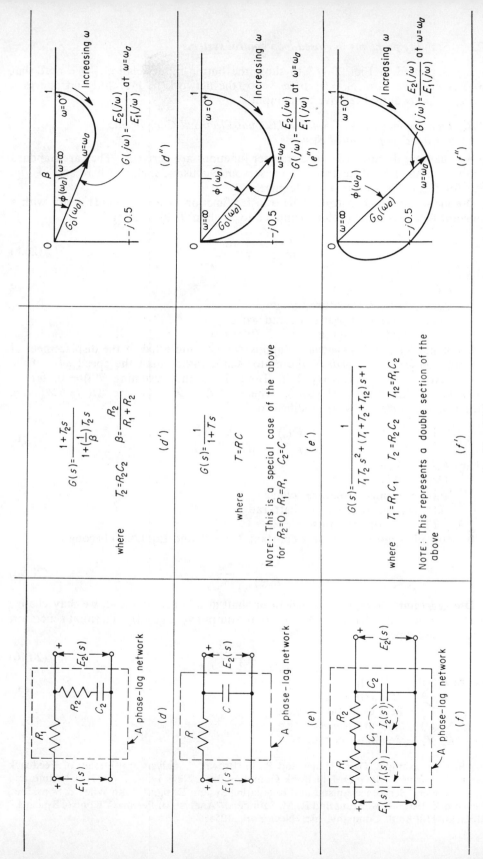

FIG. 20.1

$G(j\omega)$ is plotted in Fig. 20.1f'' to show the output-input relation. We note that $\phi(\omega)$ is negative from $\omega = 0^+$ to $\omega = \infty$; the network in Fig. 20.1f introduces a *phase lag* in its output relative to its input.

B. Transfer Functions of Some Additional Electrical Components in Closed-loop Control Systems

We shall not discuss how these transfer functions are derived. They are standard expressions used in all textbooks† on servomechanisms, included here and in Fig. 20.2 for future illustration and reference.

D-c motor for speed control.   The transfer function of a d-c (shunt) motor with a constant field excitation (voltage) applied to its shunt field winding is

$$\frac{\Omega(s)}{E_a(s)} = \frac{K_m}{1 + T_m s} \tag{20.8}$$

where $\Omega(s) = \mathscr{L}[\omega(t)]$
$E_a(s) = \mathscr{L}[e_a(t)]$
$e_a(t) = $ applied armature *voltage*
$\omega(t) = $ *speed* of motor shaft, rad/sec
$K_m, T_m = $ motor constants

D-c motor for position control.   Suppose we are interested in the displacement of the position $\theta(t) = \int \omega(t)\, dt$ of the motor shaft, rather than the speed $\omega(t)$ of the shaft. According to property 3 in Table 11.3, and assuming $\theta(0) = 0$, $\theta(t) = \int \omega(t)\, dt$ implies $\Theta(s) = (1/s)\Omega(s)$, where $\Theta(s) = \mathscr{L}[\theta(t)]$ and $\Omega(s) = \mathscr{L}[\omega(t)]$. Equation (20.8) may now be modified to

$$\frac{\Theta(s)}{E_a(s)} = \frac{K_m}{s(1 + T_m s)} \tag{20.9}$$

where $E_a(s) = \mathscr{L}[e_a(t)]$
$\Theta(s) = \mathscr{L}[\theta(t)]$
$e_a(t) = $ applied armature *voltage*
$\theta(t) = $ *position* of motor shaft, rad
$K_m, T_m = $ motor constants

In some pilot motors, the time constant $T_m = 0$, and Eq. (20.9) becomes

$$\frac{\Theta(s)}{E_a(s)} = \frac{K_m}{s} \tag{20.9a}$$

D-c generator.   Keeping the generator shaft at a constant speed, we may change the field excitation voltage $e_f(t)$ to control the output voltage $e_a(t)$ of a shunt generator. The transfer function is

$$\frac{E_a(s)}{E_f(s)} = \frac{K_g}{1 + T_g s} \tag{20.10}$$

where $E_f(s) = \mathscr{L}[e_f(t)]$
$E_a(s) = \mathscr{L}[e_a(t)]$
$e_f(t) = $ field excitation *voltage*
$e_a(t) = $ output *voltage*
$K_g, T_g = $ generator constants

† See, for example, G. J. Thaler and R. G. Brown, "Analysis and Design of Feedback Control Systems," McGraw-Hill Book Company, Inc., New York, 1960; H. Chestnut and R. W. Mayer, "Servomechanisms and Regulating System Design," John Wiley & Sons, Inc., New York, 1951; R. A. Bruns and R. M. Saunders, "Analysis of Feedback Control Systems," McGraw-Hill Book Company, Inc., New York, 1955.

An amplidyne, as a modified d-c shunt motor with one armature coil short-circuited, has a transfer function in the form of (20.10).

Tachometer.   A tachometer generates a d-c voltage $e(t)$ proportional to the speed $\omega(t)$ of its rotating shaft, which is driven by some source; that is, $e(t) = K_t\omega(t)$. This implies

$$\frac{E(s)}{\Omega(s)} = K_t \tag{20.11}$$

where $\Omega(s) = \mathscr{L}[\omega(t)]$
$\quad\quad E(s) = \mathscr{L}[e(t)]$
$\quad\quad \omega(t) = speed$ of shaft, rad/sec
$\quad\quad e(t) = output\ voltage$

Suppose we wish to consider the displacement of the position $\theta(t) = \int \omega(t)\,dt$ of the shaft, rather than the speed $\omega(t)$ of the shaft, as input.   According to property 3 in Table 11.3, and assuming $\theta(0) = 0$, $\theta(t) = \int \omega(t)\,dt$ implies $\Theta(s) = (1/s)\Omega(s)$, where $\Theta(s) = \mathscr{L}[\theta(t)]$ and $\Omega(s) = \mathscr{L}[\omega(t)]$.   Equation (20.11) may now be modified to

$$\frac{E(s)}{\Theta(s)} = K_t s \tag{20.12}$$

where $\Theta(s) = \mathscr{L}[\theta(t)]$
$\quad\quad E(s) = \mathscr{L}[e(t)]$
$\quad\quad \theta(t) = position$ of shaft, rad
$\quad\quad e(t) = output\ voltage$

Phase-sensitive potentiometer.   From the arrangement in Fig. 20.2g, it is easy to see that the output $e(t)$ of the potentiometer is proportional to the displacement $\theta(t)$ of the pointer from the center, in radians, that is, $e(t) = K_p\theta(t)$.   This implies

$$\frac{E(s)}{\Theta(s)} = K_p \tag{20.13a}$$

where $\Theta(s) = \mathscr{L}[\theta(t)]$
$\quad\quad E(s) = \mathscr{L}[e(t)]$
$\quad\quad \theta(t) = position$ of pointer, rad
$\quad\quad e(t) = voltage$

Synchrogenerator.   The output voltage $e(t)$ of a synchrogenerator is proportional to the position $\theta(t)$ of the shaft in radians, that is, $e(t) = K_s\theta(t)$.   This implies

$$\frac{E(s)}{\Theta(s)} = K_s \tag{20.13b}$$

where $\Theta(s) = \mathscr{L}[\theta(t)]$
$\quad\quad E(s) = \mathscr{L}[e(t)]$
$\quad\quad \theta(t) = position$ of shaft, rad
$\quad\quad e(t) = output\ voltage$

Amplifier.   We shall use only amplifiers whose output $e_2(t)$ is always directly proportional to the input $e_1(t)$; that is, $e_2(t) = K_a e_1(t)$.   This implies

$$\frac{E_2(s)}{E_1(s)} = K_a \tag{20.14}$$

where $E_1(s) = \mathscr{L}[e_1(t)]$
$\quad\quad E_2(s) = \mathscr{L}[e_2(t)]$
$\quad\quad e_1(t) = input\ voltage$
$\quad\quad e_2(t) = output\ voltage$
$\quad\quad K_a = gain$ of amplifier

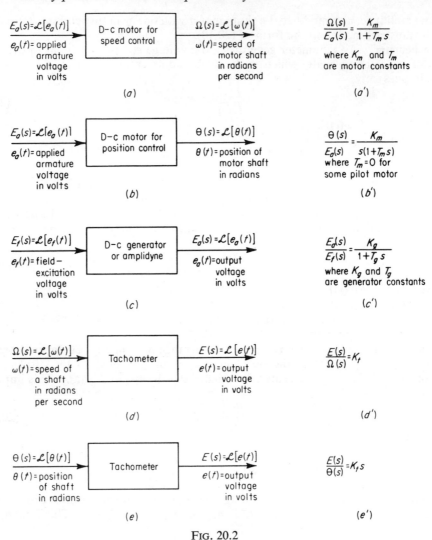

FIG. 20.2

D-c generator-motor combination.   Suppose the output of a d-c generator is used to run a motor, as in Fig. 20.2*i*.   The transfer function of the combined setup is

$$\frac{\Theta(s)}{E_f(s)} = \frac{\Theta(s)}{E_a(s)}\frac{E_a(s)}{E_f(s)} = \frac{K_m K_g}{s(1 + T_m s)(1 + T_g s)} \qquad (20.15)$$

Reference is made to Fig. 20.2*b* and *c* for the individual elements.

Remarks about combinations.   We have just combined a generator and a motor into a composite control element.   In combining two or more control elements into a *composite* element, we observe:

> *The output of the preceding element and the input of the subsequent element must represent the same physical quantity*   (20.16*a*)

For example, we may use a *potentiometer-amplifier-amplidyne-motor* combination (reference is made to Fig. 20.2).   Note that the output of the preceding element and

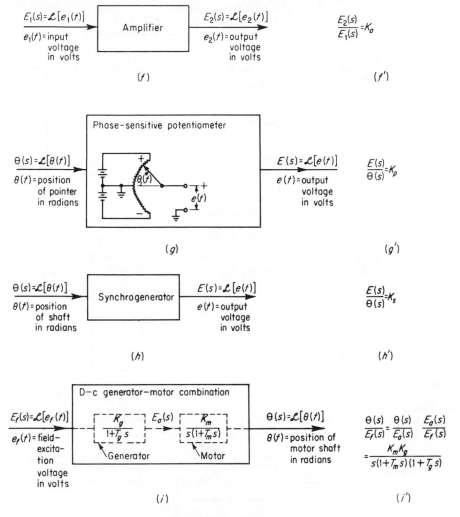

FIG. 20.2 (*continued*)

the input of the subsequent element represent the *same* physical quantity. On the other hand, we cannot have an amplifier-tachometer combination; since the output of an amplifier is a *voltage* and the input of a tachometer is a *speed*, an amplifier cannot be expected to drive a tachometer.

> The transfer function of the composite element is equal to the products of the transfer functions of the individual elements   (20.16b)

Equation (20.15) serves as an illustration.

C. Forward and Open-loop Transfer Functions of a Closed-loop Control System

We have seen above that a control element may consist in a number of component elements as in Fig. 20.3a. As a matter of fact, the feedback element may also consist in more than one single element; for example, we may have $H(s) = H_1(s)H_2(s) = B(s)/C(s)$, where $H_1(s)$ and $H_2(s)$ are the transfer functions of two component elements.

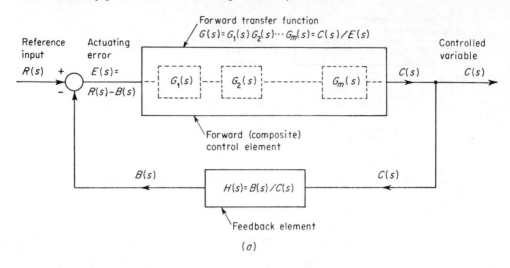

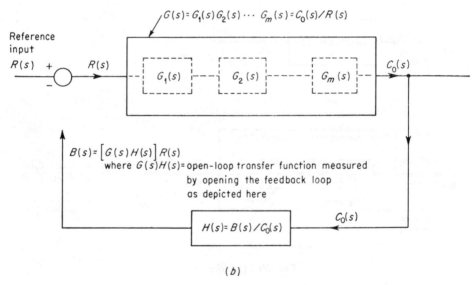

FIG. 20.3

Forward transfer function: transfer function of the forward control element. With reference to Fig. 20.3, we shall call that portion of the closed-loop control system which has the actuating error $E(s)$ as input and the controlled variable $C(s)$ as output the *forward control element;* its transfer function

Forward transfer function:

$$G(s) = G_1(s)G_2(s) \cdots G_m(s) \tag{20.17}$$

is the *forward transfer function* of the system.

Open-loop transfer function or return ratio. We have already defined the open-loop transfer function in (19.21), i.e.,

Open-loop transfer function:

$$G(s)H(s) = [G_1(s)G_2(s) \cdots G_m(s)]H(s) = \frac{B(s)}{R(s)} \tag{20.18}$$

where $R(s)$ is a reference input and $B(s)$ is the open-loop feedback as indicated in Fig. 20.3b.

Some authors call $G(s)H(s)$ the *return ratio*, since it represents the ratio of the open-loop feedback $B(s)$ to the reference input $R(s)$. However, the term *return ratio* is commonly used in the study of feedback amplifiers (a special category of closed-loop control systems to be studied in Art. 20.4A) rather than for closed-loop control systems in general. For transistor feedback amplifiers as studied in Chaps. 15 through 17, $T(s)$ or $T_{p'p}$, rather than $G(s)H(s)$, is the notation for the return ratio.

20.2. Classification of a closed-loop control system according to its forward transfer function

A. Remarks about Classification

Two methods of classification. We may classify a closed-loop control system according to (1) the general representation of its *forward transfer function G(s)* or (2) the general representation of its *open-loop transfer function G(s)H(s)*. For most (but not all) practical problems, two classifications of the same system are the same.

Classification according to the general representation of the forward transfer function $G(s)$. Once we know the classification of a closed-loop control system according to its forward transfer function $G(s)$, we know something about the system. This classification gives us some *system characteristics* concerning the relations (1) between the error and the controlled variable (e.g., a position or a displacement) *and* (2) between the error and the derivatives of the controlled variable (e.g., velocity and acceleration). For the interpretations of the terms *error* and *controlled variable*, see Fig. 20.3 or 18.5.

We shall classify closed-loop control systems into a number of types according to the forward transfer function $G(s)$ in Art. 20.2B, and discuss the system characteristics associated with each type in Art. 20.2C.

Classification according to the general representation of the open-loop transfer function. Once we know the classification of a closed-loop control system according to its open-loop transfer function $G(s)H(s)$, we also know something about the system. This classification gives us a general indication of *system stability*.

We shall classify closed-loop control systems into a number of types according to the open-loop transfer function $G(s)H(s)$ in Art. 20.3A, and discuss *system stability* for each type in Art. 20.3B. Methods of modifying an unstable system to a stable one will be discussed in Chap. 21.

B. Classification According to Forward Transfer Function G(s)

Let us assume that the forward transfer function has the general form

$$G(s) = \frac{K[(1 + \tau_1 s)(1 + \tau_2 s) \cdots (1 + 2\delta_m \tau_m s + \tau_m{}^2 s^2) \cdots]}{s^n[(1 + T_1 s)(1 + T_2 s) \cdots (1 + 2\eta_k T_k s + T_k{}^2 s^2) \cdots]} \qquad (20.19)$$

where $(1 + \tau_i s)$ and $(1 + 2\delta_j \tau_j s + \tau_j{}^2 s^2)$ are typical factors inside the brackets in the numerator, and $(1 + T_i s)$ and $(1 + 2\eta_j T_j s + T_j{}^2 s^2)$ in the denominator.

A closed-loop system is called a *type 0* system if it has a forward transfer function in the form (20.19) with $n = 0$, a *type 1* system if $n = 1$, and a *type 2* system if $n = 2$. Because of instability problems, as will be discussed later, we usually avoid using a forward transfer function representable as (20.19) with $n \geq 3$. However, for particular reasons or theoretical interest, we may have a *type n* system, where n is an arbitrary integer, and $n \geq 3$.

A type 0 system may have a forward transfer function $G(s) = K/[(1 + T_1s)(1 + T_2s)]$; a type 1 system, $G(s) = K/[s(1 + T_1s)(1 + 2\eta_2T_2s + T_2^2s^2)(1 + 2\eta_3T_3s + T_3^2s^2)]$; a type 2 system, $G(s) = K(1 + \tau_1s)/[s^2(1 + T_1s)(1 + T_2s)]$.

C. System Characteristics

Description of problem.   For

$$E(s) = \mathscr{L}[e(t)] \qquad\qquad C(s) = \mathscr{L}[c(t)]$$
$$e(t) = \text{actuating error} \qquad c(t) = \text{controlled variable} \tag{20.20}$$

the forward transfer function $G(s) = C(s)/E(s)$ of the closed-loop system in Fig. 20.3a or 18.5a relates the actuating error and the controlled variable.

Assuming a forward transfer function

$$G(s) = \frac{C(s)}{E(s)} = \frac{K}{s^n(1 + T_1s)(1 + T_2s)(1 + T_3s)(1 + T_4s)} \tag{20.21}$$

we shall derive relations between the controlled variable $c(t)$ and the actuating error $e(t)$ for type 0, 1, and 2 systems.   We shall then investigate the actuating error necessary for a particular type of controlled variable.

We further assume that the controlled variable represents a position representable by a Taylor's expansion about $t = T$:

$$c(t) = c_0 + c_1(t - T) + \frac{c_2}{2!}(t - T)^2 + \frac{c_3}{3!}(t - T)^3 + \frac{c_4}{4!}(t - T)^4 + \cdots \tag{20.22}$$

where $c_0 = c(t)|_{t=T} = c(T) = \text{position at } t = T$

$$c_1 = \frac{dc(t)}{dt}\bigg|_{t=T} = c'(T) = \text{velocity at } t = T$$

$$c_2 = c''(T) = \text{acceleration at } t = T \tag{20.22a}$$

$$c_3 = c'''(T) = \text{first derivative of acceleration at } t = T$$

$$c_4 = c^{(4)}(T) = \text{second derivative of acceleration at } t = T$$

In the analysis to follow, we are interested in the value of $c(t)$ in the neighborhood of $t = T$.   Therefore, we shall neglect the higher-order terms in (20.22) and use the first five terms only.   Rearranging (20.21), we have

$$E(s) = \frac{1}{K}s^nC(s) + \frac{\Sigma_1}{K}s^{n+1}C(s) + \frac{\Sigma_2}{K}s^{n+2}C(s) + \frac{\Sigma_3}{K}s^{n+3}C(s) + \frac{\Sigma_4}{K}s^{n+4}C(s) \tag{20.23}$$

where $\Sigma_1 = T_1 + T_2 + T_3 + T_4$

$$\Sigma_2 = T_1T_2 + T_1T_3 + T_1T_4 + T_2T_3 + T_2T_4 + T_3T_4$$
$$\Sigma_3 = T_1T_2T_3 + T_1T_2T_4 + T_1T_3T_4 + T_2T_3T_4 \tag{20.23a}$$
$$\Sigma_4 = T_1T_2T_3T_4$$

We shall analyze the *actuating-error–controlled-variable relation* for each type of system in the following paragraphs.

Type 0 system.   For $n = 0$, (20.23) becomes

$$E(s) = \frac{1}{K}C(s) + \frac{\Sigma_1}{K}sC(s) + \frac{\Sigma_2}{K}s^2C(s) + \frac{\Sigma_3}{K}s^3C(s) + \frac{\Sigma_4}{K}s^4C(s) \tag{20.24}$$

where Σ_1, Σ_2, Σ_3, and Σ_4 are defined in (20.23a). According to property 2 in Table 11.3, with the notation in (20.22a), we have

$$sC(s) = \mathcal{L}\left[\frac{d}{dt}c(t)\right] + c(0)$$

$$s^2C(s) = \mathcal{L}\left[\frac{d^2}{dt^2}c(t)\right] + c(0)s + c'(0)$$

$$s^3C(s) = \mathcal{L}\left[\frac{d^3}{dt^3}c(t)\right] + c(0)s^2 + c'(0)s + c''(0) \tag{20.25}$$

$$s^4C(s) = \mathcal{L}\left[\frac{d^4}{dt^4}c(t)\right] + c(0)s^3 + c'(0)s^2 + c''(0)s + c'''(0)$$

where

$$c(0) = [c(t)]_{t=0} \qquad\qquad c'(0) = \left[\frac{d}{dt}c(t)\right]_{t=0}$$

$$c''(0) = \left[\frac{d^2}{dt^2}c(t)\right]_{t=0} \qquad c'''(0) = \left[\frac{d^3}{dt^3}c(t)\right]_{t=0} \tag{20.25a}$$

Substituting (20.25) into (20.24) and letting

$$c(0) = c'(0) = c''(0) = c'''(0) = 0$$

i.e., assuming the system is at rest at $t = 0$, we have

$$\mathcal{L}[e(t)] = \frac{1}{K}\mathcal{L}[\text{Eq. (20.22)}] + \frac{\Sigma_1}{K}\mathcal{L}\left[\frac{d}{dt}\text{Eq. (20.22)}\right] + \frac{\Sigma_2}{K}\mathcal{L}\left[\frac{d^2}{dt^2}\text{Eq. (20.22)}\right]$$

$$+ \frac{\Sigma_3}{K}\mathcal{L}\left[\frac{d^3}{dt^3}\text{Eq. (20.22)}\right] + \frac{\Sigma_4}{K}\mathcal{L}\left[\frac{d^4}{dt^4}\text{Eq. (20.22)}\right] \tag{20.26}$$

Taking the inverse transform of (20.26), we obtain the actuating error

$$e(t) = \frac{c_0 + \Sigma_1 c_1 + \Sigma_2 c_2 + \Sigma_3 c_3 + \Sigma_4 c_4}{K} + \frac{c_1 + \Sigma_1 c_2 + \Sigma_2 c_3 + \Sigma_3 c_4}{K}(t - T)$$

$$+ \frac{c_2 + \Sigma_1 c_3 + \Sigma_2 c_4}{K(2!)}(t - T)^2 + \frac{c_3 + \Sigma_1 c_4}{K(3!)}(t - T)^3 + \frac{c_4}{K(4!)}(t - T)^4 \tag{20.27}$$

for values of t in the neighborhood of $t = T$, where Σ_1, Σ_2, Σ_3, and Σ_4 are defined in (20.23a).

For a type 0 system, we now state the following:

> *The larger the gain, the smaller the error for a particular value of the controlled variable* (20.28a)

Equation (20.27) indicates that the actuating error $e(t)$ is inversely proportional to the system gain K. Therefore, the error necessary to obtain a particular value of the controlled variable decreases as K increases.

> *A constant actuating error $e_0 = c_0/K$ is needed to produce a constant controlled variable $c(t) = c_0$* (20.28b)

For a constant controlled variable, $c_1 = c_2 = c_3 = c_4 = 0$ in (20.22) and Eq. (20.27) reduces to $e(t) = c_0/K$.

> *For a controlled variable in (20.22) with small c_1, c_2, c_3, c_4 and/or a forward transfer function in (20.21) with small time constants T_1, T_2, T_3, T_4, the actuating error is approximated by $e(t) = c_0/K$ in the neighborhood of $t = T$* (20.28c)

Small T_1, T_2, T_3, and T_4 imply small Σ_1, Σ_2, Σ_3, and Σ_4 in (20.23a). For small c_1, c_2, c_3, and c_4 and/or small Σ_1, Σ_2, Σ_3, and Σ_4, c_0/K is the dominating term in (20.27).

Type 1 system. We now have $n = 1$ in (20.23). Treatment similar to the above will lead to an expression for the actuating error corresponding to (20.27) for the type 0 system:

$$e(t) = \frac{c_1 + \Sigma_1 c_2 + \Sigma_2 c_3 + \Sigma_3 c_4}{K} + \frac{c_2 + \Sigma_1 c_3 + \Sigma_2 c_4}{K(2!)}(t - T)$$

$$+ \frac{c_3 + \Sigma_1 c_4}{K(3!)}(t - T)^2 + \frac{c_4}{K(4!)}(t - T)^3 \quad (20.29)$$

for values of t in the neighborhood of $t = T$, where Σ_1, Σ_2, and Σ_3 are defined in (20.23a).

For a type 1 system, we now state the following:

> *The larger the gain, the smaller the error for a particular value of the controlled variable* $\qquad$ (20.30a)

We note in (20.29) that the actuating error $e(t)$ is inversely proportional to the system gain K. Therefore, the error necessary to obtain a particular value of the controlled variable decreases as K increases.

> *No constant actuating error is needed to produce a constant controlled variable $c(t) = c_0$* $\qquad$ (20.30b)

For a constant controlled variable, that is, $c_1 = c_2 = c_3 = c_4 = 0$ in (20.22), Eq. (20.29) reduces to $e(t) = 0$. Therefore, no constant actuating error is needed to produce a constant displacement in the controlled variable.

> *A constant actuating error $e_0 = c_1/K_1$ is needed to produce a constant rate of change in the controlled variable* $\qquad$ (20.30c)

The controlled variable must now have the form $c(t) = c_0 + c_1(t - T)$. This means that $c_2 = c_3 = c_4 = 0$ in (20.22a); under these conditions Eq. (20.29) reduces to $e(t) = c_1/K$. Therefore, for the controlled variable to have a constant velocity, the error must be constant and equal to c_1/K_1.

> *For a controlled variable in (20.22) with small c_2, c_3, c_4 and/or a forward transfer function in (20.21) with small time constants T_1, T_2, T_3, T_4, the actuating error is approximated by $e(t) = c_1/K$ in the neighborhood of $t = T$* $\qquad$ (20.30d)

Small T_1, T_2, T_3, and T_4 imply small Σ_1, Σ_2, Σ_3, and Σ_4 in (20.23a). For small c_2, c_3, and c_4 and/or small Σ_1, Σ_2, Σ_3, and Σ_4, c_1/K is the dominating term in (20.29).

Type 2 system. We now have $n = 2$ in (20.23). Treatment similar to that for the type 0 system leads to an expression for the actuating error corresponding to (20.27) for the type 0 system:

$$e(t) = \frac{c_2 + \Sigma_1 c_3 + \Sigma_2 c_4}{K(2!)} + \frac{c_3 + \Sigma_1 c_4}{K(3!)}(t - T) + \frac{c_4}{K(4!)}(t - T)^2 \quad (20.31)$$

for values of t in the neighborhood of $t = T$, where Σ_1 and Σ_2 are defined in (20.23a).

For a type 2 system, we now state the following:

> *The larger the gain, the smaller the error for a particular value of the controlled variable* $\qquad$ (20.32a)

We note in (20.31) that the actuating error $e(t)$ is inversely proportional to the system gain. Therefore, the error necessary to obtain a particular value of the controlled variable decreases as K increases.

> *No constant actuating error is needed to produce a constant controlled variable $c(t) = c_0$* (20.32b)

For a constant controlled variable, that is, $c_1 = c_2 = c_3 = c_4 = 0$ in (20.22), Eq. (20.31) reduces to $e(t) = 0$. Therefore, no constant actuating error is needed to produce a constant displacement in the controlled variable.

> *No constant actuating error is needed to produce a constant rate of change in the controlled variable* (20.32c)

The controlled variable must now have the form $c(t) = c_0 + c_1(t - T)$. This means that $c_2 = c_3 = c_4 = 0$ in (20.22a); under these conditions Eq. (20.31) reduces to $e(t) = 0$. Therefore, no constant actuating error is needed to produce a controlled variable with a constant rate of change.

> *A constant actuating error $e_0 = c_2/2K$ is needed to produce a controlled variable with a constant second derivative* (20.32d)

The controlled variable must now have the form $c(t) = c_0 + c_1(t - T) + (c_2/2)$ $(t - T)^2$. This means that $c_3 = c_4 = 0$ in (20.22a); under these conditions Eq. (20.31) reduces to $e(t) = c_2/2K$. Therefore, for the controlled variable to have a constant acceleration, the error must be constant and equal to $c_2/2K$.

> *For a controlled variable in (20.22) with small c_3, c_4 and/or a forward transfer function in (20.21) with small time constants T_1, T_2, T_3, T_4, the actuating error is approximated by $e(t) = c_2/2K$ in the neighborhood of $t = T$* (20.32e)

Small T_1, T_2, T_3, and T_4 imply small Σ_1, Σ_2, Σ_3, and Σ_4 in (20.23a). For small c_3 and c_4 and/or small Σ_1, Σ_2, Σ_3, and Σ_4, $c_2/2K$ is the dominating term in (20.31).

20.3. Classification of a closed-loop control system according to its open-loop transfer function

A. Classification According to Open-loop Transfer Function

Let us assume that the open-loop transfer function has the general form

$$G(s)H(s) = \frac{K[(1 + \tau_1 s)(1 + \tau_2 s) \cdots (1 + 2\delta_m \tau_m s + \tau_m^2 s^2) \cdots]}{s^n[(1 + T_1 s)(1 + T_2 s) \cdots (1 + 2\eta_k T_k s + T_k^2 s^2) \cdots]} \quad (20.33)$$

where $(1 + \tau_i s)$ and $(1 + 2\delta_i \tau_i s + \tau_i^2 s^2)$ are typical factors inside the brackets in the numerator; $(1 + T_j s)$ and $(1 + 2\eta_j T_j s + T_j^2 s^2)$, in the denominator.

A closed-loop system is called a *type* 0 system if it has an open-loop transfer function in the form of (20.33) with $n = 0$; a *type* 1 system, if $n = 1$; a *type* 2 system if $n = 2$. Because of instability problems to be discussed in Art. 20.3B, we usually avoid using an open-loop transfer function representable as (20.33) with $n \geq 3$. However, for particular reasons or theoretical interest, we may have a *type n* system, where n is an arbitrary integer and $n \geq 3$.

A type 0 system may have an open-loop transfer function $G(s)H(s) = K/(1 + T_1 s)$ $(1 + T_2 s)(1 + T_3 s)$; a type 1 system, $G(s)H(s) = K/s(1 + T_1 s)(1 + T_2 s)$; a type 2 system, $G(s)H(s) = K(1 + \tau_1 s)/s^2(1 + T_1 s)(1 + T_2 s)$.

B. System Stability

Description of problem.   We are interested in knowing the general indications of *system stability* for the various types of systems defined above.

For the determination of system stability, we have studied the fundamental criterion for stability in Art. 18.3, Routh's criterion for stability in Art. 18.4, and the Nyquist criterion for stability in Art. 19.3.

Reference is now made to the Nyquist criterion for stability in Art. 19.3C.   In applying it, we use the open-loop transfer function $G(s)H(s)$ in the construction of a Nyquist diagram; this Nyquist diagram usually gives an indication of whether or not the closed-loop system is stable.

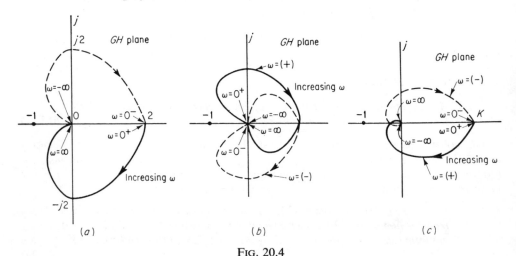

FIG. 20.4

We shall now illustrate typical Nyquist diagrams of type 0, 1, and 2 systems and remark about the stability properties of each system; we shall then discuss how an unstable system can be modified and made stable.

Nyquist diagrams of type 0 systems.   We consider the following illustrations:
Illustration 1.   Let

$$G(s)H(s) = \frac{K}{1 + 2\eta Ts + T^2 s^2} \tag{20.34}$$

$$G(s)H(s) = \frac{2}{1 + s + s^2} \tag{20.34a}$$

In plotting the Nyquist diagram $G(j\omega)H(j\omega)$, we (1) replace $s = j\omega$ in (20.34a),

$$G(j\omega)H(j\omega) = \frac{2}{(1 - \omega^2) + j\omega} = \frac{2[(1 - \omega^2) - j\omega]}{(1 - \omega^2)^2 + \omega^2} \tag{20.34b}$$

(2) compute† $G(j\omega)H(j\omega)$ for positive values of ω from $\omega = 0^+$ to $\omega = \infty$, and (3) plot $G(j\omega)H(j\omega)$ using the results of the computation for the positive-frequency portion, as depicted by the solid curve in Fig. 20.4a.   The negative-frequency portion may be computed through symmetry with respect to the real horizontal axis (dashed curve in Fig. 20.4a).

† For example, $GH = G(j\omega)H(j\omega) = 2$ at $\omega = 0$, $GH = 1.99 - j1$ at $\omega = 0.1$, $GH = -j2$ at $\omega = 1$, $GH = -0.46 - j0.31$ at $\omega = 2, \ldots$, and $GH = 0$ at $\omega = \infty$.

In considering the direction along which this $G(j\omega)H(j\omega)$ diagram approaches the origin as $\omega \to \infty$, we note that, for $s = j\omega$ and $\omega \to \infty$, s^2 is the dominating term in the denominator of (20.34a), and $G(j\omega)H(j\omega) \simeq 2/(j\omega)^2 = (2/\omega^2)\underline{/-180°}$. This means that $G(j\omega)H(j\omega)$ approaches the origin horizontally as $\omega \to \infty$.

We have now completed the Nyquist diagram for (20.34a) in Fig. 20.4a, and we obtain the following information: (1) $P = 0$ by inspection of (20.34a) and (2) $N = 0$, where

$$P = \text{number of poles of } G(s)H(s) \text{ in right-hand half of } s \text{ plane}$$
$$N = \text{number of clockwise encirclements of Nyquist diagram around } -1 \qquad (20.34c)$$

According to the Nyquist criterion in Art. 19.3C, this is a stable system.

By changing the gain $K = 2$ in (20.34a) to $K = 200$, we enlarge the Nyquist diagram in Fig. 20.4a proportionally. However, it still will not encircle the critical point -1, and $N = 0$ still holds. The system remains stable for any value of the gain.

Illustration 2.   Let

$$G(s)H(s) = \frac{Ks^2}{(1 + T_1 s)(1 + T_2 s)(1 + T_3 s)} \qquad (20.35)$$

$$G(s)H(s) = \frac{2s^2}{(1 + 0.5s)(1 + s)(1 + 1.5s)} \qquad (20.35a)$$

Following the above illustration, we construct the Nyquist diagram for (20.35a) in Fig. 20.4b. Again, $P = 0$ and $N = 0$. According to the Nyquist criterion, this is also a stable system.

By changing the gain $K = 2$ in (20.35a) to $K = 200$, we enlarge the Nyquist diagram in Fig. 20.4b proportionally. However, it still will not encircle the critical point -1, and $N = 0$ still holds. The system remains stable for any value of the gain.

A remark about stability for type 0 systems.   We have illustrated above and shall also find in other examples that

$$\textit{Most type 0 physical systems are stable} \qquad (20.36)$$

Let us now consider an unstable type 0 system for illustration. The Nyquist diagram for $G(s)H(s) = K/(1 + 2s)(1 + s + s^2)$ is plotted in Fig. 20.4c for small K. When K is made much larger, the Nyquist diagram is proportionally enlarged, and it encircles the critical point -1. The system then becomes unstable. To make it stable again, we must reduce the gain K.

Nyquist diagrams of type 1 systems.   We now consider the following illustrations:
Illustration 3.   Let

$$G(s)H(s) = \frac{K}{s(1 + T_1 s)(1 + T_2 s)} \qquad (20.37)$$

$$G(s)H(s) = \frac{10}{s(1 + 0.05s)(1 + 0.5s)} \qquad (20.37a)$$

Following the procedure in Illustration 1 above, we construct the positive-frequency portion of the Nyquist diagram $G(j\omega)H(j\omega)$ in Fig. 20.5a (solid curve) for $\omega = 0^+$ to $\omega = \infty$; we then construct the negative-frequency portion through symmetry with respect to the real axis (dashed curve) for $\omega = -\infty$ to $\omega = 0^-$. We connect the points associated with $\omega = 0^-$ and $\omega = 0^+$ with an arbitrarily large semicircle such that a representative point on it moves *clockwise* in the direction of increasing frequency, i.e., from $\omega = 0^-$ to $\omega = 0^+$, as suggested in Remark 2 of Art. 19.3C and illustrated in Fig. 19.15b.

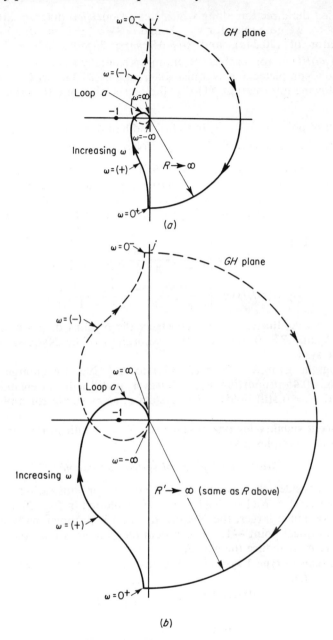

FIG. 20.5

In considering the direction along which this $G(j\omega)H(j\omega)$ diagram approaches infinity as $\omega \to 0^+$, we note that, for $s = j\omega$ and $\omega \to 0^+$, $G(j\omega)H(j\omega) \simeq 1/j\omega = (1/\omega)\underline{/-90°}$. This means that $G(j\omega)H(j\omega)$ approaches infinity vertically as $\omega \to 0^+$, as indicated by the solid curve in Fig. 20.5a.

We have now completed the Nyquist diagram for (20.37a) in Fig. 20.5a, and we obtain the following information: (1) $P = 0$ by inspection of (20.37a) and (2) $N = 0$, where P and N are interpreted in (20.34c). According to the Nyquist criterion in Art. 19.3C, this is a stable system.

By changing the gain $K = 10$ in (20.37) to a much larger value, say $K = 50$ or more, we enlarge the Nyquist diagram in Fig. 20.5a proportionally. The small loop a in Fig. 20.5a, which did not contain the critical point -1, now contains this critical point, as shown in Fig. 20.5b. This means that $P = 0$, as before, but $N = 2$, as the Nyquist diagram $G(j\omega)H(j\omega)$ encircles the critical point -1 twice. According to the Nyquist criterion, this system is unstable. By reducing the gain, we again obtain a stable system.

Illustration 4. Let

$$G(s)H(s) = \frac{K(1 + \tau_1 s)}{s(1 + T_1 s)(-1 + T_2 s)} \tag{20.38}$$

$$G(s)H(s) = \frac{1 + 2.5s}{s(1 + 0.05s)(-1 + 0.5s)} \tag{20.38a}$$

Following the procedures in Illustrations 1 and 3 above, we may construct the Nyquist diagram $G(j\omega)H(j\omega)$ for (20.38a) as in Fig. 20.6a. Here we have $P = 1$, as the factor $-1 + 0.5s$ is responsible for a pole in the right-hand half of the s plane; $N = -1$ for one counterclockwise encirclement. According to the Nyquist criterion in Art. 19.3C this is a stable system.

Illustration 5. For

$$G(s)H(s) = \frac{K(1 + \tau_1 s)(1 + \tau_2 s)}{s(1 + T_1 s)(1 + T_2 s)(1 + T_3 s)(1 + T_4 s)} \tag{20.39}$$

with an appropriate set of positive constants K, τ_1, τ_2, T_1, T_2, T_3, and T_4, we plot the Nyquist diagram $G(j\omega)H(j\omega)$ in Fig. 20.6b in the manner of the previous illustrations. Here we have $P = 0$ and $N = 0$. Therefore, the system is stable.

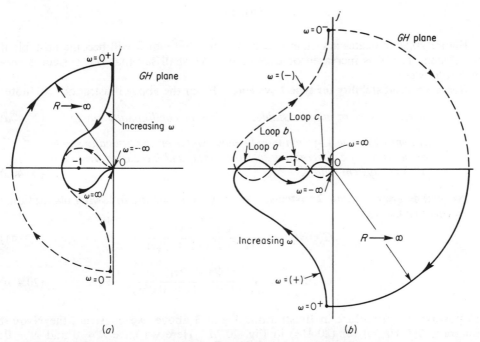

(a)   (b)

FIG. 20.6

Suppose we increase the system gain K in (20.39).   This means that the Nyquist diagram in Fig. 20.6b is proportionally enlarged; the critical point -1 is now contained in loop c instead of loop b.   We find that this new Nyquist diagram encircles the critical point -1 twice in the clockwise direction.   We now have $P = 0$ and $N = 2$; the system is unstable.

Suppose we now decrease the system gain K in (20.39).   The Nyquist diagram in Fig. 20.6b is diminished proportionally; the critical point -1 is now contained in loop a instead of loop b.   We find that this new Nyquist diagram encircles the critical point -1 twice in the clockwise direction.   We now have $P = 0$ and $N = 2$; the system is unstable.

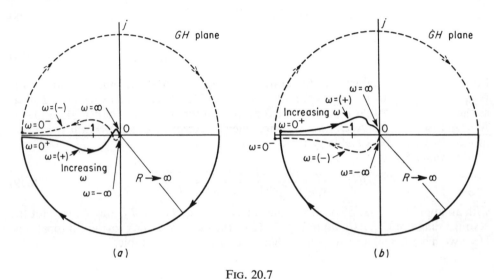

(a) (b)

FIG. 20.7

Figure 20.6b indicates a system which is stable, but which will become unstable if the system gain K is increased or decreased.   We shall say that this system is *conditionally stable*.

Remarks about stability for type 1 systems.   From the above illustrations, we note:

> *A type 1 system may be stable, unstable, or conditionally stable*   (20.40a)

> *An unstable type 1 system may be made stable or conditionally stable by adjusting (i.e., decreasing in most cases, and increasing occasionally) the system gain K*   (20.40b)

Nyquist diagrams of type 2 systems.   We now consider the following illustrations:
Illustration 6.   Let

$$G(s)H(s) = \frac{K(1 + \tau_1 s)}{s^2(1 + T_1 s)(1 + T_2 s)} \tag{20.41}$$

$$G(s)H(s) = \frac{4(1 + 2s)}{s^2(1 + 0.1s)(1 + 0.05s)} \tag{20.41a}$$

Following the procedure in Illustrations 1 and 3 above, we construct the Nyquist diagram $G(j\omega)H(j\omega)$ for (20.41a) in Fig. 20.7a.   Here we have $P = 0$ and $N = 0$; the system is stable.

Illustration 7.   Let

$$G(s)H(s) = \frac{K(1 + \tau_1 s)}{s^2(1 + T_1 s)(1 + T_2 s)} \qquad (20.42)$$

$$G(s)H(s) = \frac{1.5(1 + 0.4s)}{s^2(1 + 0.25s)(1 + 0.6s)} \qquad (20.42a)$$

Following the procedure in Illustrations 1 and 3 above, we construct the Nyquist diagram $G(j\omega)H(j\omega)$ for (20.42a) in Fig. 20.7b. Here we have $P = 0$ and $N = 2$; the system is unstable.

If we decrease the system gain K in (20.42), the Nyquist diagram in Fig. 20.7b is diminished proportionally. However, it still encircles the critical point -1; the system remains unstable.

In Illustrations 6 and 7 we note that, for $s = j\omega$ and $\omega \rightarrow 0^+$,

$$G(j\omega)H(j\omega) \cong \frac{K}{(j\omega)^2} = \frac{K}{\omega^2} \underline{/180°}$$

This means that $G(j\omega)H(j\omega)$ approaches infinity horizontally along the negative real axis as $\omega \rightarrow 0^+$. As observed in Fig. 20.7a and b, both the positive-frequency portion and the negative-frequency portion of the Nyquist diagram $G(j\omega)H(j\omega)$ are relatively close to the negative real axis. The chances that the Nyquist diagram encircles the critical point -1 are much higher for type 2 systems than for type 0 and type 1 systems, since the Nyquist diagrams for type 2 systems are usually closer to the negative real axis. Therefore, type 2 systems are *more likely* to be unstable than type 0 and type 1 systems.

Remarks about stability for type 2 systems. From the above illustrations and discussions, we note:

> *A type 2 system is more likely to be unstable than a type 1 system*   (20.43a)

> *An unstable type 2 system cannot be made stable by merely adjusting the system gain K*   (20.43b)

The problem of improving the stability of a type 2 system is a difficult one, and that for a type n system, for $n \geq 3$, is even worse. Since the type 0, 1, and 2 systems will handle most practical problems, type n systems, for $n \geq 3$, are not commonly used.

Remarks about compensation. The stability of a closed-loop control system as depicted in Fig. 20.3a is determined by its open-loop transfer function $G(s)H(s)$, which prescribes the Nyquist diagram $G(j\omega)H(j\omega)$. $G(s)$ is the forward transfer function; $H(s)$ is the transfer function of the feedback element of the system.

If a system is found to be unstable, we may either (1) modify its forward transfer function, as will be discussed in Art. 21.2, or (2) modify the transfer function of its feedback element, as will be seen in Art. 21.2, so that the open-loop transfer function $G(s)H(s)$ of the "modified" system indicates stable system behavior. These methods of modification or compensation are intended to improve both system *stability* and *accuracy*. "Accuracy" refers to small errors in system operation.

20.4. Type 0 closed-loop control systems—regulator systems

We shall give two illustrations of type 0 systems. A type 0 system is often a regulator system, e.g., a "voltage regulator" or "speed regulator," used to regulate a physical quantity, e.g., voltage speed. A type 0 closed-loop system, as compared

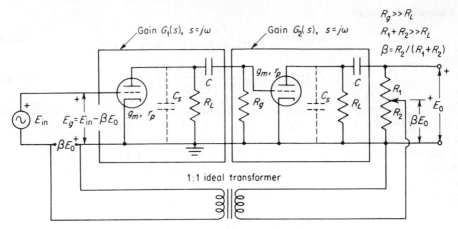

$$R_g \gg R_L$$
$$R_1 + R_2 \gg R_L$$
$$\beta = R_2 / (R_1 + R_2)$$

Gain $G_1(s)$, $s = j\omega$ Gain $G_2(s)$, $s = j\omega$

1:1 ideal transformer

Phase reversal introduced

g_m = transconductance of vacuum tube in mhos
r_p = plate resistance of vacuum tube in ohms
C_s = shunt capacitance from plate to ground
(*a*)

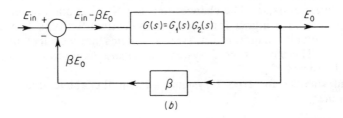

(*b*)

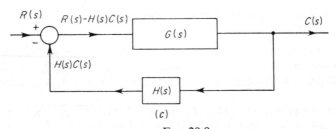

(*c*)

Fig. 20.8

with an open-loop system, performs better in the sense that it is less susceptible to (1) noise or disturbance, (2) frequency distortion, and (3) unreliability of individual system components.   We shall discuss these points in the following illustrations.

A. *Illustration* 1: *Negative-feedback Amplifier*

Description of circuit arrangement.   The a-c circuit of a two-stage *RC*-coupled amplifier with feedback loop is depicted in Fig. 20.8*a*.   The 1:1 turns-ratio transformer is purposely introduced so that the schematic of this amplifier (Fig. 20.8*b*) can be compared with a typical schematic of a closed-loop system (Fig. 20.8*c*).   In practice, this transformer is not used, and the phase reversal of βE_0 can be taken care of by other arrangements.†

† See J. D. Ryder, "Electronic Engineering Principles," fig. 9.22*c*, p. 258, Prentice-Hall, Inc., Englewood Cliffs, N.J., 1952.

Open-loop and overall transfer functions. We note the similarity between the schematics in Fig. 20.8b and c. Corresponding to the open-loop transfer function $G(s)H(s)$ in Fig. 20.3b, we now have

Open-loop transfer function:

$$G(s)H(s) = G(s)\beta \qquad (20.44)$$

Corresponding to the overall transfer function

$$G'(s) = \frac{C(s)}{R(s)} = \frac{G(s)}{1 + G(s)H(s)}$$

we now have

Overall transfer function:

$$G'(s) = \frac{E_o}{E_{in}} = \frac{G(s)}{1 + G(s)\beta} = \frac{G_1(s)G_2(s)}{1 + G_1(s)G_2(s)\beta} \qquad (20.45)$$

which is also called the *closed-loop gain* of the amplifier.

Voltage relations. $G(s)$ and $G'(s)$, for $s = j\omega$, are functions of the frequency ω. We shall now choose a typical frequency ω_1 and use numerical values $G = G(j\omega_1)$ and $G' = G'(j\omega_1)$ to illustrate the effects of negative feedback. Let us assume

$$G_1 = 10/\underline{180°} = -10 = \text{first-stage amplifier gain}$$

$$G_2 = 10/\underline{180°} = -10 = \text{second-stage amplifier gain}$$

$$G = G_1G_2 = 100/\underline{360°} = 100 = \text{two-stage gain without feedback} \qquad (20.46a)$$

$$\beta = \frac{R_2}{R_1 + R_2} = 0.09$$

$$E_{in} = 10/\underline{0°} = 10 \text{ volts} = \text{signal input}$$

Through computation, we find

$$G' = \frac{100}{1 + 0.09 \times 100} = 10$$

$$E_o = G'E_{in} = 100 \text{ volts} \qquad (20.46b)$$

$$-\beta E_o = -9 \text{ volts}$$

The voltage relations are depicted in Fig. 20.9. We note that the feedback voltage $-\beta E_o$ opposes the signal input E_{in} in polarity, and $|E_g| < |E_{in}|$. We shall say that we now have a *negative-feedback* amplifier. In general, when $|G'| < |G|$, we have negative feedback.

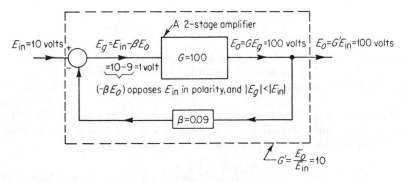

FIG. 20.9

Effects of negative feedback.   We shall now try to summarize some of the effects of negative feedback.

1. *Reduction in Gain.*   We have demonstrated in Fig. 20.9 that, for $G = 100$ without feedback, we have $G' = 10$ with negative feedback.   This means that we have a reduction in gain due to the negative feedback.   However, negative feedback also offers many attractive features to offset this disadvantageous gain reduction.

Usually we are not too concerned with the reduction in gain introduced by negative feedback.   Additional amplifier stages may be used to make up the reduction.

2. *Closed-loop Gain G' Made Independent of Fluctuations.*   For $s = j\omega$ and $|G(j\omega)\beta| \gg 1$, we may approximate Eq. (20.45) with

$$G'(j\omega) = \frac{G(j\omega)}{1 + G(j\omega)\beta} \cong \frac{G(j\omega)}{G(j\omega)\beta} = \frac{1}{\beta} \tag{20.47}$$

This means that, under the condition $|G(j\omega)\beta| \gg 1$, or a very large forward control-element gain $|G(j\omega)| \gg |1/\beta|$, we can make the closed-loop gain $G'(j\omega)$ at any frequency ω almost *constant* and independent of any fluctuations in the system (e.g., fluctuations in the d-c supply voltage due to unfiltered a-c components, fluctuations in circuit parameters due to aging or unreliability of circuit elements, etc.).   This implies that we may use inexpensive nonprecision circuit elements to build a reliable negative-feedback amplifier.

3. *Reduction of Noise in Output as a Negative-feedback Effect.*   For the amplifier depicted in Figs. 20.8 and 20.9, we now consider an internal noise source placed between the two stages of amplification as shown in Fig. 20.10a.   Let us treat the signal and the noise independently.   To differentiate between the two, boldface letters are used to represent "noise quantities" in Fig. 20.10.

For a signal input E_{in}, Eq. (20.45) dictates the output:

$$E_o = \frac{G}{1 + G\beta} E_{\text{in}} \qquad G = G_1 G_2 \tag{20.48a}$$

For a noise input $\mathbf{N}_{\text{in}}$, let us designate $\mathbf{N}_o$ as the noise output.   Taking the feedback effect into consideration, we have, between the two stages, (1) noise input $\mathbf{N}_{\text{in}}$ and (2) equivalent input $-G_1\mathbf{N}_o\beta$ from the feedback.   This amounts to an input $\mathbf{N}_{\text{in}} - G_1\mathbf{N}_o\beta$ to the second stage, which yields an output

$$\mathbf{N}_o = G_2(\mathbf{N}_{\text{in}} - G_1\mathbf{N}_o\beta)$$

Rearranging the above equation, we find

$$\mathbf{N}_o = \frac{G_2}{1 + G\beta} \mathbf{N}_{\text{in}} \qquad G = G_1 G_2 \tag{20.48b}$$

We shall now take β, G_1, G_2, G, and G' as specified in (20.46) and assume a noise input $\mathbf{N}_{\text{in}} = 1$ volt.   Let us now try to find the signal/noise ratios for an open-loop arrangement and a closed-loop arrangement for the same signal output $E_o = 100$ volts.

For the *open-loop arrangement* in Fig. 20.10b, $E_o = 100$ volts and $G = 100$ imply that we need an input signal $E_{\text{in}} = E_o/G = 1$ volt.   From the quantities in the figure, we have the following signal/noise ratio in the output:

$$\frac{\text{Signal}}{\text{Noise}} = \left| \frac{E_o}{\mathbf{N}_o} \right| = 10 \tag{20.49a}$$

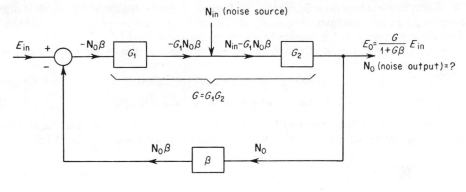

For signal alone, Eq. (20.45) implies: $E_0 = \dfrac{G}{1+GB} E_{in}$

For noise alone, $N_0 = G_2 (N_{in} - G_1 N_0 B)$ implies: $N_0 = \dfrac{G_2}{1+GB} N_{in}$

(a)

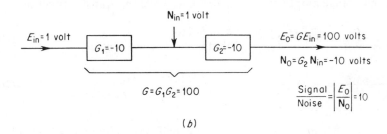

(b)

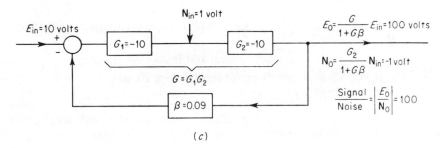

(c)

FIG. 20.10

For the *closed-loop arrangement* in Fig. 20.10c, $E_o = 100$ volts and $G' = 10$ as obtained in (20.46b) imply that we need an input signal $E_{in} = E_o/G' = 10$ volts. The noise output may be computed with the aid of (20.48b) to be $N_o = -1$ volt. We now have the following signal/noise ratio in the output:

$$\frac{\text{Signal}}{\text{Noise}} = \left| \frac{E_o}{N_o} \right| = 100 \qquad (20.49b)$$

It is always desirable to have a high signal/noise ratio. Comparing Eqs. (20.49), we note an improvement with negative feedback in a closed-loop arrangement.

4. *Reduction in Frequency Distortion as Another Negative-feedback Effect.* It is often desirable to have a uniform frequency characteristic for an amplifier, i.e., to have a relatively constant gain for a wide range of frequency.

Let us consider an amplifier with severe frequency distortion. For example, assume gains

$$G_a = 100 \qquad \text{at frequency } f_a = 1,000 \text{ cps} \qquad (20.50a)$$

and

$$G_b = 200 \qquad \text{at frequency } f_b = 2,000 \text{ cps} \qquad (20.50b)$$

We shall improve the system with negative feedback. Suppose we use the arrangement in Fig. 20.8a with $\beta = 0.09$. We now find that, with negative feedback,

$$G_a' = \frac{G_a}{1 + G_a\beta} = \frac{100}{1 + 100 \times 0.09} = 10 \qquad \text{at } f_a = 1,000 \text{ cps} \quad (20.51a)$$

and

$$G_b' = \frac{G_b}{1 + G_b\beta} = \frac{200}{1 + 200 \times 0.09} = 10.5 \qquad \text{at } f_b = 2,000 \text{ cps} \quad (20.51b)$$

Comparing (20.51) with (20.50), we note a marked reduction in frequency distortion with negative feedback.

Classification of a negative-feedback amplifier as a type 0 system. For a "single stage" in the two-stage amplifier in Fig. 20.8a, we have the transfer function or gain†

$$G_1(s) = \begin{cases} \dfrac{-g_m R_L}{1 + \omega_1/s} = \dfrac{-g_m R_L T_1 s}{1 + T_1 s} & \begin{array}{l} s = j\omega; \text{ for } \omega < \omega_0, \\ \text{that is, for } \textit{low frequencies} \end{array} & (20.52a) \\[4mm] \dfrac{-g_m R_L}{1 + s/\omega_2} = \dfrac{-g_m R_L}{1 + T_2 s} & \begin{array}{l} s = j\omega; \text{ for } \omega > \omega_0, \\ \text{that is, for } \textit{high frequencies} \end{array} & (20.52b) \end{cases}$$

where

$$\omega_1 = \frac{1}{R_g C} = \frac{1}{T_1} = \text{low half-power frequency, rad/sec}$$

$$\omega_2 = \frac{1}{R_L C_s} = \frac{1}{T_2} = \text{high half-power frequency, rad/sec}$$

$$\omega_0 = \sqrt{\omega_1 \omega_2} = \text{midband frequency} \qquad (20.53)$$

$$g_m, R_L, R_g, C, C_s, \beta = \text{circuit parameters in Fig. 20.8a}$$

$$K = (g_m R_L)^2$$

For the two-stage amplifier in Fig. 20.8a, assuming identical stages, that is, $G_1(s) = G_2(s)$, the forward transfer function is $G(s) = G_1(s)G_2(s) = [G_1(s)]^2$; that is,

Forward transfer function:

$$G(s) = \begin{cases} G_{\text{low}}(s) = \dfrac{K T_1^2 s^2}{(1 + T_1 s)^2} & \begin{array}{l} s = j\omega; \text{ for } \omega < \omega_0, \\ \text{that is, for } \textit{low frequencies} \end{array} & (20.54a) \\[4mm] G_{\text{high}}(s) = \dfrac{K}{(1 + T_2 s)^2} & \begin{array}{l} s = j\omega; \text{ for } \omega > \omega_0, \\ \text{that is, for } \textit{high frequencies} \end{array} & (20.54b) \end{cases}$$

† See MIT Electrical Engineering Staff, "Applied Electronics," pp. 470–485, John Wiley & Sons, Inc., New York, 1946. Approximations made here are $R_L \simeq R_{\text{eq}}$ and $R_g \simeq R_{\text{eq}}'$ for practical circuits with $R_L \ll r_p \ll R_g$. Similar expressions are derived in this text [Eqs. (14.41) and (14.31)] for transient study.

where K, T_1, T_2, and ω_0 are defined in (20.53). Comparing (20.54) with (20.19), we see that the feedback amplifier in Fig. 20.8a is a type 0 system according to the general representation of its forward transfer function (20.54).

According to (20.44), we now have

Open-loop transfer function:

$$
G(s)H(s) =
\begin{cases}
G(s)\beta = G_{\text{low}}(s)\beta = \dfrac{K\beta T_1{}^2 s^2}{(1 + T_1 s)^2} & \begin{array}{l} s = j\omega\,;\text{ for } \omega < \omega_0,\text{ that}\\ \text{is, for } \textit{low frequencies} \end{array} & (20.55a)\\[3ex]
G_{\text{high}}(s)\beta = \dfrac{K\beta}{(1 + T_2 s)^2} & \begin{array}{l} s = j\omega\,;\text{ for } \omega > \omega_0,\text{ that}\\ \text{is, for } \textit{high frequencies} \end{array} & (20.55b)
\end{cases}
$$

where K, β, T_1, T_2, and ω_0 are defined in (20.53). Comparing (20.55) with (20.33), we see that the feedback amplifier in Fig. 20.8a is also a type 0 system according to the general representation of its open-loop transfer function.

Remarks about the system characteristics of a negative-feedback amplifier. We have seen that the negative-feedback amplifier in Fig. 20.8a is a type 0 system. We now note:

1. A constant actuating error, that is, $E_g = E_{\text{in}} - \beta E_o$ in our present notation, is needed to produce a constant controlled variable, that is, E_o here; this may be seen in the numerical illustration in Fig. 20.9. This is consistent with (20.28b), which is characteristic of all type 0 systems.

2. For a negative-feedback amplifier, our concern is to have a reliable E_o, and we are assured of it in the above discussion. The need for an actuating error $E_g = E_{\text{in}} - \beta E_o$ does not worry us. However, the term *error* is perhaps not appropriate in this case.

Stability of a negative-feedback amplifier as a type 0 system. We shall now investigate the Nyquist diagram $G(j\omega)H(j\omega)$, that is, $G(j\omega)\beta$, for the negative-feedback amplifier in Fig. 20.8a. We merely replace $s = j\omega$ in (20.55), plot the positive-frequency portion of $G(j\omega)\beta$, and then construct the negative-frequency portion through symmetry with respect to the real axis.

Assuming a set of values for the parameters in (20.55), we plot the positive-frequency portion of the Nyquist diagram in Fig. 20.11a. Note that, for the upper half, we used Eq. (20.55a); for the lower half, Eq. (20.55b).

Since the positive-frequency portion of the Nyquist diagram is symmetrical with respect to the real axis, the negative-frequency portion is congruent to the positive-frequency portion. For clarity, we reproduce the positive-frequency portion of the Nyquist diagram in Fig. 20.11a' and the negative-frequency portion in Fig. 20.11b. To trace the complete Nyquist diagram is to trace the heart-shaped figure in Fig. 20.11a twice, once for $\omega = 0^+$ to $\omega = \infty$, and once for $\omega = -\infty$ to $\omega = 0^-$, in the clockwise direction. We now have $P = 0$ [by inspection of (20.55)] and $N = 0$, where P and N are interpreted in (20.34c). According to the Nyquist criterion in Art. 19.3C this is a stable system.

By changing the gain K to a much larger value, we enlarge the Nyquist diagram in Fig. 20.11a proportionally. However, the Nyquist diagram can never encircle -1 for any value of K; the amplifier is therefore *always stable*.

B. Illustration 2: Speed Regulator

A simple speed-regulator system is described in Fig. 20.12a with individual transfer functions taken from Fig. 20.2.

Forward and open-loop transfer functions.   We easily recognize that

Forward transfer function:

$$G(s) = \frac{K_a K_m}{1 + T_m s} \tag{20.56a}$$

and

Open-loop transfer function:

$$G(s)H(s) = \frac{K}{1 + T_m s} \qquad K = K_a K_m K_t \tag{20.56b}$$

This speed-regulator system is a type 0 system, as is evident if Eqs. (20.56) are compared with (20.19) and (20.33).

The effects of the feedback loop in this case are much like the effects of negative feedback in the previous illustration, except for notation.

Stability of a speed-regulator system.   Replacing $s = j\omega$ in (20.56b), we plot the Nyquist diagram $G(j\omega)H(j\omega)$ of the above-described speed-regulator system in Fig. 20.12b.   We now have $P = 0$ [by inspection of (20.56b)] and $N = 0$, where P and N are interpreted in (20.34c).   According to the Nyquist criterion in Art. 19.3C, this is a *stable* system.

By changing the gain K to a much larger value, we enlarge the Nyquist diagram in Fig. 20.12b proportionally.   However, it can never encircle -1 for any value of K; this speed-regulator system is always stable.

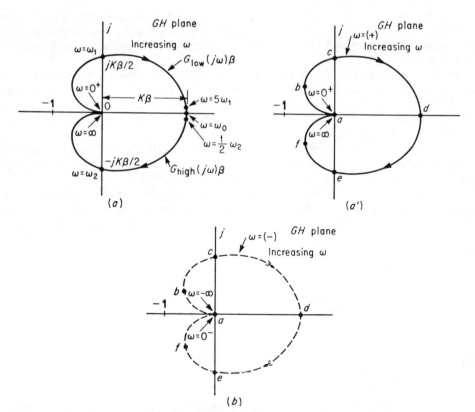

FIG. 20.11

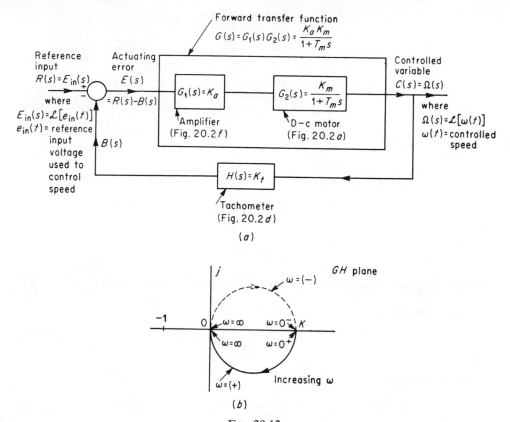

Fig. 20.12

C. Remarks about Type 0 Closed-loop Control Systems

Some characteristics of a type 0 system. From the illustrations we note the following:

1. A type 0 system is suitable for use as a regulator system, for it is less susceptible to component unreliability, disturbances or noises, and distortions than type 1 and 2 systems.

2. A constant actuating error is needed to produce a constant controlled variable. For other characteristics of a type 0 system, see the statements in (20.28).

System stability. From the Nyquist diagrams for type 0 systems in Figs. 20.4, 20.11, and 20.12b, we note:

1. Most type 0 physical systems are stable.

2. If a type 0 system is unstable, we may make it stable by reducing its system gain K or employing compensation, which will be discussed in Chap. 21.

3. The stability problem is not a severe one in type 0 systems as compared with type 1 and 2 systems.

20.5. Type 1 closed-loop control systems

A. Illustration: A Position Control System

A simple position control system is described in Fig. 20.13 with individual transfer functions taken from Fig. 20.2.

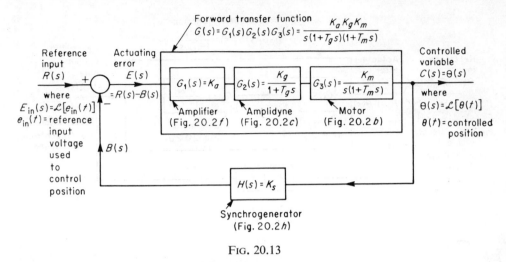

FIG. 20.13

Forward and open-loop transfer functions.   We easily recognize that

Forward transfer function:

$$G(s) = \frac{K_a K_g K_m}{s(1 + T_g s)(1 + T_m s)} \tag{20.57a}$$

and

Open-loop transfer function:

$$G(s)H(s) = \frac{K}{s(1 + T_g s)(1 + T_m s)} \qquad K = K_a K_g K_m K_s \tag{20.57b}$$

This position control system is a type 1 system, as is evident if Eqs. (20.57) are compared with (20.19) and (20.33).

Nyquist diagram.   Comparing (20.57b) with (20.37a), we see that, for $K = 10$, $T_m = 0.05$, and $T_g = 0.5$, the Nyquist diagram $G(j\omega)H(j\omega)$ of the system in Fig. 20.13 is the one depicted in Fig. 20.5a.   For a much larger K, we have the Nyquist diagram given in Fig. 20.5b.

B. *Remarks about Type 1 Closed-loop Control Systems*

We have discussed the *system characteristics* of type 1 systems in (20.30).   They are, of course, applicable to the position control system under discussion.

The statements in (20.40) give the *stability* properties of type 1 systems.   Although an unstable type 1 system may be made stable by adjusting the system gain K, a reduction in gain induces a larger error, as predicted by (20.30a), and is, therefore, often undesirable.   Different methods of compensation are available for improving the stability of a type 1 system, as will be seen in Chap. 21.

20.6. Type 2 closed-loop control systems

A. *Illustration: A Position Control System*

Suppose we modify the system in Fig. 20.13 with additional control elements in the forward branch: $G_4(s) = K_p$ for a *potentiometer* as in Fig. 20.2g and $G_5(s) = K_m' K_g'/s(1 + T_m' s)(1 + T_g' s)$ for a *generator-motor combination* as in Fig. 20.2i.

Forward and open-loop transfer functions. Changing notation, we have

Forward transfer function:

$$G(s) = \frac{K_f}{s^2(1 + T_1 s)(1 + T_2 s)(1 + T_3 s)(1 + T_4 s)} \tag{20.58a}$$

and

Open-loop transfer function:

$$G(s)H(s) = \frac{K}{s^2(1 + T_1 s)(1 + T_2 s)(1 + T_3 s)(1 + T_4 s)} \qquad K = K_f K_s \quad (20.58b)$$

Here we have a type 2 system, as is evident if (20.58) is compared with (20.19) and (20.33).

B. Remarks about Type 2 Closed-loop Control Systems

We have discussed the *system characteristics* of type 2 systems in (20.32). They are, of course, applicable to the position control system under discussion.

The statements in (20.43) give the *stability* properties of type 2 systems. Different methods of compensation are available for improving the stability of a type 2 system, as will be seen in Chap. 21.

PROBLEMS

Construct the Nyquist diagrams and determine the system stability for the return ratios or open-loop transfer functions in Probs. 20.1 through 20.9:

20.1. $G(s)H(s) = \dfrac{10}{s(1 + 0.05s)(1 + 0.5s)}$

20.2. $T(s) = \dfrac{10}{(1 + 0.01s)(1 + 0.6s)(1 + 2s)}$

20.3. $T_{p'p} = \dfrac{10}{(1 + 0.1 \times 10^{-6}s)(1 + 0.25 \times 10^{-6}s)(1 + 10 \times 10^{-6}s)}$

20.4. $G(s)H(s) = \dfrac{1{,}000(1 + 0.2s)(1 + 0.4s)}{s(1 + 0.005s)(1 + 0.02s)(1 + 1.5s)(1 + 2.5s)}$

20.5. $G(s)H(s) = \dfrac{40(1 + 0.2s)}{s^2(1 + 0.05s)(1 + 0.125s)}$

20.6. $T(s) = \dfrac{40s^2}{(1 + 0.1s)(1 + 0.2s)(1 + s)(1 + 2s)}$

20.7. $-\mu\beta = \dfrac{5(2s^3 + 3s + 1)}{6s^3 + 7s^2 + 9s + 2}$

20.8. $T(s) = \dfrac{1}{s^3(1 + s)(1 + 3s)}$

20.9. $G(s)H(s) = \dfrac{-2(1 + 20s)}{(1 - 8s)(1 + 0.03s + 0.05s^2)}$

20.10. Given: The type A transistor feedback amplifier in Fig. 17.13a with the general return ratio $T_{p'p}$ given in Fig. 17.13c.

(a) Using the transistor parameter values in (17.2a) for both transistors, $R_L = 1{,}000$ ohms and $R_F = 4{,}000$ ohms, obtain the return ratio $T_{p'p}$ of this amplifier.

(b) Find the overall transfer function $A^* = I_2(s)/I_1(s)$ for the arrangement shown in Fig. P 20.10, and check it against (17.32), thus establishing that *the type A transistor feedback amplifier in Fig. 17.12a or its special case in Fig. 17.13a has the equivalent representation in Fig. P 20.10.*

(*c*) Considering Fig. P 20.10 as the equivalent representation of the amplifier in Fig. 17.13*a*, using the return ratio $T_{p'p}$ obtained in (*a*), and assuming a response of the form

$$i_2(t) = c_0 + c_1(t - T) + \frac{c_2}{2!}(t - T)^2$$

for the values of t in the neighborhood of $t = T$, determine the actuating signal $e(t)$ for the same neighborhood.

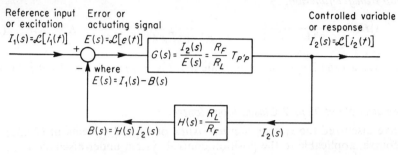

Reference input or excitation
$I_1(s)=\mathcal{L}[i_1(t)]$

Error or actuating signal
$E(s)=\mathcal{L}[e(t)]$

where
$E(s)=I_1(s)-B(s)$

$G(s) = \dfrac{I_2(s)}{E(s)} = \dfrac{R_F}{R_L}\, T_{p'p}$

$H(s) = \dfrac{R_L}{R_F}$

$B(s)=H(s)\,I_2(s)$

$I_2(s)$

Controlled variable or response
$I_2(s)=\mathcal{L}[i_2(t)]$

FIG. P 20.10

20.11. In Prob. 20.10*b*, we established that the type A transistor feedback amplifier in Fig. 17.12*a* has the equivalent representation in Fig. P 20.10.

Obtain a similar equivalent representation for the type B transistor feedback amplifier in Fig. 17.15*a*.

21 Methods of compensation for improving stability and accuracy

21.1. System stability and accuracy

There are two features desired in a closed-loop control system: *stability* and *accuracy*. We have discussed much about system stability. By accuracy, we mean "small error." In terms of the simple arrangement in Fig. 18.5a, we demand that the controlled variable $c(t)$ will follow the reference input $r(t)$ closely for small error $e(t) = r(t) - c(t)$.

Before we discuss the problem of compensation, i.e., the problem of improving stability and accuracy, we shall say a little more about these two features.

A. Stability: The Transient Characteristic of a System

Illustration 1. Let us consider the typical unstable system whose Nyquist diagram is given in Fig. 21.1a. Here we note:

1. A Nyquist diagram $G(j\omega)H(j\omega)$ that encircles the critical point -1 in the GH plane.

2. The high-frequency portion of the Nyquist diagram is close to the critical point -1, while the low-frequency portion is farther away from this critical point.

3. A runaway system response subject to a step-function input characteristic of an unstable system and exemplified in Fig. 18.6b.

Illustration 2. Now suppose we consider a system with a Nyquist diagram that passes through the critical point -1 in the GH plane, as depicted in Fig. 21.1b. This means that, in the notation of (18.5),

$$\frac{C(s)}{R(s)} = G'(s) = \frac{G(s)}{1 + G(s)H(s)} \tag{21.1a}$$

At $\omega = \omega_1$, where $G(j\omega_1)H(j\omega_1) = -1$, as indicated in Fig. 21.1b,

$$\frac{C(j\omega_1)}{R_1(j\omega_1)} = \frac{G(j\omega_1)}{1 + G(j\omega_1)H(j\omega_1)} = \infty \tag{21.1b}$$

Equation (21.1b) indicates that, for no reference input, that is, $R_1(j\omega_1) = 0$ or $r_1(t) = \mathcal{L}^{-1}[R_1(s)] = 0$, at $\omega = \omega_1$, there is a controlled variable or output, that is, $C(j\omega_1) \neq 0$ or $c(t) = \mathcal{L}^{-1}[C(s)] \neq 0$, at $\omega = \omega_1$. This closed-loop system (perhaps a feedback amplifier) actually operates like an *oscillator* in the sense that, for no input signal, there is an output signal. In a simple closed-loop system as depicted in Fig. 18.5a and b, we usually want the controlled variable $c(t)$ to follow the reference input $r(t)$ closely, so that we have small error $e(t) = r(t) - c(t)$. However,

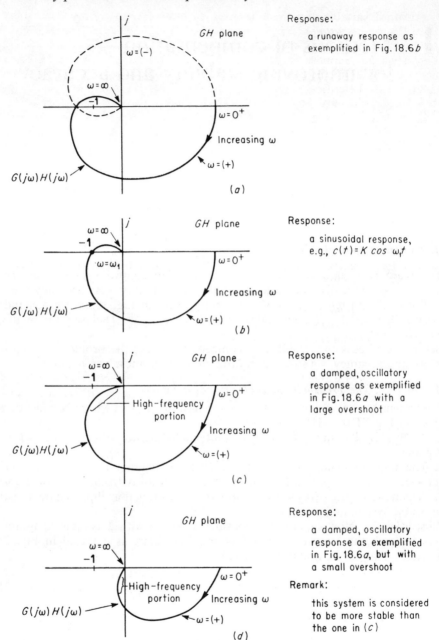

(a) Response: a runaway response as exemplified in Fig. 18.6b

(b) Response: a sinusoidal response, e.g., $c(t) = K \cos \omega_1 t$

(c) Response: a damped, oscillatory response as exemplified in Fig. 18.6a with a large overshoot

(d) Response: a damped, oscillatory response as exemplified in Fig. 18.6a, but with a small overshoot

Remark: this system is considered to be more stable than the one in (c)

FIG. 21.1   [The negative-frequency portion of the *GH* diagram is always symmetrical to the positive-frequency portion and is therefore omitted in (b), (c), and (d) as well as in future Nyquist representations.]

the controlled variable of a system whose Nyquist diagram is represented by Fig. 21.1*b* will support *sustained oscillation* and will *not* follow the reference input. We therefore must avoid using such a system.

Illustration 3. Suppose we now consider a system whose Nyquist diagram, as depicted in Fig. 21.1*c*, neither encircles the critical point −1 (as in Fig. 21.1*a*) nor passes through the critical point (as in Fig. 21.1*b*), but whose high-frequency portion is close to the critical point −1. The system behavior cannot be too different from that of the system in Fig. 21.1*b*. We shall find that its response subject to a step-function input represents *damped oscillation*, as indicated in Fig. 18.6*a*, with a *large* overshoot. This is a stable system by definition, i.e., one which does not have a runaway response subject to a finite excitation. However, its large overshoot is not a desirable feature in a closed-loop control system.

Illustration 4. A system whose Nyquist diagram (i.e., the high-frequency portion) is farther away from the critical point −1, as depicted in Fig. 21.1*d*, has a response subject to a step-function input that represents damped oscillation, as exemplified in Fig. 18.6*a*, with a *smaller* percentage overshoot $\Delta E/E$. We shall say that this system is *more stable* than the one associated with Fig. 21.1*c*.

Summarizing remarks about stability. From the above illustrations and discussions, we may state the following:

> *Of two stable systems, the one with the smaller percentage over-*
> *shoot in its controlled variable or response, subject to the same*
> *step-function reference input, is called the more stable system*   (21.2*a*)

> *In general, the closer the high-frequency portion of the Nyquist*
> *diagram of a system is to the critical point* −1 *in the GH plane, the*
> *less stable is the system*   (21.2*b*)

B. Accuracy: The Steady-state Characteristic of a System

The types of systems and their associated steady-state errors. From earlier discussions, if we consider a constant error as the steady-state error, we find from Eqs. (20.28), (20.30), and (20.32) that:

1. For a constant controlled variable, e.g., a constant position or displacement, there is a constant steady-state error associated with a type 0 system, but not with a type 1 or type 2 system.

2. For a controlled variable with a constant rate of change, e.g., a constant velocity, there is a constant steady-state error associated with type 0 and type 1 systems, but not with a type 2 system.

It is now obvious that we may eliminate a constant steady-state error by a change of system type. For example, if we can modify a type 0 system to a type 1 system, the constant steady-state error indicated in (1) above will be eliminated.

High gain at low frequencies. Closed-loop systems usually operate in the relatively low frequencies. Let us assume that the controlled variable has the form $c(t) = K \cos(\omega_0 t + \phi)$. Its frequency ω_0 will be a representative point on the low-frequency portion of the Nyquist diagram. In general, the controlled variable is not a simple sinusoidal representation. Its frequency may be changing from instant to instant, but it will remain in the low-frequency range.

From the statements in (20.28*a*), (20.30*a*), and (20.32*a*), we must have large system gain for small error for any system type. The term *error* here implies both steady-state (i.e., constant) and dynamic components. The first terms in (20.27), (20.29), and (20.31) are steady-state errors; the remaining terms in these equations are dynamic errors.

Because of the relatively low operating frequencies of closed-loop systems, we need only maintain high gain at low frequencies in order to have small steady-state error, as well as small dynamic error.

Summarizing remarks about accuracy.   From the above discussion and an earlier definition, we now state the following:

> *By accuracy of a closed-loop system we infer "small actuating error" for a desired controlled variable*   (21.3a)
>
> *To improve accuracy by eliminating constant steady-state error completely, we may modify a closed-loop system by changing its system type, e.g., from type 0 to type 1*   (21.3b)
>
> *To improve accuracy by reducing constant steady-state error, we may attempt to increase the system gain at low frequencies*   (21.3c)

21.2. Remarks about compensation

The problem of compensation is the problem of improving the stability and accuracy of a closed-loop control system.

A. Approaches to the Problem of Compensation

Suppose we have a closed-loop system with very poor performance and we wish to improve its performance in both stability and accuracy with "compensating" or stabilizing networks.

Let us consider the typical arrangement in Fig. 20.3a.   We have learned in earlier sections that:

1. The forward transfer function $G(s)$ determines certain system characteristics concerning "small error" or "accuracy," as discussed in Art. 20.2B and C.

2. The open-loop transfer function $G(s)H(s)$ determines system stability, since the Nyquist diagram $G(j\omega)H(j\omega)$, obtained by replacing $s = j\omega$ in $G(s)H(s)$, gives indications of system stability, as discussed in Art. 20.3B.

We may now compensate a closed-loop system for better performance with the following approaches:

Approach 1.   Modify $G(s)$ so that (1) the new open-loop transfer function $G(s)H(s)$ will assure a more stable system in the sense of (21.2) and/or (2) this forward transfer function $G(s)$ will assure more system accuracy.

Approach 2.   Modify $H(s)$ so that the new open-loop transfer function $G(s)H(s)$ will assure a more stable system, while the forward transfer function $G(s)$ remains unchanged.

B. Methods of Compensation

The approaches discussed above, with consideration of the remarks in (21.2) and (21.3), suggest the following methods of compensation:

Series compensation.   We may modify $G(s)$ by adding a compensating network in series with the original control element (Fig. 21.2a).   Several *RC* networks that can be used for series compensation are shown in Fig. 20.1.   The methods of series compensation will be discussed in Arts. 21.3 through 21.5.

The terms *compensation* and *stabilization* are often used interchangeably to mean "compensating for better system performance in stability as well as accuracy." Strictly speaking, compensation is associated with the improvement of stability and accuracy; stabilization, with the improvement of stability alone.   The commonly used terms series stabilization, stabilizing networks, etc., are actually meant to be series compensation, compensating networks, etc.

New forward transfer function $G(s) = G_N(s)\, G_1(s)$

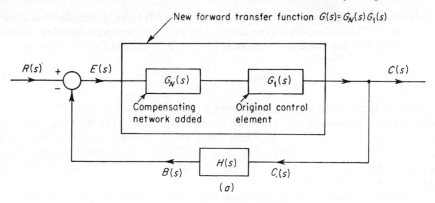

(a)

New forward transfer function $G(s) = \dfrac{G_1(s)}{1 + G_1(s)\, H(s)}$

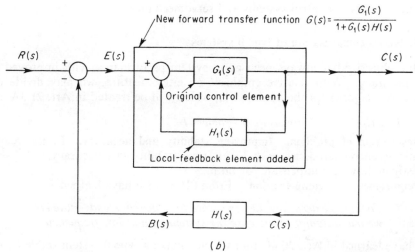

(b)

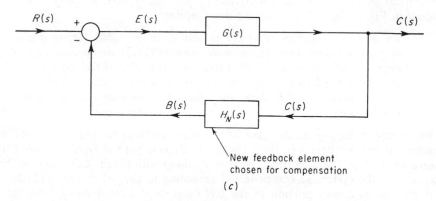

(c)

FIG. 21.2

Local-feedback compensation. We may modify $G(s)$ by local feedback (Fig. 21.2b). With the local-feedback element added, the new forward transfer function, which is obtained in the same manner as $G'(s)$ in (18.5) except for notation, is

$$G(s) = \frac{G_1(s)}{1 + G_1(s)H_1(s)} \tag{21.4}$$

The method of local-feedback compensation will be discussed in Art. 21.6.

Feedback-loop compensation. We may modify $H(s) = H_N(s)$ by choosing a new feedback element (Fig. 21.2c). The new $H(s)$ must assure a more stable Nyquist diagram $G(j\omega)H(j\omega)$ in the sense described in (21.2). Since the forward transfer function $G(s)$ remains unchanged, we expect the system characteristics, including accuracy, to *remain unchanged.*

We shall not attempt to treat this method. Reference† is made to textbooks on the subjects of control systems and servomechanisms.

21.3. Series compensation of type 0 systems

Our objective has always been good system performance with improved stability and accuracy. With relative emphasis on either feature, we may divide our task into two categories, problems I and II, which will be treated in Art. 21.3A and B.

A. Description of Compensation Problem I

Description of problem. Improving stability and accuracy. In the majority of problems encountered, we wish to improve stability *and* accuracy. We shall now investigate how to compensate for both.

Requirements for compensation. From (21.3c), we have learned:

> *To improve accuracy, i.e., to reduce the constant steady-state error,*
> *we may attempt to increase the system gain at low frequencies* (21.5a)

We have learned in Art. 20.4C that we may make a type 0 system stable by reducing its gain so that its Nyquist diagram will not encircle the critical point -1 in the GH plane. In general, the high-frequency portion of the Nyquist diagram is close to the critical point, while the low-frequency portion is farther away from it, as is evident in Fig. 21.3a. Therefore, we may require:

> *To improve stability, that is, to make an unstable system stable*
> *or a stable system more stable in the sense of (21.2), we may attempt to*
> *decrease the system gain at high frequencies, so that the high-frequency*
> *portion of the Nyquist diagram will not encircle the critical point -1,*
> *and, if possible, will be kept away from the immediate vicinity of the*
> *critical point* (21.5b)

If we interpret $|G(j\omega)|$ as the gain of a control element having $G(s)$ as its transfer function at the frequency ω, then Fig. 21.3a depicts (1) the G_1H diagram (Nyquist diagram) of a type 0 uncompensated system, along with (2) the GH diagram (Nyquist diagram) of the system as compensated according to the principles in (21.5). Note that the low-frequency portion of the GH diagram is farther away from the origin than that of the G_1H diagram, indicating an increase in gain at low frequencies for improved accuracy, as suggested by (21.5a) and illustrated in Fig. 21.3c. Also note that the high-frequency portion of the GH diagram is closer to the origin than that

† See, for example, H. Chestnut and R. W. Mayer, "Servomechanisms and Regulating System Design," pp. 273–278, John Wiley & Sons, Inc., New York, 1951.

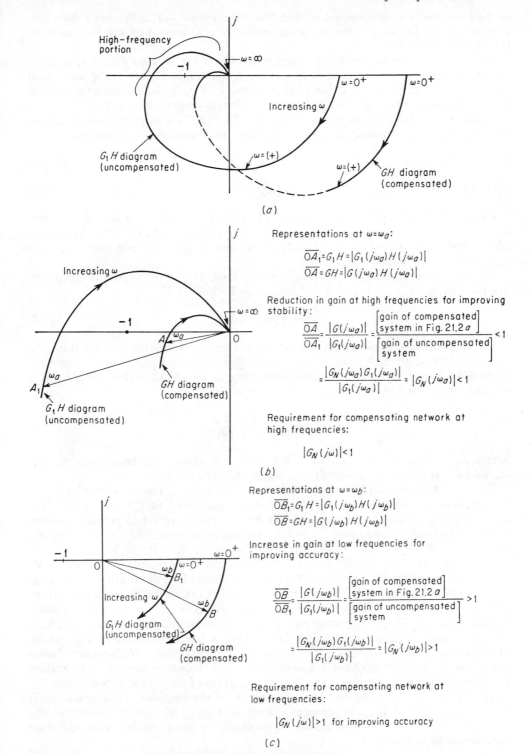

Representations at $\omega = \omega_a$:

$$\overline{OA_1} = G_1 H = |G_1(j\omega_a)H(j\omega_a)|$$
$$\overline{OA} = GH = |G(j\omega_a)H(j\omega_a)|$$

Reduction in gain at high frequencies for improving stability:

$$\frac{\overline{OA}}{\overline{OA_1}} = \frac{|G(j\omega_a)|}{|G_1(j\omega_a)|} = \frac{\left[\begin{array}{c}\text{gain of compensated}\\\text{system in Fig. 21.2}a\end{array}\right]}{\left[\begin{array}{c}\text{gain of uncompensated}\\\text{system}\end{array}\right]} < 1$$

$$= \frac{|G_N(j\omega_a)G_1(j\omega_a)|}{|G_1(j\omega_a)|} = |G_N(j\omega_a)| < 1$$

Requirement for compensating network at high frequencies:

$$|G_N(j\omega)| < 1$$

(b)

Representations at $\omega = \omega_b$:

$$\overline{OB_1} = G_1 H = |G_1(j\omega_b)H(j\omega_b)|$$
$$\overline{OB} = GH = |G(j\omega_b)H(j\omega_b)|$$

Increase in gain at low frequencies for improving accuracy:

$$\frac{\overline{OB}}{\overline{OB_1}} = \frac{|G(j\omega_b)|}{|G_1(j\omega_b)|} = \frac{\left[\begin{array}{c}\text{gain of compensated}\\\text{system in Fig. 21.2}a\end{array}\right]}{\left[\begin{array}{c}\text{gain of uncompensated}\\\text{system}\end{array}\right]} > 1$$

$$= \frac{|G_N(j\omega_b)G_1(j\omega_b)|}{|G_1(j\omega_b)|} = |G_N(j\omega_b)| > 1$$

Requirement for compensating network at low frequencies:

$$|G_N(j\omega)| > 1 \text{ for improving accuracy}$$

(c)

FIG. 21.3   (b) High-frequency portion of (a) enlarged; (c) low-frequency portion of (a).

of the G_1H diagram and does not encircle the critical point -1, indicating a reduction in gain at high frequencies for improved stability, as suggested by (21.5b) and illustrated in Fig. 21.3b.

We have omitted the negative-frequency branch of the Nyquist diagram, which is always symmetrical to the positive-frequency branch with respect to the horizontal axis. We can easily see that the G_1H diagram in Fig. 21.3a encircles the critical point -1 (compare it with Fig. 21.1a), while the GH diagram does not.

Requirements for a compensating network. To fulfill the requirements in (21.5), we may use a compensating network with a transfer function $G_N(s)$ such that

At high frequencies: $$|G_N(j\omega)| < 1 \tag{21.6a}$$

At low frequencies: $$|G_N(j\omega)| > 1 \tag{21.6b}$$

Equation (21.6a) reduces the system gain $|G(j\omega)| = |G_N(j\omega)G_1(j\omega)|$ at high frequencies and thus improves stability, as illustrated in Fig. 21.3b; Eq. (21.6b) increases the system gain $|G(j\omega)| = |G_N(j\omega)G_1(j\omega)|$ at low frequencies and thus improves accuracy, as illustrated in Fig. 21.3c.

In some systems, we may want to improve stability at the expense of accuracy. We then require (21.6a) for high frequencies and allow

$$|G_N(j\omega)| \leq 1 \tag{21.7}$$

for low frequencies.

Use of phase-lag compensating networks. We may compensate the type 0 system with the G_1H diagram (Nyquist diagram) in Fig. 21.4b with a phase-lag arrangement as in Fig. 21.4a. This arrangement, consisting in an amplifier (Fig. 20.2f) and a phase-lag network† (Fig. 20.1d), has the transfer function

$$G_N(s) = K_a \frac{1 + T_2 s}{1 + (1/\beta)T_2 s} \tag{21.8}$$

where $T_2 = R_2 C_2$, and $\beta = R_2/(R_1 + R_2)$. We may choose the parameters K_a, R_1, R_2, and C_2 so that (21.8) satisfies requirements (21.5) and (21.6).

For simplicity, we shall illustrate with $K_a = 1$ in (21.8). For $\omega = 0^+$, $G_N(j\omega) = 1$; for $\omega = \infty$, $G_N(j\omega) = \beta = R_2/(R_1 + R_2)$. According to (21.5) and the Nyquist diagram of the compensated system in Fig. 21.4b, we are improving *stability* with some sacrifice of accuracy. We may further improve stability by reducing R_2, that is, $\beta = R_2/(R_1 + R_2)$. If necessary, we may make $R_2 = 0$ and $\beta = 0$.

Let us now see how the GH diagram of the compensated system is obtained. We shall assume that the G_1H diagram of the uncompensated system is available to us in Fig. 21.4b; a compensating network is chosen which has the auxiliary diagram given in Fig. 20.1d'' and reproduced in Fig. 21.4b. At $\omega = \omega_a$, we have two known vectors $\mathbf{OA_1}$ and $\mathbf{OA_2}$ terminating on the G_1H diagram and the auxiliary diagram. The procedure for finding the vector $\mathbf{OA} = \mathbf{OA_2} \times \mathbf{OA_1}$ is outlined in Fig. 21.4b. $\mathbf{OA}$ terminates on the GH diagram of the compensated system. We have now found the point on the GH diagram associated with the frequency $\omega = \omega_a$. Repeating for other frequencies, we obtain the Nyquist diagram of the compensated system.

To improve *accuracy*, we may raise the gain K_a of the amplifier. For any $K_a > 1$, the GH diagram of the compensated system in Fig. 21.4b will be proportionally enlarged. To ensure stability, it may be necessary to use a smaller value of β than that indicated in the figure.

---

† Other phase-lag networks in Fig. 20.1 may also be used.

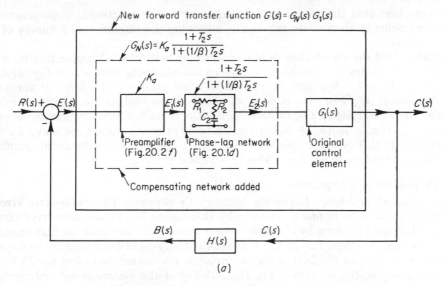

New forward transfer function $G(s) = G_N(s)\,G_1(s)$

$$G_N(s) = K_a \frac{1 + T_2 s}{1 + (1/\beta)\,T_2 s}$$

$\dfrac{1 + T_2 s}{1 + (1/\beta)\,T_2 s}$

K_a

$R(s)+$ $E(s)$ $E_1(s)$ $E_2(s)$ $G_1(s)$ $C(s)$

Preamplifier   Phase-lag network   Original
(Fig. 20.2 f)   (Fig. 20.1 d)   control
element

Compensating network added

$B(s)$ $H(s)$ $C(s)$

(a)

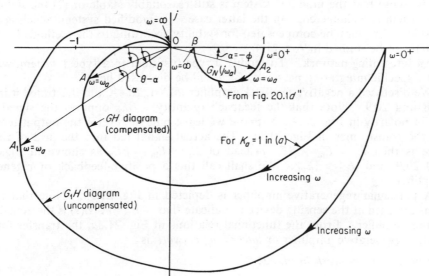

$\omega = \infty$

-1 0 β 1

$\alpha = -\phi$ $\omega = 0^+$ $\omega = 0^+$

θ $\omega = \infty$ $G_N(j\omega_a)$ A_2

A $\omega = \omega_a$ $\theta - \alpha$ $\omega = \omega_a$

α From Fig. 20.1 d ''

GH diagram
(compensated)

For $K_a = 1$ in (a)

A_1 $\omega = \omega_a$

Increasing ω

$G_1 H$ diagram
(uncompensated)

Increasing ω

Representations:
Vector $\mathbf{OA_1}$:

$\qquad G_1(j\omega_a)H(j\omega_a)$ from uncompensated $G_1 H$ diagram

Vector $\mathbf{OA_2}$:

$\qquad\qquad G_N(j\omega_a)$ from auxiliary diagram

Vector $\mathbf{OA} = vector\ \mathbf{OA_2} \times vector\ \mathbf{OA_1}$:

$\qquad G(j\omega_a)H(j\omega_a) = [G_N(j\omega_a)G_1(j\omega_a)]H(j\omega_a)$
$\qquad\qquad\qquad = G_N(j\omega_a)[G_1(j\omega_a)H(j\omega_a)]$ on compensated GH diagram

Finding the vector $\mathbf{OA}$:
Magnitude: $\qquad\qquad\qquad \overline{\mathbf{OA}} = \overline{\mathbf{OA_2}} \times \overline{\mathbf{OA_1}}$
Phase: $\qquad\qquad\qquad$ As shown in illustration

(b)

F I G. 21.4

We note here that the use of a phase-lag compensating network in conjunction with an amplifier is an effective means for improving the stability and accuracy of a type 0 system.

Remarks about the use of phase-lead compensating networks.   Suppose that we use a phase-lead network in Fig. 20.1a to replace the phase-lag network in Fig. 21.4a, and we use $K_a = 1$.   We note in Fig. 20.1a'' that $G_0(\omega) = |G_N(j\omega)| < 1$ for any finite frequency; $|G_N(j\omega)| \to 1$ as $\omega \to \infty$.   This means that we are reducing system gain $|G(j\omega)| = |G_N(j\omega)G_1(j\omega)|$ for low frequencies as well as high frequencies, except for $\omega = \infty$.   If $\alpha = R_2/(R_1 + R_2)$ in Fig. 20.1a' is properly chosen, we may be able to make this type 0 system stable according to (21.5b), but at a substantial sacrifice of accuracy according to (21.5a).   This is not good practice.

B. Description of Compensation Problem II

Description of problem.   Improving accuracy to eliminate the steady-state error. Sometimes we wish to improve accuracy by eliminating the steady-state error completely.   This may be done by changing system types.   For instance, we may modify a type 0 system to a type 1 system; the constant steady-state error inherent in a type 0 system according to (20.28b) is then completely eliminated according to (20.30b). However, two possibilities arise: (1) The stability of the system is not endangered in the sense that the modified system is still reasonably stable or (2) the stability of the system is endangered.   In the latter case, this modified system, which is a type 1 system now, may be compensated for stability according to the methods for type 1 systems to be studied in Art. 21.4.

An integrating network.   To modify a type 0 system to a type 1 system, we shall use a specific integrating network which will be discussed here.

We discussed a negative-feedback amplifier in Art. 20.4A and illustrated it in Figs. 20.8 and 20.9.   Note that the feedback quantity $-\beta E_0$ opposes the signal input E_{in} in polarity in Fig. 20.9.   Suppose we leave out, or reverse the output terminals of, the transformer in Fig. 20.8a.   The actual signal fed into the grid of the first tube is then $E_g = E_{in} + \beta E_0$, instead of $E_g = E_{in} - \beta E_0$ as shown in Figs. 20.8 and 20.9, and $|E_g| > |E_{in}|$.   We shall call this a positive-feedback or regenerative amplifier.

A particular regenerative amplifier is depicted in Fig. 21.5a.   Note that two $+$ signs are used at the sensing device to indicate that $+E_1(s) + B(s)$ is the actual input to the amplifier.   From the functional relations in Fig. 21.5a, the transfer function of this regenerative amplifier or *integrating network* is

For integrating network in Fig. 21.5:

$$G(s) = \frac{1 + Ts}{Ts} \qquad T = RC \qquad (21.9)$$

The reason for calling this regenerative amplifier an integrating network is self-explanatory in Fig. 21.5b, where we obtain the integral relation

$$e_2(t) = \frac{1}{T} \int_0^t e_1(t) \, dt + e_1(t) \qquad (21.10)$$

$e_2(t)$ is a linear combination of $e_1(t)$ and its integral.   It can be easily verified that the integrating network in Fig. 21.5a is a phase-lag network.   From (21.9) and Fig. 21.5b,

$$\frac{E_2(j\omega)}{E_1(j\omega)} = G(j\omega) = \frac{1 + Tj\omega}{Tj\omega}$$

$$= \frac{(1 + T^2\omega^2)^{\frac{1}{2}}/\tan^{-1} T\omega}{T\omega/90°} = \frac{(1 + T^2\omega^2)^{\frac{1}{2}}}{T\omega} \underline{/\theta}$$

where $\theta = \tan^{-1} T\omega - 90°$. For any values of ω and T, θ is *negative*. This means that the output $E_2(j\omega)$ *lags* behind the input $E_1(j\omega)$ by $\phi = -\theta$ deg, and we have a *phase-lag* network.

We often call a phase-lag network an integrating network, and a phase-lead network a differentiating network.

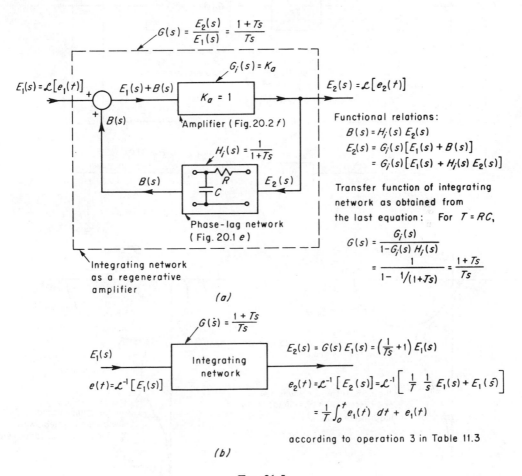

FIG. 21.5

Illustration showing the change of system type. Without the compensating network in Fig. 21.6a, we have a type 0 system which may very well depict the simple speed-regulator system discussed in Art. 20.4B and described in Fig. 20.12a. With the compensating arrangement, we have an open-loop transfer function

$$G(s)H(s) = \frac{K(1 + Ts)}{s(1 + T_1 s)} \qquad K = \frac{K_a K_1 K_h}{T} \qquad (21.11)$$

and the modified system is obviously a type 1 system. Figure 21.6b compares the Nyquist diagrams of the uncompensated type 0 system under discussion and the compensated system which is now a type 1 system. We have used $K_a = 1$ for easy

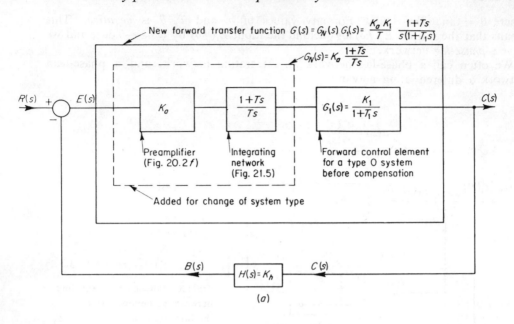

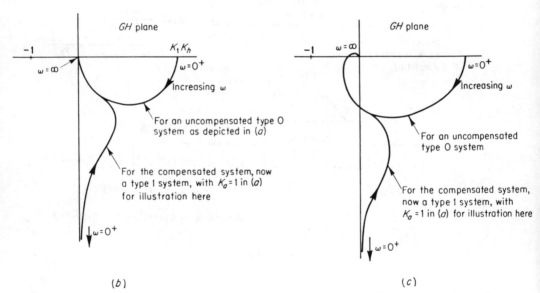

FIG. 21.6

comparison.   Note that

$$G_N(j\omega) = \frac{1 + j\omega}{j\omega} \cong 1$$

and

$$G(j\omega)H(j\omega) = [G_N(j\omega)G_1(j\omega)]H(j\omega) \cong G_1(j\omega)H(j\omega)$$

for *large* ω.   This is why the Nyquist diagram $G_1(j\omega)H(j\omega)$ for the uncompensated system and the Nyquist diagram $G(j\omega)H(j\omega)$ for the compensated system coincide at high frequencies.

Figure 21.6c provides another comparison for a different system.

21.4. Series compensation of type 1 systems

A. Requirements for Compensation

Examining the typical Nyquist diagram of an unstable type 1 system in Fig. 20.5*b*, we note that requirements (21.5) for improving the accuracy and stability of a type 0 system also apply here. This means that the use of *phase-lag compensating networks* is ideal for type 1 systems.

If we interpret $|G(j\omega)|$ as the gain of a control element, we see that a type 1 system has very high gain at low frequencies. Although high gain implies small error and high accuracy, a type 1 system can afford to sacrifice some of its accuracy (more so than a type 0 system), and we may relax requirement (21.5*a*) for type 1 systems. For this reason, the use of a *phase-lead compensating network* is also a well-accepted means of compensating a type 1 system.

B. Illustrations: Series Compensation of Type 1 Systems

Illustration 1. Use of a phase-lag compensating network. We may assume that the arrangement in Fig. 21.4*a*, without the compensating network, is an uncompensated type 1 system similar to the position control system in Fig. 20.13. We now compensate this system with a phase-lag network as in Fig. 21.4*a*. Figure 21.7*a* compares the Nyquist diagrams of the uncompensated and compensated systems for $K_a = 1$, which is used only for easy comparison and should be adjusted for good system performance in accuracy as well as stability. The *GH* diagram of the compensated system is obtained from the G_1H diagram of the uncompensated system and the auxiliary diagram of the compensating network. For example, at $\omega = \omega_a$ we have two known vectors $\mathbf{OA_1}$ and $\mathbf{OA_2}$ terminating on the G_1H diagram and the auxiliary diagram. The procedure for finding the vector $\mathbf{OA} = \mathbf{OA_2} \times \mathbf{OA_1}$ is the same as outlined in Fig. 21.4*b*. $\mathbf{OA}$ terminates on the *GH* diagram of the compensated system. We have now found the point on the *GH* diagram associated with the frequency $\omega = \omega_a$. Repeating for other frequencies, we obtain the Nyquist diagram of the compensated system. Note that the *GH* diagram of the compensated system does not encircle the critical point -1, while the G_1H diagram does.

Illustration 2. Use of a phase-lead compensating network. We now replace the phase-lag network in Illustration 1 with a phase-lead network (Fig. 20.1*a*). Figure 21.7*b* compares the Nyquist diagrams of the uncompensated and compensated systems for $K_a = 1$.

21.5. Series compensation of type 2 systems

A. Advancement of Phase as a Requirement for Compensation

Examining the typical Nyquist diagram of an unstable type 2 system in Fig. 20.7*b*, we note that, unlike the type 0 and type 1 systems, we cannot make a type 2 system stable merely by reducing the gain.

Figure 21.8 suggests that an advancement of phase will stabilize this system. In this oversimplified and idealized illustration, we have merely rotated the Nyquist diagram counterclockwise for a certain angle. This means that we have advanced the *same* phase angle for all frequencies.

To actually advance phase angle, we may use a *phase-lead compensating arrangement* consisting in a preamplifier and a phase-lead network as in Fig. 21.9*a*. Using the phase-lead network in Fig. 20.1*a*, we advance *different* phase angles for different frequencies. Note in Fig. 20.1*a''* that $\phi(0^+) = 0$, $\phi(\omega_a) = \phi_a$, $\phi(\omega_b) = \phi_b, \ldots, \phi(\infty) = 0$. This will serve our purpose very well, since we are interested only

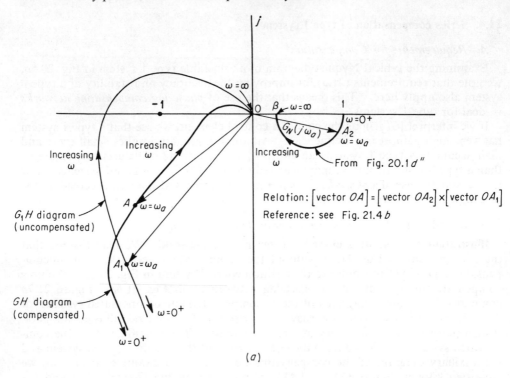

(a)

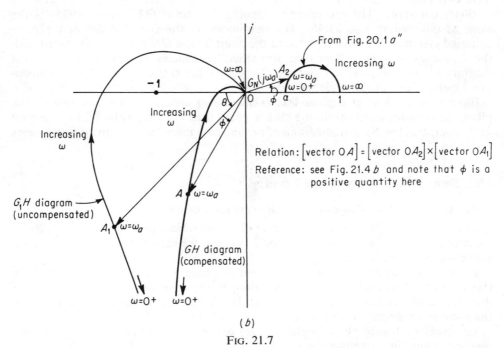

(b)

FIG. 21.7

in bringing the portion between ω_1 and ω_2 of the Nyquist diagram in Fig. 21.8 *below* the critical point -1, so that it will not encircle it; we are not too much concerned about the advancement of phase at $\omega = 0^+$ and $\omega = \infty$. The gain K_a of the preamplifier must be adjusted for good system performance in accuracy as well as stability.

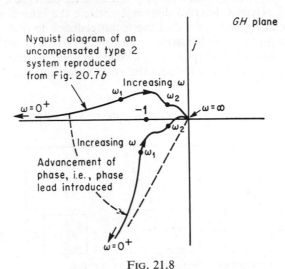

FIG. 21.8

B. *Illustration: Use of a Phase-lead Network in Compensating a Type 2 System*

We may assume that the arrangement in Fig. 21.9a, without the compensating network, is an uncompensated type 2 system as discussed in Art. 20.6A. We now compensate this system with the compensating arrangement in Fig. 21.9a. Figure 21.9b compares the Nyquist diagrams of the uncompensated and compensated systems. The GH diagram (i.e., the Nyquist diagram) of the compensated system is obtained from the G_1H diagram of the uncompensated system and the auxiliary diagram. The procedure for finding the vector $\mathbf{OA} = \mathbf{OA_2} \times \mathbf{OA_1}$ is the same as outlined in Fig. 21.4b. $\mathbf{OA}$ terminates on the GH diagram of the compensated system. We have now found the point on the GH diagram associated with the frequency $\omega = \omega_a$. Repeating for other frequencies, we obtain the Nyquist diagram for the compensated system. Note that the GH diagram of the compensated system does not encircle the critical point -1, while the G_1H diagram does.

21.6. Local-feedback compensation

A. *Description of Problem*

Control systems containing a number of local-feedback loops are called multiple-loop systems. We shall not treat the general category of multiple-loop systems.† We shall deal only with those systems whose local-feedback loops are used to modify the individual control elements, as exemplified in Fig. 21.10, and therefore compensate the system, improving its stability and accuracy. With relative emphasis on either improving stability or improving accuracy, we have two categories of problems to be discussed in Art. 21.6B and C.

† See J. G. Truxal, "Automatic Feedback Control System Synthesis," pp. 147–150, McGraw-Hill Book Company, Inc., New York, 1955, for the stability of multiple-loop systems.

B. Improving Stability as Primary Objective

Direct local feedback used in the change of system type.   We know that a type 0 system is usually stable, while type 1 and type 2 systems are less inclined to be stable, as indicated in (20.36), (20.40a), and (20.43a).   Let us assume that the arrangement in Fig. 21.11a, less the local-feedback loop, is a near-unstable type 1 or type 2 system in the sense that its Nyquist diagram does not encircle the critical point -1, but is close to it.   It can easily be shown that the local-feedback loop will transform this system into a more stable type 0 system.   The *stability* is now well taken care of. To improve the *accuracy* of this type 0 compensated system, we may increase the gain K_a of the amplifier, which in turn reduces the error according to (20.28a).

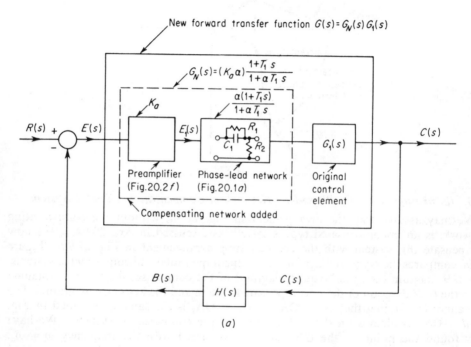

New forward transfer function $G(s) = G_N(s) G_1(s)$

$G_N(s) = (K_a a) \dfrac{1 + T_1 s}{1 + a T_1 s}$

$\dfrac{a(1 + T_1 s)}{1 + a T_1 s}$

K_a

$R(s)$ $E(s)$ $E_1(s)$

Preamplifier   Phase-lead network   Original
(Fig. 20.2f)   (Fig. 20.1a)   control
element

Compensating network added

$B(s)$ $C(s)$

$H(s)$

(a)

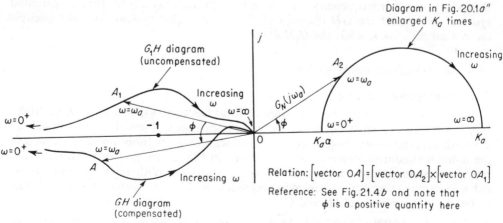

Diagram in Fig. 20.1a''
enlarged K_a times

$G_1 H$ diagram
(uncompensated)

A_2 Increasing
ω

A_1 Increasing
ω $\omega = \omega_a$

$\omega = 0^+$ $G_N(j\omega)$ $\omega = w_a$

-1 ϕ $\omega = \infty$ ϕ $\omega = 0^+$ $\omega = \infty$

$\omega = 0^+$ $\omega = \omega_a$ $K_a a$ K_a

A

Increasing ω

GH diagram
(compensated)

Relation: $[\text{vector } OA] = [\text{vector } OA_2] \times [\text{vector } OA_1]$

Reference: See Fig. 21.4b and note that
ϕ is a positive quantity here

(b)

FIG. 21.9

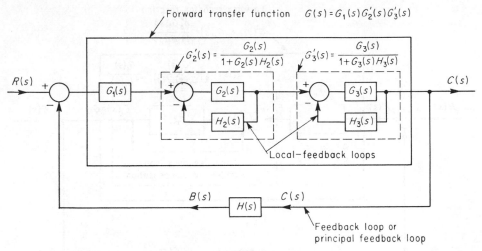

Forward transfer function $G(s) = G_1(s)G_2'(s)G_3'(s)$

$$G_2'(s) = \frac{G_2(s)}{1 + G_2(s)H_2(s)}$$ $$G_3'(s) = \frac{G_3(s)}{1 + G_3(s)H_3(s)}$$

Local-feedback loops

Feedback loop or principal feedback loop

FIG. 21.10

Illustration. Let us assume that, for the arrangement in Fig. 21.11a *less* the local-feedback loop, we have

$$G_1(s) = \frac{K}{s(1 + T_1 s)} \tag{21.12a}$$

$$H(s) = K_h \tag{21.12b}$$

Uncompensated system:

Open-loop transfer function $= K_a G_1(s) H(s) = \dfrac{K_1}{s(1 + T_1 s)} \tag{21.13}$

where $K_1 = K_a K K_h$; this obviously represents a type 1 system.

Let us now add the local-feedback loop in the arrangement indicated in Fig. 21.11a. We now have

$$G(s) = \frac{K_a G_1(s)}{1 + G_1(s)} = \frac{K_a K/s(1 + T_1 s)}{1 + K/s(1 + T_1 s)} = \frac{K_a K}{K + s + T_1 s^2} \tag{21.14a}$$

$$H(s) = K_h \tag{21.14b}$$

Compensated system:

Open-loop transfer function $= G(s) H(s) = \dfrac{K_1}{K + s + T_1 s^2} \tag{21.15}$

where $K_1 = K_a K K_h$; this obviously represents a type 0 system.

Nyquist diagrams. For $K_a = 1$, and with values assigned to K, K_h, and T_1, the Nyquist diagrams of the uncompensated and compensated systems are depicted as the $G_1 H$ and the GH diagrams in Fig. 21.11b. The Nyquist diagram of a compensated system with the increased gain $K_a > 1$ necessary for improving accuracy is also depicted.

A feature that accompanies the use of a direct local-feedback loop. We shall find that the use of a direct local-feedback loop will also help increase accuracy in the sense that the control element will *respond faster* in following its input. For example, for the same input $e_1(t)$ in Fig. 21.13e, (1) the response of the control element without

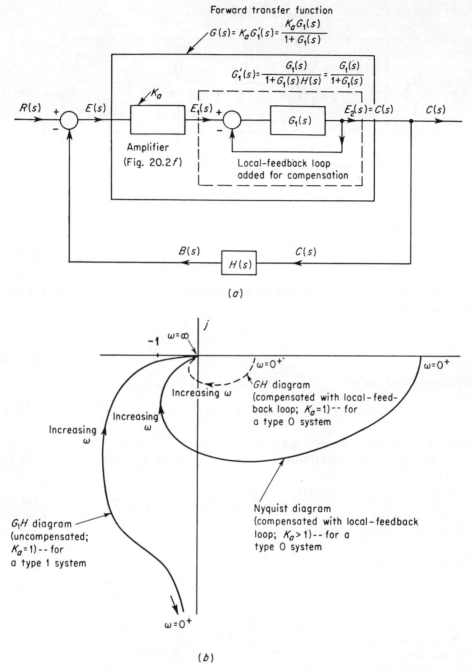

FIG. 21.11

a local-feedback loop (Fig. 21.12a) may be represented by the dashed curve $e_2(t)$ in Fig. 21.13e and (2) the response of the control element with a local-feedback loop (Fig. 21.12b) may be represented by the solid curve $e_2(t)$ in Fig. 21.13e. Comparing $e_2(t)$ with $e_1(t)$ in Fig. 21.13e, we note that the solid curve $e_2(t)$ responds faster in following $e_1(t)$.

We shall now illustrate that the above-discussed *faster response* is a result of adding a local-feedback loop. For simplicity and clear presentation, the system used in this illustration is a type 0 system *before* as well as *after* the local-feedback loop is added. It can also be demonstrated that, with appropriate system constants, the addition of a local-feedback loop to a type 1 or type 2 system can induce a faster response.

Illustration. Let us consider the arrangements in Fig. 21.12a and b, the respective forward control elements of the system in Fig. 21.11a without and with a local-feedback loop. We assume, in Fig. 21.12a, that

Without local-feedback loop:

$$G_1(s) = \frac{K_a}{1 + T_a s} \tag{21.16}$$

and compute, in Fig. 21.12b,

With local-feedback loop:

$$G_1'(s) = \frac{G_1(s)}{1 + G_1(s)} = \frac{K_b}{1 + T_b s} \tag{21.17}$$

where

$$T_b = \frac{T_a}{1 + K_a} \qquad K_b = \frac{K_a}{1 + K_a} \tag{21.17a}$$

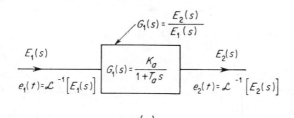

(a)

where $T_b = \dfrac{T_a}{1+K_a}$ $K_b = \dfrac{K_a}{1+K_a}$

$E_1(s)$

$e_1(t) = \mathcal{L}^{-1}[E_1(s)]$

$$G_1(s) = \frac{K_a}{1+T_a s}$$

$E_2(s)$

$e_2(t) = \mathcal{L}^{-1}[E_2(s)]$

See Fig. 21.11a

(b)

Fig. 21.12

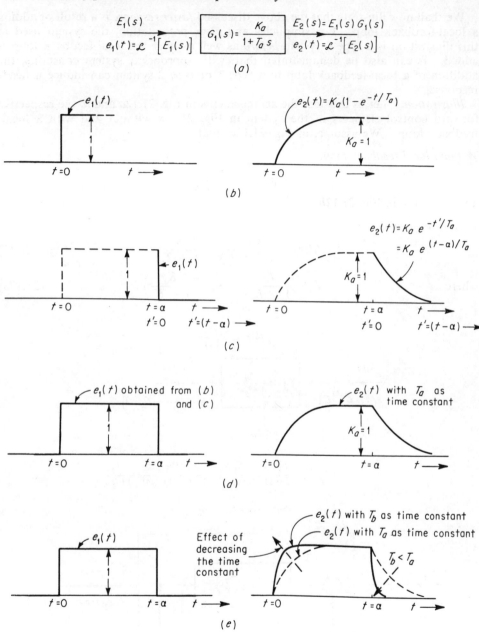

FIG. 21.13

It is obvious that $T_b < T_a$ for positive K_a. Here we have a *diminished time constant* T_b as a result of adding the local-feedback loop. We also have a reduction in gain from K_a to K_b. However, we may easily make up this reduction in gain with a pre-amplifier preceding $G_1'(s)$, as indicated in Fig. 21.11a. But what is the significance of the diminished time constant? We shall find that it is responsible for the faster response mentioned above.

The meaning of the time constant. We shall consider the arrangement in Fig. 21.13a and assume that the input is the square-topped pulse $e_1(t)$ in Fig. 21.13d. In finding the response $e_2(t) = \mathscr{L}^{-1}[E_2(s)] = \mathscr{L}^{-1}[E_1(s)G_1(s)]$, we (1) consider the rising portion in Fig. 21.13b as a unit-step input and find the response using the Laplace-transformation method discussed in Chaps. 12 and 13 and (2) consider the decaying portion in Fig. 21.13c, again using the techniques in Chaps. 12 and 13. Combining Fig. 21.13b and c, we obtain Fig. 21.13d.

If we compare the waveforms of $e_2(t)$ in Fig. 21.13b and c with those in Fig. 14.7c and d, we see that our present time constant T_a corresponds to the time constants τ_1 and τ_2 in the earlier figures. Referring to Eqs. (14.20), we now have

$$T_1 = 2.3 \times \text{time constant} = 2.3T_a \qquad (21.18a)$$

and
$$T_2 = 2.3 \times \text{time constant} = 2.3T_a \qquad (21.18b)$$

where T_1 and T_2 are the respective rise time and decay time defined in (14.20a) and (14.20b). It is now obvious that *the smaller the time constant, the faster the response* (either the rising portion or the decaying portion).

We choose $K_a = 1$ in Fig. 21.13 for easy comparison of $e_1(t)$ and $e_2(t)$.

The response $e_2(t)$, for the arrangement without a local-feedback loop (Fig. 21.12a) and with the forward transfer function $G_1(s)$ in (21.16) with time constant T_a, is now depicted by the dashed curve in Fig. 21.13e. The response $e_2(t)$, for the arrangement with a local-feedback loop (Fig. 21.12b) and with the forward transfer function $G_1'(s)$ in (21.17) with time constant $T_b < T_a$, is depicted by the solid curve in Fig. 21.13e with adjusted magnitude scales for comparison of the response times. We note that *an improvement in accuracy in terms of "faster" response is achieved by the use of a local-feedback loop.*

C. Improving Accuracy as Primary Objective

In Art. 21.3B we discussed how to *series-compensate* a type 0 system by modifying it to a type 1 system, improving its accuracy by eliminating the steady-state error. This method of compensation is demonstrated in Fig. 21.6a.

Suppose we replace the integrating network in Fig. 21.6a with the detailed arrangement in Fig. 21.5a. Here we notice a local-feedback loop consisting in a phase-lag network. Therefore, we may also consider that *local-feedback compensation* is employed in the arrangement in Fig. 21.6a. Reference is made to Art. 21.3B for more detailed discussion of this problem. It makes no difference whether we call the method (1) *series compensation*, if the arrangement in Fig. 21.5a is considered merely as a building block of the system in Fig. 21.6a, or (2) *local-feedback compensation.*

PROBLEMS

21.1. Given: A type 1 system with a control element

$$G_1(s) = \frac{K}{s(1 + 0.05s)(1 + 0.2s)} \qquad K = 50$$

and a direct feedback loop

$$H(s) = 1$$

as depicted in Fig. 21.4a with the compensating network removed.

(a) Construct the Nyquist diagram $G_1(j\omega)H(j\omega)$, and determine system stability. *Answer:* Unstable.

(b) Choose a compensating network

$$G_N(s) = K_a \frac{1 + T_2s}{1 + (1/\beta)T_2s}$$

with $K_a = 20$, $T_2 = 3.2$, and $1/\beta = 20$, and construct an auxiliary diagram $G_N(j\omega)$ in the plane of the G_1H diagram, similar to those shown in Fig. 21.4b or 21.7a.

(c) Perform vector operation on the G_1H and G_N diagrams, as demonstrated in Fig. 21.4b or 21.7a, to construct the Nyquist diagram $G(j\omega)H(j\omega) = [G_N(j\omega)G_1(j\omega)]H(j\omega) = G_N(j\omega)[G_1(j\omega)H(j\omega)]$ of the compensated system. Determine system stability. *Answer:* Stable.

Compare the present compensating technique with the one used in Probs. 19.7 and 19.8, where we reduced the system gain K to improve "stability" at the expense of "accuracy"; refer to the remarks in Prob. 19.9.

21.2. Given: The uncompensated system described in Prob. 21.1.

(a) Find the overall transfer function with the aid of (18.5):

$$G'(s) = \frac{C(s)}{R(s)} = \frac{G_1(s)}{1 + G_1(s)H(s)}$$

where $G_1(s)$ is given in Prob. 21.1, and $H(s) = 1$.

(b) Find the controlled variable (i.e., response) $c(t) = \mathscr{L}^{-1}[C(s)]$ of this uncompensated system subject to a unit-step reference input (i.e., excitation) $r(t) = u(t)$. Sketch $c(t)$, and note that it is an unstable response.

21.3. Given: The compensated system described in Prob. 21.1.

(a) Find its overall transfer function with the aid of (18.5):

$$G'(s) = \frac{C(s)}{R(s)} = \frac{G(s)}{1 + G(s)H(s)} = \frac{G_N(s)G_1(s)}{1 + G_N(s)G_1(s)}$$

where $G_1(s)$ and $G_N(s)$ are given in Prob. 21.1 and $H(s) = 1$.

(b) Find the controlled variable (i.e., response) $c(t) = \mathscr{L}^{-1}[C(s)]$ of this compensated system subject to a unit-step reference input (i.e., excitation) $r(t) = u(t)$. Sketch this compensated response, and compare it with the uncompensated response obtained in Prob. 21.2b. Is there any improvement?

21.4. Given: The two simple systems, without and with feedback loop, depicted in Fig. 21.12a and b, where $K_a = 9$ and $T_a = 1$ (and consequently $K_b = \frac{9}{10}$ and $T_b = \frac{1}{10}$).

(a) Plot $|G_1(j\omega)|$ for the system without feedback loop in Fig. 21.12a, and measure its equivalent bandwidth. Consider the half-power frequency ω_1 at which $|G_1(j\omega)|$ drops to 70.7 per cent of its maximum value as the edge of the equivalent bandwidth.

(b) Plot $|G_1'(j\omega)|$ for the system with feedback loop in Fig. 21.12b, and measure its equivalent bandwidth.

Note that the addition of a feedback loop has broadened the bandwidth at the expense of the system gain, which drops from $K_a = 9$ to $K_b = \frac{9}{10}$; this increase in bandwidth is responsible for the faster response observed in Art. 21.6B and discussed in the paragraphs following (21.18).

21.5. Repeat Prob. 21.1 with a new compensating network consisting in a preamplifier K_a and a phase-lead network $G_N(s) = \alpha(1 + T_1 s)/(1 + \alpha T_1 s)$ as depicted in Fig. 20.1a. Choose appropriate values for K_a, α, and T_1.

Index